Heat and Thermodynamics

BLACKIE & SON LIMITED
5 FITZHARDINGE STREET
LONDON·W.1
17 STANHOPE STREET
GLASGOW·C.4.

BLACKIE & SON
(INDIA) LIMITED
103-5 FORT STREET
BOMBAY

BLACKIE & SON
(CANADA) LIMITED
TORONTO

FIFTH EDITION

Heat and Thermodynamics

by

J. K. ROBERTS, Sc.D.(Cantab.), F.R.S.

Late Fellow of Christ's College, and University Lecturer in Physics at the Cavendish Laboratory, Cambridge

revised by

A. R. MILLER, Ph.D.(Cantab.), F.Inst.P.

London . **BLACKIE & SON LIMITED** . Glasgow

First edition 1928
Second edition 1933
Third edition 1940
Fourth edition 1951
Fifth edition 1960
Reprinted 1960, 1961, *1962*

First published 1928
Fifth edition © *A. R. Miller* 1960

Printed in Great Britain by Blackie & Son, Limited, Glasgow

Preface to the First Edition

This book has been written at the request of the publishers for the use of students taking a University Honours Course in Physics.

The book in general has been written from the experimental point of view, and the thermodynamical theory (Chapters XII to XIX) has been developed from the strictly thermodynamical point of view; that is to say, considerations belonging to statistical mechanics have not been introduced into these chapters. Where in other places the elucidation or application of the experimental work required some results from statistical mechanics, such results have been quoted with the briefest explanation, as any attempt to deduce them would have been out of place and would have lengthened the book to an impossible extent. The reader who wishes to study these matters in detail should refer to R. H. Fowler, *Statistical Mechanics, The Theory of the Properties of Matter in Equilibrium* (Cambridge University Press), and to the work by Jeans mentioned in the text.

In a book of this size it has not been possible to describe every slight modification of a particular class of experiment. Typical experiments have therefore been selected and described so that all the important methods of dealing with any particular problem can be studied, and footnotes referring directly or indirectly to the other experiments of the same class have been given. It is hoped that the usefulness of the book for purposes of reference may be increased by the fact that all such footnotes have been fully indexed.

It is a great pleasure to acknowledge my indebtedness to Dr. D. R. Hartree of Christ's College, Cambridge, who has kindly read through the proofs and has pointed out a number of errors, obscurities, and omissions, and made many valuable suggestions.

J. K. ROBERTS

CAVENDISH LABORATORY, CAMBRIDGE
September 1928

Preface to the Fourth Edition

The preparation of this new edition was begun in January 1949 and the whole book has been brought up to date to that time. In places it has been possible to include an account of important new work that has appeared up till as late as July 1950. In preparing the new edition, the framework of the earlier editions has been retained deliberately.

More new material has been added to the discussion of low-temperature phenomena than to any other section; and it will be appreciated (by some in particular) how appropriate this is. This additional material will be found in the new chapter on higher-order phase transitions, as well as in the chapters on the production of low temperatures and the third law. The chapter formerly headed "The Nernst Heat Theorem" is now headed "The Third Law of Thermodynamics" and has been greatly extended in scope. It now takes account of the significance, in this connexion, of the typically low-temperature phenomena. The chapter on the theory of the specific heats of solids has been recast in the light of the perspective now afforded by the lattice theory of specific heats. The re-naming of this chapter and also that on the third law indicates the shift of emphasis.

The earlier editions of this book gave the classical discussion of the second law, and the analytical methods of Willard Gibbs were used in applying it to particular systems. This procedure has been followed in the new edition, but at the same time it has been felt desirable to indicate the phenomenological approach to the laws of thermodynamics which is due to Carathéodory.

The recommendations of the International Unions of Physics and of Chemistry concerning units, symbols, and the temperature scale, have been taken into account. Accordingly, the joule has been adopted as the unit of heat. Happily, this book was the only one in English which already used the symbols recommended there for the thermodynamical functions, so that no major changes were necessary.

John Keith Roberts was well known for his experimental and theoretical research on various topics of thermodynamical interest. He intended, on returning to Cambridge after the war, to continue these thermodynamical inquiries and to extend them to other fields. We had agreed to continue our co-operation begun in 1938, and I greatly looked forward to this. I eventually accepted an invitation to revise this book out of an awareness of my indebtedness to him as a teacher. I have striven to revise it as he would have done.

It is a pleasure to thank those colleagues whose day-to-day discussions with me may be reflected in these pages. My thanks are also due to all those who in their very different ways have encouraged and stimulated me in this task.

A. R. MILLER

ROYAL SOCIETY MOND LABORATORY
CAVENDISH LABORATORY
UNIVERSITY OF CAMBRIDGE
 September 1950

Preface to the Fifth Edition

In preparing this edition, the aim has been to take account of all work which was published up to June 1958. In a few instances it has been possible to include results which had been published by mid-1959.

Since the previous edition of this book was published, the International Unions of Physics and Chemistry have agreed first, that the size of the degree on the international temperature scale shall continue to be defined in terms of the temperature interval between two fundamental fixed points and secondly, on the numerical value to be assigned to the triple point of water on the thermodynamic temperature scale, thus defining the size of the degree on that scale. Accordingly, in this edition, after pointing out that these two methods can be used to define the size of the degree, the definition in terms of a single fixed point is used in speaking of the thermodynamic scale, while that in terms of a temperature interval is used in considering the international scale, the interpolation instruments which are used to realize it, and the particular gas thermometers by use of which these interpolation instruments are calibrated.

Opportunity has been taken in this edition to revise the list of engineering texts referred to at the end of the chapter on power cycles, to include recent work on the principle of corresponding states, on magnetic cooling, and on the Bunsen ice calorimeter which, in recent years, has been developed, at the United States National Bureau of Standards, as a high-precision instrument.

It is a pleasure to express my thanks to the Librarian of the University of Melbourne for making available to me the facilities of the University Library and to Sir Leslie Martin, F.R.S. for his encouragement.

A. R. MILLER

MELBOURNE
January 1960

Acknowledgments

This opportunity is taken of expressing indebtedness and thanks to various authors, societies, and publishers for permission to use plates which have appeared in the following books and periodicals:

Ewing, *The Mechanical Production of Cold.*

Henning, *Temperaturmessung.*

Jeans, *Report on Radiation and the Quantum Theory.*

Nernst, *Grundlagen des neuen Wärmesatzes*; *Theoretical Chemistry* (English translation).

Partington and Shilling, *The Specific Heats of Gases.*

Preston, *Theory of Heat.*

A Dictionary of Applied Physics.

Handbuch der Experimentalphysik.

Müller-Pouillets Lehrbuch der Physik.

Proceedings of the Royal Society.

Philosophical Transactions of the Royal Society.

Proceedings of the Physical Society of London.

Reports on Progress in Physics of the Physical Society of London.

Philosophical Magazine.

Nature.

Physical Review.

Berichte der deutschen physikalischen Gesellschaft.

Verhandlungen der deutschen physikalischen Gesellschaft.

Annalen der Physik.

Zeitschrift für Physik.

Physikalische Zeitschrift.

Zeitschrift für physikalische Chemie.

Leiden Communications.

Journal of Research of the National Bureau of Standards, Washington.

Contents

Chapter I

Temperature

SECT.   PAGE

THE CONCEPT OF TEMPERATURE - - - - - - 1
2 Thermal Equilibrium - - - - - - - - - 1
3 Temperature as a Property of a System - - - - - - 3
4 The Size of the Degree - - - - - - - - 6
GAS THERMOMETERS - - - - - - - - 9
6 The Constant-pressure Thermometer - - - - - - - 9
7 The Constant-volume Thermometer - - - - - - - 10
8 Some Properties of Gas Thermometers - - - - - - 10
The Properties of Gases and their Use in Thermometers - - - - 12
9 Boyle's Law - - - - - - - - - - 12
10 The Actual Behaviour of Gases - - - - - - - 14
11 The Theory of Gas Thermometer Corrections - - - - - 16
12 Comparison of Scales using Different Gases - - - - - - 18
THE AVOGADRO SCALE OF TEMPERATURE - - - - 20
14 Numerical Values of the Corrections - - - - - - 20
Fixed Points - - - - - - - - - - 22
16 The Ice Point - - - - - - - - - - 22
17 The Steam Point - - - - - - - - - 23
18 The Sulphur Boiling-point - - - - - - - - 24
19 Boiling-points of Naphthalene and of Benzophenone - - - - 26
20 Melting-points - - - - - - - - - - 26
21 Melting-points at High Temperatures - - - - - - 27
22 The International Temperature Scale - - - - - - - 28
PLATINUM THERMOMETRY - - - - - - - 31
24 Platinum Thermometry at High Temperatures - - - - - 33
Practical Arrangements - - - - - - - - 33
25 The Thermometer - - - - - - - - - 33
26 Resistance of Leads - - - - - - - - - 34
27 Heating Effect of Measuring Current - - - - - - - 35
28 Thermo-electric Effects - - - - - - - - 35
29 Bridges for Thermometric Work - - - - - - - 35
THERMO-ELECTRIC THERMOMETRY - - - - - 36
31 The Potentiometer Circuit - - - - - - - - 37
32 Thermocouples at High Temperatures - - - - - - 38
MERCURY-IN-GLASS THERMOMETRY - - - - - 39
THE ABSOLUTE SCALE OF TEMPERATURE - - - - 39

SECT.   PAGE
34 The Gas Scale - - - - - - - - - - - 39
35 The Numerical Value of the Constant a - - - - - - - 41
36 The Thermodynamic or Absolute Scale of Temperature - - - - 43
37 Two Independent Temperature Scales - - - - - - - 44
38 The Gas Constant - - - - - - - - - - - 44
    EXAMPLE - - - - - - - - - - - 46

Chapter II

Quantity of Heat

THE NATURE OF HEAT - - - - - - - - 47
3 Davy's Experiment - - - - - - - - - - 48
4 Joule's Experiments - - - - - - - - - - 49
5 Specific Heat and Thermal Capacity - - - - - - - - 51
6 Summary of Results - - - - - - - - - - 52
7 The Exact Definition of the Calorie - - - - - - - - 53
8 Heat Losses in Calorimetry - - - - - - - - - 54
    THE MECHANICAL EQUIVALENT OF HEAT - - - - 55
    Direct Methods - - - - - - - - - - - 55
10 Joule, Rowland, Reynolds and Moorby - - - - - - - 55
11 Laby and Hercus - - - - - - - - - - - 56
    Electrical Methods - - - - - - - - - - - 58
13 Griffiths, Schuster and Gannon, Callendar and Barnes, Bousfield and Bousfield - 59
14 Jaeger and Steinwehr - - - - - - - - - - 59
15 Osborne, Stimson and Ginnings - - - - - - - - 62
16 Value of the Mechanical Equivalent of Heat - - - - - - 63
17 The Specific Heat of Water - - - - - - - - - 64
18 Internal Energy - - - - - - - - - - - 65
19 The First Law of Thermodynamics - - - - - - - - 67
    EXAMPLES - - - - - - - - - - - 68

Chapter III

The Kinetic Theory of Gases

THE STRUCTURE OF THE PERFECT GAS - - - - 70
3 Calculation of the Pressure - - - - - - - - - 71
4 Avogadro's Law - - - - - - - - - - - 72
5 Boyle's Law and Dalton's Law - - - - - - - - - 73
6 Introduction of the Temperature - - - - - - - - 73
7 The Determination of Avogadro's Number - - - - - - - 75
    EXAMPLE - - - - - - - - - - - 77
    THE STEADY STATE: MAXWELL'S LAW OF THE DISTRIBU-
    TION OF VELOCITIES - - - - - - - - - 77
9 The Mean Velocity - - - - - - - - - - 80
10 The Most Probable Velocity - - - - - - - - - 80
11 Expressions for Maxwell's Law - - - - - - - - - 81
12 Graphical Representation - - - - - - - - - 81

SECT.   PAGE
13   Experimental Test of Maxwell's Law-   -   -   -   -   -   -   -   82
     THE MEAN FREE PATH   -   -   -   -   -   -   -   -   84
15   Mean Free Path and Number of Collisions -   -   -   -   -   -   85
16   Probability of Path of Given Length -   -   -   -   -   -   -   85
     COLLISIONS WITH A SOLID BOUNDARY: KNUDSEN'S COSINE
       LAW -   -   -   -   -   -   -   -   -   -   -   -   86
     MAXWELL'S LAW AND THE PROPERTIES OF GASES AT VERY
       LOW PRESSURES   -   -   -   -   -   -   -   -   -   88
     Stationary Streaming through Narrow Tubes   -   -   -   -   -   -   88
19   Theory of Streaming   -   -   -   -   -   -   -   -   -   -   88
20   Streaming Experiments -   -   -   -   -   -   -   -   -   -   92
21   The Flow of a Gas through a Small Opening   -   -   -   -   -   -   93
     The Knudsen Absolute Manometer -   -   -   -   -   -   -   -   94
23   Thermo-molecular Pressure   -   -   -   -   -   -   -   -   -   97
     Thermal diffusion   -   -   -   -   -   -   -   -   -   -   98
     TABLE OF INTEGRALS -   -   -   -   -   -   -   -   -   99

Chapter IV

Equation of State for Gases

2   Andrews' Experiments -   -   -   -   -   -   -   -   -   -   101
3   The Equation of Van der Waals   -   -   -   -   -   -   -   -   103
4   Other Equations of State   -   -   -   -   -   -   -   -   -   109
    Expression of the Equation of State of Gases by means of Series   -   -   -   -   109
6   Equations of State and the Second Virial Coefficient: the Boyle Temperature   -   115
7   Principle of Corresponding States   -   -   -   -   -   -   -   -   118
    EXPERIMENTAL METHODS -   -   -   -   -   -   -   -   122
8   Compressibility   -   -   -   -   -   -   -   -   -   -   122
10 Compressibility of Liquids   -   -   -   -   -   -   -   -   -   123
    Critical Phenomena -   -   -   -   -   -   -   -   -   -   123
12 The Properties of a Substance near the Critical Point -   -   -   -   -   125
    EXAMPLES   -   -   -   -   -   -   -   -   -   -   129

Chapter V

The Production and Measurement of Low Temperatures

2   The Pictet or Cascade Process -   -   -   -   -   -   -   -   -   130
3   The Linde Method—the Joule Effect and the Joule-Kelvin Effect   -   -   -   131
4   The Claude Method   -   -   -   -   -   -   -   -   -   -   134
5   The Liquefaction of Helium   -   -   -   -   -   -   -   -   -   135
6   Helium Liquefiers -   -   -   -   -   -   -   -   -   -   136
    The Measurement of Low Temperatures   -   -   -   -   -   -   -   139
7   The International Scale and the Gas Scale from 0° to $-182\cdot97°$ C. (Int. 1948) -   139
8   The Measurement of Temperatures down to $-190°$ C.   -   -   -   -   140
9   Temperatures between 14° and 80° K.   -   -   -   -   -   -   -   141
10 Temperatures between 5° and 14° K.   -   -   -   -   -   -   -   142
11 Temperatures below 5° K.   -   -   -   -   -   -   -   -   -   142
12 Constant-temperature Baths   -   -   -   -   -   -   -   -   -   147

SECT. PAGE

The Equilibrium between Different States of Helium and Hydrogen at Low Temperatures 148

13 The Solidification of Helium - - - - - - - - - 148
14 Two States of Liquid Helium - - - - - - - - - 150
15 The Extension of the Melting Curve of Helium and Hydrogen to High Pressures 150

Cooling by Adiabatic Demagnetization - - - - - - - - 153

16 Theory of the Method - - - - - - - - - - 153
17 Relation between T^* and the Thermodynamic Temperature - - - - 160
18 Two-stage Demagnetization - - - - - - - - - 167
19 Nuclear Demagnetization - - - - - - - - - 168
EXAMPLES - - - - - - - - - - - 169

Chapter VI

The Specific Heats of Gases

Difference between the Specific Heats at Constant Pressure and at Constant Volume 172

2 Perfect Gases - - - - - - - - - - - 172
3 Actual Gases - - - - - - - - - - - 173

The Measurement of the Specific Heat at Constant Volume - - - - 175

4 The Joly Steam Calorimeter - - - - - - - - - 175
5 Eucken's Experiments on Hydrogen at Low Temperatures - - - - 176
6 The Explosion Method - - - - - - - - - - 177

The Measurement of the Specific Heat at Constant Pressure - - - - 179

8 Regnault's Experiments - - - - - - - - - - 179
9 Holborn and Henning's Experiments - - - - - - - 180
10 The Continuous-flow Method - - - - - - - - - 181
11 Experiments of Blackett, Henry, and Rideal - - - - - - 182

THE RATIO OF THE SPECIFIC HEATS OF A GAS - - - 184

Adiabatic Changes - - - - - - - - - - 184

13 Perfect Gases - - - - - - - - - - - 185
14 Actual Gases - - - - - - - - - - - 187
15 Experimental Methods - - - - - - - - - - 190

The Velocity of Sound - - - - - - - - - - 194

17 The Velocity of Sound in Free Air - - - - - - - - 196
18 The Velocity in a Tube - - - - - - - - - - 198
19 Experimental Methods - - - - - - - - - - 199
20 Dust Figure Methods - - - - - - - - - - 199
21 The Method of Partington and Shilling - - - - - - - 200
22 The Method of Dixon - - - - - - - - - - 202

RESULTS - - - - - - - - - - - - 202

24 Degrees of Freedom - - - - - - - - - - 202
25 The Equipartition of Energy - - - - - - - - - 203
26 Experimental Values - - - - - - - - - - 205
27 Hydrogen at Low Temperatures - - - - - - - - 206

The Quantum Theory - - - - - - - - - - 207

28 Rotation - - - - - - - - - - - - 207
29 Internal Vibrations - - - - - - - - - - 210
30 Theory of Dispersion of Sound in Gases - - - - - - - 213
EXAMPLE - - - - - - - - - - - 216

Chapter VII

The Specific Heats of Solids and Liquids

SECT.		PAGE
2	The Nernst Calorimeter - - - - - - - - -	217
3	The "Adiabatic Vacuum Calorimeter" of Simon and Lange - - - -	220
4	Other Methods - - - - - - - - - -	220
5	Specific Heats at Constant Pressure and at Constant Volume - - -	221
	Experimental Results - - - - - - - - -	222
6	Dulong and Petit's Law - - - - - - - - -	222
7	General Results - - - - - - - - - -	223
	Experiments at High Temperatures - - - - - - - -	226
	THE SPECIFIC HEATS OF LIQUIDS - - - - - -	228

Chapter VIII

Vaporization

		PAGE
	THE MEASUREMENT OF VAPOUR PRESSURE - - - -	230
	Non-metals - - - - - - - - - -	230
2	Direct or Static Methods - - - - - - - -	230
3	Boiling-point Method - - - - - - - - -	232
	Metals - - - - - - - - - -	233
5	Knudsen's Method - - - - - - - - -	233
6	Methods depending on the Rate of Vaporization: Langmuir's Work -	235
7	The Coefficient of Condensation - - - - - - -	238
	Results of Vapour-pressure Measurements - - - - - -	238
9	The Kirchhoff Formula - - - - - - - -	240
10	The General Equation - - - - - - - -	241
11	The Chemical Constant - - - - - - - -	241
12	The Latent Heat of Vaporization at the Absolute Zero - - - -	241
	THE MEASUREMENT OF LATENT HEAT OF VAPORIZATION	242
	Evaporation Methods - - - - - - - - -	242
15	Henning's Experiments - - - - - - - -	243
16	Experiments at Low Temperatures - - - - - - -	244
17	Dieterici's Experiments - - - - - - - -	245
	Condensation Methods - - - - - - - - -	245
18	Berthelot's Apparatus - - - - - - - -	245
19	Awbery and Griffiths' Apparatus - - - - - - -	247
20	The Joly Steam Calorimeter - - - - - - -	248
	Results - - - - - - - - - -	248
21	Trouton's Rule - - - - - - - - -	248
	THE DETERMINATION OF VAPOUR DENSITY - - - -	250
	NUMERICAL VALUES FOR THE CHEMICAL CONSTANT -	251
23	Agreement between Theoretical and Experimental Values - - -	251
	NOTE ON THE APPLICABILITY OF THE GAS LAWS TO VAPOURS - - - - - - - - -	252
	THE SEPARATION OF ISOTOPES - - - - - -	255

SECT.   PAGE
     ADSORPTION -   -   -   -   -   -   -   -   -   -   - 257
27   Elementary Kinetic Theory   -   -   -   -   -   -   •   •   - 258
     EXAMPLES   -   -   -   -   -   -   -   -   -   •   - 259

Chapter IX

Fusion

     The Measurement of the Latent Heat of Fusion of Ice   -   -   -   •   •   - 260
2   The Method of Mixtures   -   -   -   -   -   -   -   •   - 260
3   The Bunsen Ice Calorimeter   -   •   -   -   -   -   -   •   - 261
4   Electrical Method -   -   -   -   -   -   •   -   -   •   - 263
     The Measurement of the Latent Heat of Fusion of Metals   -   •   •   - 264
     The Measurement of Latent Heats of Fusion at Low Temperatures   -   •   •   - 267
     The Relation between the Latent Heat of Fusion and the Melting-point   •   •   - 267

Chapter X

Thermal Expansion

     EXAMPLE   -   -   -   -   -   -   -   -   -   -   - 269
     THE MEASUREMENT OF THE LINEAR EXPANSION OF SOLIDS   270
     Optical Methods   -   -   -   -   -   -   -   -   -   - - 270
3   Fizeau's Method   -   -   •   -   -   -   -   -   -   •   - 270
4   The Optical Lever Method   -   -   -   -   -   -   •   •   - 271
     Results   -   -   -   •   -   -   -   -   -   •   - 273
5   The Grüneisen Law   -   -   -   -   -   -   -   -   •   - 273
6   Anisotropic Bodies   -   -   -   -   -   -   -   -   •   - 274
     EXAMPLES   -   -   -   -   -   -   -   -   -   •   - 275
     THE EXPANSION OF LIQUIDS AND GASES   -   -   •   - 275
8   The Weight Thermometer   -   -   -   -   -   -   •   •   - 275
9   The Absolute Expansion of Liquids   -   -   -   -   •   -   •   - 277
10   The Expansion of Water   -   -   -   -   -   •   •   •   - 279

Chapter XI

The Transfer of Heat by Conduction and Convection

     A. CONDUCTION   -   -   -   -   -   -   -   -   -   - 280
3   Thermal Resistivity and Resistance   -   -   -   -   -   -   •   - 281
4   Practical Methods -   -   -   -   -   -   •   -   •   - 281
     GASES   -   -   -   -   -   -   -   -   •   •   - 282
5   Hercus and Laby's Method   -   -   -   -   -   -   •   - 282
6   Hot-wire Method -   -   -   -   -   -   -   -   •   - 283
7   Elementary Theory of Thermal Conductivity in Gases   -   -   •   •   - 284
8   Viscosity of Gases -   -   -   -   -   -   -   -   •   •   - 285
9   Ratio of the Thermal Conductivity and the Coefficient of Viscosity   -   •   - 287
10   The Molecular Diameter and the Mean Free Path   -   -   •   •   - 288

SECT.

PAGE

11   The Thermal Conductivity of Gases at Very Low Pressures - - - - 288
      LIQUIDS - - - - - - - - - - - - 291
      METALS - - - - - - - - - - - 292
      Direct Methods - - - - - - - - - - 292
      Electrical Methods - - - - - - - - - - 294
15   Experiments of Jaeger and Diesselhorst - - - - - - 296
16   Meissner's Experiments - - - - - - - - - 298
17   High Temperatures - - - - - - - - - 299
      Theoretical - - - - - - - - - - 299
19   Experimental Results - - - - - - - - - 300
20   Difficulties of the Theory - - - - - - - - 302
      SOLID NON-METALS - - - - - - - - 303
22   Thermal Conductivity of Crystals at Low Temperatures - - - 305
      Theoretical - - - - - - - - - - 306
      B. CONVECTION - - - - - - - - - 308
      Natural Convection - - - - - - - - - 308
26   Practical Applications of the Formula - - - - - - 310
      EXAMPLE - - - - - - - - - - 311
      Forced Convection - - - - - - - - - 312
28   The Propagation of Heat in a Conducting Medium - - - - 314

Chapter XII

The Second Law of Thermodynamics

2   Reversible Processes - - - - - - - - - 316
3   The Carnot Cycle - - - - - - - - - 317
4   The Second Law of Thermodynamics - - - - - 319
5   The Efficiency of a Reversible Heat Engine - - - - - 320
6   The Thermodynamic Scale of Temperature - - - - - 321
7   Comparison of Thermodynamic and Gas Scales of Temperature - - 322
      Entropy - - - - - - - - - - 325
9   Change of Entropy in a Carnot Cycle - - - - - - 326
10   Change of Entropy in any Reversible Cycle - - - - - 326
11   Analytical Statement - - - - - - - - 327
12   Carathéodory's Principle - - - - - - - - 329

Chapter XIII

Thermodynamic Relations and their Use

2   Maxwell's Four Thermodynamic Relations - - - - - - 332
3   Specific Heats - - - - - - - - - 333
      THE JOULE-KELVIN EFFECT - - - - - - 335
5   Theory of the Joule-Kelvin Effect - - - - - - 337
6   The Enthalpy - - - - - - - - - 338
7   Equation of State based on Measurement of the Joule-Kelvin Effect - - 339
8   Determination of Absolute Thermodynamic Temperatures from Measurements
          made on an Empirical Temperature Scale - - - - - 339
9   The Numerical Value Assigned to the Triple Point of Water - - - 340
      EXAMPLES - - - - - - - - - 341

Chapter XIV

Power Cycles

SECT.   PAGE
2   The Working Substance -   -   -   -   -   -   -   -   -   -   - 344
    STEAM-ENGINES   -   -   -   -   -   -   -   -   -   -   - 345
    The Reciprocating Steam-engine   -   -   -   -   -   -   -   - 348
4   The Rankine Cycle   -   -   -   -   -   -   -   -   - 346
5   The Entropy-temperature Diagram   -   -   -   -   -   -   - 347
6   Rankine Cycle with Superheated Steam   -   -   -   -   -   - 347
7   The Calculation of the Efficiency of the Rankine Cycle   -   -   - 345
8   The Use of Steam Tables   -   -   -   -   -   -   - 350
9   Numerical Calculations -   -   -   -   -   -   -   -   - 351
10 Mollier's Total Heat-Entropy Diagram   -   -   -   -   -   - 353
11 The Measurement of the Performance of a Steam-engine   -   -   - 355
12 Multiple-expansion Engines   -   -   -   -   -   -   -   - 356
    The Steam-turbine   -   -   -   -   -   -   -   -   - 357
14 The Reaction Turbine   -   -   -   -   -   -   -   - 358
15 The Work Obtainable from a Turbine   -   -   -   -   -   - 359
16 The Theory of Jets   -   -   -   -   -   -   -   -   - 361
    INTERNAL-COMBUSTION ENGINES   -   -   -   -   -   - 363
    Actual Cycles -   -   -   -   -   -   -   -   -   -   - 365
18 The Otto Cycle   -   -   -   -   -   -   -   -   -   - 365
19 The Diesel Cycle -   -   -   -   -   -   -   -   -   - 366
20 Heat Losses -   -   -   -   -   -   -   -   -   -   - 369
    REFRIGERATION   -   -   -   -   -   -   -   -   - 369
22 The Working Substance -   -   -   -   -   -   -   -   - 370
23 The Cycle of an Actual Refrigerating Machine   -   -   -   - 370
24 The Use of the Mollier Diagram   -   -   -   -   -   - 371
25 Numerical Calculations -   -   -   -   -   -   -   -   - 373
26 The Electrolux Refrigerator   -   -   -   -   -   -   - 373
    REFERENCES -   -   -   -   -   -   -   -   -   -   - 375

Chapter XV

The Principle of the Increase of Entropy

2   The Entropy of a Perfect Gas -   -   -   -   -   -   -   - 376
3   Entropy of a Mixture of Two Perfect Gases   -   -   -   -   - 377
4   The Change of Entropy when Two Gases diffuse into One Another -   -   - 378
5   The Principle of the Increase of Entropy   -   -   -   -   - 379

Chapter XVI

The Conditions of Equilibrium of a Physical or Chemical System

    General Laws governing Changes in a Physical or Chemical System -   -   -   - 383
2   Adiabatic Changes -   -   -   -   -   -   -   -   -   - 384
3   Isothermal Changes   -   -   -   -   -   -   -   -   - 385

SECT.   PAGE

   Conditions of Equilibrium - - - - - - - - - - - 387
6 Equilibrium in a Thermally Isolated System. Adiabatic Equilibrium - - - 388
7 Isothermal Equilibrium - - - - - - - - - - - 388
  THE EQUILIBRIUM BETWEEN TWO STATES OF THE SAME
    SUBSTANCE - - - - - - - - - - - 389
8 Clausius-Clapeyron Equation - - - - - - - - - - 389
9 The Specific Heat of a Saturated Vapour - - - - - - - 394
  HETEROGENEOUS SYSTEMS- - - - - - - - 396
10 Definition of Phase, Component - - - - - - - - 396
11 Complete Description of a Phase - - - - - - - - 397
12 Relations between the Thermodynamical Functions - - - - - 397
13 Chemical Equilibrium between Phases - - - - - - - 399
14 The Phase Rule - - - - - - - - - - - 401
15 Gibbs-Duhem Relation - - - - - - - - - - 402
  EXAMPLES - - - - - - - - - - - 404

Chapter XVII

Transformations of Higher Order

1 Thermodynamical Functions - - - - - - - - - 408
  LIQUID HELIUM - - - - - - - - - - 412
2 Properties of Liquid Helium - - - - - - - - - 412
3 Energy Relations for Helium - - - - - - - - - 418
4 Model of a Second-order Transition - - - - - - - - 419
5 Other Examples of Second-order Transitions - - - - - - 421
6 Co-operative Assemblies - - - - - - - - - - 421
  SUPERCONDUCTIVITY - - - - - - - - - 422
7 Properties of a Metal in the Superconducting State - - - - - 422
8 Thermodynamics of the Transition in a Magnetic Field - - - - 426
9 Thermodynamic Functions of the Superconducting State - - - - 428
  EXAMPLES - - - - - - - - - - - 431

Chapter XVIII

Chemical Equilibria

  Equilibrium in a Gaseous System at Constant Pressure and Temperature - - - 434
3 The Heat of Reaction - - - - - - - - - - 436
4 The Effect of Change of Temperature on the Reaction Constant - - - 436
5 The Effect of Change of Pressure on the Reaction Constant - - - 437
6 The Principle of Le Chatelier - - - - - - - - - 437
7 Equilibrium in Terms of Partial Pressures - - - - - - 438
8 Separation of Isotopes - - - - - - - - - - 438
  Reactions at Constant Temperature and Pressure in which Solids or Liquids take part - 440
10 Equilibrium Condition - - - - - - - - - - 440
11 Heat of Reaction - - - - - - - - - - - 441
12 Effect of Temperature on the Heat of Reaction - - - - - 443
  Numerical Calculations - - - - - - - - - 443
  The Activity - - - - - - - - - - - 446

SECT.		PAGE
15	Change of Activity with Pressure	446
16	Application to Equilibrium Problems	447
	THE MEASUREMENT OF EQUILIBRIUM CONSTANTS	448
18	Comparison of Values obtained using the Various Methods	453
	Electromotive Force and Equilibrium Measurements	454
20	Reversible and Irreversible Cells	455
21	The Reversible Electromotive Force	456
22	Quantity of Electricity	457
23	Sign Convention	458
24	Concentration Gas Cells	459
25	Applications of the Method	460
	THE MEASUREMENT OF HEATS OF REACTION	463
27	Heats of Reaction at Constant Pressure and Constant Volume	465
	EXAMPLE	465

Chapter XIX

The Third Law of Thermodynamics

1	The Nernst Heat Theorem	466
2	The Proof of the Nernst Heat Theorem	471
3	The Chemical Constants	475
4	Heterogeneous Reactions	481
5	Low-temperature Phenomena	482
6	Liquid Helium	483
7	The Superconducting State	485
8	Adiabatic Demagnetization	485

Chapter XX

Radiation

	Instruments for the Detection and Measurement of Radiant Heat	487
3	Bolometers	487
4	Thermopiles	488
5	Radiometers	489
	General Theory of Emission and Absorption	489
6	Prévost's Theory of Exchanges	489
7	Emission and Absorption	490
8	Kirchhoff's Law	490
9	The Full Radiator (Black Body) and Full (Black-body) Radiation	493
10	The Principle of Detailed Balancing	494
	The Stefan-Boltzmann Law	495
11	Thermodynamical Deduction	495
12	The Total Emissive Power of a Full Radiator	496
13	The Experiment Proof of the Stefan-Boltzmann Law and the Determination of the Stefan-Boltzmann Constant	499
	Wien's Displacement Law	504
15	Planck's Formula	511

SECT.   PAGE

16 The Experimental Verification of Wien's Law and the Determination of the Constant C_2 in Planck's Radiation Formula - - - - - - - 515
    RADIATION PYROMETRY - - - - - - - - 516
17 The Temperature Scale at High Temperature - - - - - - 516
18 Optical Pyrometers - - - - - - - - - - 517
19 The Total-radiation Pyrometer - - - - - - - 519
20 Comparison of Total-radiation and Optical Pyrometers - - - - 520
21 Emissivity and the Temperature of Bodies other than Full Radiators - - - 521
22 Optical Pyrometers and the Determination of High-temperature Melting-points - 522
23 The Temperature of the Sun - - - - - - - - - 523

Chapter XXI

Planck's Radiation Formula

2 Number of Independent Vibrations of a Continuous Medium - - - - 526
3 Rayleigh's Radiation Formula - - - - - - - - 529
4 The Quantum Theory - - - - - - - - - 529

Chapter XXII

The Theory of the Specific Heats of Solids

1 Introduction of Quantum Theory by Einstein - - - - - - 532
2 Frequency Spectrum - - - - - - - - - - 533
3 Debye's Theory - - - - - - - - - - 535
4 Comparison with Experiment - - - - - - - - 536
5 The T^3 Law - - - - - - - - - - 539
6 Born's Theory - - - - - - - - - - 540
7 Extension of the Theory - - - - - - - - - 542
8 The Entropy of Solids - - - - - - - - - 543
9 Specific Heats at High Temperatures - - - - - - - 544
10 The Energy of an Oscillator at the Absolute Zero - - - - 544
11 Blackman's Lattice Theory of Specific Heats - - - - - 545
12 Anomalies in the Specific Heats of Solids - - - - - - 548

Chapter XXIII

The Equation of State for Solids

2 The Virial Law of Clausius - - - - - - - - 553
    The Theory of the Solid State - - - - - - - 555
4 The Total Potential Energy of the Atoms in a Gram-atom - - - 556
5 Atomic Oscillations - - - - - - - - - 558
6 Change of Frequency with Volume - - - - - - - 560
7 The Equation of State for Solids - - - - - - - 561
8 The Direct Measurement of the Value of γ - - - - - 562
9 Thermal Expansion: Grüneisen's Law - - - - - - 563

SECT.   PAGE
10   Debye's Deduction of the Equation of State   -   -   -   -   -   -   565
11   The Thermal Expansion of Anisotropic Bodies   -   -   -   -   -   -   568
12   The Latent Heat of Vaporization at the Absolute Zero -   -   -   -   -   -   569
13   The Energy of Crystalline Salts -   -   -   -   -   -   -   -   -   571
     THE THEORY OF FUSION   -   -   -   -   -   -   -   -   573
15   Recent Theories of Melting and of Liquids -   -   -   -   -   -   -   575
     REFERENCE   -   -   -   -   -   -   -   -   -   -   583

     APPENDIX: THERMODYNAMIC RELATIONS AND THE THER-
        MODYNAMIC PROPERTIES OF STEAM   -   -   -   -   585
        1   Thermodynamic Relations   -   -   -   -   -   -   -   -   585
        2   The Properties of Steam -   -   -   -   -   -   -   -   -   587
        3   Steam Tables   -   -   -   -   -   -   -   -   -   589

     INDEX   -   -   -   -   -   -   -   -   -   -   -   **593**

CHAPTER I

Temperature

THE CONCEPT OF TEMPERATURE

1. All thermal experiments involve measurements of temperature. We shall, therefore, commence our study of the science of heat by considering the concept of temperature and how it is measured.

The physiological sensation of hotness and coldness is an experience common to us all. The ideas of temperature and of temperature scale were introduced historically to give a precise quantitative form to the qualitative idea derived from these perceptions. One of the earliest attempts to construct a temperature scale was that of Newton,[*] who arranged simple processes such as the freezing of water, the melting of wax, water boiling violently, and so forth, in an order, and assigned numerical values to them on two different scales. One of these scales was in arithmetical, and the other in geometrical, progression. The idea of temperature, or of hotness and coldness, is, like length and mass, for example, one of the primary concepts in terms of which natural phenomena are described. It is first necessary to examine this concept; and this we now do by considering the results of a number of simple experiments on fluids, more particularly on gases.[†]

2. Thermal Equilibrium.

From a macroscopic point of view, the state of a thermodynamical system can be determined by the specification of its mass, composition, and one or more *pairs* of quantities. One member of each of these pairs of quantities is a generalized force and the other is a generalized displacement; e.g. the state of a given mass of a pure gas can be specified by its pressure and its volume. Because it was on gases that the experiments which established the nature of the temperature concept were first carried out, as well as for simplicity and convenience, the discussion which follows will be given in terms of the pressure and the volume of a gas. Its generalization to other systems, the states

---

[*] Newton, *Phil. Trans.*, Vol. 22, p. 824 (1701).

[†] Compare Born, *Physik. Zeits.*, Vol. 22, pp. 218, 249, 282 (1921); also Balamuth, Wolfe and Zemansky, *Amer. Journ. Phys.*, Vol. 9, p. 199 (1941).

of which are specified by other pairs of variables, is straightforward.

Any state of the gas in which the pressure and volume remain unaltered as long as the external conditions remain unaltered is called an *equilibrium state*. It is a fact of experience that the existence of an equilibrium state depends upon the presence of other systems in the same neighbourhood and of the kinds of walls separating them. Consider two gases which are separated by a wall. If the pressure and volume of the first gas are unaltered however the pressure and volume of the second gas are altered, the wall separating the two gases is said to be *adiabatic*. If when the pressure and the volume of one of the gases is changed, those of the other gas change spontaneously until the combined system of two gases is in an equilibrium state, the wall is said to be *diathermic* and the two systems are said to be in *thermal equilibrium*. In each of these cases it is assumed that the wall is able to withstand the stresses associated with the difference in pressures. To say that two systems are in thermal equilibrium means that if they are allowed independently to come to equilibrium while they are separated by an adiabatic wall, then there is no change in the pressure and volume of either when the adiabatic wall is replaced by a diathermic wall.

Consider two systems A and B which are separated by an adiabatic wall, and a third system C from which each is separated by a diathermic wall. When such an experimental arrangement is set up, it is found that both A and C, and also B and C, reach thermal equilibrium. If the adiabatic wall between A and B is now replaced by a diathermic wall, no changes are observed in the pressure and volume of either, that is, A and B are also in thermal equilibrium with one another. This is an important experimental fact, and can be stated concisely in the form:

If each of two systems is in thermal equilibrium with a third, they are in thermal equilibrium with one another.

This experimental finding is the basis of the existence of the concept of temperature.

It is to be noted that one of the systems could be a liquid confined in a glass bulb and a capillary tube, in such a way that its change in volume is measured by the length of liquid in the capillary. It will be seen below that such an arrangement provides a thermometer, and the length of the capillary thread provides an empirical temperature scale. Of such a character was Newton's linseed-oil thermometer, and is the mercury-in-glass thermometer. Or again, one of the systems could be a metal wire (or strip) the electrical resistance of which can be measured. Platinum and lead resistance thermometers are of this character. At present, however, we are concerned to point out only that the use of such thermometers depends on the law of thermal equilibrium which has been stated above.

3. Temperature as a Property of a System.

Consider a system A in a state in which its pressure is p_a and its volume V_a, and in thermal equilibrium with a system B in the state p_b, V_b. A whole series of states p_a', V_a'; p_a'', V_a'', ... of system A can be found experimentally, each of which is in thermal equilibrium with the original state of system B. Practically, system A could be a flask of gas whose pressure and volume can be varied, and the system B could be a mercury-in-glass thermometer. To establish the existence of the series of states p_a', V_a'; p_a'', V_a'', ... of the system A is simply the experiment usually carried out to verify Boyle's law. All of these

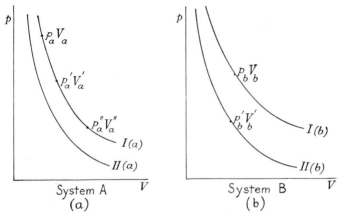

Fig. 1.1.—Pressure-volume curves for two systems in thermal equilibrium

states are in thermal equilibrium with the initial state of the system B, and so must also be in thermal equilibrium with one another. All of these states can be represented on a diagram which has the measures of pressure and volume as ordinate and abscissa. The locus of all points representing states of system A which are in thermal equilibrium with a *given* state of system B is termed an *isotherm* of system A. Experiments with simple substances indicate that usually at least a portion of an isotherm is a continuous curve In the same way another isotherm of system A can be constructed, such that each point of it represents a state which is in thermal equilibrium with another given state p_b', V_b' of system B. In this way, the family curves shown in fig. 1.1(a) can be constructed. The equation of this family of curves is

$$\vartheta_a = F_a(p_a, V_a), \quad . \quad . \quad . \quad . \quad . \quad (1.1)$$

where ϑ_a is a parameter, the value of which depends on the particular isotherm. Likewise, a family of isotherms can be constructed for the

system B (fig. 1.1(*b*)). Every state of B which is represented by a point
on the isotherm which passes through the point p_b, V_b must be in thermal
equilibrium with every state of A which is represented by a point on the
isotherm of system A which passes through the point p_a, V_a. These are
called *corresponding isotherms* (curves I(*a*) and I(*b*) in fig. 1.1). The
isotherms of B can be represented by a family of curves

$$\vartheta_b = F_b(p_b,\ V_b). \qquad \dots \dots \dots \quad (1.2)$$

In this way we can mark off pairs of corresponding isotherms from
the families of curves in fig. 1.1. Let

$$\vartheta_a{}',\ \vartheta_b{}';\ \vartheta_a{}'',\ \vartheta_b{}'';\ \vartheta_a{}''',\ \vartheta_b{}''';\ \dots$$

be the values of the two parameters ϑ_a and ϑ_b which specify corresponding isotherms of the two systems. The existence and identification of
pairs of corresponding isotherms in this way mean * that there is a
set of corresponding values of the two parameters: given a value of
ϑ_a, the value of ϑ_b appropriate to the corresponding isotherm of B is
determined. This ensures that there is a functional relationship between
ϑ_a and ϑ_b; and the one-to-one correspondence between members of the
two families of isotherms implies that, in general, it is a single-valued
function for either parameter as a function of the other. Whether or not
this relationship can be expressed in terms of elementary functions is
irrelevant in the present connexion. All that matters is that it exists.

Let this functional relationship be expressed by an equation

$$\Theta_a(\vartheta_a) = \Theta_b(\vartheta_b).$$

If we now write $f(p,\ V)$ for $\Theta\left\{F(p,\ V)\right\}$ then

$$f_a(p_a,\ V_a) = \vartheta = f_b(p_b,\ V_b). \qquad \dots \dots \quad (2)$$

where ϑ has been written for the common value of $\Theta_a(\vartheta_a)$ and $\Theta_b(\vartheta_b)$.
From another, less analytical, point of view, all states of correspond-
ing isotherms of different systems have something in common, namely,
that they are in thermal equilibrium. The systems may be said to
have a property such that, when the same numerical values can be
assigned to this property for two systems, they are in thermal equilibrium. This property is called the temperature. Clearly, an essential
condition for the existence of this concept is the law of thermal equilibrium stated in Section 2. The existence of temperature—or of the law
of thermal equilibrium from which this concept derives—can be referred
to as the zeroth law of thermodynamics.

There is another aspect † of thermal equilibrium which it is convenient to examine at this stage.

---

* A. R. Miller, *Amer. Journ. Physics*, Vol. 20, p. 491 (1952).
† C. Carathéodory, *Math. Ann.*, Vol. 167, p. 386 (1909).

For particular values of the parameters in equations (1.1) and (1.2) we have corresponding isotherms, that is, each state of A represented by the particular isotherm of the system A is in thermal equilibrium with each state of B represented by the corresponding isotherm of the system B. It has been seen above that this implies that the values of the pressures and volumes of the two systems are not all independent; in other words, there is a functional relationship between these four variables. This functional relationship can be written in the form

$$\phi_1(p_a, V_a; p_b, V_b) = 0. \quad \ldots \quad (3.1)$$

Consider a third system C, which consists of a given mass of fluid, and whose states are specified by its pressure p_c and its volume V_c. If this system is also in thermal equilibrium with the system B, then there is also a functional relationship between the pressures and volumes of equilibrium states of B and C. This relation can be written

$$\phi_2(p_b, V_b; p_c, V_c) = 0. \quad \ldots \quad (3.2)$$

It has already been seen that if each of two systems A and C are in thermal equilibrium with a third system B, then the systems A and C are in thermal equilibrium with one another. There is therefore a functional relationship between the values of the pressures and volumes of equilibrium states of A and of C. Thus the two relations (3.1) and (3.2) imply also a relation

$$\phi_3(p_c, V_c; p_a, V_a) = 0. \quad \ldots \quad (3.3)$$

More generally, the law of thermal equilibrium which has been stated in the preceding section requires that the truth of any two of the equations (3) implies also the truth of the third of them.

Carathéodory asserted that this is true when and only when the three relations (3) are equivalent to a set of relations

$$f_a(p_a, V_a) = f_b(p_b, V_b) = f_c(p_c, V_c). \quad \ldots \quad (4)$$

It must be pointed out that Carathéodory was careful to restrict his discussion to a particular class of physical systems and this restriction imposed mathematical limitations on the functions ϕ. Most commentators * on this subject have accepted Carathéodory's assertion without explicit statement of the restricted context within which he made it. The sufficiency of the condition given by equation (4) can be verified very simply; whether the condition is necessary is a matter of somewhat greater difficulty and its examination † indicates the precise mathe-

---

* M. Born. *Physik. Zeits.*, Vol. 20, p. 218 (1921); A. Landé, *Handbuch der Physik*, Julius Springer, Berlin (1926), Band IX, Kap. 4; T. Ehrenfest-Afanasjewa, *Zeits. f. Physik*, Vol. 33, p. 933 (1925); S. Chandrasekhar, *Stellar Structure*, Chicago (1939), Chap. 1, p. 11.

† G. Whaples, *Journ. Rational Mech. and Anal.*, Vol. 1, p. 301 (1953).

matical conditions which the functions ϕ must satisfy. When these conditions are met, then the relations

$$f_a(p_a, V_a) = f_b(p_b, V_b) = f_c(p_c, V_c) = \vartheta \quad . \quad . \quad . \quad (5)$$

are satisfied when thermal equilibrium is established.

The parameter ϑ in equations (2) and (5) is a measure of the common temperature of the systems in thermal equilibrium and is referred to as the *empirical temperature*. It is a measure of the temperature on a certain empirical temperature scale which is defined by the way in which the functions $f_a, f_b, \ldots$ are constructed from the pressures and volumes for states of the various systems which are in thermal equilibrium with one another.

The establishment of a temperature scale consists in the adoption of a set of rules, by use of which it is possible to assign one number to one set of corresponding isotherms, and a different number to a different set of corresponding isotherms. The necessary and sufficient condition for thermal equilibrium between two systems is that they have the same temperature, that is, each is in thermal equilibrium with the thermometric substance. Further, if two systems have different temperatures they cannot be in thermal equilibrium.

This implies that to determine the temperature of a body we place a thermometer in contact with it until the two are in thermal equilibrium. The reading of the thermometer is an indication of the temperature of the body. It is then necessary to decide how to standardize the readings of various thermometers—in other words, what is to be the standard scale of temperature.

4. The Size of the Degree.

The discussion in the preceding section indicates how a property of a substance can be used to provide a measure of its temperature on an arbitrary scale. In order to assign numerical values to the different isotherms for the system, it is necessary to *define* the size of the degree. To do this it is sufficient to specify a value to be assigned to one fixed point. This was pointed out by Kelvin * and has been emphasized in recent years by Giauque.† The International Union of Pure and Applied Physics has accepted ‡ this viewpoint and has decided that the triple point of water be chosen as the fixed point.

Consider how temperatures are specified on this basis. The thermo-

---

* W. Thomson (Lord Kelvin), *Phil. Trans. Roy. Soc.* A, Vol. 144, p. 350 (1854).

† W. F. Giauque, *Nature*, London, Vol. 143, p. 623 (1939).

‡ International Union of Pure and Applied Physics, document S. G. 48–6 (1948); see also, H. F. Stimson, *Journ. Res. Natl. Bur. Stand.*, Washington, Vol. 42, p. 209 (1949);   C. R. Barber and J. A. Hall, *Brit. Journ. Appl. Phys.*, Vol. 1, p. 81 (1950).

metric substance and the particular property (specified by, say, X) of it which is to be used to measure the temperature have been chosen. Let θ^* be the numerical value assigned to the selected fixed point to specify the size of the degree and let X^* be the value of the property X at this fixed point. The value θ which is to be assigned to the temperature at which the thermometric property has the value X is then given by the relation

$$\theta = \frac{X}{X^*}\, \theta^*. \qquad \ldots \ldots \ldots \quad (6)$$

An arbitrary additive constant θ_0 can be included in one member of this equation; its only effect is to shift the origin of the scale and this may be convenient for some purposes. Thus

$$\theta + \theta_0 = \frac{X}{X^*}\, \theta^*.$$

We shall see later that equation (6) is the basis used to define temperature on the scale based on the laws of thermodynamics (see Section 36 and Chapter XIII).

We shall now consider another procedure by which it has been usual to fix the size of the degree, for this method is still of practical utility: it is the method prescribed for the *practical* and *legal* realization of the thermodynamical scale defined in terms of equation (6) above (see Section 22). Two fixed points which are easily and accurately reproducible are chosen. The temperature between them is defined as the *standard temperature interval*. The size of the degree is fixed by specifying the number of degrees in the standard temperature interval. The fixed points which have been chosen for this purpose are: (1) the melting-point of pure ice; (2) the boiling-point of pure water under standard atmospheric pressure (760 mm. of mercury at sea-level in latitude 45°). The interval between these two temperatures is called one hundred degrees celsius.

On the *celsius scale* † the melting-point of pure ice is called zero (0° C.). The boiling-point of water is then one hundred degrees (100° C.). By using a suitable technique,‡ crushed ice in a simple Dewar flask can be used to establish and maintain a temperature of 0° C. with a certainty of $\pm 0.001°$ C. On the *fahrenheit scale*, which is sometimes used, the melting-point of ice is defined as 32°, and the boiling-point of water as 212°.

When the size of the degree is specified in this way, the temperature

---

† The Ninth General Conference of Weights and Measures decided that henceforth this scale should be re-named, dropping the words " centigrade " or " centésimale " in the name of the scale.

‡ Roger, *Journ. Amer. Chem. Soc.*, Vol. 60, p. 866 (1938)

at which the thermometric property has the value X is determined by the relation

$$t = 100\, \frac{X - X_{\text{ice}}}{X_{\text{steam}} - X_{\text{ice}}}, \quad \cdots \cdots \quad (7)$$

where X_{ice} and X_{steam} respectively are the values of the thermometric property at the ice and steam points.

The choice between these two specifications of the size of the degree was clearly stated by Kelvin * in 1854. We cannot do better than to quote his summary of the position:

> To fix on a unit or degree for the numerical measurement of temperature, we may either call some definite temperature, such as that of melting ice, unity or any number we please; or we may choose two definite temperatures, such as that of melting ice and that of saturated vapour of water under the pressure 29·9218 inches of mercury in the latitude 45°, and call the difference of these temperatures any number we please, 100 for instance. The latter assumption is the only one that can be made conveniently in the present state of science, on account of the necessity of retaining a connexion with practical thermometry as hitherto practised; but the former is far preferable in the abstract and must be adopted ultimately. In the meantime it becomes a question, what is the temperature of melting ice if the difference between it and the standard boiling-point be called 100 degrees? When this question is answered within a tenth of a degree or so, it may be convenient to alter the foundation on which the degree is defined, by assuming the temperature of melting ice to agree with that which has been found in terms of the old degree; and then to make it an object of further experimental research to determine by what minute fraction the range from freezing to the present standard boiling-point exceeds or falls short of 100.

With the exception that we are concerned now not with accuracy to a tenth but to a thousandth of a degree, Kelvin's words of 1854 state precisely the position which faced the Tenth General Conference on Weights and Measures in 1954 when it considered the temperature scale.

The precise definitions adopted will be considered below. At this stage, it is sufficient to say that it was agreed that:

(i) The thermodynamic or absolute scale of temperature should be defined by assigning a value to a single fixed point. The triple point of water was chosen for this purpose. By an *absolute* scale is meant one independent of the properties of any particular substance. Its precise significance and the use of the term *thermodynamic* in this connexion will become clear below (Section 36 and Chapter XIII).

(ii) The scale for the practical realization of temperatures in the laboratory and for legal purposes (called the international temperature scale) should continue to be defined in terms of 100 degrees temperature interval between the ice point and the steam point.

These decisions on the question of temperature measurement have

---

* W. Thomson, *Phil. Trans. Roy. Soc.* A, Vol. 144, p. 350 (1854).

been stated at this point because they indicate the topics which must be considered in detail to give an account of temperature measurement. We now turn to these topics in the following sections of this chapter.

GAS THERMOMETERS

5. It has been seen that to measure temperatures use is made of the fact that many of the physical properties of a body change when its temperature changes. We choose one of these properties of a given body whose changes can be accurately measured, and use the changes in this property to indicate or measure the changes in the temperature of the body or of any other body with which it is in thermal equilibrium.

To be more definite we shall consider a particular property of a particular kind of thermometric substance. Our choice is a given mass of a pure gas, for, as we shall see later, a gas has proved the most satisfactory body to use for a thermometer. There are two cases of practical importance. In the first, the pressure of the gas is kept constant and we measure its changes of volume when its temperature changes. In the other, we measure the changes of pressure as the temperature changes when the volume of the gas is kept constant. We shall see also that a gas thermometer in which the product of the pressure and volume is used as the thermometric property is of great theoretical significance.

6. The Constant-pressure Thermometer.

The gas is contained in a glass bulb A (see fig. 1.2) to which a capillary tube is attached. By opening the stopcock and raising or lowering the reservoir of mercury, the pressure in the bulb can be kept constant. The change in the volume occupied by the gas can be measured from the movement of the mercury in the capillary. The bulb is placed in contact with the body whose temperature is required. A small correction is necessary for the fact that the small amount of gas in the capillary (called the " dead space ") is not at the temperature of the bulb, but it is unnecessary to deal with this correction here.

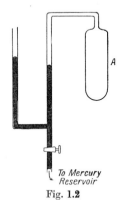

Fig. **1.2**

We first place the bulb in melting ice and leave it until it is in thermal equilibrium, that is, until the volume of the gas has become constant. Let the volume be v_0. We then place the bulb in steam and again wait until it is in thermal equilibrium. Let the volume of the gas be v_{100}. We now allow the bulb to come into thermal equilibrium with a body whose temperature we require to know. Let the volume of the gas now be v.

We *define* the temperature, t_p, of the body, measured on the constant-pressure scale with this particular thermometer, by the relation

$$t_p = \frac{v - v_0}{v_{100} - v_0} \times 100. \quad \ldots \ldots \quad (8)$$

We thus have a means of dividing the standard interval and also of measuring temperatures that lie outside the interval.

7. The Constant-volume Thermometer.

In this case the volume of the gas in the bulb is kept constant by adjusting the mercury so that the top of the column is always at the same point of the capillary. The pressure is measured by observing the difference between the height of the two mercury surfaces in the capillary tube.

Let the pressure when the bulb is in temperature equilibrium with melting ice be p_0. When it is in equilibrium with steam, let it be p_{100}. When it is in equilibrium with the body whose temperature we require, let the pressure be p.

We *define* the temperature, t_v, of the body, measured on the constant-volume scale with this particular thermometer, as

$$t_v = \frac{p - p_0}{p_{100} - p_0} \times 100. \quad \ldots \ldots \quad (9)$$

Equation (9) gives us another method of measuring temperatures.

A description of a high-precision constant-volume gas thermometer has been given by Beattie and his colleagues.* Nitrogen is used as the gas. The thermometer assembly is of the same general design as that used by earlier workers, but includes some improvements to make it possible to determine necessary corrections with greater certainty. They have used this thermometer to compare the absolute scale with that given by platinum resistance thermometers (see below) at temperatures up to the boiling-point of sulphur.

8. Some Properties of Gas Thermometers.

We shall now consider three general properties of gas thermometers which indicate their potential suitability for providing the standard temperature scale.

(1) When a gas thermometer is heated, not only does the gas itself expand but also the glass bulb which contains it. We measure the difference between these two expansions. Fortunately the expansion of the glass is small compared with that of the gas. If we know the

---

* Beattie, Jacobus, Gaines, Benedict, and Blaisdell, *Proc. Amer. Acad. Arts and Sciences*, Vol. 74, p. 327 (1941).

law according to which the glass expands, we can make the necessary correction. This can be done with great accuracy because the correction is a small one. Thus the final scale that we obtain depends only on the properties of the gas itself. We shall see the importance of this when we consider the problem of making temperature measurements at different times and places. A pure gas can be expected to have the same properties, wherever or whenever it is prepared. On the other hand, it is impossible to prepare two lots of glass which shall have exactly the same properties. If the expansion of the glass is relatively so small that it can be effectively eliminated,* the measurements will depend only on the gas; this is all that is required to satisfy the condition of reproducibility.

TABLE I

Thermometer		Temperature indicated		
Constant-volume	hydrogen..	50·003	199·976	—
,,	helium ..	50·001	199·994	449·949
,,	neon ..	50·001	199·997	449·92
,,	nitrogen ..	50·010	199·978	449·84
,,	air ..	50·013	199·976	—
,,	argon ..	50·014	199·971	449·89
,,	oxygen ..	50·016	199·929	—
Constant-pressure	hydrogen..	50·004	199·976	—
,,	helium ..	50·000	199·999	449·992
,,	neon ..	50·002	199·990	449·92
,,	nitrogen ..	50·032	199·877	449·36
,,	air ..	50·033	199·874	—
,,	argon ..	50·034	199·863	449·33
,,	oxygen ..	50·035	199·839	—

(2) After heating, a glass bulb does not necessarily recover exactly its original volume on returning to its original temperature. Provided that the bulb has been well annealed and aged, and that it is not heated to such temperatures that changes in the structure of its material take place, such changes are negligible compared with the volume changes of the gas; if they do occur they can be easily detected.

(3) It is found that different gas thermometers give practically the same scales, and that it makes little difference whether we use a constant-pressure or a constant-volume thermometer. Table I illustrates this.† The table shows the measures of three different temperatures

---

* This is not true, for example, of liquid-in-glass thermometers, such as the mercury thermometer.

† These figures are based on the measurements of Holborn and Otto (see Sections 10, 12, and 14).

which are indicated by various gas thermometers. The initial pressure, that is, the pressure at 0° C., is in all cases 1000 mm. of mercury; a variation of the initial pressure affects the reading slightly.

Although the differences in Table I are small they are appreciable in accurate work. We are, therefore, forced to make a choice as to the ultimate standard. We could, of course, choose a thermometer filled with one particular gas at a definite initial pressure to define the standard scale. But such a choice would be entirely arbitrary.

Fortunately we are not compelled to make this arbitrary choice. Although different gases give slightly different temperature scales when the initial pressure of the gas is finite, it has long been evident that, as the initial pressure is decreased, the differences between the scales given by different gases diminish; as the initial pressure approaches zero, the differences between the scales given by different gases (and by constant-volume and constant-pressure thermometers) vanish altogether. It is this *extrapolated* gas scale that we choose as the standard temperature scale. The choice has as little arbitrariness as the choice of a physical standard can have—it depends on the properties of gases in general, but not on the properties of any *particular* gas.

We must now consider the experimental proof of the statements in the last paragraph. This involves a general consideration of the properties of gases. We shall be able to give a formal definition of the standard temperature scale in the course of our investigation.

The Properties of Gases and their Use in Thermometers

9. Boyle's Law.

Early experiments by Boyle indicated that, if a given mass of gas is compressed at constant temperature, it obeys the law

$$pv = \text{constant}, \quad \ldots \quad \ldots \quad (10)$$

where p is the pressure and v the corresponding volume. This is called Boyle's law.

It is now known that Boyle's law is only approximately true. It is a convenient starting-point, however, to consider some further deductions that we can make concerning a gas that obeys Boyle's law.

Let us take a given mass of gas at 0° C. occupying a volume v_0 under a pressure p_0. We may write Boyle's law as

$$p_0 v_0 = (pv)_0, \quad \ldots \quad \ldots \quad \ldots \quad (11)$$

where $(pv)_0$ is a constant for the given mass of gas at 0° C.

Let us now keep the pressure constant and heat the gas up to a temperature t. The actual value of t need not be known. Let the volume occupied by the gas be v_t. Now define a quantity c_t by the relation

$$\frac{v_t - v_0}{v_0} = c_t. \quad \cdot \quad \cdot \quad \cdot \quad \cdot \quad \cdot \quad \cdot \quad (12)$$

Keeping the volume constant and equal to v_0, again heat the gas to temperature t, and let the pressure be p_t. Now define a quantity b_t by the relation

$$\frac{p_t - p_0}{p_0} = b_t. \quad \cdot \quad \cdot \quad \cdot \quad \cdot \quad \cdot \quad \cdot \quad (13)$$

Boyle's law at temperature t may be written

$$p_0 v_t = p_t v_0 = (pv)_t, \quad \cdot \quad \cdot \quad \cdot \quad \cdot \quad \cdot \quad (14)$$

where $(pv)_t$ is a constant for the given mass of gas depending only on the temperature.

Multiplying the left side of equation (12) above and below by p_0, and the left side of equation (13) above and below by v_0, and using equation (14), we obtain

$$c_t = b_t = \frac{(pv)_t - (pv)_0}{(pv)_0},$$

or

$$\frac{v_t - v_0}{v_0} = \frac{p_t - p_0}{p_0} = \frac{(pv)_t - (pv)_0}{(pv)_0}. \quad \cdot \quad \cdot \quad \cdot \quad (15)$$

Comparing this with equations (8) and (9), which define the constant-pressure and constant-volume scales of a given gas thermometer, we see that

For a gas which obeys Boyle's law the constant-pressure and constant-volume scales are identical, and each agrees with the scale defined by the relation

$$t = \frac{(pv)_t - (pv)_0}{(pv)_{100} - (pv)_0} \times 100. \quad \cdot \quad \cdot \quad \cdot \quad \cdot \quad (16)$$

(D 837)

10. The Actual Behaviour of Gases.

The experimental data on gases at finite pressures cannot be expressed precisely * by Boyle's law nor by any simple algebraic modification of it. Onnes had the idea of developing the pressure as a convergent double infinite series in powers of the reciprocal molar volume and of the absolute temperature. At each temperature, the series can be summed over each power of $1/V$ to give (for p) an infinite power series in the reciprocal of the molar volume. Thus, with slight rearrangement,

$$pV = A[1 + B/V + C/V^2 + D/V^3 + \ldots]. \qquad (17)$$

The coefficients $A(= RT$ for one gram-molecule), B, C, D, $\ldots$, are constants at any particular temperature; they are, of course, functions of the temperature. They are called *virial coefficients*. From the known experimental fact that at a given pressure the volume of a gas is proportional to its mass, it follows that the coefficients of this power series are proportional to the mass of gas.

In practice, the convergent infinite series must be replaced by a polynomial with a remainder term; for example

$$pV = A[1 + B/V + C/V^2] + Z. \qquad \ldots \quad (18)$$

The number of terms appropriate to a particular case depends on the range of densities covered by the measurements. The coefficients can be determined only when the number of terms is fairly small. For sufficiently low densities the remainder Z can be neglected and the values of the coefficients determined unambiguously.

The virial expansion, equation (17), can be solved for V to give an infinite series in powers of p. Thus, we obtain

$$pV = A' + B'p + C'p^2 + D'p^3 + \quad \ldots \quad (19)$$

where A', B', C', D', $\ldots$, are constants at any given temperature. The values of A', B', C', D', $\ldots$, can be expressed in terms of the virial coefficients. It is sometimes more convenient to use an expansion in the form of equation (19).

Holborn and Otto † carried out a very careful and accurate series of experiments on nitrogen, air, helium, hydrogen, argon, neon, and oxygen at pressures from about 1 metre of mercury up to 80 metres of mercury and at temperatures from $-258°$ C. to $400°$ C. (as measured on a gas thermometer). They showed that, within these limits, the

---

* H. Kammerlingh Onnes, *Leiden Comm.*, No. 71 (1901); H. Kammerlingh Onnes and W. H. Keesom, *Leiden Comm. Supp.*, No. 23 (1912); L. Holborn and J. Otto, *Zeits. f. Physik*, Vol. 38, p. 366 (1926).

† Holborn and Otto, loc. cit.

behaviour of all these gases could be accurately represented by a formula containing four constants; that is,

$$pV = A' + B'p + C'p^2 + D'p^3. \quad . \quad . \quad . \quad (20)$$

B'/A' is of order 10^{-3} and C'/A' is of order 10^{-5} or 10^{-6} if p is measured in metres of mercury; the term $D'p^3$ is generally negligible.

In connexion with the subject matter of this chapter, it is important to note that an expression of this kind does not contain the temperature explicitly. It can, therefore, be used to represent experimental results *before* we have any knowledge of the final temperature scale that we are going to use. Such results can conveniently be set out in tabular form as below.

Reading of ther- mometer	A	B	C	D	E
t_1	A_1	B_1	C_1	D_1	E_1
t_2	A_2	B_2	C_2	D_2	E_2
t_3	A_3	B_3	C_3	D_3	E_3

The thermometer readings are quite arbitrary. Such a table means that, when the gas is at a temperature corresponding to a reading say t_2 of the given arbitrary thermometer, its behaviour is accurately represented by a formula of the form (17), in which the coefficients have the numerical values given in the table.

At very low pressures it is found that the remainder term as well as the terms in $1/V$ and $1/V^2$ become negligibly small compared with the first term, so that provided we work only in the region of very low pressures the gas may be assumed to obey Boyle's law. In this region equation (15) will apply with a degree of accuracy which we may make as high as we please by making the pressure small enough.

At very low pressures, then, the constant-pressure and constant-volume scales of a thermometer employing a *given* gas agree with one another, and each agrees with the scale obtained by using the variation of the quantity pv for the given gas.

From the experimental results we have to show that the scale obtained is independent of the gas employed, provided that we work at sufficiently low pressures. In other words, we have to show that the measure of a given temperature

$$t_{(\text{lim})} = \frac{\underset{p \to 0}{\text{Lim}} (pv)_t - \underset{p \to 0}{\text{Lim}} (pv)_0}{\underset{p \to 0}{\text{Lim}} (pv)_{100} - \underset{p \to 0}{\text{Lim}} (pv)_0} \times 100 \quad . \quad (21)$$

is independent of the gas in the thermometer.

To state the question explicitly, first consider thermometers of a particular kind employing a particular gas. We shall suppose then that we use a constant-pressure helium thermometer, the pressure being p_0. We use this thermometer to measure the temperatures when we are carrying out our compression experiments on helium gas. We thus obtain a series of values of the constants A, B, C, corresponding to various temperatures t_p (as measured on the particular helium thermometer). The question is: how can we use these experimental results to determine the measures of the same temperatures that would have been obtained if we had used a helium thermometer at very low pressures?

To do this it is necessary to consider the corrections which must be applied to the readings obtained with a gas thermometer to allow for the pressure of the gas.

While we are considering this question we shall not confine ourselves to constant-pressure thermometers, but shall deal also with constant-volume thermometers.

11. The Theory of Gas Thermometer Corrections.

Equation (20) gives the relation between the pressure and the volume of a given mass of gas. It can therefore be applied to the gas in a constant-volume, or a constant-pressure, gas thermometer. At the pressures used in gas thermometry, the terms in the virial expansion containing the square and higher powers of p are negligibly small. To represent the behaviour of the gas in a gas thermometer accurately, we may therefore omit the terms involving C and D in equation (20). This gives the equation

$$pv = A + Bp \qquad \cdots \quad \cdots \quad \cdots \quad (22)$$

to represent the behaviour of the gas at the pressures relevant to gas thermometry.

(a) The Constant-volume Thermometer. We consider first the correction of the readings of a constant-volume thermometer to vanishingly low pressure. Let the fixed volume of the gas be v_0. At temperatures $0°$, $100°$, and $t°$ on the celsius scale, equation (22) gives

$$p_0 v_0 = A_0 + B_0 p_0,$$

$$p_{100} v_0 = A_{100} + B_{100} p_{100},$$

$$p_t v_0 = A_t + B_t p_t,$$

where p_0, p_{100}, and p_t are the measured pressures at these temperatures.

The temperature t_v on the constant-volume scale is defined by

$$t_v = 100 \, \frac{p_t - p_0}{p_{100} - p_0}.$$

We have, therefore,

$$t_v = 100 \frac{A_t - A_0 + B_t p_t - B_0 p_0}{A_{100} - A_0 + B_{100} p_{100} - B_0 p_0}$$

$$= 100 \frac{A_t - A_0}{A_{100} - A_0} \left\{ \frac{1 + (B_t p_t - B_0 p_0)/(A_t - A_0)}{1 + (B_{100} p_{100} - B_0 p_0)/(A_{100} - A_0)} \right\}.$$

If we expand the right-hand member of this equation, neglecting the square and higher powers of the pressures, we get

$$t_v = t_{(\lim)} \left\{ 1 + \frac{B_t p_t - B_0 p_0}{A_t - A_0} - \frac{B_{100} p_{100} - B_0 p_0}{A_{100} - A_0} \right\}.$$

This gives the correction.

If we write a for the constant $(A_{100} - A_0)/100 A_0$, then equation (21) leads to the exact relation

$$A_t = A_0 (1 + a t_{(\lim)}) \quad \cdots \cdots \cdots \quad (23)$$

for A_t. The expression for the difference $t_{(\lim)} - t_v$ can be simplified if we substitute for A_{100} and A_t from the above equation and use the approximate relation

$$p_t = p_0 (1 + a t_{(\lim)}).$$

This last relation is very nearly true and is sufficiently accurate for determining the correction. Furthermore, we shall write t_v for $t_{(\lim)}$ in the expression for the correction. We thus obtain

$$t_{(\lim)} - t_v = \frac{p_0}{A_0} \left\{ B_{100} \left(1 + \frac{1}{100a} \right) t_v + B_0 \left(\frac{1}{a} - \frac{t_v}{100a} \right) - B_t \left(\frac{1}{a} + t_v \right) \right\}. \quad (24)$$

(b) *The Constant-pressure Thermometer.* We now consider the correction of the readings of a constant-pressure thermometer. Let this constant pressure be equal to p_0. At temperatures $0°$, $100°$, and $t°$ on the celsius scale, equation (22) gives

$$p_0 v_0 = A_0 + B_0 p_0,$$
$$p_0 v_{100} = A_{100} + B_{100} p_0,$$
$$p_0 v_t = A_t + B_t p_0,$$

where v_0, v_{100}, and v_t are the measured volumes at these temperatures.

The temperature t_p on the constant-pressure scale is defined by the relation

$$t_p = 100 \frac{v_t - v_0}{v_{100} - v_0}.$$

We have, therefore,

$$t_p = 100 \frac{A_t - A_0 + p_0(B_t - B_0)}{A_{100} - A_0 + p_0(B_{100} - B_0)}.$$

We can then proceed as from the corresponding point in the discussion of the correction of the readings of a constant-volume thermometer. But it is more direct and free of mathematical approximations * to proceed as follows.

---

* I am indebted to Messrs. D. D. Swift and R. J. Dutton of Manchester University for pointing out to me that this direct and exact reduction is possible.

Since from equations (21) and (22)

$$t_{(\text{lim})} = 100 \frac{A_t - A_0}{A_{100} - A_0},$$

we have

$$t_p = \frac{t_{(\text{lim})} + 100 p_0 (B_t - B_0)/(A_{100} - A_0)}{1 + p_0(B_{100} - B_0)/(A_{100} - A_0)},$$

which leads to

$$t_{(\text{lim})} - t_p = \frac{p_0}{A_{100} - A_0} \{(B_{100} - B_0)t_p - 100(B_t - B_0)\}$$

or

$$t_{(\text{lim})} - t_p = p_0 \left\{ \frac{B_{100} - B_0}{100 a A_0} t_p - \frac{B_t - B_0}{a A_0} \right\}, \quad \cdot \quad \cdot \quad \cdot \quad \cdot \quad \cdot \quad \cdot \quad (25)$$

in which we have introduced the constant a defined above.

12. Comparison of Scales using Different Gases.

Having thus established the scale given by one particular gas at vanishingly low pressure, we have to show that exactly the same scale would be given by any other gas at vanishingly low pressure. The simplest way of doing this is to show by experiment that for any other gas the quantity

$$\frac{A_t - A_0}{A_0} \frac{1}{t_{(\text{lim})}}$$

does not depend on the temperature. A_t and A_0 refer to the gas in question, while $t_{(\text{lim})}$ is the scale obtained by extrapolation from the results of one particular gas which we have taken to be helium.

For this purpose the accurate experiments of Holborn and Otto * are available. Holborn and Otto did not actually use a gas thermometer to measure their temperatures, but they used a platinum thermometer which effectively had been directly compared with a helium thermometer.† They carried out experiments as described in Section 10

---

* Holborn and Otto, *Zeits. f. Physik.*, Vol. 33, p. 5 (1925); Vol. 38, p. 364 (1926).

† The platinum thermometer was standardized at the boiling-point of sulphur (444·600° C.). This value is obtained by correcting the reading of a helium thermometer to infinitely low pressure. For low temperatures, see Chapter V, Sections 7 and 8.

with helium from —258° to 400° C., with neon from —208° to 400° C., with hydrogen from —208° to 250° C., and with argon and nitrogen from —100° to 400° C. The experiments were not, in fact, carried out or reduced with the object of establishing the point that we are interested in. Their object was to obtain for any given temperature in the range the most accurate empirical formula possible of the type of equation (18) to represent the variation of the quantity pv with pressure. With this object in view, the experimental results were reduced on the assumption that the quantity

$$\frac{A_t - A_0}{A_0 t_{(\text{lim})}}$$

had the same value for all gases and for all values of the temperature $t_{(\text{lim})}$. The results were all consistent with this assumption and, as the experiments were carried out with a high degree of precision, any departure from constancy of this quantity amounting to one part in three thousand would have been detected. The constancy thus established indicates in the case of helium that the calibrated platinum thermometer reproduces accurately the extrapolated helium scale, and for any of the other gases considered that the quantity $\underset{p \to 0}{\text{Lim}} (pv)_t$ is a linear function of the temperature as measured on a helium thermometer with the helium at an infinitely low pressure. We may prove from this that the scale obtained with a gas thermometer is independent of the gas, provided the pressure is sufficiently low. The proof is as follows.

We have as the result of experiment the linear relation

$$(pv)_t = (pv)_0 (1 + at_{(\text{hel.})}),$$

in which for convenience we have left out the sign to indicate that this is only true in the limiting case $p \to 0$; $t_{(\text{hel.})}$ is the temperature measured on a helium thermometer with the helium at infinitely low pressure, and (pv) refers to any other gas, say nitrogen. The measure of the same temperature using a nitrogen thermometer with the nitrogen at infinitely low pressure is by definition

$$t_{(\text{nit.})} = \frac{(pv)_t - (pv)_0}{(pv)_{100} - (pv)_0} \times 100.$$

Substituting from the last equation in this and using the definition of a, we obtain immediately

$$t_{(\text{hel.})} = t_{(\text{nit.})}.$$

THE AVOGADRO SCALE OF TEMPERATURE

13. Summarizing these results, we define the Avogadro scale of temperature as that given by a gas thermometer filled with a gas at vanishingly low pressure. The melting-point of ice is defined as 0° and the boiling-point of water under standard atmospheric pressure as 100°. We shall call this scale the *Avogadro temperature scale*, or simply the *gas scale*. Henceforward we shall use simply the symbol t to indicate such temperatures.

We have shown that it can be proved by direct experiment that the scale obtained is independent of the gas employed in the thermometer, and also of whether we use a constant-volume or a constant-pressure thermometer.

Further, we have shown how the readings of an ordinary gas thermometer can be corrected so as to give the temperatures that would be obtained using a thermometer at infinitely low pressure (see equations (24) and (25)).

14. Numerical Values of the Corrections.

We give in Table II the corrections that must be applied to the readings of various thermometers to reduce them to the Avogadro scale. The corrections all refer to thermometers in which the initial pressure at 0° C. is 1 m. of mercury; as will be seen from equations (24) and (25), the correction is proportional to the initial pressure at the pressures used in practice.

Any attempt to correct gas-thermometer readings outside the range of temperatures for which compressibility measurements have been made ultimately depends on success in finding a formula to represent the temperature variation of the second virial coefficient (see equation (18)) for the gas in question. This formula is then used to extrapolate from the measured results. This method was used by Berthelot (for his equation, see Chapter IV, Section 4) with considerable success before accurate compressibility experiments over a wide range of temperatures were available. He thus calculated, for example, that the correction to the constant-volume nitrogen thermometer at 1000° C. is $+0.77°$. Apart from its value in giving the actual corrections, this method is particularly useful in that it indicates that above 450° C. the corrections to the Avogadro scale are less than the experimental errors of gas thermometry.

An entirely independent method of correcting gas-thermometer readings is to use the measurements of the Joule-Kelvin effect (see Chapter XIII). This method has been developed by Callendar and others.   The independent check which it affords is of great value. Unfortunately measurements have been made only over a limited temperature range, and wide extrapolation is necessary.   Further measurements are needed in order that the method may be applied with greater certainty.

Tables of corrections based on earlier experimental results will be found in any book of physical constants.   One of the most important differences between the figures given in Table II and the earlier ones

TABLE II

t ($°$ C.)	Constant pressure			Constant volume		
	He	H_2	N_2	He	H_2	N_2
+ 450	+ 0·012	—	+ 0·670	+ 0·061	—	+ 0·190
+ 400	+ 0·010	—	+ 0·550	+ 0·046	—	+ 0·150
+ 350	+ 0·008	—	+ 0·430	+ 0·034	—	+ 0·110
+ 300	+ 0·006	—	+ 0·320	+ 0·023	—	+ 0·080
+ 250	+ 0·004	+ 0·035	+ 0·225	+ 0·015	+ 0·032	+ 0·050
+ 200	+ 0·002	+ 0·020	+ 0·132	+ 0·008	+ 0·017	+ 0·027
+ 150	+ 0·001	+ 0·008	+ 0·056	+ 0·003	+ 0·007	+ 0·011
+ 100	0·000	0·000	0·000	0·000	0·000	0·000
+ 50	0·000	− 0·003	− 0·025	− 0·001	− 0·002	− 0·004
0	0·000	0·000	0·000	0·000	0·000	0·000
− 25	+ 0·001	+ 0·007	+ 0·039	+ 0·002	+ 0·003	+ 0·006
− 50	+ 0·002	+ 0·018	+ 0·112	+ 0·004	+ 0·006	+ 0·015
− 75	+ 0·004	+ 0·032	+ 0·228	+ 0·006	+ 0·010	+ 0·029
− 100	+ 0·006	+ 0·052	+ 0·399	+ 0·009	+ 0·015	+ 0·052
− 125	+ 0·011	+ 0·084	+ 0·686	+ 0·013	+ 0·021	+ 0·084
− 150	+ 0·018	+ 0·139	—	+ 0·018	+ 0·028	—
− 175	+ 0·028	+ 0·230	—	+ 0·023	+ 0·037	—
− 200	+ 0·046	+ 0·368	—	+ 0·028	+ 0·047	—
− 225	+ 0·077	—	—	+ 0·034	+ 0·060	—
− 250	+ 0·195	—	—	+ 0·043	—	—
− 260	+ 0·500	—	—	+ 0·048	—	—

Corrections to gas-thermometer readings to reduce them to the thermodynamic scale.   The corrections are deduced from the direct measurements of the departure of the gases from Boyle's law by Holborn and Otto (*Zeits. f. Physik*, Vol. 33, p. 10 (1925), and Vol. 38, p. 366 (1926)).   The values for constant-volume thermometers below −180° agree with those determined by Onnes and his co-workers (see Holborn and Otto, *loc. cit.*).

The initial pressure of the gas at 0° C. is 1000 mm. of mercury.

is that the present figures indicate greater departures from the thermodynamic scale of the constant-volume hydrogen and helium thermometers.   The differences, however, are only of about the same order as the experimental errors in thermometry.   As far as corrections based on the departure of the gas from Boyle's law are concerned, this way is preferable to one employing an extrapolation formula (e.g. Berthelot's), provided that the experimental data are available.

A check of the accuracy of the corrections to gas-thermometer readings can be obtained by comparing the readings of two gas thermometers containing different gases, when they are placed side by side in the same constant-temperature bath.*

Another important check of the accuracy of the corrections is to carry out measurements using the same gas at different initial pressures, and by a process of graphical extrapolation to find the reading that would have been obtained if the initial pressure had been zero. This gives the temperature on the Avogadro gas scale.†

Fixed Points

15. Gas thermometers are not convenient for ordinary use in experiments involving temperature measurements, and we shall not, therefore, consider the purely technical difficulties of using them and of correcting their readings for various small errors. Details of such corrections will be found in the papers just cited.‡ In practice we use resistance thermometers, thermocouples, or some other convenient type of thermometer.

In order to reduce the readings given by any thermometer we may be using to the gas scale we use certain fixed points. These are the melting- or boiling-points of certain pure substances. For practical purposes we take the temperatures of these points on the gas scale as fixed by standard determinations. We determine the readings of whatever thermometer we are using at suitable fixed points, and by comparison with the temperatures of the fixed points on the gas scale obtain a calibration of the thermometer. We shall consider here the fixed points above 0° C. Those at low temperature are dealt with in Chap. V.

The most important fixed points are the ice point and the steam point. For the purposes of practical measurement these two fixed points still retain a special place as " fundamental fixed points " compared with the other basic and secondary fixed points.§

16. **The Ice Point.**

The ice point is defined as the temperature of equilibrium between ice- and air-saturated water at normal atmospheric pressure. The most convenient method of measuring the ice point of a thermometer is to

---

* See Chappuis, *Trav. et Mem. du Bur. Int.*, Vol. 13 (1907); Travers, Senter, and Jaquerod, *Zeits. f. phys. Chem.*, Vol. 45, p. 416 (1923); Holborn and Henning, *Ann. d. Physik*, Vol. 35, p. 761 (1911); Heuse and Otto, *Ann. d. Physik*, Vol. 9, p. 491 (1931).

† See Eumorfopoulos, *Proc. Roy. Soc.*, A, Vol. 90, p. 189 (1914).

‡ See also Chappuis and Harker, *Phil. Trans.*, Vol. 194, p. 37 (1900).

§ See Tables IV and V below and J. A. Hall, *Brit. Journ. Appl. Phys.*, Vol. 7, p. 233 (1956).

fill a Dewar flask with finely powdered ice and a small quantity of distilled water. The thermometer must be well immersed in the ice, which must be pressed round it. Great care must be taken that the thermometer has remained long enough in the ice to have reached a steady condition. After a measurement has been made, it is as well to withdraw the thermometer slightly so as to decrease the depth of immersion. If the reading of the thermometer is unchanged, we can be sure that the original immersion was sufficient.

A Dewar flask is a double-walled glass vessel. The space between the walls is evacuated so that there is no air to conduct heat across this space, and the walls are silvered to prevent the passage of heat by radiation (see Chapter XX) into or out of the vessel. Such a vessel has very high heat-insulating properties. It provides an adiabatic wall.

17. The Steam Point.

The steam point is defined as the temperature of equilibrium between liquid water and its vapour at the pressure of one standard atmosphere. For measuring the steam point we use an apparatus of the type shown in fig. 1.3. This apparatus is called a hypsometer. The steam from the boiling water passes in the direction shown by the arrows. The thermometer is placed in the position shown. It will be noticed that the steam surrounding the thermometer is jacketed by another layer of steam. This ensures that the walls surrounding the thermometer shall be at the temperature of the steam, and that there shall be no loss of heat from the thermometer by radiation.

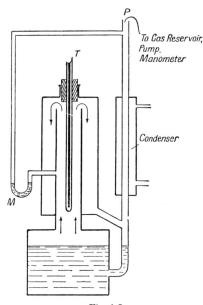

Fig. 1.3

The thermometer is placed in steam and not in the boiling water, because it is found that small quantities of impurity appreciably affect the temperature of boiling water, but have no effect on the temperature of the steam. It must be placed sufficiently above the surface of the water not to be splashed by the boiling.

The rate of boiling should be varied, and it should be ascertained that this does not affect the temperature. The immersion should be varied as in the case of the ice point.

The effect of pressure on the boiling-point is given by the following formula, which gives the equilibrium temperature as a function of pressure:

$$t = 100 + 28{\cdot}012\left(\frac{p}{p_0} - 1\right) - 11{\cdot}64\left(\frac{p}{p_0} - 1\right)^2 + 7{\cdot}1\left(\frac{p}{p_0} - 1\right)^3,$$

where p is the pressure and p_0 stands for one standard atmosphere. This gives the boiling-point to an accuracy of $0{\cdot}001°$ C. for pressures from 660 to 860 mm. of mercury.

The tube at P can be connected to a gas reservoir in which the pressure can be adjusted to any desired value, but in general it is left open to the air, since the effect on the boiling-point of small variations in the external (atmospheric) pressure is accurately known. In this case it is necessary to measure the barometric pressure with considerable accuracy, because a change of 1 mm. of mercury in pressure produces a change of about $\frac{1}{27}$ deg. in the boiling-point. The reading of the barometer must be corrected for: (1) the effect of temperature on the density of the mercury and on the length of the scale used to measure the length of the column, (2) the effects of latitude and of height above sea-level on the value of the acceleration of gravity. All these corrections are given in any book of physical constants. Having reduced the length of the mercury column to what it would be if the pressure had been measured under the standard conditions (0° C. at sea-level in latitude 45°), the effect on the boiling-point of its departure from the standard pressure of 760 mm. of mercury can be obtained from tables.* The water manometer M gives the difference between the pressure near the bulb of the thermometer and that at the point P.

18. The Sulphur Boiling-point.

An arrangement which will give satisfactory and consistent sulphur points is described in the report of the international committee on the temperature scale.* The sulphur is contained in a tube of porcelain or of fused silica. The thermometer is provided with a cylindrical shield provided with a conical portion at the top which closely fits the tube of the thermometer. This shield prevents losses by radiation, and also prevents liquid sulphur which has condensed near the top of the thermometer from running down and cooling the lower part. It is necessary to test that vertical displacement of the thermometer does not affect the readings, as in the case of the ice and steam points. For full details reference should be made to the report of the recommendations of the international committee. With this arrangement an accuracy of between 0·01° and 0·02° can be obtained.†

* See, for example, Burgess, *Journ. Res. Bur. Stand.*, Washington, Vol. 1, p. 635 (1928).

† Beattie, Benedict, and Blaisdell, *Proc. Amer. Acad. Arts and Sciences*, Vol. 71, p. 327 (1937).

In some recent high-precision measurements,* the thermometer was not immersed directly in the sulphur vapour. A vertical furnace was used, and it contained an aluminium block (the comparison block) which was provided with wells in which platinum resistance thermometers could be placed. Alternate layers of insulating material and of aluminium were placed outside the block. Above it, and separated from it, there was a guard block through which the thermometers passed. In this way, the interior of the shield approximated to a black body, but with sufficient openings to ensure the free circulation of sulphur vapour. The comparison block and the guard block were provided with electric heaters for the precise regulation of the temperature and to control the losses from the walls. With this equipment an accuracy of about one millidegree was obtained.

The boiling-point of sulphur under standard atmospheric pressure on the thermodynamic scale is 444·600° C. The effect of change of pressure on the boiling-point is given by the relation

$$t = 444\cdot6 + 69\cdot010\left(\frac{p}{p_0} - 1\right) - 27\cdot48\left(\frac{p}{p_0} - 1\right)^2 + 19\cdot14\left(\frac{p}{p_0} - 1\right)^3,$$

where p is the pressure and p_0 stands for one standard atmosphere. This formula gives the temperature to an accuracy of about 0·001° C. for pressures between 660 and 800 mm. of mercury.

Actual observations of the boiling-point are given in Table III, which is based on that given by Blaisdell and Kaye.† The values in the final column are computed from the observed values using the formulæ for the virial coefficients and the method of reduction given by Keyes.‡

The average of all these values is 444·64. That of the determinations (with two different thermometers) by Beattie and his colleagues at the Massachusetts Institute of Technology is 444·72. The latter determination is the only one that has been made since the Seventh General Conference on Weights and Measures accepted the value of 444·60° C. for the sulphur point. Although these later results suggest that this value is too low, the Ninth General Conference on Weights and Measures decided not to alter the value assigned to the sulphur point.

---

* Hoge and Brickwedde, *Journ. Res. Bur. Stand.*, Washington, Vol. 28, p. 217 (1942).

† Blaisdell and Kaye, *Temperature: its Measurement and Control in Science and Industry*, Reinhold Publishing Corporation (1941), pp. 127–140.

‡ Keyes, *ibid.*, pp. 45–59

TABLE III.—BOILING-POINT OF SULPHUR

Observer	Thermometer			Temperature	
	Gas	Con-stant	p_0	Observed	Thermo-dynamic
Callendar and Griffiths (1891) ..	Air	p	760	444·53	444·50
Chappuis and Harker (1902) ..	N$_2$	v	529	444·7	444·8
Eumorfopoulos (1908)	Air	p	761	444·5	445·0
Holborn and Henning (1911) ..	H$_2$	v	623⎫	444·51	444·53
	He	v	613⎭		
Day and Sosman (1912)	N$_2$	v	502	444·45	444·52
Eumorfopoulos (1914)	N$_2$	p	792	444·125	444·616
			415	444·356	444·613
Chappuis (1917)	N$_2$	v	560	444·49	444·57
Beattie (M.I.T.) (1939)	N$_2$	v	600	444·6556	444·7428
			450	444·6738	444·7392
			333	444·6919	444·7403
Beattie (M.I.T.) (1939)	N$_2$	v	600	444·6035	444·6907
			450	444·6336	444·7037
			333	444·6496	444·7130

19. Boiling-points of Naphthalene and of Benzophenone.

The boiling-points of naphthalene and of benzophenone are also used as fixed points. They may be determined in apparatus similar to that used for the sulphur point. Their values are:

Boiling-point of naphthalene $= 217 \cdot 96° + 0 \cdot 208 \, (t + 273 \cdot 2) \log_{10}(p/760)$.

Boiling-point of benzophenone $= 305 \cdot 9° + 0 \cdot 194 \, (t + 273 \cdot 2) \log_{10}(p/760)$.

In each of these formulæ p mm. of mercury is the pressure.

20. Melting-points.

The melting-points of various pure metals are convenient fixed points. They are determined by taking a cooling curve of the molten metal when it is slowly cooling. At the melting-point the temperature remains stationary until all the metal has solidified. For practical reasons it is not convenient to put a gas thermometer directly into a molten metal. The value of a melting-point on the gas scale is, there-fore, determined by using a thermocouple or a platinum thermometer (see Sections 23 *et seq.*) as a transfer instrument. The reading of the thermocouple is taken when it is in contact with the freezing metal, and the thermocouple is then transferred to a suitable constant-tem-perature bath in which it is placed side by side with the gas ther-mometer. The temperature of the bath is adjusted until the thermocouple gives the same reading as it did at the freezing-point of the metal. This temperature is read off on the gas thermometer.

Suitable constant-temperature baths are as follows:

At temperatures below the boiling-point of water, a water bath.

At temperatures between this and 200° to 250°, an oil bath containing cotton-seed oil.

At temperatures between 220° and about 600° or 630°, a bath of fused sodium nitrate and potassium nitrate in the proportions 45 per cent sodium nitrate and 55 per cent potassium nitrate.

Above 600° C. an air bath must be used. This must be carefully designed to give a uniform temperature.*

In a liquid bath careful attention must be given to the question of stirring. Heat should not be applied directly to the part of the bath containing the thermometer.†

21. Melting-points at High Temperatures.

The extension of the gas scale to temperatures above 500° C. is a problem which presents the following very considerable difficulties. These have been overcome in the ways indicated.

(a) The bulb, if made of porcelain or fused silica, has an uncertain and variable expansion and at the highest temperatures (i.e. above 1000° C.) either softens or devitrifies. A bulb of platinum can be used, but this also becomes soft. An alloy of platinum and iridium has been used, but the iridium volatilizes and contaminates the thermocouples. Such bulbs also tend to develop leaks.

Day and Sosman ‡ finally solved the problem by using an alloy of platinum, 80 per cent, and rhodium, 20 per cent.

(b) Bulbs of platinum and of platinum alloys are permeable to hydrogen at high temperatures.

Nitrogen is therefore used in the thermometer. The furnaces must be heated electrically, otherwise there is danger that one of the furnace gases may penetrate the bulb. Electric heating has the further advantage of being steadier and more easily controlled.

(c) At high temperatures the pressure inside the bulb of a constant-volume thermometer becomes high and this produces a change in the volume of the bulb.

This difficulty is overcome by surrounding the bulb with a gas whose pressure is always adjusted to be equal to that of the gas inside the bulb.

Using these methods, Day, Sosman, and Allen have determined the values of various melting-points up to 1550° C. The reading of a thermocouple of platinum and platinum-rhodium was determined when it was

---

* See Day and Clement, *Sill. Journ.*, Vol. 26, p. 405 (1908).

† For technical details, see Ezer Griffiths, *Methods of Measuring Temperature* (Griffin), 2nd edition (1925).

‡ See Day and Sosman, " The Realization of the Absolute Scale of Temperature ", *A Dictionary of Applied Physics* (Glazebrook), Vol. I.

at the temperature of the melting metal. The same thermocouple was then placed side by side with the bulb of the gas thermometer in an electrically heated air bath which was carefully designed to produce a uniform temperature over the whole length of the bulb. The temperature of the bath was raised until the thermocouple had the same reading as when it was in contact with the melting metal, and the gas thermometer was read at this temperature. The initial pressure of the nitrogen in the thermometer was 350 mm. of mercury.

22. The International Temperature Scale.

The thermodynamical scale can be realized practically only through the medium of the gas thermometer, either directly or indirectly in the way that has been indicated in the preceding paragraphs. In 1927, the International Committee of Weights and Measures adopted a practical scale of temperature called the *international temperature scale*. This scale was amended in certain particulars at a further meeting in 1948 but it was expressly stated that the international scale was not to be affected in any way by the decision to define the thermodynamic scale in terms of a single fixed point. It was designed to conform with the thermodynamical scale as closely as is compatible with present knowledge. It was designed to be definite, reproducible, and capable of determining any temperature within the range uniquely.

The international temperature scale * consists of a number of basic fixed points (of which two, the ice and steam points are to be regarded as fundamental fixed points), of secondary fixed points (whose values are known accurately), and selected interpolation instruments calibrated according to a specified procedure. The fixed points are those of which the determination has been described in Sections 16 to 21 above, together with the temperature of equilibrium between liquid and gaseous oxygen at a pressure of one standard atmosphere. These fixed points can be regarded as giving the results of the experiments which have been described in Sections 16 to 21. The basic fixed points, adopted in 1927 and amended † at the Ninth General Conference of Weights and Measures in 1948, are summarized in Table IV and the secondary fixed points in Table V. It should be noted that at temperatures above 500° C. the correction which has to be applied to the gas scale to give the thermodynamical scale is less than the experimental error in determining melting-points in this temperature region.

---

* See Day and Sosman, " The Realization of the Absolute Scale of Temperature ", *A Dictionary of Applied Physics* (Glazebrook), Vol. 1; National Physical Laboratory, *Annual Reports for 1928*, p. 31; W. H. Keesom, *Ned. T. Natuurk.*, Vol. 7, p. 1 (1940); *Procès Verbaux des Séances du Comité International des Poids et Mesures*, p. 21 (1948); *The International Temperature Scale of 1948*, National Physical Laboratory, Teddington (1949); Stimson, *Journ. Res. Bur. Stand.* Washington, Vol. 42, p. 209 (1949).
† *The International Temperature Scale of 1948*, National Physical Laboratory (1949).

TABLE IV.—BASIC FIXED POINTS

Basic fixed points	Degrees celsius
Boiling-point of oxygen	−182·97
Ice point (fundamental fixed point) ..	0
Steam point (fundamental fixed point) ..	100
Boiling-point of sulphur	444·600
Freezing-point of silver	960·8
Freezing-point of gold	1063

TABLE V.—SECONDARY FIXED POINTS

Secondary fixed points	Degrees celsius
Freezing-point of carbon dioxide	−78·5
Melting-point of mercury	−38·7
Triple point of water	0·0100
Transition point of sodium sulphate decahydrate ..	32·38
Triple point of benzoic acid	122·36
Condensing-point of naphthalene vapour	218·0
Freezing-point of tin	231·9
Condensing-point of benzophenone vapour	305·9
Freezing-point of cadmium	320·9
Freezing-point of lead	327·3
Condensing point of mercury	365·58
Freezing-point of zinc	419·5
Freezing-point of antimony	630·5
Freezing-point of aluminium	660·1
Freezing-point of copper (reducing atmosphere) ..	1083
Freezing-point of nickel	1453
Freezing-point of cobalt	1492
Freezing-point of palladium	1552
Freezing-point of platinum	1769
Freezing-point of rhodium	1960
Freezing-point of iridium	2443
Melting-point of tungsten	3380

The interpolation instruments and the procedure according to which they are to be used can be summarized as follows:

(a) a platinum resistance thermometer, using a quartic formula for the resistance as a function of temperature, from the boiling-point of oxygen to 0° C.;

(b) a platinum resistance thermometer, using a quadratic formula for the resistance as a function of temperature, from 0° C. to the freezing-point of antimony;

(c) a platinum-rhodium platinum thermocouple from the freezing-point of antimony to the freezing-point of gold;

(d) an optical pyrometer for temperatures above the freezing-point of gold, using the Planck radiation formula (see Chapter XX, Section 15) with the constant C_2 equal to 1·438 cm. degree (see equation (34) of Chapter XX).

The primary and secondary fixed points, apart from the two triple points, are to be determined as the equilibrium temperature between the two phases indicated at a pressure of one standard atmosphere. One standard atmosphere is *defined* as 1,013,250 dyne cm.$^{-2}$, which is the pressure exerted by a column of mercury 760 cm. high, having a density of 13·5951 gm. cm.$^{-3}$, and subject to a gravitational attraction of 980·665 dyne gm.$^{-1}$. The specified density is that of ordinary mercury at the ice point. Certain requirements concerning purity of specimen materials and the method of making the measurement must be observed in determining these equilibrium points. There are also certain requirements regarding the purity of the materials of which the interpolation instruments are constructed; these are specified by certain limits to the values of the constants which occur in the various interpolation formulæ, and are given in detail below.

Between the ice point and 200° C., the differences between the international scale and the thermodynamic celsius scale probably do not exceed 0·05°. Recent work at the Massachusetts Institute of Technology * has shown that there are somewhat greater differences between 200° C. and the boiling-point of sulphur. The differences found between the thermodynamic $t_{\text{therm.}}$ and international $t_{\text{int.}}$ scales were represented by a formula

$$t_{\text{therm.}} - t_{\text{int.}} = \frac{t}{100}\left(\frac{t}{100} - 1\right)(0·04217 - 7·481 \times 10^{-5}t).$$

The boiling-point of sulphur on the thermodynamic scale was found to be 444·74° C., the results obtained with two gas thermometers differing by about 0·05 degree. In the range from the ice point to the boiling-point of oxygen, the differences between the two scales are less than 0·05 degree.

The use of the interpolation instruments specified above to measure temperatures between the fixed points is dealt with in the following sections. Temperatures above 1063° C. are considered in Chapter XX, and temperatures below the ice point are considered in Chapter V.

---

* Beattie, Benedict, and Kaye, *Proc. Amer. Acad. Arts and Sciences*, Vol. 74, p. 343 (1941); Blaisdell and Kaye in *Temperature: its Measurement and Control in Science and Industry*, pp. 127–140, Reinhold Publishing Corporation (1941); J. A. Beattie, M. Benedict, B. E. Blaisdell and J. Kaye, *Proc. Amer. Acad. Arts and Sciences*, Vol. 77, p. 255 (1949).

PLATINUM THERMOMETRY

23. We have already mentioned that the gas thermometer is not convenient for use in ordinary work involving temperature measurements. For these measurements we use thermometers of other types whose readings can be reduced to agree with the gas scale. Of such thermometers those depending on changes in certain electrical properties are the most satisfactory and convenient.

The electrical resistance of metals changes with temperature, and, developing the work of Siemens, Callendar has shown that in the case of platinum this property can be used to give a very accurate and convenient scale of temperature. It is necessary to use a noble metal to avoid contamination by oxidation.

Temperatures measured on the platinum scale are defined as follows.

Let R_0 be the resistance of a given sample of platinum wire when it is at the temperature of melting ice. Let R_{100} be its resistance when it is at the temperature of steam. Let R be its resistance at any other temperature.

We *define* the value of this last temperature on the platinum scale as

$$t_{Pt} = \frac{R - R_0}{R_{100} - R_0} \times 100. \quad \ldots \ldots \quad (26)$$

This *assumes* a linear relation between resistance and temperature. The quantity $(R_{100} - R_0)$ is called the fundamental interval of a thermometer.

We now consider the relation between the measures of temperatures on the gas and platinum scales.

Callendar and later workers have shown by many experiments on different samples of platinum that the resistance R_t of a platinum wire at a temperature t on the gas scale, between the ice point and the antimony point, is given by the relation

$$R_t = R_0(1 + at + bt^2), \quad \ldots \ldots \quad (27)$$

where a and b are constants for the given wire. This is, of course, the interpolation formula which has to be used to realize the international temperature scale.

The platinum temperature is corrected to the parabolic relation, equation (27), by introducing the difference coefficient, δ. This is defined by

$$t - t_{Pt} = \delta(t - 100)t \, 10^{-4} = \delta\left\{\left(\frac{t}{100}\right)^2 - \left(\frac{t}{100}\right)\right\}. \quad \bullet \quad (28)$$

By substituting equation (27) in equation (26), the platinum temperature is obtained in terms of a and b, the constants of the thermometer. This gives

$$t_{Pt} = \frac{(a + bt)t}{a + 100b},$$

from which it follows that

$$\delta = -\frac{10^4 b}{a + 100b}. \quad \cdot \quad \cdot \quad \cdot \quad \cdot \quad \cdot \quad (29)$$

In this way, the quadratic formula, equation (27), is replaced by a difference formula, equation (28), which expresses the difference between the quantity required (the temperature on the gas scale) and one (the platinum temperature) that can be calculated from a linear relation. This greatly simplifies the calculations. Since the difference formula is used to give a small correction, the platinum temperature can be used in place of t to determine the correction and then we can proceed by the method of successive approximations.

For a pure platinum wire the value of δ lies between 1·488 and 1·498; impure platinum usually has a high value of δ. Tables which give (a) the gas scale temperature corresponding to a measured platinum temperature, for a thermometer with a given standard value of δ, and (b) the change in the gas scale temperature for a small change in δ, have been constructed.* Such tables simplify the task of calculation and can be used to determine the gas scale temperature from the platinum temperature for the particular thermometer which is being used.

The platinum used for making thermometers should be of such purity that R_{100}/R_0 is not less than 1·390, and $R_{444\cdot6}/R_0$ not less than 2·645. The diameter of the wire should be not smaller than 0·05 mm. and not larger than 0·2 mm., and it should be annealed at a temperature of at least 660° C. Once we have determined the value of δ for a given sample of platinum, we can reduce the platinum scale temperatures obtained with this sample to gas scale temperatures. The practical procedure is as follows. We first determine the ice and steam points of the thermometer. This enables us to determine platinum scale temperatures. We must next measure the difference between the gas scale temperature t and the platinum scale temperature t_{Pt} at the boiling-point of sulphur, for which t is known; that is, all we have to do is to measure t_{Pt} at this point. Using equation (28) we can then determine δ. A platinum thermometer calibrated in this way can be relied on to

---

* Kaye and Laby, *Tables of Physical and Chemical Constants*, 12th edition, Longmans, Green and Co. (1959), pp. 45–6.

reproduce the gas scale between 0° and 630° C. with an error not greater than two or three hundredths of a degree. For practical and legal purposes it has been decided that a platinum thermometer so used shall provide the standard international temperature scale between these temperature limits.* A detailed comparison of platinum resistance thermometers in the temperature range −190° C. to 445° C. has been carried out at the Bureau of Standards.†

24. Platinum Thermometry at High Temperatures.

Before the melting-point of gold (1063° C.) had been directly determined on the gas scale by Day, Sosman, and Allen, a determination had been made by Heycock and Neville using a platinum thermometer calibrated at the ice, steam, and sulphur points. Such a determination involves an extrapolation of about 600 degrees and is of no real value in fixing the gold point; but the fact that the value they obtained agrees closely with that determined later directly on the gas scale shows that the platinum thermometer will give accurate results up to this temperature.

Moser ‡ has shown that for high temperatures it is best to use thermometers of wire 0·5 or 0·6 mm. in diameter, the resistance at the ice point being 0·13 to 0·25 ohm. One of the chief difficulties in using platinum thermometers at high temperatures is alteration in the ice point reading. This is probably due in part to slight changes in the impurities in the wire. Moser uses a procedure based on Matthiesen's rule, which states that a small amount of impurity in a given metal produces a resistance change Δ which is almost independent of the temperature. He has shown that by working in a specified manner with resistance differences the effect of such ice point changes can be very considerably reduced.

Practical Arrangements

25. The Thermometer.

The thermometer itself consists of a spiral of wire wound on a mica or porcelain cross (see fig. 1.4). The resistance of the spiral is made equal to 2·56 or 25·6 ohms; in the former case the fundamental interval is 1 ohm, and in the latter 10 ohms. The leads are kept apart by passing them through holes in a number of pieces of mica. These pieces of mica also serve the purpose of preventing convection currents in the tube of porcelain or fused silica which contains the thermometer. If some other method of insulating the leads is used, trouble from convection currents may arise and should be watched for.

---

* See, for example, Burgess, *Journ. Res. Bur. Stand.*, Washington, Vol. 1, p. 635 (1928).

† Hoge and Brickwedde, *Journ. Res. Bur. Stand.*, Washington, Vol. 28, p. 217 (1942).

‡ Moser, *Ann. d. Physik*, Vol. 6, p. 852 (1930).

The leads, which are of heavy platinum wire, are soldered to small metal cups containing fusible metal, and into these the external leads are fused. For work up to 500° C. the leads can be of silver, provided that a short length of stout platinum is introduced between the fine wire of the spiral and the silver to prevent contamination of the fine wire in welding the leads. Above 500° C. silver volatilizes and contaminates the thermometer.

After inserting the thermometer in the tube the gas in it should be either removed or dried and the tube sealed in order to prevent insulation leaks.

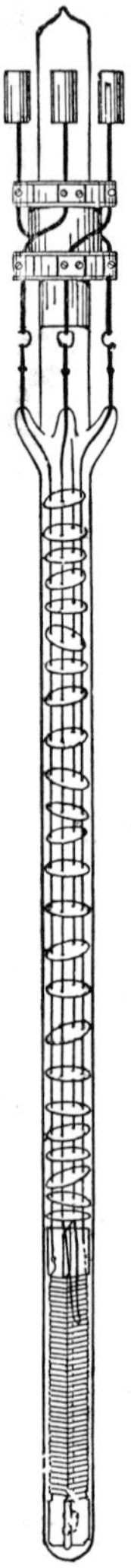

26. Resistance of Leads.

In the resistance measurements involved in platinum thermometry, troubles due to lead resistances are more serious than in ordinary resistance measurements. The leads are necessarily long, and they cannot be heavy, so their resistance is appreciable. Moreover, when the temperature of the thermometer changes the temperature of the leads also changes, and the effect of such changes must be eliminated. On the other hand, reference to equation (26) shows that we are concerned only with *changes* of resistance, and that, if a lead or contact resistance remains constant, it need not trouble us. In this respect these resistance measurements are simpler than ordinary resistance measurements.

Lead resistances may be eliminated in various ways which we now consider.

Callendar used the method of " compensating leads ". The bridge arrangement is shown in fig. 1.5. The thermometer is connected at P, and the compensating leads in the opposite arm of the bridge at C. R_1 and R_2 are the equal ratio arms of the bridge. W is a variable resistance. Each thermometer which is to be used with a bridge of this type must be provided with compensating leads. These leads are of the same wire as those connected with the thermometer itself, and of the same length; they run as near as possible to them in the thermometer tube, so that they are at as nearly as possible the same temperature. They are short-circuited inside the thermometer tube at the end near the platinum spiral by a short piece of the wire of which the spiral is made. The copper leads which connect them to the bridge should be of the same wire and the same length as those from the thermometer, and should run side by side with them. Since the compensating leads are in the opposite arm of the bridge from the

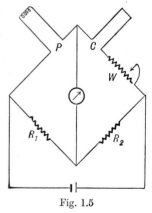

Fig. 1.5

Fig. 1.4

thermometer leads, and since they are similar and are so arranged that temperature changes affect both equally, any effect of such changes of temperature on the lead resistance will be eliminated, and we shall measure only the change in the resistance of the platinum spiral itself.

Another method that can be used is illustrated in fig. 1.6. The thermometer has three leads, AB, CD, and CE. CD and CE are one continuous wire and the spiral is soldered on to a point C on it. The thermometer is connected to the bridge as shown, so that CD is in the galvanometer arm of the bridge. If AB and CE are equal in length and run everywhere side by side, the effect of variations in their temperature will be eliminated.

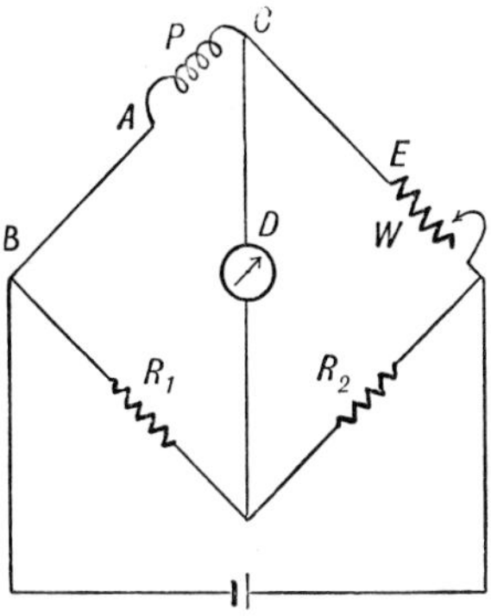

It should be mentioned here that the copper leads used with a platinum thermometer should never be made of stranded wire, in which strands tend to break and so cause variations in the resistance.

27. Heating Effect of Measuring Current.

The sensitiveness of a bridge is increased by increasing the measuring current, but so also is the heating effect of the current in the thermometer. The thermometer must be made of fine wire in order that for a reasonably large resistance the thermometer may be small. This is absolutely necessary if the thermometer is to be of any practical use. In such a fine wire (usually about 0·15 mm. in diameter) the heating effect of the bridge current is very appreciable. Callendar showed that, with a current of 0·01 amp. flowing through a thermometer of the usual construction made of wire 0·15 mm. in diameter, the heating produces a rise of temperature of 0·16 deg. at 0° C., and a rise of 0·17 deg. at 100° C.*

The effect does not reach its maximum immediately the current begins to flow. The result is that, if we leave the battery circuit open and close it only for making measurements, the readings will not be steady and the galvanometer will show a gradual drift. For this reason it is necessary to leave the current flowing through the bridge all the time (see next section).

Fig. 1.6

28. Thermo-electric Effects.

Owing to the difference of temperature between different parts of the bridge circuit and to the variety of metals employed, thermo-electric effects can become quite large. A simple but satisfactory method of eliminating these, and also of keeping the current through the thermometer flowing all the time (see preceding section), is to insert an ordinary reversing switch of the rocking type in the battery circuit. Once the preliminary adjustments have been made, the galvanometer circuit remains closed, and the resistances are adjusted until there is no movement of the galvanometer when the current is reversed. Usually effects due to induction are negligible and the above method can be used. If this is not the case, a key of the type designed by Griffiths must replace the ordinary rocking key, so that during the reversal of the current the galvanometer circuit is momentarily opened.

29. Bridges for Thermometric Work.

A bridge suitable for work with platinum thermometers has been designed by Callendar and Griffiths.† Each coil is double the coil below it, and the fine

* For further details, see Callendar, *Phil. Trans.*, A, Vol. 178, p. 161 (1887).

† Callendar and Griffiths, *Phil. Trans. Roy. Soc.*, A, Vol. 182, pp. 43, 119 (1891); see also Callendar and Barnes, *loc. cit.*

adjustment is made by using a bridge wire. In the latest forms of the bridge mercury contacts are used, so as to make the effects of contact resistance as small as possible. The calibration of such a bridge is simple. The ratio arms are equal.

A most accurate and convenient bridge has been designed by Müller.* Although this bridge is capable of giving results of the highest accuracy it is extremely simple to use and calibrate. Effects due to variable contact resistances are eliminated in an ingenious manner by arranging the positions of all such contacts so that they are in series with large enough resistances for the variations to be relatively negligible. The use of a bridge wire, which is always a disadvantage, is avoided by using the method of varying a large shunt on a small resistance to give the fine adjustments. A decade system of arrangement of coils is used. The ratio arms, as in the Callendar-Griffiths bridge, are equal, which is a great advantage. For full details the original paper should be consulted.

Other types of bridge have been designed by Smith.†

THERMO-ELECTRIC THERMOMETRY

30. If two wires of different metals are joined together at both ends and the junctions of the metals are at different temperatures, an electromotive force acts round the circuit so formed. It can be measured by cutting one of the wires and joining the ends to a potentiometer. The electromotive force depends on the difference between the temperatures of the junctions and can therefore be used to measure temperature.

In practice one of the junctions is usually kept at constant temperature (the melting-point of ice). This junction is called the cold junction. The other junction—the hot junction—is at the temperature which we wish to measure.

Various combinations of metals can be used for thermocouples. For temperatures up to 300° C. couples of copper and constantan or of iron and constantan can be used. Constantan is an alloy of copper and nickel. Such couples give a comparatively large electromotive force (for copper-constantan about 40 microvolts per degree difference between the junctions) and are, therefore, convenient; but they must not be used above 300° C., because here they deteriorate rapidly.

For copper-constantan couples from 0° C. to 350° C., Adams found

$$E = At - B(1 - e^{-Ct}),$$

where E is the electromotive force, t is the temperature of the hot junction, and A, B, C are constants. In practice for such couples the most satisfactory procedure is to use tables giving the electromotive force of typical thermocouples such as those that have been drawn up by Adams.‡ These tables were prepared by inserting in the formula

---

* Müller, *Bull. Bur. Stand.*, Vol. 13, p. 547 (1916).

† F. E. Smith, *Phil. Mag.*, Vol. 24, p. 541 (1912).

‡ Adams, *Amer. Inst. of Mining and Metall. Engineers*, p. 165 (September, 1919).

average values of the constants obtained experimentally for various samples of wire. A given couple is calibrated by measuring its electromotive force at a number of fixed points (see Sections 15 *et seq.*) and by plotting a curve of corrections giving, as a function of the reading of the thermocouple, the difference between the tabulated value of the electromotive force at the given temperature and the electromotive force given by the couple. This curve can be used in conjunction with the tables to convert the couple readings into temperatures.

For higher temperatures couples of platinum and an alloy, platinum-rhodium, should be used. For standard couples the platinum should be of such purity that R_{100}/R_0 is initially not less than 1·390 (see Section 23). With one junction at 0° and the other at the freezing-point of gold the couple must develop an electromotive force of not less than 10,200 and not more than 10,400 microvolts. The diameter of the wires used should lie between 0·35 and 0·65 mm. With the cold junction in ice the electromotive force E is given by

$$E = A + Bt + Ct^2,$$

where t is the temperature of the hot junction. If the values of the constants A, B, C are determined by measuring the electromotive force at the freezing-point of antimony (the value for the antimony used being obtained by measurement with a standard platinum thermometer), the silver point and the gold point, the couple gives the standard international temperature scale between 660° and 1063° C. The effect of calibrating standard couples at other temperatures has been considered by Roeser.[*]

31. The Potentiometer Circuit.

The accuracy with which the temperatures are required determines the quality of the potentiometer that must be used for the measurements. It is difficult to make measurements closer than 1 microvolt, and a potentiometer reading to microvolts is all that is required for most purposes. Using a copper-constantan thermocouple 1 microvolt corresponds approximately to $\frac{1}{40}$ deg. The sensitiveness can be increased by using a number of thermocouples in series.

The chief sources of error in making thermo-electric measurements are: [†]

(*a*) *Insulation leaks.*—Great care must be taken to insulate the thermocouple circuit, particularly if there is another circuit in the apparatus. Very slight insulation faults may easily give entirely fallacious results. The difficulties of satisfactory insulation become great at high temperatures. At such temperatures furnaces should be heated by alternating current.

[*] Roeser, *Journ. Res. Bur. Stand.*, Washington, Vol. 3, p. 343 (1929). Valuable practical details concerning the use of thermocouples are given in this paper.

[†] See also Walger and F. R. Lorenz, *Zeits. f. techn. Physik*, Vol. 11, p. 242 (1930).

(b) *Stray thermo-electromotive forces arising from the various metallic contacts in the circuits involved in the measurements.*—Such effects can usually be eliminated by a careful arrangement of the contacts so that they cancel each other in pairs. In Table VI we give the approximate values of thermo-electric forces, so that

TABLE VI

Thermo-electromotive forces against platinum in microvolts per degree

Antimony	..	47	Nickel	..	−16·4
Bismuth	..	−65	Silver	..	7·1
Copper	..	7·4	Brass	..	4
Iron	..	16	Constantan	..	−34·4
Mercury	..	0	Manganin	..	5·7

the magnitude of effects likely to arise can be estimated. If any pair of metals form a circuit the current flows across the hot junction towards the metal with the algebraically higher value. The E.M.F. of any pair of metals can be obtained by taking the algebraic difference of the numbers for those metals. Thus brass and copper give 3·4 microvolts per degree difference between two opposing brass-copper junctions. The E.M.F. between copper connecting wires and brass terminals on the apparatus is, therefore, important. To take an example of how these effects can be minimized, consider the connexion of the galvanometer to the potentiometer illustrated in fig. 1.7. If the brass-copper junctions A and B are at the same

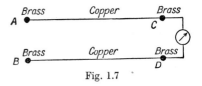

Fig. 1.7

temperature their net effect will be zero, and the same applies to C and D. A satisfactory way of ensuring that this will be the case is to make the actual contacts with the terminals A and B with two stout brass wires, and to solder the copper leads on to these brass wires. The two soldered joints can then be immersed in a vessel of highly insulating oil so as to keep them at very nearly the same temperature. For the most accurate work copper terminals, copper switches, and an all-copper galvanometer should be used.

(c) *It is found that the E.M.F. of a thermocouple is altered if the wire is in any way strained.*—This makes it desirable to calibrate the couple in the position in which it is to be used, whenever this is possible.

32. Thermocouples at High Temperatures.

Platinum thermocouples can be used outside the range specified in Section 30 and up to 1600° C., provided they are carefully calibrated at a sufficient number of suitable fixed points. Tables similar to those for use with copper-constantan couples have been drawn up by Adams. Used in conjunction with such tables, platinum thermocouples will give nitrogen scale temperatures—which for practical purposes are identical with thermodynamic temperatures—with an accuracy of about 3 degrees at 1500° C.

MERCURY-IN-GLASS THERMOMETRY

33. The mercury-in-glass thermometer, like all " pointer " instruments, has the great advantage of being easy to read and of giving a direct reading. For accurate work, however, the corrections that must be applied to its readings make it inconvenient, and in physical measurements it has been almost entirely replaced by the platinum thermometer or by thermocouples. We shall only consider it very briefly.*

A mercury thermometer is calibrated by putting it in ice, and noting the point on the stem to which the mercury rises. It is then put into steam and the point to which the mercury rises is again noted. The distance between the two marks is then divided into one hundred equal parts, each part corresponding to a degree. Owing to the fact that there is some obscurity in connexion with the coefficient of expansion of mercury (see Chapter X, Section 9), and also to the fact that the coefficient of expansion of glass is not small compared with that of mercury, the correction to the gas scale can be made satisfactorily only by comparing a mercury thermometer directly with a gas thermometer—or with another thermometer that itself has been directly compared with a gas thermometer—at a large number of points. This is a great disadvantage. Another serious disadvantage is that some of the corrections can be made satisfactorily only when working under ideal conditions which can seldom be completely realized in actual experiments—as distinct from calibration tests. The following are the errors for which corrections must be made:

(1) Lack of uniformity in the bore of the capillary.

(2) Error in marking the ice and steam points correctly.

(3) Effect due to the weight of the mercury column—the thermometer gives a different reading in the horizontal and vertical positions.

(4) Effect due to external pressure on the bulb.

(5) Change in the ice point. This is a serious difficulty. Glass shows marked thermal hysteresis. If a thermometer is heated to the steam point and then placed in ice it will give a certain reading. If it is left in the ice its reading will gradually creep up (increase) and it may take a day or more before it becomes stationary. With even the best glass thermometers this effect is not by any means small and amounts to 0·03 deg.—a serious error. It can actually in some thermometers amount to 0·5 deg. We may mention that ageing a thermometer does not remove this effect.

(6) Emergent stem correction. A correction is necessary for the fact that the mercury which is in the capillary is not always at the same temperature as that in the bulb of the thermometer.

THE ABSOLUTE SCALE OF TEMPERATURE

34. The Gas Scale.

We must now return to the gas scale, and to a further consideration of the experiments mentioned in Section 12. These experiments indicate that a gas at very low pressures provides the most satisfactory thermometer and that, in the limit of vanishingly low pressure, the indications of constant-pressure and constant-volume thermometers are the same

---

* For full details of the use of mercury thermometers, see Ezer Griffiths, *Methods of Measuring Temperature* (Griffin), 2nd edition, revised (1925).

for all gases and are identical with the temperature scale determined by using the product pV for the gas. We have considered these results in terms of the international temperature scale defined by two fundamental points. They could equally well have been discussed in terms of a temperature scale defined by a single fixed point as the absolute or thermodynamic temperature scale is now defined.

In particular, these experiments indicate that for any gas we may write

$$\mathop{\rm Lim}_{p\to 0} (pV)_t = \mathop{\rm Lim}_{p\to 0} (pV)_0(1 + at). \quad \cdot \quad \cdot \quad \cdot \quad (30)$$

In this expression a has been written for $(A_{100} - A_0)/100A_0$ where the constants A are the values of the first virial coefficient at the fixed points indicated by the suffixes and t is the temperature on the gas scale. The experiments also show that a has the same value for all gases. This is the content of Charles's law.

The quantity a also provides the connexion between numerical values on the international temperature scale and those on the thermodynamic scale. It is desirable * to assign the numerical value of the single fixed point on the thermodynamic scale (the triple point of water) so that the size of the degree on that scale will be the same, within the limits of existing experimental accuracy, as the degree on the international temperature scale defined by the interval between the fundamental fixed points. We shall suppose that this has been done and write θ_{tr} for the thermodynamic temperature of the triple point of water. Then if t is a temperature on the international scale and θ is the corresponding temperature on the thermodynamic scale

$$\theta = \theta_0 + t$$

where θ_0 is the thermodynamic temperature of the ice point. We then have the following relations. On the international temperature scale

$$X_t = X_0(1 + at),$$

and on the thermodynamic scale

$$\theta_0 + t = \theta = \frac{X_t}{X_{tr}}\,\theta_{tr}, \quad \theta_0 = \frac{X_0}{X_{tr}}\,\theta_{tr},$$

where X is used to specify the thermometric property which is being used to measure temperatures. For instance, X may stand for $\mathop{\rm Lim}_{p\to 0}(pV)$. It follows that

$$1 + at = \frac{X_t}{X_0} = \frac{\theta_0 + t}{\theta_0} = 1 + \frac{t}{\theta_0},$$

whence $$\theta_0 = 1/a.$$

* Compare the quotation from Kelvin given in Section 4.

Thus, the reciprocal of a in equation (30) is the thermodynamic temperature of the ice point.

The quantity a is intimately related to the coefficients of volume expansion and of pressure change for a gas It will be seen that its value can be determined from measurements of these quantities at different pressures. The coefficient of expansion α_p at the temperature t is defined by

$$\alpha_p = \frac{1}{V}\left(\frac{\partial V}{\partial t}\right)_p$$

the pressure remaining constant. The coefficient of pressure change β_V at temperature t is defined by

$$\beta_V = \frac{1}{p}\left(\frac{\partial p}{\partial t}\right)_p$$

the volume remaining constant.

35. The Numerical Value of the Constant a.

The most usual method of determining the value of a is to extrapolate to zero pressure the values of the coefficients of expansion, α, and of pressure change, β, measured on various gases at various initial pressures p_0. This can be done either graphically or algebraically, using the formula $pv = A + Bp$. The results of a number of measurements by Heuse and Otto,[*] which were made between 0° and 100° C., and are therefore independent of any temperature measurement, are given in Table VII.

TABLE VII

p_0 (cm. of mercury)	Helium		Hydrogen		Nitrogen	
	α	β	α	β	α	β
39·024	·0036595	36611	36604	36617	36664	36673
53·310	36594	36602	36604	36613	36668	36671
72·717	36587	36611	36593	36620	36699	36709
99·450	36579	36604	36589	36621	36734	36740

Using the algebraic method of extrapolation they obtain the following limiting values:

	From α	From β
He	0·0036607	36609
H$_2$	36611	36610
N$_2$	36609	36606

[*] Heuse and Otto, *Ann. d. Physik*, Vol. 2, p. 1022 (1929).

The mean value from α is 0·0036609; from β it is 0·0036608, the mean being taken as 0·0036609. Using the graphical method they obtained 0·0036610. It will be seen that in spite of the difference between the measured values at finite pressures the extrapolated values agree closely, which is a further confirmation of the correctness of the idea that at infinitesimal pressures all gases approximate to the same behaviour. Taking into account earlier determinations, Heuse and Otto finally adopted the value *

$$a = 0\cdot0036608.$$

From this value of a, we obtain 273·16° for the absolute temperature of the ice point. There have been many determinations of this value. From analyses of the existing data, Roebuck and Murrill † give a value 273·170° and Beattie ‡ gives a value of 273·165°. In the same paper, Beattie describes his own work in this field; two different methods of reducing his data yield the values 273·165° and 273·167°. From these data, Birge § concluded that the best value of the absolute temperature of the ice point is

$$T_0 = 273\cdot16 \pm 0\cdot01°.$$

It should be noted that in experiments at the Kammerlingh Onnes Laboratory at Leiden, a value 273·144° K. had been found for the ice point. Keesom and Tuyn ‖ recommended to the Institut International du Froid that

$$273\cdot15 \pm 0\cdot02°$$

should be adopted as the ice point. Included amongst the determinations of the ice point on which Birge's recommendation was based, was that made at the Physikalisch Technische Reichsanstalt from which the value 273·158° was obtained. In 1952, independent calculations of these results were made by H. van Dijk of Leiden and by J. Otto of the Physikalisch Technische Bundesanstalt. Both of these recalculations led to the lower value 273·149° for the ice point. From a consideration of all these data, the Tenth General Conference on Weights and Measures adopted ¶ 273·16° K. exactly as the numerical value of the triple point of water on the thermodynamic scale with one fixed point. The ice point is then defined to be 0·0100 degree below the triple point.

---

* See also Heuse and Otto, *Ann. d. Physik*, Vol. 4, p. 778 (1930).

† Roebuck and Murrill, *Temperature: its Measurement and Control in Science and Industry*, Reinhold Publishing Co., New York, 1941, pp. 60–74.

‡ Beattie, *ibid.*, pp. 74–89.

§ Birge, *Reports on Progress in Physics*, Vol. 8, p. 110 (1941).

‖ See Casimir, *Nature*, Vol. 143, p. 465 (1939).

¶ *Nat. Bur. Stand., Washington, Tech. News Bull.*, Vol. 39, p. 13 (1955); J. A. Hall, *Brit. Journ. Appl. Phys.*, Vol. 7, p. 233 (1956).

For the specification of the absolute temperature, it follows that

$$T = t + \frac{1}{a}. \quad \ldots \ldots \quad (31)$$

At the temperature $t = -\frac{1}{a}$

we have $T = 0,$

and this temperature is called the *absolute zero*.

36. The Thermodynamic or Absolute Scale of Temperature.

Temperatures on the thermodynamic or absolute scale of temperature are determined, in terms of a single fundamental point, by the relation

$$T = T_{tr} \lim_{p \to 0} (pV) \big/ \lim_{p \to 0} (pV)_{tr}, \quad \ldots \ldots \quad (32)$$

where the suffix *tr* is used to denote a value measured at the triple point of water and T_{tr} is the numerical value assigned to the triple point of water to specify the size of the degree on this scale. The appropriateness of the term *thermodynamic* to designate this temperature scale will become clear from the considerations advanced in Chapter XIII, Section 7. We have seen that T_{tr} is given the value 273·16° K.; and that the choice of this value is dictated by the practical requirement of defining the scale so that existing measurements can be retained without recalculation.

The relations between temperatures on the international and on the thermodynamic scales can now be set out very simply. The following diagrammatic scheme was evolved * by the Comité Consultatif de Thermométrie in 1954.

International Scale

International temperature	International Kelvin temperature
t	$\longrightarrow T_{int} = t + 273\cdot15$ (exactly)
Indicated by: °C. (Int. 1948) degrees celsius (international 1948)	Indicated by: °K. (Int. 1948) degrees Kelvin (international 1948)

Thermodynamic Scale

Thermodynamic celsius temperature	Thermodynamic temperature
$t_{th} = T - 273\cdot15$ (exactly) $\longleftarrow$	T
Indicated by: °C. (therm) degrees celsius (thermodynamic)	Indicated by: °K. degrees Kelvin

* H. F. Stimson, *Amer. Jour. Phys.*, Vol. 23, p. 614 (1955); J. A. Hall, *Brit. Journ. Appl. Phys.*, Vol. 7, p. 233 (1956).

37. Two Independent Temperature Scales.

When the international temperature scale was introduced in 1928, it was designed to be the closest possible practical realization of the thermodynamic scale. This correspondence is modified in one particular by the decision, reached in 1948 and 1954, to define the thermodynamic scale in terms of one fixed point without affecting in any way the existing international scale which remains the recommended practical scale and which is still defined by a temperature interval between two fundamental fixed points.

This means that there are now two scales independently defined. The degrees on the two scales are indistinguishable in size *at the present time* but they must, in fact, be slightly different. As greater precision is achieved in temperature measurements, the differences will no doubt become appreciable in relation to the limits of accuracy then attainable. We shall then be faced with the problem of bringing the two scales into line. By that time, it will probably be possible to secure agreement to defining the size of the degree on the international scale also by one fundamental point. This could be done by defining the steam point as a " primary " instead of as a " fundamental " point on the international scale. Its value on this scale can then be amended as more precise measurements are made, in the same way as the numerical values attached to some of the other equilibrium points of the international temperature scale were amended in 1948. This implies that when that happens the interval between the ice and the steam points will no longer be precisely 100 degrees celsius: but the certainty of this happening at some time is one of the inevitable consequences of the adoption in 1954 of the recommendations of the Comité Consultatif de Thermométrie about the definition of the thermodynamic and the international scales.

38. The Gas Constant.

Using the relation
$$t = T - \frac{1}{a} \qquad \ldots \ldots \ldots \quad (33)$$

in equation (30), we obtain

$$\lim_{p \to 0} (pv)_T = \lim_{p \to 0} (pv)_0 \cdot aT, \qquad \ldots \ldots \quad (34)$$

where $(pv)_0$ is the value of pv for the given mass of gas at the melting-point of ice.

Now *Avogadro's law* states that: *At the same temperature and pressure equal volumes of all gases contain the same number of molecules.* This law is as far as we know *exactly true* when the pressure under consideration approaches zero. The law cannot in a sense be called the direct result of experiment, but we do know that relative molecular

weights deduced from the measurement of gaseous densities by assuming
the law agree as closely as possible with those determined by purely
chemical methods. It follows immediately from Avogadro's law that,
if we consider a gram-molecule of *any* gas, the quantity

$$\mathrm{Lim}_{p \to 0} (pV)_0$$

is a constant independent of the particular gas that we choose. We
have written V to indicate that we are dealing with a gram-molecule,
a convention that we shall use henceforth throughout this book. We
have already seen that a is a constant independent of the particular
gas. It follows then that equation (34) becomes, for a gram-molecule
of any gas,

$$\mathrm{Lim}_{p \to 0} (pV) = RT, \quad \ldots \ldots \quad (35)$$

where T is the absolute temperature, and R is a universal constant for
all gases, called the *gas constant*. R is actually given by

$$R = \mathrm{Lim}_{p \to 0} (pV)_0 . a, \quad \ldots \ldots \quad (36)$$

and can thus be determined experimentally from the value of a, which
is given in Section 35, and from measurements of gaseous densities at
the melting-point of ice.

It is important to realize that for the range of temperatures for
which we have direct experimental data (roughly shown for various
gases in Section 14, Table II), equation (35) may be regarded as
experimentally exactly true. We have every reason to suppose that,
apart from effects of dissociation, gases continue to obey the law to
the highest temperatures, but very little is known about their behaviour
in the neighbourhood of the absolute zero. It is not possible at this
stage to discuss the meaning of the term absolute zero, but the validity
of equation (35), with T as defined in Section 35, for temperatures
excluding only a small range in the neighbourhood of the absolute
zero, does not depend on such a discussion.

For the determination of $\mathrm{Lim}_{p \to 0} (pV)_0$ the only gas that can be considered is
oxygen, whose molecular weight is fixed by definition; the molecular weights of
other gases must be determined by chemical methods and are therefore subject
to inaccuracy. Henning [*] collected the most accurate experimental data for
oxygen, and arrived at the result

$$\mathrm{Lim}_{p \to 0} (pV)_0 = 22 \cdot 414 \text{ litre atmospheres.}$$

More recent measurements are now available and have been examined in

[*] Henning, *Zeits. f. Physik*, Vol. 6, p. 69 (1921).

detail by Birge.* Usually, observations of this character have been confined to pressures of one atmosphere and less. In an exhaustive investigation, Cragoe † has shown that a more reliable result can be obtained by the use of data at higher pressures. His work on the isotherms of oxygen covers the range from 0 to 100 atmospheres. Using Cragoe's results, the recalculated data of Bateucas,‡ and the data of Moles, Toral and Escribano,§ Birge obtains finally

$$\lim_{p \to 0} (pV)_0 = 22\cdot4140 \pm 0\cdot0006 \text{ litre atmos. mole}^{-1},$$

where the unit of pressure is the atmosphere in terms of *standard* gravity $(980\cdot665 \text{ cm. sec.}^{-2})$. This value is in terms of atomic weights on the chemical scale. It is equivalent, on the physical scale of atomic weights, to

$$\lim_{p \to 0} (pV)_0 = (2271\cdot78 \pm 0\cdot03) \times 10^7 \text{ erg mole}^{-1}$$

which is the value adopted by Bearden and Thomsen.‖

Using the value of the triple point of water given in Section 35 and this value of $\lim (pV)_0$, we obtain

$$R = 0\cdot082082 \pm 0\cdot000004 \text{ litre atmos. deg.}^{-1} \text{ mole}^{-1}.$$

If the volumes are measured in cubic centimetres and the pressure in dynes per square centimetre, we get

$$R = (8\cdot3170 \pm 0\cdot0001) \times 10^7 \text{ erg deg.}^{-1} \text{ mole}^{-1}.$$

EXAMPLE

1. Show that the relations between the coefficients of successive terms in the virial expansion (for one gram-molecule of gas) and the expansion in powers of p are

$$A' = RT = A, \quad B' = B,$$

$$RTC' = C - B^2, \quad R^2T^2D' = 2B^3 - 3BC + D.$$

* Birge, *Rev. Mod. Phys.*, Vol. 1, p. 1 (1929); Birge and Jenkins, *J. Chem. Phys.*, Vol. 2, p. 167 (1934); Birge, *Reports on Progress in Physics*, Vol. 8, p. 102 (1941).

† Cragoe, *Journ. Res. Bur. Stand.*, Washington, Vol. 26, p. 495 (1941).

‡ Bateucas, *Boletin de la Universidad de Santiago*, 1935.

§ Moles, Toral and Escribano, *Trans. Faraday Soc.*, Vol. 35, p. 1439 (1939).

‖ J. A. Bearden and J. S. Thomsen, *Nuovo Cimento*, Supplemento al Vol. 5, p. 292 (1957).

CHAPTER II

Quantity of Heat

1. It is natural to ask what happens when the temperature of a body changes. From the earliest times this question has been answered by saying that, when the temperature of a body rises or falls, the amount of *heat* in the body increases or diminishes. In other words, it was postulated that there is an agent called heat, and that an increase in it corresponds to a rise in the temperature of the body. This, however, begs the question, unless we have explained the nature of this concept, that is, what is meant by *heat*. We shall first trace the historical development of this concept, describing some of the classical experiments which have led to our present ideas.

THE NATURE OF HEAT

2. From the earliest times there have been two rival theories about the nature of heat. Neither of these originally had a satisfactory experimental basis. The more popular theory always appears to have been the *caloric* theory, according to which heat or caloric is an indestructible fluid which fills up the interstices between the molecules of matter and flows from a hotter to a colder body. According to the other doctrine, heat is due to a rapid vibration of the molecules. This theory found few supporters until the middle of the nineteenth century; it has now entirely superseded the other.

Bacon appears to have been the first to attempt to base his theory on experimental results. Considering the way in which heat could be produced by friction or percussion, he concluded that " heat is motion ". Bacon's conclusion was not generally accepted, and the calorists maintained that in hammering or rubbing some of the caloric is squeezed out of the matter and makes its presence known by rise of temperature.

We need not go into the details of the caloric theory, but may pass on to the first definite experimental investigation of the subject by Count Rumford.* He rotated by horse-power a hollow gun-metal cylinder which had a blunt borer pressed against it. After it had made 960 revolutions in half an hour, he noticed that the temperature had

---

* Rumford, *Phil. Trans.* (1798).

risen from 16° C. to 55° C., while the amount of powder produced by the boring was only 54·2 grams.

Rumford pointed out that the essential fact was that the supply of heat was inexhaustible. If, as the supporters of the caloric theory maintained, the heat were rubbed out of the material, a stage would finally be reached at which no further heat would be available. No such stage was observed. The rise in temperature which was observed did not depend in any way on the rise that had previously been observed or on the amount of hammering it had received. The continued rise in temperature depended only on the continued working.

Rumford carried out further experiments in which the metal was placed under water which was made to boil by the heat generated by the working. The following is Rumford's summary of the results of his experiments, and of their bearing on the question of the nature of heat.

" In meditating over the results of all these experiments, we are naturally brought to the great question which has so often been the subject of speculation by philosophers, namely:

" ' What is heat? Is there any such thing as an *igneous fluid*? Is there anything that can with propriety be called *caloric*?'

" We have seen that a very considerable quantity of heat may be excited by the friction of two metallic surfaces, and given off in a constant stream or flux *in all directions*, without interruption or intermission, and without any signs of diminution or exhaustion. . . .

" In reasoning on this subject we must not forget that most remarkable circumstance, that the source of the heat generated by friction in these experiments appeared evidently to be *inexhaustible*.

" It is hardly necessary to add that anything which any *insulated* body or system of bodies can continue to furnish without *limitation* cannot possibly be a *material substance*; and it appears to me to be extremely difficult, if not quite impossible, to form any distinct idea of anything capable of being excited and communicated in the manner the heat was excited and communicated in these experiments except it be *motion*."

3. Davy's Experiment.

Humphry Davy (1799) first showed that two pieces of ice, or of wax, tallow, resin, or any substance fusible at a low temperature, can be melted merely by rubbing them together. This result, as we shall see, made the caloric theory entirely untenable.

Black had earlier * carried out experiments in which he exposed a mass of ice-cold water by suspending it in a vessel in a large hall. He noticed that its temperature rose to 4° C. in half an hour. He noticed further that, if he exposed an equal mass of ice in the same room under the same conditions, it took about ten hours to melt, without changing its temperature.

---

* An account of Black's experiments is contained in his *Lectures on the Elements of Chemistry*, which were published in 1803, four years after his death.

Before the time of Black it was thought that when a solid changed into a liquid no supply of heat was necessary to effect the transformation, and that any heat supplied always caused a rise of temperature which could be detected by a thermometer. Black wrote of his experiments: " The opinion I formed from attentive observation of the facts and phenomena is as follows. When ice, for example, or any other solid substance, is changing into a fluid by heat, I am of opinion that it receives a much greater quantity of heat than what is perceptible in it immediately after by the thermometer. A great quantity of heat enters into it on this occasion without making it apparently warmer when tried by this instrument. This heat, however, must be thrown into it, in order to give it the form of a fluid; and I affirm that this great addition of heat is the principal and most immediate cause of the fluidity induced."

The explanation from the point of view of the caloric theory was that caloric could not only exist in the free state, in which it is sensible and affects a thermometer, but that it could also exist in combination with matter, when it would become latent or inactive and could not be detected by a thermometer. Thus water on the caloric theory consists of ice combined with a certain quantity of caloric, that is, water contains a greater quantity of caloric than ice.

We can now see the impossible position in which Davy's experiment leaves the calorists. The experiment shows that ice by friction is converted into water. According to the calorists' explanation of Rumford's experiment the effect of friction is to squeeze caloric out of matter and to diminish the quantity of caloric which it contains. Applying this argument to Davy's experiment we are forced to the conclusion that water contains *less* caloric than ice. The experiments of Black, however, show that, on the caloric theory, ice must have an absolute quantity of caloric added to it before it can be converted into water, and that therefore, according to the caloric theory, water contains *more* caloric than ice. This contradiction is fatal to the theory.

The difficulty disappears completely if we suppose that the rise in temperature is actually produced by friction. We know that (as Davy says) " a motion or vibration of the corpuscles of bodies must be necessarily generated by friction or percussion. Therefore we may reasonably conclude that this motion or vibration is heat."

Later (in 1812) Davy wrote: " The immediate cause of the phenomena of heat is motion, and the laws of its communication are precisely the same as the laws of the communication of motion."

4. Joule's Experiments.

The principles enunciated by Rumford and Davy were not, however, generally accepted even in 1840 when Joule commenced his investigations.

It had probably occurred to Rumford that there was some definite relation between the amount of the work expended and the rise in temperature. Joule carried out experiments to determine exactly the rise in temperature of a given mass of a given fluid as a result of the expenditure of a definite amount of work, all the work being expended in this way, that is, his experiments were done under adiabatic conditions.

In Joule's experiments, the water in a copper vessel was stirred by a rotating paddle; the motion of the water was destroyed by vanes fixed to the sides of the containing vessel. The paddle was turned by falling weights, so that the work spent in stirring the water could be estimated from the loss in potential energy of the weights in their fall (a small correction was necessary for the kinetic energy which the weights possessed at the end of their fall). He measured the rise in temperature of the water and its mass (a correction being added to allow for the containing vessel and paddle). As a result of a large number of experiments with this apparatus Joule proved that the rise in temperature of a given mass of water depended linearly on the work expended. He showed that the work done in raising the weight of 1 lb. through 772 ft. at Manchester * will, if it is all expended in this way, raise the temperature of 1 lb. of water one degree fahrenheit.

Between 1840 and 1849, Joule carried out a series of experiments of this kind. In one set of experiments, he observed the rise in temperature of mercury in an iron container when it was stirred by an iron paddle. In other experiments the mechanical work was done by rubbing together two iron rings which were immersed in mercury. To compare the rise in temperature of the iron with that of the water in his earlier experiments, Joule made use of the results of Black's experiments on the temperature of mixtures of substances initially at different temperatures.

Black † had shown that when equal amounts of different substances at different temperatures were mixed, the equilibrium temperature which was finally reached by the mixture depended on the particular substances. Black carried out experiments in which given masses of different substances were mixed and allowed to come to thermal equilibrium. He measured the initial temperatures of the two substances and the temperature of the mixture when thermal equilibrium had been reached. As a result of these experiments, it was possible to assign values s_1, s_2, s_3, . . . characteristic of each substance, so that if m_1 grams of one substance at temperature t_1 were mixed with m_2 grams of another substance at temperature t_2 ($t_2 < t_1$) and the final temperature were t, then

$$m_1 s_1 (t_1 - t) = m_2 s_2 (t - t_2). \quad . \quad . \quad . \quad . \quad (1)$$

---

* The work done in raising 1 lb. weight through 1 ft. varies from place to place on account of variations in the acceleration due to gravity.   † Black, *loc. cit.*

The numerical values of s_1, s_2, . . . were determined by assigning the value unity to this parameter for water.

Using the values which had been determined in this way, Joule was able to show that in his experiments on mercury, the rise in temperature, when converted to the equivalent rise in temperature of water, agreed with his earlier experiments to within one per cent. It should also be noted that the results expressed by equation (1) were used to allow for the rise in temperature of the stirring mechanism which he used in all these experiments.

In other experiments, Joule measured the rise in temperature which was produced when an electrical current was passed through a wire immersed in a fluid. This was compared with the electrical energy which was dissipated. He again obtained results which agreed with his earlier experiments to within one per cent. In other experiments he measured the change in temperature which occurred when air was compressed and expanded, and the mechanical work which was expended by the frictional resistance to water flowing through a tube. In none of these experiments did his results differ by more than five per cent. In all of these experiments, all the mechanical, or other, work which was expended was used to raise the temperature of the fluid and not to produce any other effect.

The work of Joule is of very great importance. In the first place, he used a very great variety of methods. Secondly, he put thermal measurements of this kind on a quantitative basis. His work was of quite extraordinary accuracy when we consider the resources at his disposal in those days.

The results of Joule's experiments can be summarized by writing the equation

$$W = Jsm\Delta t, \quad \ldots \ldots \ldots \quad (2)$$

where J is a constant independent of the substance whose rise in temperature is measured, W is the amount of mechanical or electrical energy which is expended, that is, the work done, Δt is the rise in temperature of a mass m of the substance, and s is a constant characteristic of the substance.

5. Specific Heat and Thermal Capacity.

These quantitative, reproducible results indicated that the parameter s, which occurs in equations (1) and (2), is a measure of some property of the particular substance. This property is called the *specific heat*. Corresponding to this, the product of the specific heat and the mass is called the *thermal capacity* of the system. Thus, the specific heat is the thermal capacity of unit mass of the substance. These experiments also make it possible to specify what is meant by *heat*. They indicate that when work is done on a system it suffers a change of state which can be manifest by a rise in its temperature. The amount by which the energy of the system changes can then be measured by the product which occurs on the right-hand side of equation (2). It measures the change in a property which changes when the temperature of the system rises as a result of the expenditure of mechanical, or other, work on it. The quantity which is measured by the product of the thermal capacity of the substance and its rise in temperature when work is done on it, is called the *quantity of heat* which it has gained. Remembering that, in assigning values to the specific heat, water was taken as a standard, it has been customary to define the unit of heat as the amount of heat which is absorbed by one gram of water when its temperature rises one degree celsius. This unit is called the *calorie*, although it will be appreciated that once Joule had established the equivalence of heat and mechanical energy, a separate "unit of heat" is superfluous. This has now been recognized by international agreement and the joule (10^7 ergs) is specified as the unit of heat.*

It cannot be assumed *a priori* that the same amount of heat is given out by one gram of water when its temperature falls by one degree. This requires experimental proof, which is provided by the agreement between the results of Callendar's experiments on the specific heat of water using both the electrical method and the thermal interchanger (see section 13). Other experiments, in which given masses of fluids at different temperatures are mixed, indicate that the amount of heat required to raise the temperature of a given mass of material through one degree is very nearly independent of the temperature. This is not quite so, but the departures are so small that, except in high-precision work, they can be neglected.

6. Summary of Results.

Experiments of the kind carried out by Joule have, since his day, been performed with greater accuracy. They will be considered in detail in Sections 10 to 15 below. Meanwhile, it is sufficient to say that they confirm precisely the relation (2) which was deduced from the results of Joule's experiments.

The quantitative and reproducible results of Joule's experiments made the caloric theory no longer tenable. As soon as it was realized that the temperature of a body could be changed simply by using an external agency to do work on it, without the temperature of any other body being altered, the notion of caloric lost all meaning. Following this, the idea of heat as a form of energy was accepted by Joule

* H. F. Stimson, *Journ. Res. Bur. Stand.*, Washington, Vol. 42, p. 209 (1949); J. A. Hall and C. R. Barber, *Brit. Journ. Appl. Phys.*, Vol. 1, p. 81 (1950); H. F. Stimson, *Amer. Journ. Phys.*, Vol. 23, p. 621 (1955); J. A. Hall, *Brit. Journ. Appl. Phys.*, Vol. 7, p. 236 (1956).

and Kelvin, and maintains its position to this day. At the end of this chapter we shall indicate an alternative way of looking at these experiments * which is logically more satisfying, but for the present we shall examine these questions in the light of the ideas which followed in the wake of Joule's experiments.

They established an exact equivalence between heat and mechanical energy, and can be summarized by writing

$$W = JH, \quad \ldots \ldots \ldots \quad (3)$$

where W is the amount of work expended to change the temperature of the working substance, H is the amount of heat produced (that is, as specified in the preceding section), and J is a constant called the " mechanical equivalent of heat ". In fact, J is the specific heat of water (at the temperature of the experiment) measured in mechanical units. If heat is measured in calories, then J is the amount of work which must be expended to produce one calorie. Before considering the exact experiments, mentioned at the beginning of Section 5, which have been carried out to determine the precise value of the constant J, we shall deal with two questions of general importance in calorimetry.

7. The Exact Definition of the Calorie.

Although, as has been stated in Section 5, the unit of heat is the joule, the results of many calorimetric experiments are still expressed in terms of the calorie; and this was the universal practice until recent years. Furthermore, the energy required to raise the temperature of a given mass of water through one degree depends on the temperature of the water. Careful experiments by the method of mixtures show this; and the experiments which are considered in Sections 10 to 15 below confirm it. Indeed, this is one of the reasons for adopting the unit of mechanical energy also as the unit of heat. It also indicates that we must be more precise in our definition of the calorie; it is necessary to specify the temperature at which it is measured. There are two calories in common use.

The 15° calorie is defined as the amount of heat required to raise the temperature of 1 gm. of water from 14·5° to 15·5° C.

The mean calorie is one-hundredth of the amount of heat required to raise the temperature of 1 gm. of water from 0° to 100° C.

The experiments which are described in Sections 10 et seq. give the most accurate method of determining the variation of the specific heat of water, that is, the determination of the ratio of the amount of heat (or, what is the same thing, of work) required to raise the temperature

---

* Born, *Phys. Zeits.*, Vol. 22, p. 249 (1921).

of 1 gm. of water through one degree at any given temperature to that required to raise it from 14·5° to 15·5° C.

They also give a method of determining the ratio of the mean calorie to the standard or 15° calorie.

8. Heat Losses in Calorimetry.

A difficulty that is common to all the experiments that we are to consider, in fact to all experiments in which we attempt to measure quantity of heat, is due to heat losses. We may therefore briefly consider here the methods that are used to deal with them.

No first-class thermal insulator is known which can compare with electrical insulators in common use. The result is that it is impossible to isolate from its surroundings a system on which thermal experiments are being made, and in consequence heat is flowing all the time from the system to the surroundings or vice versa.

We have to determine the amount of heat that is so lost and correct for it. The law governing such losses was discovered by Newton * and is called *Newton's law of cooling*. It states that the rate at which a body loses heat to its surroundings is proportional to the temperature difference between the body and its surroundings. Actually the law is true only for small differences of temperature unless the system is cooling by forced convection (see Chapter XI, Section 27), but in accurate calorimetric experiments we always arrange that the difference of temperature between the body and its surroundings is small, and that the rate of loss of heat is small compared with the rate at which heat is supplied. With this assumption let us suppose that we have a body originally at the same temperature as its surroundings and that we supply heat to it at a uniform rate for a certain time. During this time its temperature rises at a definite rate; let it be t_2 at the end of the heating, t_1 being the initial value. The rate of loss of heat to the surroundings is proportional to the temperature difference between the body and the surroundings. At the beginning of the experiment this temperature difference is zero and at the end it is $(t_2 - t_1)$; the rate of rise of temperature is uniform. The total loss is therefore the same as if the body were to remain at the mean temperature $\frac{1}{2}(t_1 + t_2)$, i.e. as if the excess above the surroundings were $\frac{1}{2}(t_2 - t_1)$, for the whole time of the heating. The total loss of heat may therefore be written

$$k \times \tfrac{1}{2}(t_2 - t_1) \times \text{(time for experiment)}.$$

k is a constant which is determined by measuring the rate of fall of the temperature of the body, when no heat is supplied to it and when its temperature is in excess of its surroundings by various known amounts. The proportionality between rate of loss of heat and temperature excess can be verified in this way.

In other calorimetric experiments it may be required to maintain a steady temperature. Such an apparatus is termed a thermostat. In an ideal thermostatic system the rate of loss of heat to its surroundings at every instant is equal to the rate of supply of heat from the source. The chief difficulties in maintaining a constant temperature are as follows.†

(a) *Time-lag in the Control of the Heat Supply.*—In any thermostat there is a lag between the change in temperature of the system and the change in the rate of supply of heat. From a theoretical study it has been shown ‡ that for stable

* Newton, *Phil. Trans. Roy. Soc.*, Vol. 22, p. 828 (1701).

† Laby, *Proc. Phys. Soc.*, Vol. 54, p. 55 (1942).

‡ Callendar, Hartree and Porter, *Phil. Trans. Roy. Soc.*, Vol. 235, p. 415 (1936).

control of temperature, the supply of heat to the thermostat must return quickly to its normal value, and there must be positive damping in the controlling system. This means that the thermometer which controls the heat supply must follow temperature changes rapidly and regulate the supply of heat from the source with the least possible delay.

(b) *Depth of Penetration of Temperature Fluctuations.*—Temperature fluctuations of short period penetrate an insulator only to a small depth. An enclosure constructed of alternate layers of good and bad conductors of heat is an effective shield against temperature fluctuations.

(c) *Thermal Shielding.*—In an enclosure of alternate layers of conductors and non-conductors of heat, the non-conductor eliminates short-period fluctuations, because of the effect mentioned under (b), whereas a layer of a good conductor brings all points inside it to the same temperature.

(d) *Position of Thermometer.*—If the thermometer which regulates the supply of heat is placed inside the thermostat, temperature changes, at least sufficient to actuate the thermometer, occur in the region from which it is the purpose of the thermostat to exclude any temperature change. If a resistance thermometer is used for this purpose, it can be readily wound on an external surface of the enclosure whose temperature is to be controlled.

THE MECHANICAL EQUIVALENT OF HEAT

9. The experiments that have been made to determine the value of the mechanical equivalent of heat may be divided into two main groups, (1) those in which mechanical energy is turned directly into heat, (2) those in which electrical energy is so converted.

At this stage we shall describe these experiments in terms of the " mechanical equivalent of heat "; for the primary purpose of the men who first carried out experiments such as these was to examine whether there *was* a mechanical equivalent of heat and, if so, to determine its value, that is, the precise equivalence between the calorie and the units of mechanics. The student must, however, appreciate that in these experiments the quantity that is measured is the specific heat of water (or other working substance) in energy units (mechanical or electrical) at the temperature of the experiment.

We shall first consider the (direct) experiments in which the energy is measured mechanically.

Direct Methods

10. Joule, Rowland, Reynolds and Moorby.

After Joule had completed the work we have already described, he made a more accurate determination * of the mechanical equivalent of heat by measuring the rise in temperature of the water in a container when it was stirred by a paddle driven mechanically. Similar experi-

* J. P. Joule, *Phil. Trans. Roy. Soc.*, Vol. 169, p. 365 (1878).

ments were carried out by Rowland.* Reynolds and Moorby † used a continuous-flow method in which as the water flowed through a Froude hydraulic brake its temperature changed from about 0° C. to about 100° C.

11. Laby and Hercus.

Laby and Hercus ‡ have carried out a determination by a direct method and in spite of the many difficulties involved have attained the same order of accuracy as other workers who have used the electrical method.

An electromagnetic brake or induction dynamometer was used. The electromagnet with poles N, S and winding W (see fig. 2.1) was similar in construction to the field magnet of a direct-current dynamo, but with magnetizing windings taken to slip rings R. It was rotated about a vertical axis by a driving belt on the pulley P.

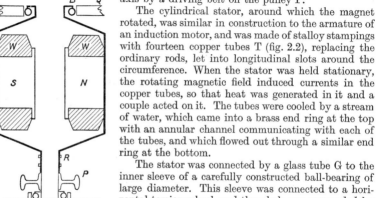

Fig. 2.1

The cylindrical stator, around which the magnet rotated, was similar in construction to the armature of an induction motor, and was made of stalloy stampings with fourteen copper tubes T (fig. 2.2), replacing the ordinary rods, let into longitudinal slots around the circumference. When the stator was held stationary, the rotating magnetic field induced currents in the copper tubes, so that heat was generated in it and a couple acted on it. The tubes were cooled by a stream of water, which came into a brass end ring at the top with an annular channel communicating with each of the tubes, and which flowed out through a similar end ring at the bottom.

The stator was connected by a glass tube G to the inner sleeve of a carefully constructed ball-bearing of large diameter. This sleeve was connected to a horizontal torsion wheel, and the whole was suspended by a torsion wire which was carried on a frame supported by the plate Q (fig. 2.1). This plate carried the fixed part of the upper ball-bearing B of the rotor, and was rigidly fixed to the base plate A by three uprights. The glass tube served to insulate the stator thermally, and the glass-metal joints were made with sealing-wax. The frame carrying the stator was provided with levelling screws and its position on the plate Q was adjustable. The stator could thus be accurately centred between the pole pieces N and S.

The couple was measured as in Rowland's experiments by weights hanging on tungsten wires which were attached to the torsion wheel. Preliminary experiments with cone, ball, and other types of bearings showed that, if the couple were to be measured to 1 in 10,000, none of these bearings was suitable for the pulleys over which the wires passed from the hanging weights to the torsion wheel. Pulleys supported by agate knife-edges were used, and correction was made for

    * H. A. Rowland, *Proc. Amer. Acad. Arts and Sciences*, Vol. 16, p. 38 (1880).

    † O. Reynolds and W. H. Moorby, *Phil. Trans. Roy. Soc.*, Vol. 190, p. 301 (1897).

    ‡ Laby and Hercus, *Phil. Trans.*, A, Vol. 227, p. 63 (1927); Hercus, *Proc. Phys. Soc.*, Vol. 48, p. 282 (1936).

the slight displacement of the knife-edges from the centres of the pulleys. In order that the couple acting on the stator should correspond fully to the heat produced, the axis of rotation of the stator was made parallel to that of the rotating magnet by means of suitable levelling screws and sliding plates, and the rotating magnet was so mounted on S.K.F. ball-bearings as to avoid any motion parallel to the axis of rotation, which would produce heat but no couple. Measurement of the couple and of the number of rotations of the magnet gave the work performed.

The heat produced was obtained by measuring the rise of temperature of the stream of water by means of two platinum thermometers connected differentially and placed in the stream of water, one (H in fig. 2.2) before and one after it entered the stator. The thermometers were about an inch from the stator itself, and were contained in tubes which passed inside the inner sleeve of the stator ball-bearing and the tube supporting the stator. The mass of water flowing through the stator in a time corresponding to a given number of revolutions of the magnet was measured. High accuracy in the thermal measurements was attained by making the heat losses small—the total loss was less than 0·04 per cent of the heat developed. The losses took place from (1) the tubes surrounding the thermometers, (2) the stop of the stator, (3) the sides and bottom of the stator. Subsidiary experiments showed that (1) was made negligibly small by surrounding the thermometer tubes with vacuum jackets. To make (2) negligible, the temperature of the room was adjusted to be equal to that of the top of the stator; the equality was tested by a thermocouple K. (3) was made small by surrounding the stator with a vacuum flask, which was screwed on to the bottom by means of a threaded iron ring sealing-waxed into the bottom of the flask. The top of the flask was closed by a ring of round rubber pressed into the small space between the flask and the glass tube carrying the stator. The temperature difference between the inside and outside walls of the flask was determined by a thermocouple F, and the correction

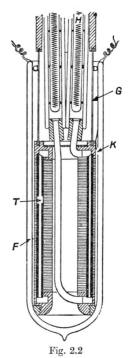

Fig. 2.2

for loss through the flask walls was determined from this temperature difference and from the results of subsidiary experiments on the flask filled with water.

Great care was taken to obtain steadiness in all conditions, i.e. magnetic field, rate of rotation, and water flow. The rate of generation of heat was thus constant, and with a constant water flow there was no appreciable change in the temperature of any part of the calorimeter during an experiment. This condition must always be fulfilled in continuous-flow calorimetry.

A modification of the Laby and Hercus method, in which a stationary magnetic field replaces the rotating one, has been suggested by Chowdri and Kothari.*

The measurements of Laby and Hercus have been criticized † on the ground that they took no specific steps to expel dissolved air and other gases. Jessel claimed that dissolved gases make a considerable

---

* Chowdri and Kothari, *Indian Journ. Phys.*, Vol. 14, p. 409 (1940).

† Jessel, *Proc. Phys. Soc.*, Vol. 46, p. 747 (1934).

difference to the measured value of the specific heat of water, and thus to the value determined for the mechanical equivalent. This criticism has been dealt with by Laby and Hercus * on thermodynamical grounds. They showed that dissolved air could not affect the measured value of the 15° calorie by more than one part in ten thousand. This conclusion, based on a thermodynamical consideration of the problem, has been well confirmed by the recent work at the Bureau of Stan-dards at Washington. As is pointed out below, the latter workers took particular care to ensure that the sample of water on which they made their measurements was free of all dissolved gases. As we shall see below, their result, when converted to the same units, agrees with that of Laby and Hercus to better than three parts in 20,000. This concordance provides direct evidence that dissolved gases have a negligible effect on the measured value of the mechanical equivalent of heat. This agreement, together with the theoretical considerations advanced by Laby and Hercus, shows that there is no justification whatever for Jessel's criticism.

Electrical Methods

12. The fundamental electrical units in the electromagnetic system of measurement are defined as multiples of the corresponding centimetre-gram-second units. Since 1 January 1948, each practical standard † has been defined in terms of the particular electromagnetic law which expresses the relation between the quantity concerned and the fundamental quantities of length, mass, and time for which standards have long been defined. The electrical units defined in this way are given the prefix " absolute ".

However, until 1948, electrical units used in practical measurements were defined in concrete terms, such as the resistance of a specified column of mercury and the current which deposits silver at a particular rate in a specified silver voltameter. These were called the international units and were sufficiently close to the corresponding fundamental units to be regarded as identical with them within the limits of accuracy of existing practice.

In the experiments to which we turn in the following sections, the measurements were made in terms of the international units and the results are expressed in terms of the corresponding energy unit, the international joule. The various national standards laboratories have compared the international units with the electromagnetic standards.

---

* Laby and Hercus, *Proc. Phys. Soc.*, Vol. 47, p. 1003 (1935); Hercus, *ibid.*, Vol. 48, p. 282 (1936).

† *Units and Standards of Measurement employed at the National Physical Laboratory: III Electricity*, London, Department of Scientific and Industrial Research (1952).

As a result of their work the ratios of the corresponding units are known with great precision. The use of these conversion factors permits comparison of the results of the experiments in which the energy is measured electrically with the results of those in which it is measured mechanically. Thus, by measuring the electrical energy required to produce a measured rise in the temperature of the physical system, an accurate value for the calorie can be determined in mechanical units.

To measure the input of electrical energy, we may measure the duration of the experiment (t sec.) and (1) E and I, (2) I and R, or (3) E and R where E is the electromotive force, I the current, R the resistance.

13. Griffiths, Schuster and Gannon, Callendar and Barnes, Bousfield and Bousfield.

In his experiments Griffiths * measured E and R while Schuster and Ganon † measured E and I. In the course of their experiments, Callendar and Barnes ‡ developed the method of continuous-flow calorimetry. They also measured the variation of the specific heat of water over a wide range of temperatures. Bousfield and Bousfield § used a combination of continuous-flow calorimetry and measurements of the rise in temperature of the water.

Detailed accounts of the experiments mentioned above and in Section 10, together with descriptions of the equipment used and criticisms of the measurements, have been given in the first four editions of this book. The student who is interested in these details should consult one of these earlier editions or the original papers to which reference has been made.

14. Jaeger and Steinwehr.‖

These workers carried out a very careful determination by the rise-of-temperature method. They aimed at an accuracy of one part in ten thousand in all their measurements. They consider the following the essential points in work of this kind.

(1) *The use of a large mass of water* (50 *Kgm.*). This makes the correction for the thermal capacity of the containing vessel proportionately small, since for a given thickness of wall the mass of the vessel itself depends on its superficial area, or on the square of the linear dimensions,

---

* E. H. Griffiths, *Phil. Trans. Roy. Soc.*, Vol. 184, p. 361 (1893); *Proc. Roy. Soc.* A, Vol. 55, p. 23 (1894).

† A. Schuster and W. Gannon, *Phil. Trans. Roy. Soc.*, Vol. 186, p. 415 (1895).

‡ H. L. Callendar, *Phil. Trans. Roy. Soc.* A, Vol. 199, p. 55 (1902); H. T. Barnes, *ibid.*, Vol. 199, p. 149 (1902); H. T. Barnes, *Proc. Roy. Soc.* A, Vol. 82, p. 390 (1909); H. L. Callendar, *Phil. Trans. Roy. Soc.* A, Vol. 212, p. 1 (1912).

§ W. R. Bousfield and W. E. Bousfield, *Phil. Trans. Roy. Soc.* A, Vol. 211, p. 236 (1911).

‖ Jaeger and Steinwehr, *Ann. d. Physik*, Vol. 64, p. 305 (1921).

while the mass of the contained water depends on their cube. For the same reason, the larger the mass of water, the smaller is the heat loss as compared with the heat supplied, for a given rise of temperature produced in a given time. An upper limit is fixed by the fact that it is desirable to weigh the vessel and the contained water on an equal-armed balance.

(2) *The use of a small temperature rise* (1·4 deg.). This ensures that Newton's law of cooling shall be strictly applicable to determine the cooling correction. It is also necessary to use a reasonably small temperature rise on account of the fact that the relation between the specific heat of water and the temperature is not linear, but ten degrees is small enough (see Example 1 on p. 68). A great disadvantage of using such a small rise is that it is necessary to measure it correct to one ten-thousandth of a degree, which means carrying out resistance measurements to one part in two million.

(3) *Efficient stirring of the water.*

(4) *Well-defined temperature of the surroundings.* This makes the heat loss definite. It was ensured by placing the calorimeter inside a double-walled metal box with the space between the walls and the lid filled with water. The temperature of this water was kept constant by running through a long copper coil submerged in it a constant stream of water the temperature of which was controlled.

A section of the calorimeter and the surrounding metal box is shown in fig. 2.3, and a drawing of the stirring arrangement and the heater in fig. 2.4.

The calorimeter consisted of a cylindrical copper vessel (fig. 2.3) lying on its side on four porcelain insulators inside the constant-temperature box. The height of the cylinder and the diameter of the ends were both 40 cm. The thickness of the walls was 0·7 mm., so that the mass of the vessel was about 4·5 Kgm. In the centre of the side of the vessel was a circular hole which served for the introduction of the heating coil H (fig. 2.4), the shaft which drove the stirrer, and the thermometer. This hole was closed by the lid D (fig. 2.4) as shown in fig. 2.3. The leads to the heating coil, the stirring shaft, and the thermometer passed through brass tubes from 2·5 to 1·7 cm. long and 6 or 8 mm. in diameter soldered in holes in the lid. Thus there was very little communication with the outer air, and the amount of evaporation that took place was negligible. (In any case the method adopted for determining the loss of heat would include any loss due to evaporation.)

The stirrer and its mounting are shown in the figure. In order to prevent large loss of heat by conduction along the shaft, a piece of vulcanite J was introduced. The stirrer rotated at the rate of about 1 revolution in 2 sec., and generated about $\frac{1}{4}$ calorie in 1 sec., i.e. about 1 watt. The energy supplied by the heater was about 800 watts.

The heating coil was of constantan wire 1 mm. in diameter and 14 m. long, resistance about 8 ohms. It was heated by a current of 10 amp. It was wound on a brass cylinder 10 cm. long and 8 cm. in diameter. This brass was originally 3 mm. thick, but it was turned down except for a band about 3 mm. wide at each end, and the wire was wound in the space so formed. The wire was silk-covered and was shellacked. After winding it a brass cover was slipped over it and soldered into place. The leads passed out through two brass tubes. They were of copper and were hard-soldered to the constantan. Thin potential leads were soldered on to the current leads above the junctions with the constantan so that any disturbance due to thermo-electric effects was avoided.

The current was measured by passing it through a standard 0·1 ohm in series with the heater, and measuring the potential drop on this with a potentiometer. The potential drop on the heater (80 volts) was measured by putting a standard

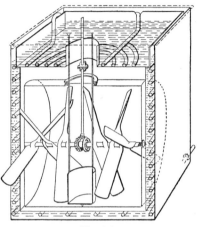

Fig. 2.3

10,000 ohms plus 127 ohms in parallel with it and measuring the drop on the 127 ohms on the potentiometer. A Weston cell was used as the standard of E.M.F. The time of switching the current on and off was automatically recorded on a chronograph on which seconds were marked by a standard clock. An experiment usually lasted 6 min.

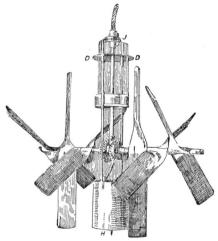

Fig. 2.4

The temperature rise was measured by a standard platinum thermometer. Observations of the temperature change before the beginning and after the end of the heating were made to determine the heat loss. This method of experimenting (putting a definite quantity of energy in and shutting off) obviated the necessity of relying entirely on measurements of a rapidly rising temperature.

The water equivalent of the calorimeter and other metal parts was only about 0·7 Kgm., or only a little over 1 per cent of the mass of water (50 Kgm.). It needed only to be known to 1 per cent and its temperature variation could be neglected (see Jaeger and Steinwehr, loc. cit., p. 318).

There were about seventy experiments over the range from 5° to 50° C.

The temperature rise of 1·4 deg. required temperature measurements to be made to 1/10,000 deg. if an accuracy of one part in ten thousand were to be attained. This was hardly possible, and, as would be expected, individual experiments showed departures of a few parts in ten thousand.

15. Osborne, Stimson and Ginnings.*

A very accurate determination of the mechanical equivalent has been carried out more recently at the Bureau of Standards at Washington. An electrical method was used. The calorimeter in which the measurements were made was well insulated from the influence of external sources of heat by enveloping it in a shell which was kept at very nearly the same temperature as the calorimeter itself. Furthermore, the temperature of the surroundings was controlled to be very nearly the same as the temperature of the calorimeter.

The apparatus consisted essentially of a calorimeter containing a quantity of water, part liquid and part vapour. An electrical heater was immersed in the water; this provided a method of adding a measured amount of energy to the water, the calorimeter, and its contents. There was also a pump to ensure turbulent circulation of the water in the calorimeter. The water was distilled to remove impurities, and then re-distilled under a pressure of a tenth of an atmosphere to remove any dissolved gases. This was done since Jessel † had suggested that dissolved air had a large effect on the measured specific heat of water.

In making the heat capacity measurements, the calorimeter with a known mass of water was heated over a measured temperature range, platinum thermometers being used to measure the temperature. The essential measurements are: the amount of water subjected to the process, the amount of energy exchanged, and the change of state produced in the water.

From their measurements, Osborne and his colleagues have prepared tables of the specific heat of water, enthalpy of liquid and vapour, heat of vaporization, and the specific volume of the vapour throughout

    * Osborne, Journ. Res. Bur. Stand., Washington, Vol. 4, p. 609 (1930); Osborne, Stimson and Ginnings, ibid., Vol. 23, p. 197 (1939).

    † Jessel, Proc. Phys. Soc., Vol. 46, p. 747 (1937).

the temperature range from the ice point to the steam point. This determination of J is probably the most accurate that has been made by an electrical method. The results are in good agreement with those of Jaeger and Steinwehr, and those of Laby and Hercus using a mechanical method.

16. Value of the Mechanical Equivalent of Heat.

In Sections 11, 14, and 15 above, the three outstanding determinations of the energy equivalent of heat have been described. Of these, one is a direct mechanical determination and the other two are electrical.

The direct measurement is that by Laby and Hercus.* Their data were recalculated by Birge,† and the recalculated value was later accepted by Laby and Hercus,‡ The value of the 15° calorie as recalculated is:

Laby and Hercus: $J_{15} = 4 \cdot 1852_6 \pm 0 \cdot 0007_0$ absolute joule cal_{15}^{-1}.

The probable error stated here is that assigned to this work by Birge.§ It is based on the average value of the residuals in the recalculated results.

The two determinations of the electrical equivalent are those of Jaeger and Steinwehr,‖ and of Osborne, Stimson and Ginnings.¶ Birge † has pointed out that the analytic expression which Jaeger and Steinwehr use does not represent their data properly. The residuals show a serious trend in the neighbourhood of 15° C., just where an accurate representation of the data is most essential. Birge has recalculated these data and, again basing his estimate of the probable error on the average residuals, gives the result:

Jaeger and Steinwehr:

$$J'_{15} = 4 \cdot 1832_7 \pm 0 \cdot 0009_0 \text{ international joule } \mathrm{cal}_{15}^{-1}.$$

Osborne, Stimson and Ginnings also noted the behaviour of the residuals in the results of Jaeger and Steinwehr, and, by an independent method, recalculated their value and obtained almost the same result (4·1832).

* Laby and Hercus, *Phil. Trans. Roy. Soc.*, A, Vol. 227, p. 63 (1927).

† Birge, *Rev. Mod. Phys.*, Vol. 1, p. 1 (1929).

‡ Laby and Hercus, *Proc. Phys. Soc.*, Vol. 47, p. 1003 (1935).

§ Birge, *Reports on Progress in Physics*, Vol. 8, p. 109 (1941).

‖ Jaeger and Steinwehr, *Ann. Phys. Lpz.*, Vol. 64, p. 305 (1921).

¶ Osborne, Stimson and Ginnings, *Journ. Res. Bur. Stand.*, Washington, Vol. 23 p. 197 (1939).

The value of the 15° calorie obtained by Osborne, Stimson and Ginnings,* with the probable error assigned to it by Birge,† is:

Osborne, Stimson and Ginnings:

$$J'_{15} = 4.1850_2 \pm 0.0004 \text{ international joule } \text{cal}_{15}^{-1}.$$

From these results, the value of the mechanical equivalent of heat adopted by Birge is

$$J_{15} = 4.1855 \pm 0.0004 \text{ absolute joule } \text{cal}_{15}^{-1},$$

and the adopted value of the electrical equivalent is

$$J'_{15} = 4.1847 \pm 0.0003 \text{ international joule } \text{cal}_{15}^{-1}.$$

The difference between the international and the absolute joule involves a factor

$$1.00020 \pm 0.00004_5.$$

Allowing for this factor, it will be observed that the mechanical determination of the energy equivalent of heat by Laby and Hercus agrees with the electrical determination by Osborne, Stimson and Ginnings to better than three parts in twenty thousand. This close agreement is of great importance in that it provides an entirely independent check of the accuracy of the electrical standards.

17. The Specific Heat of Water.

Apart from giving the value of the mechanical equivalent of heat, these experiments determine the variation of the specific heat of water with temperature. We have already referred to the work of Rowland, of Joule, and of Griffiths in this connexion. In passing, mention must be made of the very careful work of Bartoli and Stracciati and of Ludin,‡ both of whom used the method of mixtures. This method is probably subject to errors, particularly at the higher temperatures.

The most extensive investigations are those of Callendar and Barnes, of Jaeger and Steinwehr, and of Osborne, Stimson, and Ginnings. It is important to realize that the absolute values of the electrical standards are immaterial, because we are only concerned with relative amounts of energy at different temperatures.

In 1948, Professor W. J. de Haas examined all the available data. He used the values obtained by Callendar and Barnes, by Jaeger and Steinwehr, by Laby and Hercus, and by Osborne, Stimson and Ginnings

---

* Osborne, Stimson and Ginnings, *Journ. Res. Bur. Stand.*, Washington, Vol. 23, p. 197 (1939).

† Birge, *Reports on Progress in Physics*, Vol. 8, p. 112 (1941).

‡ Bartoli and Stracciati, *Beiblätter*, Vol. 15, p. 761 (1891); Ludin, *ibid.* (1897); (see *A Dictionary of Applied Physics*, Vol. I, p. 490).

to determine a weighted mean value of the specific heat of water at constant pressure at 15° C. He then used the formula developed at the National Bureau of Standards at Washington and this value at 15° C. to determine the values of the specific heat of water at all other temperatures between 0° C. and 100° C. The table of values so obtained was considered by the International Committee on Weights and Measures * and agreed. A selection of the adopted values is given in Table 1.

TABLE 1.—SPECIFIC HEAT OF WATER

Temperature, °C.	C_p abs. joule/°C./gm.	Temperature, °C.	C_p abs. joule/°C./gm.
0	4·2174	50	4·1804
10	4·1919	60	4·1841
20	4·1816	70	4·1893
30	4·1782	80	4·1961
35	4·1779	90	4·2048
40	4·1783	100	4·2156

18. Internal Energy.

The experiments which have been described in this chapter can be looked at from a different point of view. This alternative point of view,† which we shall now consider, has the advantage that by it the concept of internal energy can be introduced in a logical manner depending only on experimental results.

In all the experiments which we have been considering, work (mechanical or electrical) is expended on the working substance and its rise in temperature is measured. In all of these experiments the calorimeter forms an adiabatic system. In fact, in the experiments of Laby and Hercus, and of Osborne and his colleagues, special precautions were taken to have the calorimeter and its shield in a room whose temperature was adjusted to be as nearly equal as possible to that of the calorimeter. Thus, the calorimeter contains a working substance and a source of energy, and this forms a system which is separated adiabatically from the external world. A measured amount of energy is supplied to the working substance, and its rise in temperature is measured. The result of Joule's experiments, and of all the later determinations of the energy equivalent of heat, is just that the rise in temperature of a given amount of the working substance depends only on the amount of work expended or of energy supplied, irrespective of

* *Procès Verbaux des Séances du Comité International des Poids et Mesures*, Vol. 22, p. 92 (1950); see also H. F. Stimson, *Amer. Journ. Physics*, Vol. 23, p. 621 (1955).

† Born, *Phys. Zeit.*, Vol. 20, p. 218 (1921).

the way in which it is supplied; that is, by supplying a certain amount of energy or doing work adiabatically on the calorimeter and its contents, the state of the working substance is altered. Define a function U, called the *internal energy, which depends only on the state of the system*, and which is such that the change in U when the system goes *adiabatically* from one state to another state is equal to the external work which has to be expended on it to effect the change. Thus, for two states of the system,

$$W_{\text{(adiabatic)}} = U_2 - U_1. \quad \cdots \quad (4)$$

The definition of the internal energy in this way as a function of state of the system is made possible by the fact that when a system is caused to change from one state to another, the work that must be done on it is the same for *all adiabatic paths* by which it can pass from the one state to the other.

It should be noted that this is essentially an experimental method of introducing the quantity U as a function of state of the system; for it is precisely by an experiment performed adiabatically in this way that thermodynamical measurements are made. For instance, in measurements of the specific heat, the substance which is being investigated is itself the calorimeter, that is, as far as possible, it is adiabatically isolated. The amount of work which must be expended on it to bring about a particular change of state (usually under the condition of constant volume) is measured. This gives the change in energy in going adiabatically from the initial to the final state. Now, the change in state associated with this change in energy is manifest primarily as a change in temperature. The connexion with the idea of quantity of heat as it was developed historically, for example, as a result of experiments like those carried out by Black, is provided by using as unit of heat that energy which is required to produce a particular change of temperature of one gram of water. This amount of energy expressed in mechanical units is the mechanical equivalent of heat.

However, the concept of quantity of heat can be defined for any process at all, whether or not the changes take place adiabatically. Specifying the internal energy of the initial and final states of the system by U_1 and U_2, and the work expended on the system by W, the *quantity of heat* supplied in the process is *defined* by

$$Q = U_2 - U_1 - W. \quad \cdots \quad (5)$$

Throughout the development of thermodynamics, quantity of heat can be used in just this way, as the difference between the increase in internal energy and the work expended on the system.

This way of introducing the concept of heat shows clearly that it is a form of energy. Furthermore, from equation (5), it is clear that the quantity of heat can be measured in terms of the units of mechanical energy. It has been pointed out already that this follows from Joule's experiments, and that the International Unions of Physics and Chemistry have now adopted the unit of mechanical energy—appropriately called the *joule*—also as the unit of heat. When this is done, the determinations of the mechanical equivalent of heat which have been described in this chapter can then be regarded more simply as determinations of the specific heat (and its temperature variation) of the working substance (generally water) used in the experiments.

This also makes clear what is meant by a *flow of heat*. When two bodies at different temperatures are placed in thermal contact, so that they eventually come into thermal equilibrium, the internal energy of the colder increases at the expense of the internal energy of the hotter. This flux of energy is the meaning which must be given to a flow of heat from one to the other of two bodies in contact.

If the system consists of several adiabatically isolated bodies, the internal energy of each of which is known as a result of calorimetric experiments, the internal energy of the system is *defined* as the sum of the internal energies of the separate bodies. In general, this will not always be exactly true, but the deviation varies only as the surface, so that for large enough volumes it can be neglected. Thus, the additive character of internal energy can always be used.

19. The First Law of Thermodynamics.

The fact which is expressed by equation (5) is usually known as the *first law of thermodynamics*. It is simply an extension, by introducing the quantity of heat Q, of the experimental fact which follows from Joule's experiments, that the amount of mechanical or other work which has to be done on a system to enable it to pass from one specified state to another specified state by adiabatc changes is independent of the way in which the changes are carried out. The extension is that the work expended on the system, plus the heat supplied to it, is equal to the change in internal energy of the system in passing from one state to the other. It can also be regarded as an extension of the principle of the conservation of energy to systems in which there are changes of temperature.

EXAMPLES

1. Assuming that the variation of the specific heat of water is given by a formula

$$c = \alpha + \beta t + \gamma t^2,$$

show that the difference between the *actual* specific heat at a temperature $\frac{1}{2}(t_1 + t_2)$ and the *mean* specific heat over the range t_1 to t_2 is

$$-\gamma(t_2 - t_1)^2/12.$$

Roth [*] has given such a parabolic formula in which the constants have the values 1·0066, −0·0005696, and 0·000008742. Show that the error in assuming that the actual specific heat at the mean temperature is the same as the mean over the range does not amount to one part in ten thousand for a range of ten degrees.

2. Show that provided the appropriate specific heats are positive, then, when a body is placed in thermal contact with another at a lower temperature, there is a flux of energy from the former to the latter.

[*] Roth, *Zeits. f. phys. Chem.*, A, Vol. 183, p. 38 (1938).

CHAPTER III

The Kinetic Theory of Gases

1. We have seen in Chapter I that at very low pressures (or densities) all gases obey the following simple laws:

(1) *Boyle's Law.*—If a given mass of gas is compressed at constant temperature, the product of the pressure and the volume remains constant.

(2) *Charles's Law.*—If a given mass of gas is heated through a given range of temperature, say from 0° C. to $t°$ C., the volume remaining constant, the coefficient of pressure change is independent of the nature of the gas. Similarly, if it is heated at constant pressure, the same applies to the coefficient of expansion. Further, the coefficients of expansion and of pressure change are equal (Chapter I, Section 35).

To these we may add:

(3) *Dalton's Law of Partial Pressures.*—The pressure exerted on the walls of the containing vessel by a mixture of gases is equal to the sum of the pressures that would be exerted by the gases if they were present separately.

(4) *Joule's Law.*—The energy content of a gas is independent of its volume; that is, if a gas is allowed to expand into a vacuum, there is no loss or gain of energy involved in the process; also, if two gases diffuse into one another so that the volume occupied by each is altered, there is no change in the internal energy. Both processes must, of course, be isothermal. (For Joule's experiment, see Chapter V, Section 3.)

(5) *Gay Lussac's Law.*—The volumes in which gases combine chemically bear a simple relation to one another and to that of the resulting product if this is also gaseous. The volumes must, of course, all be measured under the same conditions of temperature and pressure.

Further, we may add a law which, though not a direct expression of an experimental result, explains the result expressed in Gay Lussac's law in a very simple way, and is now regarded as one of the fundamental laws of chemistry, in the study of which it is found that molecular weights determined from gaseous densities (at very low pressures) agree closely with those obtained by purely chemical methods.

(6) *Avogadro's Law.*—Equal volumes of all gases measured at the same temperature and pressure contain the same number of molecules; in other words, the volume occupied at a given temperature and pres-

sure by a gram-molecule (i.e. by a mass in grams equal to the molecular weight) of a gas is the same for all gases.

The fact that at very low pressures the behaviour of all gases is represented by these simple laws indicates that all have a common and simple structure. Our object now is to attempt to construct a model which shall obey these laws. It is convenient to call a gas in such a condition that it obeys the above laws exactly a *perfect gas*.

THE STRUCTURE OF THE PERFECT GAS

2. In constructing our model of a gas we shall be guided by both the molecular theory of chemistry, and the results of experiments on the nature of heat described in Chapter II. These indicate that heat is a form of energy, namely the energy involved in the motion of the molecules of which the body under consideration is made up, and that heating of a body merely increases this energy. The basis of our theory, then, must be that the molecules of matter are in constant motion.

We shall suppose that a gas consists of molecules which are all the same, and which are like minute hard spheres moving about in all directions. The actual volume occupied by the spheres is entirely negligible compared with the total volume of the gas. This last assumption is justified by the fact that we are only attempting to find a theory which shall apply to a very highly expanded gas, and that we know that when the gas is liquefied the molecules can be packed into a space which is very small compared with that which is occupied by the gas.

The molecules exert no forces on each other except when they actually collide; that is, they move in rectilinear paths the directions of which are changed only by collisions with other molecules or with the walls of the containing vessel.

The collisions between molecules and with the walls must be perfectly elastic; in other words, there is no loss of kinetic energy when they take place. If this were not the case the kinetic energy of the molecules would gradually be dissipated.*

Such a collection of molecules will exert pressure on the walls of the containing vessel, just as a blast of sand particles exerts pressure when it falls on a hard surface. We shall now calculate the magnitude of the pressure, and shall show that it varies with the volume of the gas in accordance with Boyle's law.

---

* It is perhaps more accurate to say that *on the average* collisions must be perfectly elastic. In the case of diatomic molecules, for example, at an individual collision some of the translational energy may apparently disappear, being converted into rotational energy, but at other collisions the total translational energy of the two molecules concerned will be increased. These two effects must balance each other so that on the whole there is no loss or gain of translational energy due to collisions. In our simple model we are neglecting all such effects. It is really a model of a monatomic gas, but the results can be applied to the *translational energy* of a diatomic or polyatomic gas.

3. Calculation of the Pressure.

Consider an element dS of the surface of the wall of the vessel containing the gas; for convenience we shall take dS perpendicular to the axis of x. We divide the molecules into groups such that the molecules in group 1 (n_1 per unit volume in number) all have velocity components parallel respectively to the axes of x, y, z, of u_1, v_1, w_1. The number of such molecules which will strike the element dS in time dt is the number contained in a cylinder of height $u_1 dt$, the area of whose base is dS, and whose axis is drawn parallel to the direction of the resultant velocity whose com-

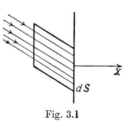

Fig. 3.1

ponents are u_1, v_1, w_1 (fig. 3.1). The volume of the cylinder is $u_1 dS dt$, so that the number of molecules of group 1 contained in this cylinder is

$$n_1 u_1 dS dt,$$

and this is therefore the number of molecules of group 1 which strike the element of area in time dt.

Since each of these molecules of mass m has momentum $m u_1$ perpendicular to the surface, the amount of momentum in a direction perpendicular to the surface brought up by this group of molecules is

$$m n_1 u_1^2 dS dt.$$

To obtain the total momentum, in a direction perpendicular to the element of the surface, which is brought up to the element, we sum this expression for all values of u_1 which are *positive*, and obtain

$$m \sum n_1 u_1^2 dS dt. \quad \dots \quad \dots \quad (1)$$

We write

$$\sum n_1 u_1^2 = \tfrac{1}{2} n \overline{u^2} / V,$$

where n is the total number of molecules and $\overline{u^2}$ is the *mean square* of the velocity components parallel to the x axis of all the molecules; that is,

$$\overline{u^2} = \frac{n_1 u_1^2 + n_2 u_2^2 + \dots}{n_1 + n_2 + \dots}.$$

The factor $\tfrac{1}{2}$ occurs because we are summing only for positive values of u.

Substituting this result in expression (1), the total amount of momentum perpendicular to the element which is brought up to it in time dt becomes

$$\tfrac{1}{2} m n \overline{u^2} dS dt / V.$$

We assume that there is no net flow of the gas in any direction. In this case the *aggregate* momentum must be exactly reversed by collision with dS. The total change of momentum perpendicular to dS in time dt is, therefore, given by

$$m n \overline{u^2} \, dS \, dt / V,$$

and this is equal and opposite to the impulse of the force exerted by the molecules on the element of area in time dt.

If p is the pressure (that is, force per unit area), the impulse on an area dS in time dt is

$$p \, dS \, dt.$$

We have, therefore, $\qquad p V \, dS \, dt = m n \overline{u^2} \, dS \, dt,$

or $\qquad\qquad\qquad\qquad p V = m n \overline{u^2}. \quad \cdots \quad \cdots \quad (1a)$

Further, if C is the *root mean square velocity*, it is defined by the relation

$$C = \left(\frac{n_1 c_1{}^2 + n_2 c_2{}^2 + \cdots}{n_1 + n_2 + \cdots} \right)^{\frac{1}{2}}, \quad \cdots \quad (2)$$

where c_1 is the resultant velocity of molecules of group 1 and so on, and we have

$$C^2 = \overline{u^2} + \overline{v^2} + \overline{w^2}. \quad \cdots \quad \cdots \quad (2a)$$

We may assume further that

$$\overline{u^2} = \overline{v^2} = \overline{w^2},$$

so that $\qquad\qquad\qquad\qquad \overline{u^2} = \tfrac{1}{3} C^2,$

and the expression for the pressure becomes

$$p = \tfrac{1}{3} m n C^2 / V,$$

or $\qquad\qquad\qquad\qquad p = \tfrac{2}{3} \cdot \tfrac{1}{2} m n C^2 / V. \quad \cdots \quad \cdots \quad (3)$

The pressure is, therefore, *two-thirds of the total kinetic energy of the molecules in unit volume.*

4. Avogadro's Law.

In order to prove that the gas obeys Avogadro's law it is necessary to use a result of the dynamical theory of gases which we shall not prove.* This result states that when two gases are brought into

---

* For a proof, see Jeans, *Dynamical Theory of Gases*, 3rd edition, Chapter V; see also Jeans, *Kinetic Theory of Gases*, Cambridge (1940), Section 11.

contact, the condition for no net transfer of energy from one to the other is that the mean translational energies of their individual molecules are equal. This result is deduced from dynamical considerations only. According to our view of the nature of heat, no net transfer of energy means that the two gases are at the same temperature. We may, therefore, write for two gases at the same temperature

$$\tfrac{1}{2}mC^2 = \tfrac{1}{2}m'C'^2, \quad \ldots \ldots \quad (4)$$

where the plain letters refer to the first gas and the dashed letters refer to the second gas.

If the pressures of the two gases are also equal and if n and n' respectively are the numbers of molecules in unit volume of the two gases, we have from equation (3)

$$mnC^2 = m'n'C'^2.$$

Using equation (4), this gives

$$n = n', \quad \ldots \ldots \ldots \quad (5)$$

which is Avogadro's law.

5. Boyle's Law and Dalton's Law.

Since kinetic energies are additive, it follows immediately from equation (3) that pressures must also be additive. Thus, the pressure exerted by a mixture of gases is the sum of the pressures exerted by the constituents of the mixture separately. This is Dalton's law of partial pressures.

It also follows from equation (3) that, if the volume of the containing vessel is allowed to change, while the number of molecules and their energy of motion (that is, temperature) are kept constant, the pressure varies inversely as the volume. This is Boyle's law.

6. Introduction of the Temperature.

Let us consider a gram-molecule of a gas. We shall call N_0 the number of molecules in a gram-molecule. N_0 is by *definition* the same for all substances.

If V is the volume occupied by a gram-molecule of a gas, we have from equation (3)

$$pV = \tfrac{2}{3} \cdot \tfrac{1}{2}mN_0C^2. \quad \ldots \ldots \quad (6)$$

According to the theory and to experiment, V at a given temperature and pressure is independent of the nature of the gas.

In order to introduce the temperature we use the empirically determined law that

$$pV = RT, \qquad \ldots \ldots \quad (7)$$

where R is the gas constant, which is proved empirically to have the same value for all gases (Chapter I, Section 38), and T is the absolute temperature as defined in Chapter I, Section 36.

Comparing equations (6) and (7), we see that

$$\tfrac{1}{2}mN_0C^2 = \tfrac{3}{2}RT. \qquad \ldots \ldots \quad (8)$$

This equation is of great importance for the following reasons:

(1) *It gives a physical meaning to the gas constant R and shows that it is equal to two-thirds of the total translational energy of the molecules in one gram-molecule of a gas at a temperature of one degree absolute*; that is, R (or k) defines the size of the degree.

(2) Since mN_0 is simply the molecular weight of the gas in grams (that is, for oxygen it is 32 gm., for hydrogen 2·016 gm., and so on), *it enables us to calculate the root mean square velocity of the molecules of any gas at a given temperature merely from a knowledge of the value of the gas constant and of the absolute temperature*; that is, merely from measurements of pressure and volume and knowledge of the molecular weight. *It should be specially noted that we do not need to know the value of* N_0.

We give in Table I the root mean square velocities of the molecules in various gases at 0° C. calculated from this equation. The mean velocities, which can only be obtained after we know the law of distribution, are also for convenience given in the table. The velocities at other temperatures can easily be obtained, since they are proportional to the square root of the absolute temperature. It will be seen that the velocities are very high—in hydrogen they are of the order 1 mile per second.

TABLE I

Gas	Molecular weight (0 = 16)	Root mean square velocity at 0° C. (cm. per sec.) (C)	Mean velocity ($\bar{c}$)
Hydrogen ··	2·016	183,900	169,400
Helium ··	4·003	131,000	120,700
Nitrogen ··	28·02	49,300	45,400
Oxygen ··	32·0	46,100	42,500
Krypton ··	83·7	28,600	26,300
Xenon ··	131·3	22,800	20,900

If we consider not a gram-molecule of gas, but a mass containing N molecules, equation (7) becomes

$$p\mathbf{V} = \frac{N}{N_0} RT = NkT, \qquad \ldots \ldots \quad (9)$$

where we have used the symbol $\mathbf{V}$ to indicate that we are not dealing with a gram-molecule, a notation which we shall use in the rest of the book. $k = R/N_0$ is called Boltzmann's constant.

7. The Determination of Avogadro's Number.

We have considered the numerical evaluation of all the constants occurring in the theory of a perfect gas except N_0, the number of molecules in a gram-molecule, which is usually called *Avogadro's number*. The most accurate value of this quantity is obtained by an indirect method depending on the determination of the absolute charge of the electron and of the charge carried by one gram-molecule of monovalent ions in a solution: the latter quantity is known with great accuracy. Assuming that each ion in a solution carries a charge equal to that carried by one electron, the ratio of the two charges gives the value of N_0.

In his early experiments on radioactivity, Rutherford [*] determined the charge carried by an alpha particle. He measured the total charge of the particles emitted in a given time by a known amount of radium and made a direct count of the number of particles by observing scintillations on a screen. This method gave the charge on the electron as $4 \cdot 65 \times 10^{-10}$ e.s.u. Millikan [†] measured the charge carried by oil drops suspended in air between charged plates. It was found that the charge was always an exact multiple of the smallest charge found, which was assumed to be e, the charge of one electron. Millikan found $e = 4 \cdot 774 \times 10^{-10}$ e.s.u. Using the accepted value for the charge carried by one gram-atom of the monovalent ion in solution, we obtain for the number of molecules in a gram-molecule $N_0 = 6 \cdot 064 \times 10^{23}$.

Later workers have determined N_0 and e from a comparison of the wave-lengths of X-rays obtained using diffraction from crystals and from ruled gratings. Using these results, the most accurate values of e and N_0 are [‡] $e = 4 \cdot 8025 \times 10^{-10}$ abs. e.s.u. and $N_0 = 6 \cdot 0228 \times 10^{23}$ mole^{-1}.

This value of N_0 agrees satisfactorily with values obtained by the application of the radiation laws (see Chapter XX, Section 15).

---

[*] Rutherford and Geiger, *Proc. Roy. Soc.*, A, Vol. 81, p. 162 (1908).

[†] Millikan, *Phil. Mag.*, Vol. 34, p. 2 (1917); *The Electron* (Chicago Univ. Press).

[‡] Birge, *Reports on Progress in Physics*, Vol. 8, p. 119 (1941).

Other extremely interesting methods have been used by Perrin,* one of which we may consider briefly. It is shown in the example at the end of this section that p, the pressure at a given point in a vertical column of gas, is given by

$$p = p_0 e^{-Mgh/RT}.$$

where h is the height of the given point above the level where the pressure is p_0, the molecular weight (referred to $O = 16$) is M, and g is the acceleration of gravity. Since for low pressures p is proportional to n, the number of molecules per unit volume, we may write

$$n = n_0 e^{-Mgh/RT}.$$

It will be noticed that the rate at which the density falls off depends on the molecular weight of the gas. For example, since the molecular weight of hydrogen is one-sixteenth of that of oxygen, the height to which we must rise to produce the same rarefaction in the two gases is sixteen times as great in hydrogen as in oxygen.

Perrin measured the vertical distribution, not in a gas, but in a suspension of colloidal particles in a liquid. In this case it is necessary to multiply g in the above equation by the factor $(1 - d/D)$, where d is the density of the liquid and D that of the grains. It is necessary to use particles all of the same size. He obtained a small number of such by a long-continued process of fractional centrifuging. One way of determining the vertical distribution was the following. A drop of the emulsion was placed in a hollow microscope slide and covered with a cover glass. The objective used had a very small depth of field. After equilibrium had been established in the emulsion, an instantaneous photograph was taken with the objective in a given position. The number of grains in the field was counted on the photograph. The objective was then moved a vertical distance x, which was directly measured on the micrometer screw of the microscope, and another photograph was taken. The distance h between the two sections thus examined is equal to x multiplied by the refractive index of the liquid.

In this way, using the known value of the gas constant, the value of M, the molecular weight of the particles referred to $O = 16$, was determined from the above equation. If m is the mass of a particle in grams, M/m is equal to N_0. The mass of a particle was determined by determining the density and the volume. The density was determined by adding potassium bromide to the emulsion until on centrifuging the grains neither rose nor sank, and determining the density of the solution. The volume was determined by the application of Stokes's law to the falling grains, thus obtaining the radius. Both determinations were carefully confirmed by independent methods.

Perrin obtained the following results: (a) the law of distribution of particles with height is that given by the above equation; (b) as the temperature is raised the particles spread out in accordance with the equation; (c) the value of N_0 is independent of the density of the particles, the size of the particles, the vis-cosity and density of the liquid, and the temperature.

We may mention that a gram-molecule of the particles used by Perrin would weigh many tons. Thus the density fell off very rapidly with height.

---

* See Perrin, *Atoms* (Constable, 1923).

Show that p, the pressure at a given point in a vertical column of gas at uniform temperature T, is given by

$$p = p_0 e^{-Mgh/RT},$$

where h is the height of the given point above the level where the pressure is p_0, M is the molecular weight, g is the acceleration of gravity, and R is the gas constant.

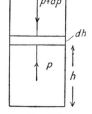

[Consider a cylindrical column of the gas of unit cross-section (see fig. 3.2). The downward force on the gas contained in an element of this cylinder of thickness dh is equal to $m'g$, where m' is the mass of gas in the element. This downward force is balanced by the difference between the pressures at the upper and lower sides of the element. We have, therefore,

$$p - (p + dp) = m'g.$$

Fig. 3.2

If V is the volume occupied by a gram-molecule of the gas at pressure p, we have $m' = M \, dh/V$, since the volume of the element is dh. Remembering that $V = RT/p$, the above equation becomes

$$\frac{dp}{p} = -\frac{Mg}{RT} \, dh.$$

Solving this equation, and remembering that $p = p_0$ when $h = 0$, we obtain the required result.]

THE STEADY STATE:
MAXWELL'S LAW OF THE DISTRIBUTION OF VELOCITIES

8. So far it has only been necessary to consider the average velocity of the molecules—the particular method of averaging giving us what we called the root mean square velocity. We now consider the actual distribution of velocity among the molecules.

The law of distribution of velocities was first guessed and partially established by Clerk Maxwell.[*] The proof of it by direct methods was given by Boltzmann.[†] The proof given by Boltzmann is well worth study because of the lively idea it gives of the processes at work in a gas.[‡] For a general proof resting on firm foundations, it is necessary to turn to the methods of statistical mechanics.[§]

It is extremely unlikely that at any moment all the molecules will possess the same kinetic energy, and there is a very large number of ways in which the total amount of energy can be divided among them. The question is whether there is any particular distribution of the energy which tends to persist once it is established, and whether a system starting from any arbitrary condition will tend to reach this steady state.

---

[*] Clerk Maxwell, *Phil. Mag.*, Vol. 19, p. 31 (1860); *Scientific Papers*, Vol. 1, p. 377.

[†] Boltzmann, *Vorlesungen über Gastheorie*, Vol. 1 (1896).

[‡] Boltzmann's demonstration will be found in Kennard, *Kinetic Theory of Gases*, McGraw-Hill (1938), Sections 21 to 28.

[§] Fowler, *Statistical Mechanics*, 2nd edition, Cambridge (1936), Section 2·6.

When we say that a gas is in the steady state, we do not imply that the velocity of any one molecule remains constant; but that, if we examine the whole of the molecules at any instant, the number having velocities between certain prescribed limits does not depend on the time at which the examination is made.

Having found from theoretical considerations the distribution in the steady state, we can by integration determine certain measurable properties of a gas. Experimental verification of these deductions furnishes evidence for the correctness of the assumptions underlying the theoretical treatment. This experimental evidence is considered in Sections 18–22: see also Section 13.

If u, v, w are the components, parallel to three mutually perpendicular axes, of the velocity of a molecule, of which there are N altogether, and if when the gas is in the steady state the number of molecules whose component velocities lie between the limits u and $u + du$, v and $v + dv$, w and $w + dw$ is

$$Nf(u, v, w)\,du\,dv\,dw,$$

our problem is to find the form of the function f.

For convenience we shall call a molecule whose component velocities lie between the above limits a molecule of class A. We shall call a molecule of class B one whose component velocities lie between the limits u' and $u' + du'$, v' and $v' + dv'$, w' and $w' + dw'$.

We shall consider collisions between molecules of class A and those of class B, which occur in such a way that at the moment of impact the direction cosines of the lines joining the centres of the colliding molecules lie between definite limits. The number of such collisions which occur in a time dt can be calculated in terms of the function f (the form of which is of course not known). If we integrate this number for all values of u', v', w', and for all values of the direction cosines mentioned above, we obtain the total number of molecules which *leave* class A in time dt.

Let us now consider another type of collision in which *after* the collision one of the molecules belongs to class A, the other to class B, and for which the direction cosines of the lines joining the centres of the colliding molecules at the moment of collision lie between certain definite limits. Given these conditions we can calculate the velocities of the two molecules before the collision, and can again calculate the number of such collisions which occur in a time dt in terms of the function f. If we integrate over all values of u', v', w', and of the direction cosines mentioned above, we obtain the total number of molecules which *enter* class A in the time dt.

If we equate the total number of molecules which leave class A in time dt to the total number of molecules which enter class A in the same time, we obtain the condition for the steady state. This equation enables us to determine the form of the function f.

The full details of the calculation are given in the papers already referred to. It is shown that the function f has the form

$$Ae^{-\beta m(u^2 + v^2 + w^2)},$$

where A and β are constants to be determined later, and m is the mass in grams of a single molecule. This means that out of a total number of molecules N the number whose component velocities lie between the limits u and $u + du$, v and $v + dv$, w and $w + dw$, is given by the expression

$$NAe^{-\beta m(u^2 + v^2 + w^2)}\,du\,dv\,dw, \qquad \cdots \cdots (10)$$

or what is the same thing,

$$NAe^{-\beta mu^2}\,du\,e^{-\beta mv^2}\,dv\,e^{-\beta mw^2}\,dw. \qquad \cdots \cdots (11)$$

For many purposes it is more convenient to consider c, the resultant velocity of the molecule. If the direction of c makes an angle θ with the z axis, and a plane through this direction and the axis of z makes an angle ϕ with the x axis, we have

$$
\left.
\begin{aligned}
u &= c \sin\theta \cos\phi, \\
v &= c \sin\theta \sin\phi, \\
w &= c \cos\theta.
\end{aligned}
\right\} \quad \ldots\ldots\ldots \quad (12)
$$

Transforming to these co-ordinates, the law of distribution becomes

$$
NAe^{-\beta mc^2} c^2 \sin\theta\, d\theta\, d\phi\, dc. \quad \ldots\ldots \quad (13)
$$

This equation gives us the number of molecules, out of a total number N, whose resultant velocities lie between c and $c + dc$, the direction of c lying between the limits θ and $\theta + d\theta$, and ϕ and $\phi + d\phi$.

In order to obtain the total number of molecules whose velocities lie between the limits c and $c + dc$ irrespective of direction, we integrate the above expression with respect to θ and ϕ. The limits of θ are from 0 to π, and of ϕ from 0 to 2π. We thus obtain for the number of molecules whose resultant velocities lie between the limits c and $c + dc$

$$
4\pi NAe^{-\beta mc^2} c^2\, dc. \quad \ldots\ldots\ldots \quad (14)
$$

The law of distribution given by equation (10), (11), or (14) is called *Maxwell's law of the distribution of velocities*.

We must now evaluate the constants A and β in terms of the quantities which determine the physical condition of the gas.

If n is the number of molecules in unit volume of the gas, and if χ is *any property* of a molecule, which may or may not be a function of the velocity of the molecule, the value of $\Sigma\chi$ per unit volume of the gas is by equation (14) with $N = n$ given by

$$
\Sigma\chi = 4\pi nA \int_0^\infty \chi e^{-\beta mc^2} c^2\, dc. \quad \ldots\ldots \quad (15)
$$

Let us put $\chi = 1$. $\Sigma\chi$ is then equal to n, the number of molecules in unit volume. We have then from equation (15)

$$
1 = 4\pi A \int_0^\infty e^{-\beta mc^2} c^2\, dc.
$$

The value of the integral is $\dfrac{1}{4}\sqrt{\dfrac{\pi}{\beta^3 m^3}}$ (see integrals evaluated at end of this chapter). Using this value, we obtain

$$
A = \left(\frac{\beta m}{\pi}\right)^{\frac{3}{2}}, \quad \ldots\ldots\ldots \quad (16)
$$

and the law of distribution becomes

$$
4\pi N\left(\frac{\beta m}{\pi}\right)^{\frac{3}{2}} e^{-\beta mc^2} c^2\, dc. \quad \ldots\ldots \quad (17)
$$

Again, let us put $\chi = c^2$ in equation (15). $\Sigma\chi$ is now equal to nC^2, where C is the *root mean square velocity* as defined in equation (2). We obtain

$$
C^2 = 4\pi A \int_0^\infty e^{-\beta mc^2} c^4\, dc.
$$

The value of the integral is $\frac{3}{8}\sqrt{\frac{\pi}{\beta^5 m^5}}$. Using this and the value of A given by equation (16), we obtain

$$\tfrac{1}{2}mC^2 = \frac{3}{4\beta}, \qquad \ldots \ldots \ldots \quad (18)$$

which gives β in terms of the mean kinetic energy of a molecule. Using equation (8), we obtain

$$\beta = \frac{1}{2}\frac{N_0}{RT} = \frac{1}{2}\frac{1}{kT}, \qquad \ldots \ldots \ldots \quad (19)$$

a relation which we shall use later.

9. The Mean Velocity.

The mean velocity of all the molecules, $\bar{c}$, is obtained by multiplying equation (17) by c, integrating, and dividing by N. Thus

$$\bar{c} = 4\pi\left(\frac{\beta m}{\pi}\right)^{\frac{3}{2}}\int_0^\infty e^{-\beta mc^2}c^3\,dc$$

$$= \frac{2}{\sqrt{\pi\beta m}}. \qquad \ldots \ldots \ldots \ldots \quad (20)$$

From equations (18) and (20) we may obtain the relation between the mean or average velocity $\bar{c}$ and the root mean square velocity C. Thus

$$\bar{c} = \sqrt{\frac{8}{3\pi}}\,C = 0 \cdot 921\,C. \qquad \ldots \ldots \ldots \quad (21)$$

We have already seen in Section 6 how C can be determined. This equation enables us to determine the value of $\bar{c}$ when C is known (see Table I).

10. The Most Probable Velocity.

Equation (17) shows us that if we plot values of the function

$$4\pi N\left(\frac{\beta m}{\pi}\right)^{\frac{3}{2}}e^{-\beta mc^2}c^2 \qquad \ldots \ldots \ldots \quad (22)$$

as ordinates, and values of c as abscissæ, we obtain a curve (see fig. 3.3, p. 82) such that, if lines are drawn parallel to the axis of ordinates through the points c and $c + dc$, the number of molecules having velocities between c and $c + dc$ is equal to the area enclosed by the two lines, the axis of abscissæ, and the curve.

This curve has a maximum, and the velocity corresponding to the maximum is the *most probable velocity*, which we shall call α.

To obtain maxima and minima we differentiate expression (22) with respect to c and equate to zero. We thus obtain

$$ce^{-\beta mc^2}(1 - \beta mc^2) = 0.$$

The solutions $c = 0$ and $c = \infty$, given by the first two factors, have obvious meanings (see fig. 3.3). The maximum is obtained by putting the third factor equal to zero, that is,

$$\alpha = \sqrt{\frac{1}{\beta m}}. \qquad \ldots \ldots \ldots \quad (23)$$

Further, we have

$$\bar{c} = \frac{2\alpha}{\sqrt{\pi}}. \qquad \ldots \ldots \ldots \quad (24)$$

11. Expressions for Maxwell's Law.

Maxwell's law can be expressed in the following equivalent ways. If N is the total number of molecules, the number lying in a range $du\,dv\,dw$ at u, v, w is

$$N \left(\frac{\beta m}{\pi}\right)^{\frac{3}{2}} e^{-\beta m(u^2 + v^2 + w^2)} du\,dv\,dw \quad \text{(equations (10) and (16));}$$

$$N \left(\frac{\beta m}{\pi}\right)^{\frac{3}{2}} e^{-\beta m u^2} du\, e^{-\beta m v^2} dv\, e^{-\beta m w^2}\, dw \quad \text{(equations (11) and (16)).}$$

These two equations refer to component velocities. The number lying in a range dc of the resultant velocity c is

$$4\pi N \left(\frac{\beta m}{\pi}\right)^{\frac{3}{2}} e^{-\beta m c^2} c^2 dc \quad \text{(equation (17));}$$

or

$$\frac{4N}{\sqrt{\pi}} \frac{1}{\alpha^3} c^2 e^{-c^2/\alpha^2} dc. \qquad \ldots \ldots \ldots \quad (25)$$

This last equation is deduced from the previous one by using equation (23); α is the most probable velocity.

The temperature may be introduced by using equation (19). We obtain

$$\frac{4N}{\sqrt{\pi}} \left(\frac{M}{2RT}\right)^{\frac{3}{2}} e^{-Mc^2/2RT} c^2 dc, \qquad \ldots \ldots \quad (26)$$

in which we have put $mN_0 = M$; M is the molecular weight referred to $O = 16$.

12. Graphical Representation.

The Maxwell distribution is represented graphically in fig. 3.3. Expression (26) is plotted for four values of T, namely 273°, 373°, 773°, and 1273° K., corresponding to celsius temperatures of 0° C., 100° C., 500° C., and 1000° C. respectively. The curves are plotted for hydrogen, that is, M is put equal to 2·016. The velocities are in the units shown on the axis of abscissæ; the units for the axis of ordinates must be chosen to make the area of the curve equal to N, the total number of molecules. All the curves have the same area, that is, they all refer to the same total number of molecules.

The maxima of the four curves occur at the points $c = 1\cdot50$, $1\cdot76$, $2\cdot53$, and $3\cdot24 \cdot 10^5$ cm. per second respectively.

It will be noticed that the higher the temperature the more scattered the distribution becomes. Illustrating the scattered nature of the distribution, it will be seen that even at 500° C. almost half of the molecules have velocities greater than the most probable velocity at 1000° C.

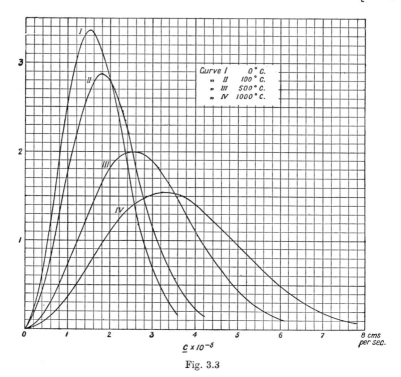

Curve I	0° C.
" II	100° C.
" III	500° C.
" IV	1000° C.

$\underline{c} \times 10^{-5}$ 8 cms per sec.

Fig. 3.3

13. Experimental Test of Maxwell's Law.

The earliest confirmation of this law was provided by the velocities of the electrons escaping from a hot metallic filament.* Various retarding potentials were put on the escaping electrons, and measurements were made of the fractions of the electrons which were travelling with speeds above a succession of specified limits. From such data the distribution of velocities of the electrons both inside and outside the filament could be determined.

Eldridge † has carried out an experiment which gives a direct test of Maxwell's law. The apparatus is shown in fig. 3.4. The system of discs shown was mounted in a large glass tube. The lowest disc acted as the rotor of an induction motor, and the system could be rotated up to 7200 revolutions per minute, the rate of rotation being measured stroboscopically. The other discs each had a hundred radial slots cut in them and when rotating acted as a velocity filter. Cadmium was contained in a side tube, which was heated by a furnace. This tube was closed except for a slit immediately under the lowest slotted disc.

The theory of the filter can be best understood by at first considering the two

* Richardson and F. C. Brown, *Phil. Mag.*, Vol. 16, pp. 353, 890 (1908); Vol. 18, p. 681 (1909); Schottky, *Ann. d. Phys.*, Vol. 44, p. 1011 (1914); Sih Ling Ting, *Proc. Roy. Soc.*, A, Vol. 98, p. 374 (1921); J. H. Jones, *ibid.*, Vol. 102, p. 734 (1923).

† Eldridge, *Phys. Rev.*, Vol. 30, p. 931 (1927); Coster, Smyth and Compton, *Phys. Rev.*, Vol. 30, p. 349 (1927); Estermann, Frisch and Stern, *Zeits. f. Physik*, Vol. 73, p. 348 (1931).

extreme discs only and supposing that they have only one slot each. If the discs rotate very slowly a deposit marking the undisplaced line is obtained on the glass target (which is cooled with liquid air). When the discs are rotating rapidly the upper disc travels a certain distance while a molecule is traversing the distance between the two discs. In this case a spread-out deposit is obtained, with the fastest molecules nearest to the undisplaced line, and by examining the deposit with a photometer the distribution of the velocities among the molecules leaving the furnace can be obtained.

To reduce the time of exposure many slots were used in each disc. In this case with only two discs confusion would arise, and with the discs rotating slowly not one undisplaced line, but several, would be obtained. Such effects were eliminated by using several slotted discs all exactly similar and mounted on the same shaft with the slots all carefully aligned.

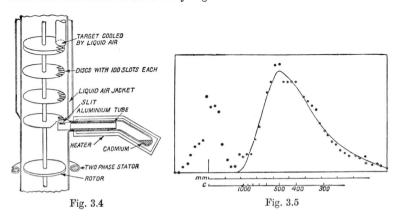

Fig. 3.4   Fig. 3.5

The results obtained are shown in fig. 3.5. The points are the observed densities of the deposit and the line was calculated on the assumption that the velocities of the vapour molecules were distributed according to Maxwell's law. For the details of the calculation reference should be made to the original paper. The observed points corresponding to the undisplaced line are also shown. The agreement between the theoretical curve and the observed points is to some extent fortuitous and is better than would be expected from the accuracy of the experiment. The results show that an accurate test of Maxwell's law is possible by this method.

The Doppler line breadth of the lines in molecular spectra provides another experimental test. This is one of the few phenomena which exhibit details corresponding to the velocity distribution itself. An experiment which incidentally confirmed the Maxwell law of the distribution of velocities was carried out by Ornstein and van Wyk.* They studied the lines emitted from an electric discharge passing through helium at low pressure. Earlier, the square-root temperature variation of the velocity distribution had been confirmed † by an experiment on the breadths of spectral lines. Experiments have also been carried out using evaporated bismuth,‡ but these are more difficult to interpret, as the bismuth atoms associate to form molecules of at least two different kinds.

* Ornstein and van Wyk, *Zeits. f. Physik*, Vol. 78, p. 734 (1932).
† Fabry and Buisson, *Compt. Rend.* (Paris), Vol. 154, p. 1224 (1912).
‡ Zartman, *Phys. Rev.*, Vol. 37, p. 383 (1931); Ko, *Journ. Franklin Inst.*, Vol. 127, p. 173 (1934)

THE MEAN FREE PATH

14. An important quantity in the study of the molecular theory of gases is the mean free path, or the mean distance that a molecule travels between collisions. The meaning of this quantity is illustrated by the following considerations.

Between collisions a molecule A moves in a rectilinear path. If σ is the *diameter* of a molecule and if the centre of another molecule lies within a distance σ of the line drawn through the centre of A in the direction of its motion, a collision takes place. In a time t the molecule A traverses a distance $\bar{c}t$, where $\bar{c}$ is the average velocity appropriate to the temperature, and, assuming that the linear dimensions of a molecule are negligible compared with the distance between molecules, the number of collisions that A makes in the time t is equal to the number of molecules whose centres lie in a volume $\pi\sigma^2\bar{c}t$. If n is the number of molecules per unit volume, the number of collisions made in time t by the molecule A is therefore $n\pi\sigma^2\bar{c}t$.

Since the molecule travels a total distance $\bar{c}t$ in time t, the mean distance λ that it travels between two collisions is given by

$$\lambda = \frac{1}{n\pi\sigma^2}. \qquad \ldots \ldots (27)$$

λ is called the *mean free path*.

This simple calculation shows the significance of the mean free path, but it is not exact, because we have made the assumption that the molecules through which the one we are considering moves are at rest. If we take their motion into account and assume velocities distributed according to Maxwell's law, we obtain for the mean free path *

$$\lambda = \frac{1}{\sqrt{2}.\,n\pi\sigma^2} = \frac{0.7071}{n\pi\sigma^2}. \qquad \ldots \ldots (28)$$

The accurate determination of the actual value of the mean free path under given conditions is extremely difficult. The difficulty is concerned among other things with the fact that the term diameter, as applied to a molecule, cannot have any very precise significance. It is, therefore, very important to realize that the theory given in the following sections does not necessitate a knowledge of the actual value of the mean free path. We merely assume that such a quantity exists.

---

* See Moelwyn-Hughes, *Physical Chemistry*, Cambridge (1940), Chapter II; Pergamon Press (1957), p. 51.

15. Mean Free Path and Number of Collisions.

If $\bar{c}$ is the mean velocity of a molecule, the total distance described in unit time by the n molecules in unit volume is $n\bar{c}$.

Let γ be the total number of collisions occurring in unit volume in unit time. Each collision terminates *two* free paths. Hence the n molecules describe 2γ free paths in unit time. Since the total distance described in unit time by the n molecules in unit volume is $n\bar{c}$, the average length λ of a free path is given by

$$\frac{n\bar{c}}{2\gamma},$$

or the total number of collisions occurring in unit volume in unit time is given by

$$\gamma = \frac{n\bar{c}}{2\lambda}. \qquad \ldots \ldots \ldots \quad (29)$$

16. Probability of Path of Given Length.

The chance of a molecule making a collision in length dL is proportional to dL (if dL is sufficiently small), say dL/λ, and is independent of the path L already traversed. We have introduced λ in this way as it then has the dimensions of length. We show that the parameter λ introduced in this way is identical with the mean free path.

We shall denote the probability that after a collision a molecule will describe a path at least equal to L by $f(L)$. After describing the distance L, the chance that it will make a collision in describing a further distance dL is given by dL/λ. The chance that it will describe the distance dL *without* making a collision is therefore $(1 - dL/\lambda)$. The chance that a molecule will describe a distance L and then a further distance dL without making a collision is, since the two probabilities are independent, given by the product $(1 - dL/\lambda)f(L)$. This is equal to $f(L + dL)$, or to

$$f(L) + \frac{df(L)}{dL}\,dL.$$

We have therefore

$$\frac{df(L)}{dL} = -f(L)/\lambda.$$

The solution of this equation is $\quad f(L) = Ae^{-L/\lambda},$

where A is an arbitrary constant of integration. If $L = 0$, $f(L)$ is obviously equal to unity, which shows that $A = 1$. We have therefore

$$f(L) = e^{-L/\lambda}.$$

Now the probability of a free path of length between L and $L + dL$ is the product of the probabilities of a free path at least L and of a collision in dL, since these are independent. That is, it is equal to $f(L)dL/\lambda$. The mean free path, which is the average value of L weighted according to the number of free paths of different lengths, is

$$\int_0^\infty \{Lf(L)/\lambda\}\,dL \Big/ \int_0^\infty \{f(L)/\lambda\}\,dL = \lambda, \qquad \ldots \ldots \quad (30)$$

so that the parameter λ which has been introduced is identified with the mean free path.

COLLISIONS WITH A SOLID BOUNDARY: KNUDSEN'S
COSINE LAW

17. In the kinetic theory we assume that equal numbers of molecules are moving in all directions in space, and that the number of molecules per unit volume is the same throughout the whole volume of a gas at rest and at uniform temperature. If we assume that these conditions also apply in the immediate neighbourhood of a solid in the gas, we can calculate the number of collisions made by molecules coming from a given direction with unit area of the wall in unit time.

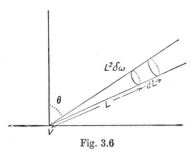

Fig. 3.6

If there are n molecules per unit volume and the mean velocity is $\bar{c}$, we have by equation (29) that the total number of collisions occurring in unit volume in unit time is $n\bar{c}/2\lambda$; therefore, from the element of volume $L^2 dL \delta\omega$ (fig. 3.6), $n\bar{c}L^2 dL \delta\omega/\lambda$ molecules per second come straight from making a collision, since two molecules are involved in each collision. Of these, if velocity directions are distributed at random in space, a fraction $dS \cos\theta/4\pi L^2$ travel in the direction of an element of area dS at V; that is, a number

$$\frac{dS \cos\theta}{4\pi} \frac{n\bar{c}}{\lambda} dL \delta\omega$$

start off from the element of volume in this direction. Of these only a fraction $e^{-L/\lambda}$ (see equation (30)) travel the distance L without making a further collision, so that the total number which reach the element dS is

$$(dS n\bar{c}/4\pi\lambda) \cos\theta \cdot e^{-L/\lambda} dL \delta\omega.$$

From the whole solid angle $d\omega$, which makes an angel θ with the normal to the surface, the element of area dS receives

$$\int_{L=0}^{L=\infty} \frac{dS}{4\pi} \cdot \frac{n\bar{c}}{\lambda} \cos\theta \cdot e^{-L/\lambda} d\omega \, dL$$

collisions per second; integrating, we obtain

$$\frac{dS}{4\pi} n\bar{c} \cos\theta \, d\omega. \qquad \ldots \ldots \quad (31)$$

If we integrate this expression over the whole solid angle 2π, we obtain the total number of collisions from all sides which unit area of the surface receives in unit time, namely

$$\tfrac{1}{4}n\bar{c}. \quad . \quad . \quad . \quad . \quad . \quad . \quad . \quad (31a)$$

If the condition that near the surface velocities in all directions are equally probable is to be fulfilled, it is necessary that the same number of molecules should leave the element dS in the direction θ as strike it coming from that direction; that is to say (see equation (31)) that in unit time

$$\frac{dS}{4\pi}\, n\bar{c}\cos\theta\, d\omega \quad . \quad . \quad . \quad . \quad . \quad . \quad (32)$$

molecules should leave the element of area dS of the surface in the solid angle $d\omega$ making an angle θ with the normal to the surface. If this were not the case, positive and negative velocities in the direction θ would not be equally favoured in an element of volume in the immediate neighbourhood of the surface. The cosine law holds, therefore, both for the number of molecules reaching and for the number of molecules leaving a given area of the surface in a given direction.

For the case discussed above of a gas and solid in equilibrium the cosine law must hold.* Knudsen makes the assumption that it holds for each individual molecule and that:

(1) *The direction in which a molecule leaves a solid surface is entirely independent of the direction from which it comes when it strikes it.*

(2) *The probability of a molecule leaving a surface in a given direction is given by the cosine law (equation* (32) *).*

The experiments of Stern † and others on the diffraction of molecules by crystal lattices have shown that for surfaces in which the atoms are regularly arranged the laws are not true. In the case of glass surfaces the experiments discussed below confirm them. They are probably true of all surfaces whose structure is irregular owing to the presence of adsorbed films probably several molecules thick.

It should be noted that equation (31) is analogous to Lambert's law in photometry. This latter applies only to a diffuse surface. It is to be expected that a corresponding restriction should apply to the collisions of gas molecules with a surface; certainly, a crystal lattice does not provide a " diffuse " surface for impinging gas molecules.

---

* See, for example, Clausing, *Ann. d. Physik*, Vol. 4, p. 533 (1930).

† Estermann, Frisch, and Stern, *Zeits. f. Physik*, Vol. 73, p. 348 (1931), and earlier papers.

MAXWELL'S LAW AND THE PROPERTIES OF GASES AT VERY LOW PRESSURES

18. An independent test of Maxwell's law could be obtained by calculating the value of some physical property of a gas, say the viscosity, from the theory. To obtain an *accurate* result, however, it is necessary to know much more than we do about the detailed laws of collisions between molecules. Knudsen has shown that we may get over this difficulty by using apparatus, the dimensions of which are small compared with the mean free paths of the gas molecules at the pressures used. We may mention that it is not necessary to know the free paths accurately. Approximate values are sufficient in order that we may be sure that the above condition is fulfilled (see Chapter XI, Table II).

Stationary Streaming through Narrow Tubes

The experiments we shall consider here are concerned with the flow of gases through tubes, the diameters of which are small compared with the mean free path of the gas molecules at the pressures used. We shall call such tubes " narrow ". We calculate the flow assuming Maxwell's law and the two laws given at the end of Section 17. The experimental and calculated results agree closely. This may be taken as a confirmation of Maxwell's law and Knudsen's assumptions together. Smoluchowski gives a more exact calculation. For a tube of circular cross-section his formula agrees with Knudsen's (equation (38) below).*

19. Theory of Streaming.

It follows from law (1) at the end of Section 17 that, after a gas molecule has struck a solid surface, it is equally likely to leave the surface on either side of the plane drawn perpendicular to the plane of incidence through the normal at the point at which it strikes the surface. If, then, n molecules, each having velocity c and each coming from the same direction, strike the wall, and if w is

---

* For a general discussion, see Clausing, *Ann. d. Physik*, Vol. 12, p. 961 (1932).
Clausing (*Ann. d. Physik*, Vol. 7, p. 569 (1930)) has carried out an investigation of non-stationary streaming. A vessel A with a long narrow tube connected to it was evacuated. At zero time the end of the tube remote from A was connected to a gas reservoir at pressure p such that the free path was large compared with the diameter of the tube. The pressure in A was measured as a function of the time and from the result the mean time that a gas molecule took to traverse the tube zigzag was calculated. From the diameter and length of the tube, and assuming Maxwell's law and Knudsen's assumptions, the mean velocity of the gas molecules was deduced. The results obtained were $5 \cdot 36 \cdot 10^4$ cm. sec.$^{-1}$ for neon and $3 \cdot 99 \cdot 10^4$ cm. sec.$^{-1}$ for argon at 294° abs. The kinetic theory values (see Sections 6 and 9) were 5·50 and $3 \cdot 96 \cdot 10^4$ cm. sec.$^{-1}$ respectively. The agreement with the kinetic theory values indicates the validity of the assumptions. A similar method at low temperatures was used to measure the mean lifetime of an argon atom on a glass or tungsten surface. This mean lifetime obviously affects the time taken by an atom in traversing the tube.

the component of the velocity parallel to the wall and m the mass of each molecule, the wall receives momentum

$$nmw,$$

because on the average the molecules leave the wall in random directions and carry away no resultant momentum in any direction parallel to the wall.

For a gas at rest the net effect of all the different streams of molecules is zero, but for a gas which is streaming the net effect is not zero.

We shall now calculate the momentum given to the wall of a tube through which a gas is streaming. We shall suppose the dimensions of the cross-section of the tube to be so small compared with the mean free path of the molecules that the effect of collisions of gas molecules with one another in the tube can be neglected. In this case the streaming of the gas down the tube cannot be due to the superposition of a streaming motion on the random motion; *but it is due to the random motion itself, and to the fact that as we pass down the tube the density changes and that on this account the numbers of molecules crossing a given cross-section in opposite directions are not exactly the same.* The detailed application of this idea is as follows.

If there are n molecules per unit volume, the number dn in unit volume having velocities between c and $c + dc$ is, according to Maxwell's distribution law (equation (25)), given by

$$dn = \frac{4n}{\sqrt{\pi}} \frac{r}{\alpha^3} c^2 e^{-c^2/\alpha^2} dc, \qquad \ldots \ldots \quad (25)$$

where α is the most probable velocity.

The total number of molecules with velocity c which in unit time strike unit area of the wall is

$$\tfrac{1}{4} c \, dn.$$

This result is obtained by applying equation (31a) to this particular case.

If the mean velocity of translation of the dn molecules parallel to the wall is w, the momentum given up to unit area of the wall by the molecules of velocity c is

$$\tfrac{1}{4} cmw \, dn \text{ per second.} \qquad \ldots \ldots \ldots \quad (33)$$

As we have said, w is not due to the superposition of a streaming motion on the ordinary molecular motion, but is due to the molecular motion and to the non-symmetrical distribution of the molecules. In fact, w depends on c and is proportional to it. We write therefore

$$w = \kappa c, \qquad \ldots \ldots \ldots \ldots \quad (34)$$

where κ is a constant independent of c. Actually κ is an averaging factor. It depends on the distribution in space of the *directions* in which molecules with velocity c are moving. The law of distribution of these directions is independent of c itself and also of dn, the total number of molecules in unit volume and moving with velocity c.

We substitute from equation (34) in (33); the amount of momentum given to unit area of the wall in unit time by molecules of velocity c becomes

$$\tfrac{1}{4} \kappa c^2 m \, dn.$$

Substituting from equation (25) and integrating, we obtain the total amount of momentum, B, given up to unit area of the wall in unit time by molecules of all velocities. That is,

$$B = \frac{n\kappa m}{\sqrt{\pi}} \int_0^\infty \frac{c^4}{\alpha^3} e^{-c^2/\alpha^2} dc = \tfrac{3}{8} n\kappa m\alpha^2.$$

The last result is obtained using the table of integrals given at the end of this chapter.

If $\bar{c}$ is the arithmetic mean velocity of the molecules, we have (see equation (24))

$$\bar{c} = \frac{2\alpha}{\sqrt{\pi}},$$

so that $$B = \frac{3\pi}{32} nm\kappa\bar{c}^2. \qquad \ldots \ldots \ldots \quad (35)$$

$\bar{c}$ is by definition equal to $\Sigma c/n$, so that

$$\kappa\bar{c} = \frac{\Sigma \kappa c}{n} = \frac{\Sigma w}{n}.$$

This quantity is the mean velocity, parallel to the wall, of all the molecules; that is, it is the velocity of the mass of gas, which we call v. We have then

$$B = \frac{3\pi}{32} nm\bar{c}v. \qquad \ldots \ldots \ldots \quad (36)$$

We suppose that the gas is streaming through a cylindrical tube of any-shaped cross-section. Let us consider an element of the tube of length dl, and let us suppose that the circumference of a normal cross-section is O, and that the area of the cross-section is A. The momentum communicated to such an element in the direction of its length in time dt is from equation (36)

$$\frac{3\pi}{32} nm\bar{c}vO\,dl\,dt.$$

We may put $nm = \rho$, the density of the gas. The mean velocity $\bar{c}$ of the gas molecules is connected with the pressure of the gas by Maxwell's law (equations (3) and (21)) by the relation $p = \tfrac{1}{3}nm\bar{c}^2$. Substituting in the above expression, we obtain for the momentum given up to the element

$$\frac{3}{8}\sqrt{\frac{\pi}{2}} \cdot \rho \sqrt{\frac{p}{\rho}} \cdot vO\,dl\,dt.$$

Assuming that the element of the tube $O\,dl$ receives all the momentum which the pressure fall $-\dfrac{dp}{dl} dl$ in the same length dl produces, that is, an amount $-A\,\dfrac{dp}{dl}\,dl\,dt$ in time dt, we have

$$\frac{3}{8}\sqrt{\frac{\pi}{2}} \cdot \rho \sqrt{\frac{p}{\rho}} \cdot vO = -A\,\frac{dp}{dl}. \qquad \ldots \ldots \ldots \quad (37)$$

The mass M which passes through the tube in unit time is given by $M = A\rho v$; that is, from equation (37)

$$M = -\frac{8}{3}\sqrt{\frac{2}{\pi}}\sqrt{\frac{\rho}{p}}\,\frac{A^2}{O}\frac{dp}{dl}.$$

Applying Boyle's law, we have $\rho/p = \rho_1$, where ρ_1 is the density at the temperature of the experiment and at a pressure of one dyne per square centimetre, so that

$$M = -\frac{8}{3}\sqrt{\frac{2}{\pi}}\ \sqrt{\rho_1}\ \frac{A^2}{O}\ \frac{dp}{dl}.$$

For stationary streaming M is constant along the length of the tube, and we have for a tube of length L and of constant cross-section

$$M = \sqrt{\rho_1}\ \frac{p' - p''}{\dfrac{3}{8}\sqrt{\dfrac{\pi}{2}}\dfrac{O}{A^2}L}.^* \quad \cdots \cdots \quad (38)$$

---

* Actually we cannot assume that the element of the tube $O\,dl$ receives all the momentum that the pressure fall in the length dl produces in the gas, but we must take into account the change in the momentum of the gas itself: equation (37) must on this account be written

$$\frac{3}{8}\sqrt{\frac{\pi}{2}}\ \rho\ \sqrt{\frac{p}{\rho}}\ vO = -A\ \frac{dp}{dl} - A\rho v\ \frac{dv}{dl},$$

$A\rho v$ being the mass of gas flowing across any section of the tube in 1 sec.; calling this M as above, we have

$$\frac{3}{8}\sqrt{\frac{\pi}{2}}\ \frac{1}{\sqrt{\rho_1}}\ \frac{O}{A^2}\ G = -\frac{dp}{dl} - \frac{M^2}{A^2\rho_1}\ \frac{d}{dl}\left(\frac{1}{p}\right);$$

the last term is obtained by writing $M/A\rho$ for v, remembering that $\rho = p\rho_1$.
Integrating over the whole length of the tube, we have

$$\frac{3}{8}\sqrt{\frac{\pi}{2}}\ \frac{1}{\sqrt{\rho_1}}\ M\int_0^L \frac{O}{A^2}\ dl = p' - p'' - \frac{M^2}{A^2\rho_1}\ \frac{p' - p''}{p'p''},$$

from which, if we put

$$W = \frac{3}{8}\sqrt{\frac{\pi}{2}}\int_0^L \frac{O}{A^2}\ dl,$$

we have

$$M = \frac{\sqrt{\rho_1}}{W}\left(p' - p''\right)\ \frac{1}{1 + \dfrac{M}{A^2\sqrt{\rho_1}W}\dfrac{p' - p''}{p'p''}};$$

that is, M is less than $\dfrac{\sqrt{\rho_1}}{W}(p' - p'')$. If then we write Z for the quantity $\left(\dfrac{M}{A^2\sqrt{\rho_1}W}\dfrac{p' - p''}{p'p''}\right)$, which occurs in the denominator of the above expression, and if we substitute in Z for M the value $\dfrac{\sqrt{\rho_1}}{W}(p' - p'')$, we obtain an upper limit for Z; that is, we have

$$Z < \frac{1}{A^2W^2}\ \frac{(p' - p'')^2}{p'p''}.$$

For a circular tube of radius R we have

$$Z < \frac{32}{9\pi}\ \frac{R^2}{L^2}\ \frac{(p' - p'')^2}{p'p''}.$$

In the experiments considered in Section 20 the largest value of R/L was $1/600$, so that even if p' is many hundred times p'' the value of U is vanishingly small compared with unity. We may therefore write without sensible error

$$M = \frac{\sqrt{\rho_1}}{W}\left(p' - p''\right),$$

as in equation (38).

We may call the quantity in the denominator which depends only on the dimensions of the tube its resistance, and we denote it by W, so that $M = \sqrt{\rho_1}\,\dfrac{p' - p''}{W}$. For a circular tube $O = 2\pi R$ and $A = \pi R^2$, where R is the radius. In this case

$$W = \frac{3}{8}\sqrt{\frac{2}{\pi}}\,\frac{L}{R^3}. \qquad \cdots \cdots \cdots \quad (39)$$

In deducing the formula $\frac{1}{4}n\bar{c}$ for the number of collisions with a solid wall (equation (31a)), we assume that the mean free path is small compared with the extent of the gas. The application of this formula to the present case, in which the mean free path is large compared with the extent of the gas, is based on the cosine law, according to which the presence of a solid wall does not in any way alter the directions of the velocities of the molecules. It follows that the number of collisions with a wall is the same for the same pressure however small the space containing the gas may be. The theory depends on the use of this formula and of the Maxwell distribution law. The verification of equation (38) by the experiments of Knudsen which we are about to consider must therefore be taken as a direct experimental verification of the Knudsen cosine law and of the Maxwell distribution law together.

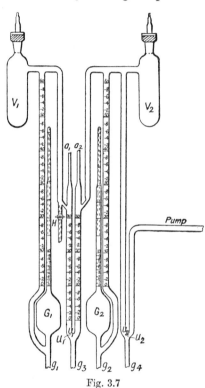

Fig. 3.7

20. Streaming Experiments.

The apparatus used by Knudsen to verify equation (38) is shown in fig. 3.7. The narrow tube to be investigated is blown on to the apparatus at a_1 and a_2. The tubes g_1, g_2, g_3, g_4 are connected by rubber tubing to mercury reservoirs so that the height of the mercury in each of the tubes can be adjusted at will. By raising the mercury in the tube g_4 the whole apparatus can be cut off from the pump. By raising it to a_1 and a_2 in g_3 communication between the gas reservoirs V_1 and V_2 can be stopped. If it is allowed to sink a little, communication is established through the tube to be investigated; and if it is lowered still further, so that the sides of the U-tube are not closed, the two sides of the apparatus are brought into direct communication. G_1 and G_2 are gauges.

A difference of pressure is established between the reservoirs V_1 and V_2, and, after the gas has flowed through the tube under investigation for a measured time, the change of pressure in each is measured. From the volumes of the reservoirs and their connecting tubes the mass of gas which has passed from one reservoir to the other can be calculated.

Various tubes were used. No. 1 was 6 cm. long and 0·01 cm. in radius; No. 2 had the same radius but was twice as long; No. 3 was 6 cm. long and 0·014 cm. in radius; No. 4 consisted of twenty-four tubes in parallel, each 2 cm. long and 0·003 cm. radius. The tubes were all carefully calibrated.

The confirmation of equation (38) by Knudsen's experiments on various gases was entirely satisfactory.

If the pressure is so high that the mean free path is no longer large compared with the dimensions of the cross-section of the tube, the flow becomes complicated. For details of this type of flow the original paper must be consulted.

21. The Flow of a Gas through a Small Opening.

Using the apparatus just described, Knudsen * investigated the rate of flow of a gas through an opening the dimensions of which were small compared with the mean free path of the gas molecules. Knudsen used a small hole in a platinum sheet which was sealed on the end of a glass tube which was in turn sealed inside the tube connecting a_1 and a_2. In one case the platinum was 0·0025 mm. thick and the hole $5 . 10^{-6}$ sq. cm. in area, and in another 0·005 mm. thick and the hole $66 . 10^{-6}$ sq. cm. in area. The measurements agreed with the following theory.

An area A of a solid wall receives $\frac{1}{4}n'\bar{c}A$ collisions per second, where n' is the number of molecules per cubic centimetre of the gas and $\bar{c}$ is their mean velocity (see equation (31a)). If there is a hole in the wall of area A, $\frac{1}{4}n'\bar{c}A$ molecules will pass out in each second through the hole to the other side. If on this side there are n'' molecules per cubic centimetre, $\frac{1}{4}n''\bar{c}A$ molecules will pass back per second, so that the net number, n, passing out in 1 sec. is

$$n = \tfrac{1}{4}\bar{c}A(n' - n'').$$

Multiplying both sides of this equation by the mass of a molecule m, we obtain for M, the mass of gas passing through the hole in 1 sec.,

$$M = \tfrac{1}{4}\bar{c}A(\rho' - \rho''),$$

where ρ' and ρ'' are the densities on the two sides of the hole.

According to Maxwell's distribution law we have (equations (3) and (21))

$$\bar{c} = \sqrt{\frac{8}{\pi\rho_1}},$$

where ρ_1 is the density of the gas under a pressure of 1 dyne per square centimetre; further, according to Boyle's law, $\rho'' = p''\rho_1$ and $\rho' = p'\rho_1$, where p' and p'' are the pressures on the two sides of the hole. Using these values, we obtain

$$M = \frac{A}{\sqrt{2\pi}} \sqrt{\rho_1}\,(p' - p''). \quad \cdots \cdots \quad (40)$$

Interpreting this equation in the same way as we did equation (38), we may call the quantity $\sqrt{2\pi}/A$ the resistance of the opening and denote it by W. We have then

$$M = \frac{\sqrt{\rho_1}(p' - p'')}{W}. \quad \cdots \cdots \cdots \quad (41)$$

Knudsen's experiments confirmed equation (40). This equation has an important application in the measurement of vapour pressures (see Chapter VIII, Section 5).

---

* Knudsen, *Ann. d. Physik*, Vol. 28, p. 999 (1909); see also Bichowsky and Wilson, *Phys. Rev.*, Vol. 33, p. 851 (1929), for a preliminary study at high temperatures.

The Knudsen Absolute Manometer

22. We can conveniently consider here the manometer devised by Knudsen * for the absolute measurement of very low pressures. The manometer is available for pressures up to about 4 or 5 dynes per square centimetre; for pressures above this it ceases to be an absolute instrument and its readings require correction by a factor which can only be determined by comparison with an instrument of some other type (see Chapter XX, Section 5).

There are various possible forms of the apparatus. Essentially they can all be represented diagrammatically as in fig. 3.8. A_1 is a fixed plate, which can be heated. Opposite it is another larger plate A_2 suspended so that it can turn about an axis O. When there is a difference of temperature between the plates, A_2 tends to turn about O, and the couple acting on it depends on the difference of temperature and on the pressure of the gas.

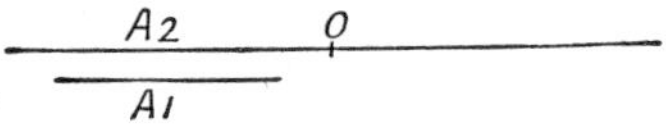

Fig. 3.8

In working out the theory, we shall assume that the distance between the plates is so small compared with their dimensions that all edge effects can be neglected; this means that we shall assume that the various effects are the same as they would be if the plates were infinite in area and we were considering a small area forming part of the infinite area. Further, we shall assume that the distance between the plates is small compared with the mean free path of the molecules, so that the molecules arrive at one plate in exactly the same condition as that in which they leave the other.

Let n_1 be the number of molecules per unit volume moving towards A_2; let $\overline{c_1}'$ be their mean velocity and C_1' their root mean square velocity. Let n_2 be the number of molecules per unit volume moving away from A_2 and let $\overline{c_2}'$ be their mean velocity and C_2' their root mean square velocity. If m is the mass of a molecule, the momentum brought up to unit area in unit time by the first stream of molecules is $\frac{1}{3}mn_1C_1'^2$, and that carried away by the second stream is $\frac{1}{3}mn_2C_2'^2$. The sum of these two quantities gives the pressure on the surface, and this multiplied by the area of A_1 gives the force acting on the particular part of A_2 opposite to A_1. The force acting on the other parts of A_2 will be the same as if A_1 were not present, and will not give rise to any couple since forces on back and front are equal. The force on the back of the part of A_2 opposite to A_1 will be pA_1. The difference between this and the force on the front, multiplied by the distance from the axis of the centre of the area under consideration, gives the couple acting on A_2. This couple is therefore equal to

$$\{\tfrac{1}{3}m(n_1C_1'^2 + n_2C_2'^2)A_1 - pA_1\}l, \quad \ldots \quad \ldots \quad (42)$$

where l is the distance between the centre of the area and the axis.

* Knudsen, *Ann. d. Physik,* Vol. 32, p. 809 (1910); see also Smoluchowski, *Ann. d. Physik,* Vol. 34, p. 182 (1911).

Now by equation (31a) the number of molecules which come up to unit area of the part of A_2 opposite to A_1 in unit time is

$$\tfrac{1}{2} n_1 \overline{c_1'}$$

(the factor $\tfrac{1}{2}$ occurs instead of the factor $\tfrac{1}{4}$ because n_1 is the number of molecules in unit volume moving in one direction only), and the number of molecules which leave unit area of this part of A_2 in unit time is

$$\tfrac{1}{2} n_2 \overline{c_2'}.$$

These two numbers must be equal, otherwise there would be an accumulation—positive or negative—of molecules at the surface of A_2. We have therefore

$$n_1 \overline{c_1'} = n_2 \overline{c_2'}.$$

Further, if for the gas *not* between the plates $\bar{c}$ is the mean velocity of the molecules and n the *total* number of molecules per unit volume, we have

$$n_1 \overline{c_1'} + n_2 \overline{c_2'} = n\bar{c};$$

for, if we suppose the boundary between the two regions to be definite, the number of molecules crossing unit area of this boundary from inside to outside in unit time is proportional to the term on the left-hand side of this equation, and the number crossing unit area in unit time in the opposite direction is proportional to the right-hand side. The two numbers must be equal or there would be an accumulation of gas between the plates. Combining the last two equations, we obtain

$$n_1 \overline{c_1'} = n_2 \overline{c_2'} = \tfrac{1}{2} n\bar{c}. \quad \ldots \quad \ldots \quad (43)$$

We shall suppose further that the apparatus is so arranged that A_2, the moving plate, is at the same temperature as the mass of the gas and as the walls containing the apparatus. In this case we have

$$p = \tfrac{1}{3} mn C^2, \quad \ldots \quad \ldots \quad \ldots \quad (44)$$

where C is the root mean square velocity of the molecules in the mass of the gas.

Substituting from equations (43) and (44) in equation (42), we obtain for the couple K acting on the plate A_2

$$K = pA_1 l \left\{ \frac{1}{2} \frac{C_1'^2/\bar{c_1} + C_2'^2/\bar{c_2'}}{C^2/\bar{c}} - 1 \right\}.$$

And since

$$\frac{C_1'}{\overline{c_1'}} = \frac{C_2'}{\overline{c_2'}} = \frac{C}{\bar{c}},$$

this becomes

$$K = pA_1 l \left\{ \frac{1}{2} \frac{C_1' + C_2'}{C} - 1 \right\}. \quad \ldots \quad \ldots \quad (45)$$

We now have to introduce the temperatures T_1 and T_2 of the plates A_1 and A_2. Considering the gas between the plates, we cannot assume that the mean temperature of the molecules leaving a surface is the same as that of the surface, but we must suppose that it will to some extent depend on the temperature of the molecules before they reach the surface. We shall suppose that the gas molecules between the plates which are moving towards the plate A_1 have the mean temperature T_2', and that those moving towards the plate A_2 have the mean temperature T_1'. Further, we shall suppose that

$$T_1' + T_2' = T_1 + T_2.$$

This equation can be deduced from the result give in Chapter XI, Section 11, equation (21), provided the surfaces of A_1 and A_2 have the same accommodation coefficient. It is equivalent to

$$C_1'^2 + C_2'^2 = C_1^2 + C_2^2,$$

where C_1 and C_2 are the root mean square velocities corresponding to temperatures T_1 and T_2 respectively. If the difference between C_1 and C_2 is small compared with C_1 and C_2 themselves, we have to the first order of small quantities

$$C_1' + C_2' = C_1 + C_2.$$

Substituting this in equation (45) and remembering that

$$C = C_2,$$

we obtain $$K = \tfrac{1}{2}pA_1l\left(\frac{C_1 - C_2}{C_2}\right),$$

or $$K = \tfrac{1}{2}pA_1l\left\{\sqrt{\frac{T_1}{T_2}} - 1\right\}. \quad \cdots \cdots \quad (46)$$

This equation enables us to determine p from the measured couple and from the temperatures of the plates, provided the difference between these temperatures is small.

The restoring couple on the suspended system is measured in the usual way by determining the moment of inertia and the period of oscillation; the couple K is deduced from the deflection of the moving system which is measured with the usual mirror and scale arrangement.

It is important to note that p is the *total pressure* of all gases and vapours present. In particular, it includes the pressure of mercury vapour, which is not measured by a MacLeod gauge. This fact is illustrated by the following measurements.* $(T_1 - T_2)$ is the difference between the temperatures of the plates, and p is the pressure in the instrument deduced from the measurement of the couple. It will be noticed that the measured value of p is independent of $(T_1 - T_2)$.

$(T_1 - T_2)$ ..	17·4	21·8	26·3	31·1	35·9	40·9	etc., to 70·9
p dynes per sq. cm.	2·72	2·72	2·82	2·76	2·81	2·75	etc.

The mean value of p measured by the absolute manometer is 2·77 dynes per square centimetre. The value of p measured on a MacLeod gauge was 0·91 dynes per square centimetre. The difference, 1·86 dynes per square centimetre, gives the vapour pressure of mercury at

* See Knudsen, *loc. cit.*

the temperature, 23° or 24° C., of the apparatus. Measurements by other methods show that the vapour pressure of mercury is 1·86 dynes per square centimetre at 22° C. This is in excellent agreement with the result obtained using the absolute manometer.

23. Thermo-molecular Pressure.

Consider two vessels separated by a partition which is a perfect heat insulator and which has a hole in it (see fig. 3.9). Let the absolute temperatures on the two sides be T_1 and T_2, and the corresponding gas pressures p_1 and p_2. The ordinary condition for equilibrium is $p_1 = p_2$. If, however, the linear dimensions of the hole are small compared with the free path of the gas molecules (so that if a molecule passes through the hole from side 1 to side 2 the probability is negligible that it returns through the hole to side 1 before it has made a large number of collisions and thus attained the temperature T_2), quite a different condition of equilibrium is obtained. In this case the number of molecules passing through the hole of area A per second from side 1 to side 2 is, by equation (31a), equal to $\frac{1}{4}An_1\bar{c}_1$, where n_1 is the number of molecules per c.c. and $\bar{c}_1$ the mean velocity on side 1; similarly the number passing through the hole in the opposite direction is $\frac{1}{4}An_2\bar{c}_2$. In the equilibrium condition these two numbers are equal, that is, we have $n_1\bar{c}_1 = n_2\bar{c}_2$, from which we obtain as the condition of equilibrium

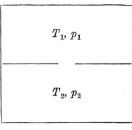

Fig. 3.9

$$\frac{p_1}{p_2} = \sqrt{\frac{T_1}{T_2}}. \quad \ldots \ldots \quad (47)$$

This result was first obtained by Osborne Reynolds.[*] He demonstrated the phenomenon by experiments with porous plates and called it *thermal transpiration*.

The same effect occurs when there is a temperature gradient in a tube containing a gas at such a pressure that the free path of the gas molecules is not negligibly small compared with the diameter of the tube. In this case it is not possible to obtain an absolutely rigorous expression for the pressure difference between the ends of the tube, but the phenomenon has been studied in considerable detail by Knudsen.[†] He has obtained semi-empirical formulæ which are valid over limited ranges of the ratio of tube diameter to free path, and has

---

[*] Osborne Reynolds, *Phil. Trans.*, Vol. 170, p. 727 (1879).

[†] Knudsen, *Ann. d. Physik*, Vol. 83, p. 797 (1927), and earlier papers.

shown that the differential equation between p and T along the tube must be of the form

$$\frac{dp}{dT} = \frac{p}{T}\,\phi\left(\frac{r}{\lambda}\right), \quad \ldots \ldots \quad (48)$$

where r is the radius and ϕ is some function. Finally, he has shown that experimental observations with hydrogen over a wide range of values of r/λ and of temperature differences can be accounted for by a single formula.* The differential equation (48) can be obtained † in a quite general form for irreversible processes of this sort by using Onsager's principle ‡ of microscopic reversibility.

These effects may be of considerable importance in measuring pressures.   For example, the ordinary type of liquid-air trap can establish a pressure difference between the two tubes leading from it. The effect is very important in measuring temperatures in the helium range with helium gas and vapour pressure thermometers (see Chapter V, Section 11).

Thermal Diffusion

24. Enskog and Chapman § each showed theoretically that if a temperature gradient is applied to a mixture of gases, the molecules of the two kinds separate. If the molecules are not too nearly equal in mass, the heavier molecules diffuse into the cooler regions. If the masses of the molecules are nearly equal, the larger molecules tend to diffuse into the cooler regions. The effect, which is called thermal diffusion, depends also on the law of force between the molecules. It is a maximum for elastic spheres and vanishes for an inverse fifth power law of repulsion. The thermal diffusion coefficient is so strongly dependent on the law of molecular interaction that it may be used to determine this law. Equilibrium is established when the effect due to thermal diffusion is balanced by the opposite effect due to ordinary diffusion in a mixture of gases when the concentration is not uniform.

The effect has been demonstrated experimentally by a number of workers and the law of force between the molecules can be deduced from a comparison of the experimentally observed separation with that calculated from the kinetic theory assuming elastic spheres. We shall not discuss the details here, but it was realized that the effect was likely to prove of very great importance when Clusius and Dickel ‖ showed that it could be made the basis of a very efficient method of separating isotopes. The gas mixture is contained in a long vertical cylinder

---

* Knudsen, *loc. cit.*, pp. 816–18. See also Sophus Weber, *Leiden Comm.*, No. 71(*b*).

† de Groot, C. R., *Acad. Sci.*, Paris, Vol. 225, p. 173 (1947); *Physica.*, Vol. 13, p. 555 (1947).

‡ Bohr, *Studier over Metallernes Elektronteorie*, Copenhagen (1913); Onsager, *Phys. Rev.*, Vol. 37, p. 405 (1931); *ibid.*, Vol. 38, p. 2265 (1931); Casimir, *Rev. Mod. Phys.*, Vol. 17, p. 343 (1945).

§ Chapman and Cowling, *Mathematical Theory of Non-Uniform Gases*, Cambridge (1939), Section 14·7.

‖ Clusius and Dickel, *Naturwiss.*, Vol. 26, p. 546 (1938); Vol. 27, p. 148 (1939). See also Korsching and Wirtz, *Naturwiss.*, Vol. 27, p. 367 (1939).

with an electrically heated wire down the middle. The lighter component is enriched at the wire owing to the effect of thermal diffusion and the heavier component is enriched at the outer wall. At the same time the upward convection current near the wire carries the light gas to the top, where it collects, and the downward convection current at the wall carries the heavy gas down. Using a tube 36 metres long they have succeeded in separating HCl so that the heavier component contained over 99 per cent of the ^{37}Cl isotope.

This method has also been used * to separate the isotopes of uranium (in the form of hexafluorides). It was used as a first stage, and the U^{235}-enriched product was fed to an electromagnetic separation plant. The production rate of the latter was thereby greatly increased. A multi-stage all-metal thermal-diffusion apparatus for the separation of isotopes in quantity has been described by Watson, Onsager and Zucker.† Full details of the construction of the equipment, and of its operation and performance in preparing Ne^{22}, are given in the paper referred to.

The thermal diffusion of vapours is utilized in studying the chemical properties of volatile compounds. If a volatile substance is introduced into a closed system in which the pressure is less than 10^{-3} mm. of mercury, its vapour diffuses rapidly through the whole system. It can then be collected in a particular part of the apparatus, designed to measure a given property, by cooling that part to a temperature at which the vapour pressure of the substance is negligible. The kinetic energy of the vapour molecules provides the motive power to transfer the substance through the system, and cooling provides a ready means of collecting it where it is wanted to investigate a particular property.

TABLE OF INTEGRALS

25. Integrals of the form

$$\int_0^\infty e^{-\alpha u^2} u^n \, du,$$

where n is an integer, occur frequently in the kinetic theory of gases. They can be evaluated, by using recurrence formulæ, in terms of the values of the particular integrals for which $n = 0$ and $n = 1$. For $n = 0$, we have the probability integral

$$\int_0^\infty e^{-\alpha u^2} \, du = \frac{1}{2}\sqrt{\frac{\pi}{\alpha}}.$$

For $n = 1$, the integral can be evaluated by taking u^2 as a new variable. This gives

$$\int_0^\infty e^{-\alpha u^2} u \, du = \frac{1}{2\alpha} \int_0^\infty e^{-\alpha u^2} \, d(\alpha u^2) = \frac{1}{2\alpha}.$$

Now consider the integral

$$I_{2r} = \int_0^\infty e^{-\alpha u^2} u^{2r} \, du,$$

* Smyth, *Rev. Mod. Phys.*, Vol. 17, p. 351 (1945); Jones and Furry, *ibid.*, Vol. **18**, p. 151 (1946).

† Watson, Onsager and Zucker, *Rev. Sci. Instr.*, Vol. 20, p. 924 (1949).

in which the exponent is even. If we differentiate under the integral sign with respect to the parameter α, we get

$$\frac{d}{d\alpha} I_{2r} = \int_0^\infty \frac{d}{d\alpha} e^{-\alpha u^2} u^{2r} du = -\int_0^\infty e^{-\alpha u^2} u^{2r+2} du = -I_{2r+2},$$

which is a general formula which holds for all values of r, and enables us to evaluate each integral in terms of the immediately preceding integral of the sequence. Thus,

$$\int_0^\infty e^{-\alpha u^2} u^2 du = I_2 = -\frac{d}{d\alpha} I_0 = -\frac{d}{d\alpha} \left(\frac{1}{2} \sqrt{\frac{\pi}{\alpha}} \right) = \frac{1}{2} \cdot \frac{1}{2} \sqrt{\frac{\pi}{\alpha^3}},$$

$$\int_0^\infty e^{-\alpha u^2} u^4 du = I_4 = -\frac{d}{d\alpha} I_2 = -\frac{d}{d\alpha} \left\{ \frac{1}{2} \cdot \frac{1}{2} \sqrt{\frac{\pi}{\alpha^3}} \right\} = \frac{1}{2} \cdot \frac{1}{2} \cdot \frac{3}{2} \sqrt{\frac{\pi}{\alpha^5}}.$$

In general, this leads to the formula

$$\int_0^\infty e^{-\alpha u^2} u^{2r} du = I_{2r} = \frac{1 \cdot 3 \cdot 5 \ldots (2r-1)}{2^{r+1}} \sqrt{\frac{\pi}{\alpha^{2r+1}}}.$$

For an odd exponent of u, we have the general form

$$I_{2r-1} = \int_0^\infty e^{-\alpha u^2} u^{2r-1} du.$$

Differentiating this under the integral sign with respect to the parameter α leads to the result

$$\frac{d}{d\alpha} I_{2r-1} = \int_0^\infty \frac{d}{d\alpha} e^{-\alpha u^2} u^{2r-1} du = -\int_0^\infty e^{-\alpha u^2} u^{2r+1} du = -I_{2r+1}.$$

Thus
$$\int_0^\infty e^{-\alpha u^2} u^3 du = I_3 = -\frac{d}{d\alpha} I_1 = \frac{1}{2} \cdot \frac{1}{\alpha^2},$$

$$\int_0^\infty e^{-\alpha u^2} u^5 du = I_5 = -\frac{d}{d\alpha} I_3 = \frac{1}{2} \cdot \frac{1 \cdot 2}{\alpha^3},$$

$$\int_0^\infty e^{-\alpha u^2} u^7 du = I_7 = -\frac{d}{d\alpha} I_5 = \frac{1}{2} \cdot \frac{1 \cdot 2 \cdot 3}{\alpha^4}.$$

In general, for an odd exponent, we have the formula

$$I_{2r-1} = \int_0^\infty e^{-\alpha u^2} u^{2r-1} du = \frac{1}{2} \frac{(r-1)!}{\alpha^r}.$$

CHAPTER IV

Equation of State for Gases

1. Gases at ordinary and high pressures depart to a measureable extent from the simple laws given at the beginning of Chapter III. As has already been pointed out in Chapter I, they do not obey Boyle's law, that is, at constant temperature pV is not exactly constant. It has already been noted that in order to represent the behaviour of gases a power series expansion can be used, in powers of the reciprocal molar volume, of the form

$$pV = A[1 + B/V + C/V^2 + D/V^3 + \ldots],$$

where A, B, C, D, $\ldots$, are functions of the temperature. For a gram-molecule of gas it is clear that A must be equal to RT.

Before Kammerlingh Onnes proposed this virial expansion, many attempts had been made to modify Boyle's law to take account of the departures from it. For the most part, these equations were based on assumptions and theoretical considerations of doubtful validity and are now of no more than historical interest, but they have been so widely used in the past and are still so frequently referred to that it will be necessary to give a brief account of them. This we shall do (Sections 3 and 4 below) after first considering some of the experimental results to explain which these equations were set up.

2. Andrews' Experiments.*

We must now attempt to account theoretically for the departures from the perfect gas laws. First we shall consider some further experiments which have a direct bearing on the matter. We shall then try to account for these experiments, not by finding an empirical formula which fits them, but by examining our assumptions concerning the dynamical model of a perfect gas and modifying them in a way that we should expect would make them represent more closely the behaviour of an actual gas.

Andrews compressed carbon dioxide in a tube at constant temperature. He measured the pressure and the volume of the gas, and

---

* Andrews, *Phil. Trans.*, Vol. 159, p. 575 (1869); Vol. 167, p. 421 (1876).

observed its behaviour. His apparatus is described in Chapter VIII, Section 2. The results obtained are illustrated by the family of *isotherms* in fig. 4.1, in which pressures in atmospheres are shown as ordinates and volumes as abscissæ; each curve corresponds to a definite temperature which is marked on the curve.

Taking the curve for 21·5° and starting from the point p corresponding to the lowest pressure, we see that, as the pressure is increased, the volume steadily decreases until the point q is reached. If, after reaching this point, we attempt to compress the gas further, some of the gas is liquefied and the pressure remains constant. We thus follow the straight line qr which is parallel to the axis of volume, more and more liquid being formed as we pass along it. At the point r the carbon dioxide is again homogeneous, being all in the liquid state. Beyond this point the gradient is very steep, a large change in pressure producing only a small change of volume.

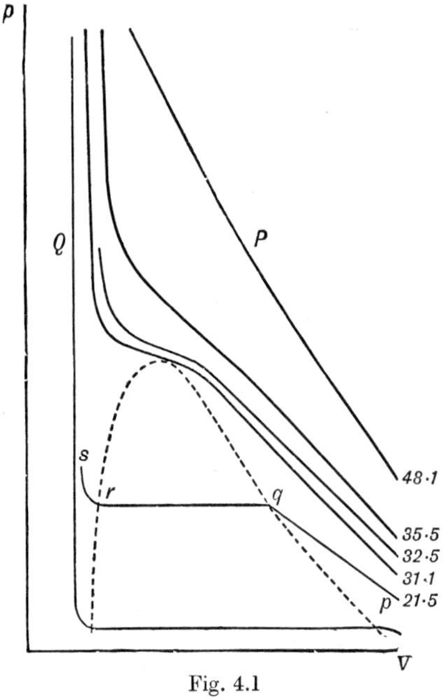

Andrews found that at a temperature of 30·9° liquefaction took place, but that at temperatures of 31° and higher no liquefaction occurred, however much the pressure was increased. On this account 30·9° C. is called the *critical temperature* for carbon dioxide, and the isotherm for this temperature is called the *critical isotherm*.

Fig. 4.1

At the point q the whole mass is in the gaseous state, while at the point r it is all in the liquid state. Two dotted curves are drawn in the figure, one through the points representing the volume of the liquid at which evaporation begins, and the other through the points representing the volume of the gas at which liquefaction begins. These two curves meet at the critical isotherm, and at this point the specific volumes of the liquid and vapour are equal (see, however, Section 12).

At the point P the substance would undoubtedly be regarded as in the gaseous state, while at the point Q it would be regarded as in the liquid state. It is possible to pass from the point P to the point Q without any discontinuity occurring, provided that we do not pass through the region bounded by the dotted curve, inside which alone heterogeneity is found. This fact is usually spoken of as the *continuity of the liquid and gaseous states.*

All gases show the same behaviour, but the critical temperatures, pressures, and volumes differ widely.

3. The Equation of Van der Waals.

Since the liquid state changes continuously into the gaseous state, it should be possible to obtain a general equation of state connecting the pressure, volume, and temperature which will apply to a substance whether it be in the gaseous or the liquid state.

The simple equation $pV = RT$, which we have obtained for a perfect gas, obviously will not apply to the general case. The first to attempt to modify this equation by removing some of the simplifying assumptions on which it is based was Van der Waals, whose work we now consider.

In the theory of the ideal gas it is assumed that the volume occupied by the molecules themselves is negligible compared with the total volume of the gas, and that the molecules exert no appreciable forces on one another. It is evident that the former assumption cannot be exactly true for actual gases; and with regard to the second assumption, if we consider the magnitude of forces of cohesion between the molecules of matter in the solid and liquid states, we see that, even when the matter is in the gaseous state, we may expect that these forces will not be entirely negligible. We shall now consider the effect of taking these two factors into account.

(a) *Derivation.* We make the fundamental assumption that, if a perfect and an actual gas are in thermal equilibrium, the mean translational energies of their molecules are equal; in other words, the mean translational energy of a molecule of an actual gas is proportional to its absolute temperature.

The effect of the fact that the volume occupied by the molecules is finite and not negligible is that the number of collisions of any molecule with other molecules or with the surface of the containing vessel in a given time is greater than the number calculated in Chapter III on the assumption that the volume occupied by the molecules is negligible. The effect as regards collisions with the wall is the same as if the molecules themselves were negligibly small, but were confined in a smaller space. Taking this factor into account, we must correct equation (9), Chapter III, by writing

$$p(\mathbf{V} - b) = NkT, \qquad \ldots \ldots \quad (1)$$

where b is the correction for the volume of the molecules themselves, and N is the total number of molecules present.

The effect of forces of cohesion can be seen by considering fig. 4.2. AB is a portion of the wall of the containing vessel. The effect of molecules farther away than a certain distance r will be inappreciable; we therefore draw round each of the molecules m_1, m_2, m_3, a sphere of radius r; the effects of molecules lying outside these spheres, and of the walls of the vessel, need not be considered.* For a molecule m_1 which is farther away from the walls than r the net effect of the forces of cohesion will on the average be zero, because the molecules on either side will exert equal and opposite forces. On the other hand, for a molecule m_3, whose distance from the wall is less than r, only the

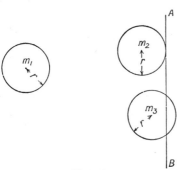

tangential forces will be balanced; with regard to the forces normal to the surface, the effect of the molecules on the side of m_3 remote from the wall will preponderate, as can be clearly seen from the figure. Since the force between molecules is an attractive one, the net result will be a field of force acting inwards on the molecules near the surface. Molecules coming up to the surface will on the average possess the mean translational energy $\frac{3}{2}kT$ (see equation (8), Chapter III) before they enter this field of force. On entering the field of force the kinetic energy of the molecules will be reduced, and the pressure p that they exert will be less than would be exerted if the cohesive forces were absent. If we represent the effect per unit area of the cohesive forces by p_1, it is $(p + p_1)$ and not p that is proportional to the mean kinetic energy of the molecule of the gas, that is, to the absolute temperature T. Using this result in equation (1), we obtain

$$(p + p_1)\,(\mathbf{V} - b) = NkT.$$

Fig. 4.2

The value of p_1 is proportional to the number of molecules striking unit area of the surface in unit time, and to the intensity of the field of force. Both of these factors are proportional to the density, ρ, of the gas, and we may therefore write

$$p_1 = c\rho^2,$$

where c is a constant. Substituting this value in the above equation, we obtain

$$(p + c\rho^2)\,(\mathbf{V} - b) = NkT;$$

* Newton's third law of motion shows that we do not have to take into account the attractive forces between the gas molecules and the wall.

and since $\rho^2 = N^2 m^2 / \mathbf{V}^2$, m being the mass of a molecule, we may write this last equation in the form

$$\left(p + \frac{a}{\mathbf{V}^2}\right)(\mathbf{V} - b) = NkT, \quad \cdots \cdots \quad (2)$$

which is Van der Waals' equation of state*.

It will be seen that a is constant for a given mass of gas, but is proportional to the square of the total mass of gas present. b is proportional to the first power of the mass of the gas.

(b) *Properties of Van der Waals' Equation.* If we are considering a gram-molecule of gas, equation (2) becomes

$$\left(p + \frac{a}{V^2}\right)(V - b) = RT,$$

where a and b are the values of the constants appropriate to a gram-molecule. This equation may be written in the form

$$p = \frac{RT}{V - b} - \frac{a}{V^2}. \quad \cdots \cdots \quad (3)$$

The general form of the curves representing this equation is shown in fig. 4.3; for each curve T remains constant, and the higher curves correspond to larger values of T.

We commence by searching for maxima and minima. Differentiating equation (3) to obtain $\partial p / \partial V$, and equating to zero to find the turning-points of the curve, we obtain

$$\frac{RT}{(V - b)^2} = \frac{2a}{V^3}. \quad \cdots \cdots \quad (4)$$

Eliminating T between this equation and equation (3), we obtain

$$p = \frac{a(V - 2b)}{V^3}. \quad \cdots \cdots \quad (5)$$

This is the equation of the locus of the maxima and minima of the family of curves obtained by giving various values to T, and is represented in the figure by the curve ARBQC.

To find the position of the maximum B of this curve, we differentiate equation (5) with respect to V and equate to zero, thus obtaining

$$\left.\begin{array}{l} V_c = 3b, \\[2mm] p_c = \dfrac{a}{27b^2} \end{array}\right\} \quad \cdots \cdots \quad (6)$$

---

* See also Eucken, *Zeits. f. phys. Chem.*, Bodenstein Festband, p. 432 (1931).

If we substitute these values in equation (3), we obtain the value of T for the curve passing through the point B,

$$T_c = \frac{8a}{27Rb}. \qquad \ldots \ldots \ldots \quad (7)$$

Actually the curve corresponding to this temperature has a point of inflexion with a horizontal tangent at the point B. For such a point we must have $\partial p/\partial V = 0$, and $\partial^2 p/\partial V^2 = 0$, that is, differentiating the original equation (3), we obtain

$$\frac{RT}{(V-b)^2} = \frac{2a}{V^3}, \text{ and } \frac{2RT}{(V-b)^3} = \frac{6a}{V^4}.$$

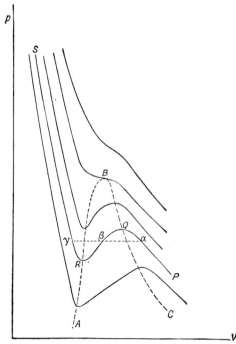

Fig. 4.3

Solving these equations and equation (3), we obtain the same values for p, V, and T as are given by equations (6) and (7). Further, we see that there is only one such point for the whole family of curves.

The curve or isotherm through this point, that is, the one corresponding to the temperature $8a/27Rb$, therefore has the following properties.

(1) *It is the only isotherm which has a point of inflexion with a horizontal tangent.*

(2) *Since it touches the curve given by equation* (5) *at the maximum point of that curve, no isotherm for a higher value of T has a horizontal tangent (that is, a maximum or minimum) at any point; and all isotherms for smaller values of T cut the curve given by equation* (5) *in two points, that is, they have both a maximum and a minimum.*

(c) *Comparison with Experiment.* A consideration of these two properties of this curve, and a general comparison of the curves in fig. 4.3 with those representing the results of Andrews' experiments (fig. 4.1), make it natural to identify this curve with the critical isotherm. Thus, according to the theory of Van der Waals, the critical point is determined by equations (6) and (7). Carrying the comparison further and considering the curves for temperatures below the critical temperature, we see that Van der Waals' equation predicts an S-shaped curve like PQRS, whereas experiments gives a curve PαβγS, with discontinuities in slope at α and γ, the portion αβγ corresponding to the heterogeneous region.

Actually, however, it is possible to realize experimentally the portions αQ and γR, which correspond to a supercooled vapour and to a superheated liquid. We could not expect to be able to realize the portion QR, which represents an essentially unrealizable condition where increase of pressure causes an increase of volume. The theory of Van der Waals gives no indication of the point α at which condensation to the liquid state begins. Demonstrations of the position of the line αβγ which depend on consideration of the work done on taking the gas through the " cycle " αQβRγβα are invalid. This follows from the character of the part QβR of the Van der Waals curve which has just been noted, for the work is not a function of state, so the work done in any process depends on the path along which the process is carried out. The position of the line αβγ can be determined by a consideration of the change in the appropriate thermodynamical function of state (see Examples 17 and 18 at the end of Chapter XVI).

The general agreement between the theory of Van der Waals and experiment is remarkable, when we consider the simplicity of the Van der Waals equation and the assumptions on which it is based.

The quantitative agreement can be tested by a comparison of the values of the constants *a* and *b* deduced, using equations (6) and (7), from the values of the critical constants (the methods of measuring which we consider later in this chapter) with those values that are required to account for the measured departures of the gas from the simple gas laws (see for example Jeans, *Dynamical Theory of Gases*, 3rd edition, pp. 135–7 and p. 148). The differences amount to 20 or 30 per cent.

Another way of showing that considerable numerical discrepancy exists is to calculate the expression RT_c/p_cV_c from equations (6) and (7) and compare with the experimental values. This quantity is called the *critical coefficient*. We obtain from equations (6) and (7)

$$\frac{RT_c}{p_cV_c} = \frac{8}{3} = 2 \cdot 667$$

for all substances. Experimental values are shown in Table I.

TABLE I.—CRITICAL CONSTANTS FOR CERTAIN INORGANIC SUBSTANCES *

Substance	Critical pressure P_c (atm.)	Critical volume V_c (c.c./gm.-mol.)	Critical temperature T_c (° abs.)	RT_c/P_cV_c
He	2·25	61·55	5·2	3·082
Ne	26·86	44·30	44·75	3·086
A	47·996	77·07	150·66	3·351
Kr	54·3	107·0	210·6	2·975
X	57·2	236·2	287·8	3·375
Rn	—	—	377·5	—
Hg	1042	40·12	1735	3·406
H_2	12·8	69·68	33·2	3·055
O_2	49·713	74·42	154·28	3·424
N_2	33·49	90·03	125·97	3·422
Cl_2	76·1	123·4	417·1	3·643
CO	34·6	90·03	134·4	3·541
NO	64	57·25	177·1	3·97
N_2O	77·5	96·92	311·9	3·408
CO_2	72·83	94·23	304·16	3·639
CS_2	72·868	172·7	546·15	3·573
SO_2	77·65	124·8	430·25	3·642
H_2O	218·5	55·44	647·3	4·385
D_2O	218·6	55·16	644·6	4·386
NH_3	112·2	72·02	405·5	4·118
CCl_4	44·98	275·8	556·25	3·681
$SnCl_4$	36·95	351·3	591·8	3·743

* Taken from Moelwyn-Hughes, *Physical Chemistry*, Pergamon Press (1957), p. 573; see also Kaye and Laby, *Tables of Physical and Chemical Constants*, twelfth edition, Longmans, Green and Co., 1959, p. 134; and K. A. Kobe and R. E. Lynn, *Chem. Rev.*, Vol. 53, p. 117 (1953).

On the whole the larger values are for the more complicated molecules, but there does not appear to be any very definite relationship with the atomicity.

(d) *Reduced Equation of State.* Before leaving Van der Waals' equation, we must consider an important property which it possesses.

Let the ratio of the temperature of a fluid to its critical temperature be θ, the ratio of its pressure to its critical pressure be π, and the ratio of its volume to its critical volume be ϕ. Thus,

$$\left.\begin{aligned} \theta &= \frac{T}{T_c}, \\[2mm] \pi &= \frac{p}{p_c}, \\[2mm] \phi &= \frac{V}{V_c}. \end{aligned}\right\} \quad \cdots \cdots \cdots \quad (8)$$

Substituting the values of p, V, and T given by equation (8) and those of p_c, V_c, and T_c given by equations (6) and (7) in Van der Waals' equation, it becomes

$$\left(\pi + \frac{3}{\phi^2}\right)(3\phi - 1) = 8\theta. \quad \cdots \cdots \quad (9)$$

This is called the *reduced equation of state* of Van der Waals, and θ, π, and ϕ are called the reduced temperature, pressure, and volume.

It will be noticed that in equation (9) there are no constants depending on the nature of the particular substance with which we are dealing; that is, if two of the quantities θ, π, and ϕ are the same for two substances, the third will also be the same. This is called the *law of corresponding states*.

4. Other Equations of State.

There have been many attempts to improve on the equation of Van der Waals. This equation fails seriously in three important respects:

(1) It predicts that the ratio RT_c/p_cV_c at the critical point will be 2·67, whereas experiment (Table I, p. 108) shows that it is greater than 3, and varies appreciably for different gases.

(2) It predicts that the relation between the critical volume V_c and V_0, the smallest volume which the molecules can be made to occupy by the application of infinite pressure at non-zero temperature, will be $V_c = 3V_0$, whereas a large number of results collected by Berthelot show that the relation is more nearly $V_c = 4V_0$. We may note that V_0 is also the volume which would be occupied by the molecules under finite pressure as the temperature approaches absolute zero.

(3) As mentioned in Section 3, the values of the constants a and b required to fit the experimental results on compressibility or thermal expansion at moderate pressures differ from those deduced from the critical constants using equations (6) and (7) by about 20 to 30 per cent.

Of the other equations proposed * we may mention the following and compare them as regards (1), (2), and (3) with that of Van der Waals.

---

* For a list of a very large number of the equations that have been proposed, see Partington and Shilling, *The Specific Heats of Gases*, pp. 29–33 (Benn, 1924); see also J. R. Partington, *An Advanced Treatise on Physical Chemistry*, London: Longmans, Green (1949), Vol. 1, Chapter 7.

(a) *Dieterici.* $$p = \frac{RT}{(V-b)}\, e^{-a/RTV}.$$

This predicts a value for the ratio RT_c/p_cV_c of 3·69, which is better than Van der Waals. As regards (2), it predicts $V_c = 2V_0$, which is worse than Van der Waals. As regards (3) it is considerably better than Van der Waals, notably as regards the value of b. Generally for moderate pressures it is much better than Van der Waals, but it is useless for high pressures. It has no sounder a theoretical basis than Van der Waals, and it gives better agreement with experiment for the inversion curve in the porous plug experiment described in Chapter V, Section 3.*

(b) *Clausius.* $$\left(p + \frac{a'}{T(V+c)^2}\right)(V-b) = RT.$$

It will be noted that this differs from Van der Waals in that the forces of cohesion are taken as inversely proportional to the absolute temperature. It also contains an additional constant c, which enables it to represent departures from the law of corresponding states. These changes are purely empirical.

The following two equations are of great practical importance; they do not attempt to represent the whole range of phenomena, but for the limited range to which they apply they are convenient and accurate.

(c) *Berthelot.*—Neglecting the constant c in the equation of Clausius, it becomes

$$\left(p + \frac{a'}{TV^2}\right)(V-b) = RT. \quad \ldots \ldots \quad (10)$$

This equation fails just as badly as does that of Van der Waals at the critical point, but at moderate pressures it agrees better with experiment than Van der Waals. Treating it exactly as we did Van der Waals' equation, we obtain for the critical constants

$$V_c = 3b,$$

$$p_c = \left(\frac{RT_c}{2b} - \frac{a'}{9T_c b^2}\right),$$

$$T_c^{\,2} = \frac{8a'}{27Rb}.$$

These equations can be used to determine the values of a' and b in terms of the critical constants of the gas, giving

$$\left.\begin{array}{l} a' = 3p_c V_c^{\,2} T_c, \\[4pt] b = \dfrac{V_c}{3}. \end{array}\right\} \quad \ldots \ldots \ldots \quad (11)$$

Using these values, equation (10) can be written

$$\left(p + \frac{3p_c}{\theta\phi^2}\right)\left(V - \frac{V_c}{3}\right) = RT, \quad \ldots \ldots \quad (12)$$

where θ and ϕ are the reduced temperature and volume respectively. It is this last equation that Berthelot discusses.

He aims at an equation that shall be valid over a wide range of temperatures for gases or vapours, but only for comparatively small pressures. Further, he

---

* See Lewis, *System of Physical Chemistry*, Vol. 2, p. 71.

aims at an equation in which the *measured* critical constants shall be the only constants depending on the particular substance under consideration; equation (12) obviously satisfies this last condition. When T is equal to zero, however, it makes the volume equal to $\frac{1}{3}V_c$. We have already mentioned that $\frac{1}{4}V_c$ is nearer to the truth. We therefore substitute $\frac{1}{4}V_c$ for $\frac{1}{3}V_c$ in equation (12). Berthelot finds further that the equation represents experimental results on compressibilities better if in the first bracket the factor 16/3 is substituted for 3. We thus obtain

$$\left(p + \frac{16}{3}\frac{p_c}{\theta\phi^2}\right)\left(V - \frac{V_c}{4}\right) = RT,$$

which can be written

$$pV\left(1 + \frac{16}{3}\frac{1}{\pi\theta\phi^2}\right)\left(1 - \frac{1}{4\phi}\right) = RT. \quad \ldots \quad (13)$$

It should be noticed that the quantities π, θ, ϕ occurring in this equation are the ratios of the pressure, temperature, and volume to the *measured* critical constants of the gas; this makes the equation particularly convenient for practical use. It is immediately obvious that the equation fails to predict the correct values of the critical constants, but this is not important as it is not meant to be used at such high pressures.

The correction terms are both small compared with unity and we may neglect squares and products of such terms. We may therefore write

$$pV = RT\left(1 - \frac{16}{3}\frac{1}{\pi\theta\phi^2} + \frac{1}{4\phi}\right). \quad \ldots \quad (14)$$

This equation may be made to assume a more convenient form in the following way. It may be seen from Table I, p. 108, that the measured ratio of RT_c to p_cV_c is approximately the same for a large number of gases. Berthelot takes the value of the ratio in round numbers as 32/9 and writes

$$p_cV_c = \tfrac{9}{32}RT_c \text{ (approx.)}.$$

Remembering that, for the pressures for which we are going to use the equation, Boyle's law is approximately true, we have

$$pV = RT \text{ (approx.)}$$

Combining these equations, we obtain

$$\pi\phi = \tfrac{32}{9}\theta \text{ (approx.)} \quad \ldots \ldots \quad (15)$$

as an approximate expression of the result of experiment. We now substitute the value of ϕ given by equation (15) in the small *correction terms* of equation (14), obtaining

$$pV = RT\left\{1 + \frac{9}{128}\frac{\pi}{\theta}\left(1 - \frac{6}{\theta^2}\right)\right\},$$

or

$$pV = RT\left\{1 + \frac{9}{128}\frac{T_c}{p_c}\frac{p}{T}\left(1 - \frac{6T_c^2}{T^2}\right)\right\}. \quad \ldots \quad (16)$$

This is a convenient form of Berthelot's equation. It may be applied to gases and vapours at all temperatures. It is the equation that should be used when direct experimental measurements of compressibilities are not available. It is extremely useful in connexion with the reduction of the results of measurements on the specific heats of gases (see Chapter VI), and in connexion with the integration of the Clausius-Clapeyron equation (see Chapter VII). When direct com-pressibility measurements are available it is better to use Berthelot's equation in the form given in equation (10).

(d) *Callendar*. $$V - b = \frac{RT}{p} - c, \quad \cdot \; \cdot \; \cdot \; \cdot \; \cdot \; \cdot \; \cdot \; \cdot \quad (17)$$

where c varies as the inverse nth power of the absolute temperature; that is,

$$c = c_0 \left(\frac{T_0}{T}\right)^n,$$

where c_0 is the value of c when $T = T_0$. The term c represents the effect of attrac-tive forces between molecules or of the coaggregation of single molecules to form associated complexes.

The equation may be applied to gases and vapours at moderate pressures. It makes no attempt to apply at the critical point, and does not apply to liquids. Its most important application is to the case of steam, and it is the equation that is always used in dealing with this substance (see Appendix).

Expression of the Equation of State of Gases by means of Series

5. We now return to consider the virial expansion of Kammerlingh Onnes

$$pV = A[1 + B/V + C/V^2 + D/V^3 + \ldots],$$

or the alternative expansion in powers of the pressure

$$pV = A' + B'p + C'p^2 + D'p^3 + \ldots.$$

We also have $A = A', = RT$ for one gram-molecule of gas, and $B = B'$.

The second virial coefficient is the most important. When B is known, the behaviour of the gas at moderate pressures is completely determined, since the terms which contain higher powers become significant only at very high pressures.

Values * of **B** for various gases are shown in fig. 4.4 as a function of the celsius temperature.† It will be seen that for all gases B varies with the temperature in a similar way. At low temperatures B has large negative values. As the temperature is increased, the value (algebraic) of B increases through zero to positive values.

The point at which B is equal to zero is of importance. It is called the *Boyle temperature*. The reason for that is that, since the coefficients C, D, . . . are all small compared with B, the terms involving them

---

* Clarendon type letters will be used to denote the values of the virial coefficients when the pressure is measured in metres of mercury and the volume is measured in litres.

† For empirical equations which fit these curves, see Holborn and Otto, *Zeits. f. Physik*, Vol. 33, p. 9 (1925); 38, p. 356 (1926). *N.B.*—The mass of gas is not 1 gram-molecule.

only become important at high pressures. If, then, B is equal to zero, the gas obeys Boyle's law with considerable accuracy up to comparatively high pressures.

For example, in the case of nitrogen at 50° C. we have

$$\mathbf{A} = 1\cdot184, \quad \mathbf{B} = -0\cdot015\,.\,10^{-3}, \quad \mathbf{C} = 3\cdot8\,.\,10^{-6},$$

where the pressure is measured in metres of mercury and the volume in litres. This may be taken as the Boyle temperature for nitrogen. Up to a pressure of 14 m. of mercury or about 19 atmospheres, the departures from Boyle's law are *less* than one part in one thousand.

On the other hand, at 0° C. the values of the coefficients are

$$\mathbf{A} = 1\cdot0, \quad \mathbf{B} = -0\cdot61\,.\,10^{-3}.$$
$$\mathbf{C} = 5\cdot4\,.\,10^{-6},$$

and the departures from Boyle's law become equal to one part in one thousand at pressures of about 2 atmospheres; and at 100° C., where the coefficients have the values

$$\mathbf{A} = 1\cdot37, \quad \mathbf{B} = 0\cdot36\,.\,10^{-3},$$
$$\mathbf{C} = 3\cdot15\,.\,10^{-6},$$

the departures from Boyle's law become equal to one part in one thousand at about 4 atmospheres.*

It has been shown † that, at very high pressures, the coefficients for carbon dioxide depend on the density region in which the measurements are made.

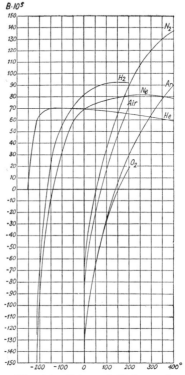

Fig. 4.4.—Values of $\mathbf{B}$ for various gases: p in metres of mercury, $\mathbf{V}$ in litres, mass of gas such that $p = 1$ when $\mathbf{V} = 1$.

The behaviour of a gas can also be shown by a diagram in which the value of $p\mathbf{V}$ for a given mass of gas at constant temperature is plotted as a function of p. Such curves are shown in fig. 4.5; each curve corresponds to a given temperature. The temperatures are proportional to the numbers marked on the curves.

Since
$$\left(\frac{\partial(pV)}{\partial p}\right)_{p=0} = B,$$

the value of B for a given temperature gives the slope of the pV curve for $p = 0$. The reverse process can be used to determine the second

* See also Example 2 at the end of this chapter.
† A. and C. Michels, *Proc. Roy. Soc.*, A, Vol. 160, p. 348 (1937).

virial coefficient. By determining the isotherms of helium, neon, argon, hydrogen, nitrogen, and oxygen, Cragoe * has determined the second virial coefficient of these gases from the slope of the pV-isotherms at $p = 0$.

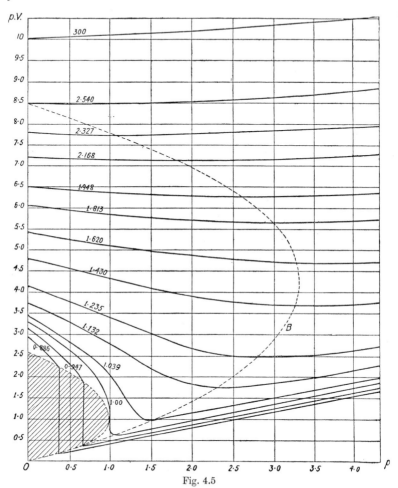

Fig. 4.5

In accordance with the results shown in fig. 4.5, the curves for the lower temperatures all begin with negative gradients. They all reach a minimum point, after which the slope is positive; this is because the value of C, the third virial coefficient, is positive. The locus of the minima is marked by the curve B.

* Cragoe, *Journ. Res. Bur. Stand.*, Washington, Vol. 26, p. 495 (1941).

The curve for the Boyle temperature is the one marked 2·540. For this curve the minimum lies on the axis $p = 0$. Curves for temperatures higher than the Boyle temperature show no minimum; for them the value of pV increases steadily with p. These curves are typical of the behaviour of all gases. The units used in plotting are arbitrary.

There have been many determinations of virial coefficients in recent years and they can be compared with values calculated from the interaction energy. The second virial coefficient is related * to the interaction energy for a pair of molecules by the expression

$$B(T) = 2\pi N \int_0^\infty \left[1 - \exp\left\{-u(r)/kT\right\}\right] r^2 \, dr.$$

If we use the Lennard–Jones † expression for the inter-molecular energy

$$u(r) = 4\epsilon[(\sigma/r)^{12} - (\sigma/r)^6]$$

where ϵ is the depth of the potential well and σ is the separation of the pair of molecules at which the interaction energy vanishes, the expression for B can be put in a form amenable to calculation. Tables of $B(T)/b$ for various values of θ/T (where b has been written for $2\pi N\sigma^3/3$ and θ has been written for ϵ/k) have been published.‡

6. Equations of State and the Second Virial Coefficient: the Boyle Temperature.

Van der Waals' equation may be written

$$pV = \frac{RT}{\left(1 + \dfrac{a}{pV^2}\right)\left(1 - \dfrac{b}{V}\right)}.$$

The correction terms a/pV^2 and b/V are both small compared with unity provided the gas is not too much compressed. Using the binomial theorem and neglecting squares and products of the correction terms, the equation becomes

$$pV = RT\left(1 + \frac{b}{V} - \frac{a}{pV^2}\right)$$

$$= RT + \frac{RT}{V}b - \frac{RT}{pV^2}a.$$

---

* See R. H. Fowler, *Statistical Mechanics*, second edition, Cambridge: at the University Press (1936), §§ 8.3, 9.7.

† J. E. Lennard-Jones, *Proc. Roy. Soc.* A, Vol. 106, p. 463 (1924); *Physica*, Vol. 4, p. 941 (1937).

‡ J. O. Hirschfelder, F. T. McClure, and I. T. Weeks, *Journ. Chem. Phys.*, Vol. 10, p. 204 (1942); W. H. Stockmayer and J. A. Beattie, *ibid.*, Vol. 10, p. 476 (1942); R. B. Bird and E. L. Spotz, *The Virial Equation of State*, University of Wisconsin, Project NOrd 9938 (10 May, 1950).

The second and third terms on the right-hand side are small correction terms. In them we substitute from the approximate relation

$$pV = RT \text{ (approx.)},$$

thus obtaining $$pV = RT + \left(b - \frac{a}{RT}\right)p. \quad \cdots \cdots \quad (18)$$

Thus according to Van der Waals' equation the second virial coefficient B is given by

$$B = b - \frac{a}{RT}. \quad \cdots \cdots \cdots \quad (19)$$

The Boyle temperature T_B is given by

$$B = 0,$$

whence $$T_B = \frac{a}{Rb}. \quad \cdots \cdots \cdots \quad (20)$$

We have for the critical temperature from equation (7)

$$T_c = \frac{8a}{27Rb}.$$

Thus, according to Van der Waals' equation,

$$\frac{T_B}{T_c} = \frac{27}{8} = 3 \cdot 375.$$

Experimental values are given in Table II. The agreement is not very satisfactory. It may be mentioned that the *constancy* of the ratio for different gases is a further indication of the extent to which the principle of corresponding states is true.

TABLE II

	He	H$_2$	Ne	N$_2$	Air	A	O$_2$
Boyle temperature*	19° abs.	104°	134°	323°	357°	410°	423°
Critical temperature	5·2°	33·2°	44·75°	126°	132·5°	149·7°	155°
$\dfrac{T_B}{T_c}$	3·65	3·15	3·00	2·56	2·67	2·73	2·72

* From the measurements of Holborn and Otto (*loc. cit.*).

Let us now consider Berthelot's equation, which may be written (see equation (16))

$$pV = RT + \frac{9}{128}\frac{RT_c}{p_c}\left(1 - \frac{6T_c^2}{T^2}\right)p.$$

According to this equation the second virial coefficient B is given by

$$B = \frac{9}{128}\frac{RT_c}{p_c}\left(1 - \frac{6T_c^2}{T^2}\right), \quad \cdots \cdots \quad (21)$$

and the Boyle temperature is given by

$$\frac{T_B}{T_c} = \sqrt{6} = 2{\cdot}45,$$

which is on the whole in slightly better agreement with the experimental values than is the value of the ratio predicted by Van der Waals' equation.

Berthelot's equation in its other form (see equation (10)) may be written

$$pV = RT + \left(b - \frac{a'}{RT^2}\right)p.$$

Thus according to this equation the second virial coefficient is given by

$$B = \left(b - \frac{a'}{RT^2}\right). \qquad \cdots \cdots \cdots \quad (22)$$

In practical applications this more general form of Berthelot's equation, or preferably an empirical expression giving B as a function of the temperature (see fig. 4.4 and the footnote on Section 5), is to be used in all cases where direct compressibility measurements are available. Examples will be found in Chapter VI, Section 3, and in Chapter VIII, Section 25. If compressibility measurements are not available, the expression for B in terms of the critical constants given in equation (21) is of great practical value.

Equations (19) (Van der Waals) and (21) (Berthelot) both indicate that, as T increases, B approaches a constant value. On the other hand, experiment (see fig. 4.4) shows that as T increases B reaches a maximum and then diminishes, but this maximum is probably not of practical importance except in the case of helium. It was to account for the maximum in this case that Lennard-Jones chose the form of intermolecular energy given in Section 5 rather than any mathematically simpler alternative. The experimental data on the inert elements in the solid state, as well as the gaseous state, can also be represented * by this interaction energy; and this is its real superiority over the simpler forms.

Slater, Kirkwood, and Keyes,† and Buckingham, Massey, and Corner,‡ have considered the forces between neutral molecules from the point of view of quantum mechanics and have found theoretically the second virial coefficient for helium and its temperature variation. The latter workers show that the calculated values of the viscosity and the second virial coefficient are in good agreement with the experimental values from 26° to 15° K. Below 15° K., the calculated values are too small; likewise the various maxima and minima of the curves (such as the Boyle temperature) occur at too low values. Inclusion of dipole-quadruple interactions reduces the discrepancy. Rice § has made similar calculations for argon.

---

* J. Corner, *Trans. Faraday Soc.*, Vol. 44, p. 914 (1948).

† See papers by Slater, Kirkwood, and Keyes, *Phys. Rev.*, Vol. 37, pp. 682, 832 (1931); Vol. 38, p. 237 (1931); see also Wohl, *Zeits. f. phys. Chem.*, Bodenstein Festband, p. 807 (1931); Kirkwood, *Phys. Zeits.*, Vol. 33, p. 57 (1932); Müller, *Proc. Roy. Soc.*, A, Vol. 154, p. 624 (1936); Herzfeld, *Phys. Rev.*, Vol. 52, p. 374 (1937).

‡ Buckingham, *Proc. Roy. Soc.*, A, Vol. 160, p. 94 (1937); Buckingham and Massey, *Proc. Roy. Soc.*, A, Vol. 168, p. 378 (1938); *ibid.*, Vol. 169, p. 205 (1939); Buckingham, Hamilton and Massey, *Proc. Roy. Soc.*, A, Vol. 179, p. 103 (1941); R. A. Buckingham and J. Corner, *Proc. Roy. Soc.*, A, Vol. 189, p. 118 (1947); O. Halpern and R. A. Buckingham, *Phys. Rev.*, Vol. 98, p. 1626 (1955); R. A. Buckingham, A. R. Davies, and D. C. Gilles, *Proc. Phys. Soc.*, Vol. 71, p. 457 (1958); see also D. ter Haar, *Proc. Phys. Soc.*, Vol. 66, p. 847 (1953).

§ Rice, *Journ. Amer. Chem. Soc.*, Vol. 63, p. 3 (1941).

7. Principle of Corresponding States.

The principle of corresponding states has been mentioned in considering the reduced form of van der Waals' equation (Section 3*d*). This principle was suggested by van der Waals in 1873 in connexion with his equation of state, but it is of a more fundamental character and of more general application than this origin would suggest. A simple statement of the principle of corresponding states is that, in terms of reduced parameters of state, the behaviour of all substances is the same. This means that, when the value of a particular physical property is calculated in terms of reduced parameters of state, the values so obtained for all gases or liquids or solids will lie on a common curve.

Such identity of behaviour must depend ultimately upon the properties of, and the interactions between, molecules.* Since matter exists in condensed states, there must be attractive forces between molecules at large distances. Since all condensed matter has a finite density, repulsive forces must predominate when molecules approach close together. These primitive facts indicate the basic features of the interaction between a pair of molecules; and their primacy ensures that these forces will generally be of the same kind, varying from one species to another only in scale, that is, in the values of the parameters in the expression for the potential energy of a pair of molecules. It is also clear that in the case of some molecular species there will be additional factors (for instance, the dipole moment of polar molecules or molecules which contain highly polar groups, or the zero-point energy of light molecules, or the shapes of large molecules like proteins and high polymers) which will cause these molecular species to depart from the behaviour of molecules simpler in structure.

The form of the intermolecular energy was examined by de Boer †
from this point of view. He showed that, when the molecular field of force is spherical and the interaction energy of a pair of molecules can be written as the product of an energy characteristic of the species and a dimensionless function which is the same for all substances, the principle of corresponding states is valid. This latter condition can be written in terms of the depth ϵ of the potential well and the separation σ of the molecules at which the interaction energy vanishes; for the principle to be valid it is necessary that the interaction energy $u(r)$ of a pair of molecules can be written as $\epsilon\phi(r/\sigma)$ where ϕ is a universal function. It should be noted that the Lennard–Jones interaction energy is of the required form as also is that used by Buckingham.‡

---

* For a discussion of intermolecular forces see J. E. Lennard-Jones in Chapter X of R. H. Fowler, *Statistical Mechanics*, Cambridge: at the University Press (1936).

† J. de Boer and A. Michels, *Physica*, Vol. 5, p. 945 (1938); J. de Boer, Thesis, Amsterdam (1940).

‡ J. E. Lennard-Jones, *Proc. Roy. Soc.* A, Vol. 106, p. 463 (1924); R. A. Buckingham, *ibid.*, Vol. 168, p. 264 (1938); see D. ter Haar, *Physica*, Vol. 19, p. 375 (1953).

Conditions which have to be satisfied for the principle to be valid have been given by Pitzer * who also examined the density, the gas-to-liquid volume ratio, and the reduced vapour pressure as functions of the reduced temperature for a number of substances. He found that argon, krypton, and xenon followed the principle most closely. Taking them as standards, he was able to explain in a general way (in terms of his conditions) the deviations of other substances from this standard behaviour. The conditions put forward by Pitzer have been critically examined by Guggenheim † who states them in the following way. The principle of corresponding states is valid provided:

(a) The effect of quantization of the translational degrees of freedom is negligible.

(b) The molecules are spherically symmetrical either actually or by virtue of free rotation.

(c) The intramolecular degrees of freedom are independent of the density.

(d) The potential energy of a pair of molecules is of the form given by de Boer.

The first condition excludes all the isotopes of the lightest molecules hydrogen and helium; the other conditions rule out highly polar molecules. It appears that many of the macroscopic properties of substances are insensitive to the precise form of $u(r)$ for small values of r so that, although the fourth condition is not rigorously true except for large values of r (even when the first three conditions are satisfied), it turns out to be a useful approximation in this connexion for many non-polar molecules. It is not possible to divide substances into those for which the principle holds and those which depart from it. It is necessary rather to say that different substances accord with the principle to a greater or lesser extent. We have already seen that it is followed most closely by the inert heavy elements; the properties of highly polar molecules, of molecules which form hydrogen bonds, and of molecules which react chemically, depart most from the principle.

The principle of corresponding states has been applied by Guggenheim ‡ to examine

(i) the critical parameters,
(ii) the virial coefficients and the Boyle temperature,
(iii) the densities of coexistent phases,
(iv) the vapour pressure, heat capacity, coefficient of thermal expansion, and surface tension of the liquid phase,
(v) the temperature and the pressure at the triple point.

* K. S. Pitzer, *Journ. Chem. Phys.*, Vol. 7, p. 583 (1939).
† E. A. Guggenheim, *Journ. Chem. Phys.*, Vol. 13, p. 253 (1945).
‡ E. A. Guggenheim, *loc. cit.*; E. A. Guggenheim and M. L. McGlashan, *Proc. Roy. Soc.* A, Vol. 206, p. 448 (1951).

Argon, krypton, xenon, and (with less accuracy) neon follow the principle with respect to all these properties; nitrogen, oxygen, carbon monoxide, and methane follow the principle with fair accuracy as vapours and liquids, but not as solids. The extent to which the principle holds is illustrated by fig. 4.6, which is taken from the paper by Guggenheim and McGlashan, and shows the reduced second virial coefficients as a function of the reduced temperature. The values of the critical constants used for hydrogen in this diagram have been calculated from

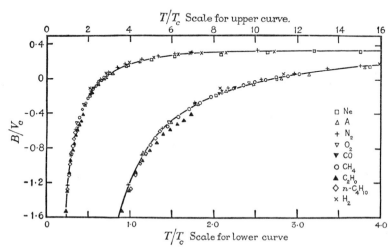

Fig. 4.6.—Experimental values of reduced second virial coefficients for pure gases plotted against the reduced temperature. The values of the critical constants used for hydrogen have been calculated from the experimental values to allow for quantal effects. [After E. A. Guggenheim and M. L. McGlashan, *Proc. Roy. Soc.* A, Vol. 206, p. 451 (1951).]

the experimental values to allow for quantal effects. More recent measurements on ethane indicate that it follows the principle more closely * than is indicated by the points for it in fig. 4.6.

The law of corresponding states has been discussed from the point of view of quantum theory by de Boer.† He introduces the characteristic energy ϵ and the characteristic length σ for each molecular species and writes the macroscopic quantities temperature, volume, and pressure in terms of molecular units as ϵ/k, $N\sigma^3$, and ϵ/σ^3, where k is Boltzmann's constant and N is the number of particles. The law of corresponding states would then require that there should be a unique relation between the pressure, volume, and temperature expressed in

* E. A. Guggenheim, *Rev. Pure and Appl. Chem.*, Vol. 3, p. 4 (1953).

† De Boer and Michels, A., *Physica*, Vol. 5, p. 945 (1938); de Boer, Thesis, Amsterdam (1940).

molecular units. It is found that the relation which is obtained depends also on a parameter

$$\Lambda^* = h/\sigma\sqrt{m\epsilon},$$

which has a characteristic value for each of the substances considered. The classical law of corresponding states is obtained in the limit as Λ^* approaches zero. This parameter measures the deviations from the law of corresponding states due to quantal effects.[*] For all but the lightest elements, Λ^* is very nearly zero, so that the classical law is obeyed.

On this basis, various properties of the gaseous elements have been examined.[†] It has been shown how, for the lighter elements, the molar volumes and the internal energy depart from the classical limit. This deviation can be related to the zero-point energy. The solid-liquid transition has also been considered, and an explanation of the fact that the helium isotope of mass 4 cannot be solidified under its equilibrium vapour pressure is given. De Boer has also calculated the molar volume, as a function of temperature, of the helium isotope of mass 3 in the liquid and gaseous states and the equilibrium vapour pressure of the liquid. The helium isotope of mass 3 was prepared in the pure state and liquefied first in 1948. Its vapour pressure curve was measured [‡] and its boiling and critical temperatures determined. The vapour pressure curve agrees fairly accurately with de Boer's predictions. More recently, the density of the liquid and the gas has been measured.[§] The density function follows de Boer's calculated values very closely. Using the principle in its quantal form de Boer and Cohen [||] have also determined the equation of state of the helium isotope of mass 3 and have calculated its viscosity. Measurements [¶] of this quantity agree with the predicted value at $4 \cdot 2°$ K. and are about 12 per cent lower than it at $1 \cdot 3°$ K.

The law of corresponding states has been extended also to solids at low temperatures, considering the frozen rare gases.[**] The method has been used to calculate the potential energy and the interatomic distances of three of neon, argon, krypton, and xenon in terms of those of the other. The quantal contribution is allowed for by assuming that the lattice theory of specific heats (see Chapter XXII) holds for all

---

[*] De Boer, *Physica*, Vol. 14, p. 139 (1948).

[†] De Boer and Blaisse, *Physica*, Vol. 14, p. 149 (1948).

[‡] Grilly, Hammel and Sydoriak, *Phys. Rev.*, Vol. 75, p. 303 (1949); Abraham, D. W. Osborne and Weinstock, *ibid.*, Vol. 80, p. 366 (1950); S. G. Sydoriak and T. R. Roberts, *ibid.*, Vol. 106, p. 175 (1957).

[§] Grilly, Hammel and Sydoriak, *Phys. Rev.*, Vol. 75, p. 1103 (1949).

[||] J. de Boer, *Physica*, Vol. 15, p. 843 (1949); J. de Boer and E. G. D. Cohen, *ibid.*, Vol. 17, p. 993 (1951).

[¶] E. W. Becker, R. Misenta, and F. Schmeissner, *Phys. Rev.*, Vol. 93, p. 244 (1954).

[**] Murphy and Rice, *Journ. Chem. Phys.*, Vol. 14, p. 518 (1946).

the solids. The characteristic temperature and the specific heat of neon, argon, and krypton were calculated from those of xenon. The agreement with the experimental values is reasonably good.

EXPERIMENTAL METHODS

8. Compressibility.

The isotherms of a fluid determine the way in which its volume and pressure vary at constant temperature. The rate of change of volume per unit volume with decreasing pressure is called the *compressibility*. The compressibility can be measured under various external constraints, for example, the compressibility can be determined under adiabatic conditions or of the vapour in equilibrium with the liquid state.

To determine the equation of state of a gas, or its isotherms, it is necessary to determine the compressibility under the constraint of constant temperature. For the isothermal compressibility we have

$$K_T = -\frac{1}{V}\left(\frac{\partial V}{\partial p}\right)_T.$$

Again, the compressibility of a saturated vapour, that is, measured along the saturation curve of a liquid and its vapour in equilibrium, is defined by

$$K_{\text{sat}} = -\frac{1}{V}\frac{dV}{dp}.$$

The complete differential is used in this equation since when the change takes place along the saturation curve there is only one independent variable. The compressibilities measured under various conditions are related. The adiabatic and the saturation compressibilities are related to the isothermal compressibility by the equations

$$K_{\text{ad}} = K_T/\gamma$$

(see Chapter VI, Section 14), and

$$K_{\text{sat}} = K_T - \alpha_p \Big/ \frac{dp}{dT}$$

(see Chapter XIII, example 8).

9. We may now consider briefly the experimental methods employed in determining the compressibility of gases. The methods may be divided into two distinct groups: (1) those in which the mass of gas remains constant and the volume is varied, (2) those in which variable masses of gas are compressed so as always to occupy the same volume.

The experiments of Andrews described in Chapter VIII, Section 2, may be taken as typical of the first group of methods, provided that some form of absolute manometer is attached to the apparatus. Two forms of manometer are available: (1) an ordinary column of mercury which is open to the air at one end,* (2) a pressure balance in which the force exerted by the pressure on a movable piston, the area of whose cross-section is accurately known, is balanced by weights.†

For work at high pressures the tube containing the gas under investigation should be arranged so that an equal pressure is applied outside and inside. For this purpose it must be contained in a steel vessel as shown in fig. 4.7, and suitable arrangements must be made for viewing the level to which the mercury rises, so that the volume of the gas may be measured.‡

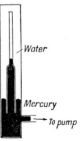

Fig. 4.7

Of the second group of methods the work of Onnes § and of Holborn and others ‖ may be taken as typical. A known mass of gas (determined by measuring its volume at atmospheric pressure and temperature) is compressed into a given volume and the pressure is measured. This method is available over a wide range of temperatures, since the mercury which is used to force the gas into the known volume can be separated from the bulk of the gas by a narrow capillary, and so, whatever the temperature in the bulb containing the mass of the gas, the mercury can be at room temperature. A correction is necessary for the amount of gas in the capillary.

10. Compressibility of Liquids.

The compressibilities of liquids up to pressures greater than 12,000 Kgm. per square centimetre (approximately 1 atmosphere = 1 Kgm. per square centimetre) have been measured by Bridgman. For details of the methods used to produce such extraordinarily high pressures and of the results obtained, reference must be made to the original papers.¶

Critical Phenomena

11. The experiments of Callendar described in the next section have shown that the simple ideas concerning critical phenomena outlined earlier in this chapter are not strictly correct and that it is more accurate to speak of a critical region than of a critical point. In this

* See Amagat, *Ann. d. Chimie et de Physique*, Vol. 29, p. 90 (1893); see also Onnes and others, *Leiden Comm.*, Nos. 44, 94b, 67, 70.

† See, for example, Holborn and Schultze, *Ann. d. Physik*, Vol. 47, p. 1089 (1915).

‡ See Amagat, *loc. cit.*

§ Onnes, *Leiden Comm.*, Nos. 69, 78, 97.

‖ Holborn and Otto, *Zeits. f. Physik*, Vol. 38, p. 359 (1926), and earlier papers; see also Scott, *Proc. Roy. Soc.*, A, Vol. 125, p. 330 (1929).

¶ See, for example, Bridgman, *Proc. Amer. Acad. Arts and Sciences*, Vol. 47, pp. 347, 439 (1912); Vol. 48, p. 307 (1913); Vol. 49, pp. 1, 627 (1914); Vol. 52, p. 609 (1917); Vol. 57, pp. 52, 100 (1922); Vol. 59, p. 171 (1924); Vol. 66, p. 185 (1931); Vol. 67, p. 1 (1932); Vol. 68, p. 1 (1933); *Rev. Mod. Phys.*, Vol. 7, p. 1 (1935); *Journ. Chem. Phys.*. Vol. 3, p. 597 (1935); Vol. 5, p. 964 (1937).

section we shall neglect this fact and shall consider briefly the ordinary methods used to determine critical constants.

In general the critical temperature and pressure may be determined by bringing the substance, contained in a tube similar to that used by Andrews, into such a condition that a minute change of temperature causes the appearance or disappearance of liquid, and by measuring the temperature and pressure.*

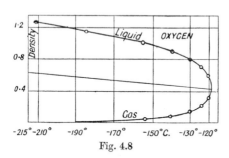

Fig. 4.8

The direct determination of the critical volume is more difficult owing to the large change of volume corresponding to a small change of pressure. The most accurate method of determining the critical volume or density is to use the law of rectilinear diameters discovered by Cailletet and Mathias. This law states that, if we plot against the temperature the densities of both liquid and vapour when they are in equilibrium, we obtain a curve roughly parabolic in shape (see fig. 4.8). The two halves of this curve meet at the critical point; if the mean of the liquid and vapour densities is plotted on the same figure, the resulting curve is almost a straight line also passing through the critical point. The liquid and vapour densities (see Chapter VIII, Section 23) are determined as near to the critical point as is practicable, and, using this law, the results are extrapolated to the point itself. A physical explanation of the law of rectilinear diameters is discussed in Chapter XXIII, Section 15.

Critical data for a few substances † are given in Table III.

TABLE III

Substance	Critical temperature, °C.	Critical pressure, atmos.	Critical density, gm./cm.³
Water	374·2	218·3	0·326
Heavy water	371·4	218·6	0·363
Sulphur dioxide	157·5	77·8	0·524
Carbon dioxide	31·04	72·85	0·468
Xenon	16·59	58·0	1·105
Ethylene	9·90	50·5	0·227
Krypton	−63·77	54·3	0·909
Oxygen	−118·4	50·1	0·41
Argon	−122·4	48·0	0·235
Nitrogen	−146·9	33·5	0·311
Deuterium (equilibrium)	−234·9	16·3	0·067
Hydrogen deuteride	−237·25	14·65	0·048
Hydrogen (equilibrium)	−240·2	12·8	0·031
Helium (isotope 4)	−267·95	2·26	0·069
Helium (isotope 3)	−269·8	1·15	0·04

* See also Onnes, Dorsman and Holst, *Leiden Comm.*, No. 145b; for further references, see the paper of Hein cited in Section 12.
† See K. A. Kobe and R. E. Lynn, *Chem. Rev.*, Vol. 52, p. 117 (1953).

12. The Properties of a Substance near the Critical Point.

A simple way of observing critical phenomena is to take a strong glass tube filled only with a liquid and its vapour. If this tube is slowly heated, the meniscus marking the separation of the liquid and the vapour gradually flattens out and ultimately disappears at the critical point. According to the simple theory we have given, this phenomenon should take place only if the tube is filled with exactly the amount of substance corresponding to the critical density. If there is less substance than this present, the meniscus should gradually move down the tube as the temperature is raised, and before the critical point is reached the tube should be completely filled with vapour. On the other hand, if there is more substance than this present, the meniscus should gradually rise in the tube as the temperature rises, and before the critical temperature is reached the tube should be completely filled with liquid. This is not what happens, however, and Hein * has shown that with carbon dioxide the disappearance of the meniscus is observed when the mean density varies from 0·341 to 0·589, or from 0·735 to 1·269 times the critical density. Further, using a method devised by Teichner, he and others have shown that large variations in density, above and below the position where the meniscus was last seen, are observed even after the critical point has been passed. The observations were made by observing the positions of a series of small spheres of different densities inside the tube. The densities of these spheres were of the same order as the critical density of the substance under investigation, and each sphere came to rest at the horizontal level at which the density of the substance was equal to its own density.

The whole problem has been elucidated by the experiments of Callendar † on water. He has shown that by removing the last traces of dissolved air from the water it is possible to obtain accurate and reproducible results in the critical region itself.

The water was sealed in quartz tubes and it was found that the densities of liquid and vapour did not, as demanded by the simple theory, become equal at 374° C. when the meniscus vanished, but that a visible difference of density persisted and could be traced nearly up to 380° C. under favourable conditions. The relation between the density of the liquid and the temperature was determined with considerable accuracy by using different weighed quantities of water sealed in tubes whose total volume was known, and by observing the temperature at which the meniscus just reached the top of the tube. Similarly, for the saturated vapour the relation between density and

---

* Traube, *Z. anorg. Chem.*, Vol. 38, p. 399 (1904); Teichner, *Ann. Phys.*, Lpz., Vol. 13, p. 595 (1904); Hein, *Zeits. f. phys. Chem.*, Vol. 86, p. 385 (1914); in the last paper full references are given to earlier work on critical phenomena.

† Callendar, *Proc. Roy. Soc.*, A, Vol. 120, p. 460 (1928).

temperature was determined by using smaller amounts of liquid and observing the temperature at which the last trace of liquid vanished. The results obtained are shown in fig. 4.9. The values for the liquid above 374° C. where the meniscus vanished were obtained by making observations on the position of the line of demarcation between liquid and vapour, which could be observed on account of the difference in density. The mass in the vapour phase was determined by extrapolation of the experimental curve as shown by the dotted line in the figure. The accuracy of the results

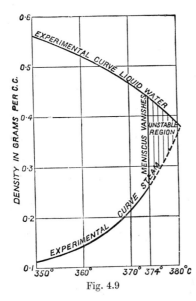

Fig. 4.9

so obtained diminished rapidly as the densities of liquid and vapour became more nearly equal. The results indicated that the densities would become equal a little above 380° C. The smallest trace of air made reliable observations in the unstable region impossible.

It was important to confirm these results by measuring some other quantity which could be determined accurately for both liquid and saturated vapour. This was particularly necessary as the very accurate observations of Holborn and Baumann * on the saturation pressure of steam in a steel cylinder by a static method similar in principle to that used by Andrews indicated the existence of a definite critical temperature at 374° C. They showed that there was no saturation pressure beyond this point but a continuous change of pressure with volume at constant temperature.† This result, as Callendar's later experiments showed, was undoubtedly due to the presence of dissolved air in the water.

Callendar therefore measured the enthalpy $U + pV$, where U is the internal energy. The measurement of this quantity is considered in Section 3 of the Appendix,‡ but the results will be given here as their significance from the present point of view will be appreciated in a general way without a detailed consideration of the meaning of the enthalpy.

---

* Holborn and Baumann, *Ann. d. Physik*, Vol. 31, p. 945 (1910).

† See also Cailletet and Colardeau, *Comptes Rendus*, Vol. 112, p. 563 (1891); *Ann. d. Chimie et de Physique* (6), Vol. 25, p. 519.

‡ In this connexion reference may also be made to the work of Bennewitz and his co-workers, Bennewitz and Andreewa, *Zeits. f. phys. Chem.*, A, Vol. 142, p. 37 (1929).

Callendar found in the first place that, when the observations were made with ordinary distilled water, and the enthalpies of water and of steam under saturation pressure were plotted against the pressure, the results, although rather irregular near the saturation line for both water and steam, lay on a parabola with its vertex at 374° C. They thus appeared to confirm the usual theory.

On the other hand, when air-free water was used the results became more regular and reproducible to an unbelievable extent, and definite values at saturation could be obtained for both water and vapour. They are shown in fig. 4.10. It will be seen that they show the same effect in the critical region as is shown in fig. 4.9. The meniscus vanished at 374° C., but the enthalpies of liquid and vapour were not, as the simple theory requires, equal at this point. The enthalpies of both liquid and vapour at saturation could be measured up to 380° C., where they became equal; that is, at this point the latent heat* of vaporization became zero and the properties of liquid and vapour were identical. The results showed that at 374° C. the latent heat of vaporization was still 300 joules per gram.

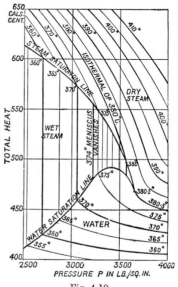

Fig. 4.10

Summarizing these results, we may say that according to the earlier simple view of critical phenomena it was supposed that at a definite temperature the meniscus between liquid and vapour disappears and that at this point, at which the surface tension vanishes, all the properties of liquid and vapour become identical. The experiments of Callendar show that in the case of water when the meniscus vanishes at 374° C. the properties of liquid and vapour are not identical, but that differences persist up to 380° C. where they do become identical. In the region between 374° and 380° C. very small traces of dissolved air cause disturbances which make reliable observations in this region impossible. All earlier experiments probably suffer from this defect, which also makes it impossible to obtain sharp and reproducible results for either liquid or vapour near saturation and thus produces rounding off of isotherms. The results of Callendar

---

* At constant temperature the difference between the enthalpy of the saturated vapour and that of the liquid under saturation pressure is equal to the latent heat of vaporization.

completely explain the earlier difficulty as to why it is possible to observe the vanishing of the meniscus with varying amounts of substance in a tube.

Similar results for other substances (carbon dioxide, ethane, ethylene) have been obtained by Maas and his co-workers.* In an extensive investigation with carefully prepared pure samples, they have shown that a heterogeneous mixture of vapour and liquid exists beyond the temperature at which the heterogeneity can be detected visually. In a series of experiments, the capsule containing the liquid under test was

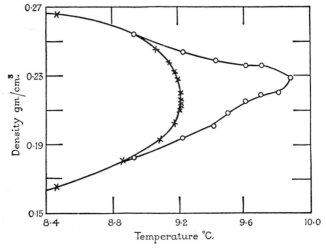

Fig. 4.11.—The coexistence curves of liquid and vapour ethylene. The crosses represent measurements made on a capsule shaken vigorously and give the points at which the visible meniscus disappears. The circles were determined in p-V-T experiments [after S. N. Naldrett and O. Maas, *Canadian Journ. Res.* B, Vol. 18, p. 119 (1940)].

rotated in a constant-temperature bath to get rid of temperature gradients in the sample, and it was shaken vigorously to promote mixing. In such samples, the temperature at which the meniscus disappeared was precisely reproducible. However the sample remained heterogeneous as it was heated above this temperature. Typical of the results is that for ethylene shown in fig. 4.11. The flat portion of the coexistence curve obtained in a bomb experiment indicates the temperature at which the meniscus disappears. At this temperature, the liquid and the vapour become completely miscible, but both phases exist above this temperature and, in the region enclosed by the two

* O. Maas and A. L. Geddes, *Phil. Trans.*, A, Vol. 236, p. 303 (1937); S. G. Mason. S. N. Naldrett and O. Maas, *Can. Journ. Res.*, B, Vol. 18, p. 103 (1940); S. N. Naldrett and O. Maas, *ibid.*, Vol. 18, p. 118 (1940); O. Maas, *Chem. Rev.*, Vol. 23, p. 17 (1938).

coexistence curves, there is a dispersion of liquid and vapour. The true critical temperature is indicated by the apex of the coexistence curve determined from p-V-T measurements. Maas concluded that the true critical temperature cannot be determined by a direct visual method and that it is always higher than the temperature at which the meniscus disappears.

EXAMPLES

1. Obtain the expressions for the critical parameters of a Van der Waals' gas without direct recourse to the calculus.

[Write Van der Waals' equation as a cubic in V. This generally has three roots; at the critical point these are all equal, to V_c, say. (Why?) Thus, at the critical point the Van der Waals' equation is equivalent to

$$(V - V_c)^3 = 0.$$

Comparison of the coefficients of the two equations gives relations (6) and (7) of this chapter.]

2. Show that, for a Van der Waals' gas, the departure, at the Boyle temperature, from perfect-gas behaviour is less than 0·01 per cent up to pressures equal to $0·27p_c$, and that, for a pressure equal to the critical pressure, the departure is not greater than 0·14 per cent.

3. The internal energy of a gram-molecule of a gas is written in the form

$$U = U_0 + U_i,$$

where U_0 is its internal energy in the perfect-gas condition and U_i is the energy arising from the mutual interactions between the gas molecules. Assuming that an expansion as far as the third power of p is required to represent the equation of state of the gas, show that, neglecting the variation of the virial coefficients with temperature,

$$U_i = -\tfrac{1}{2}Cp^2 - \tfrac{2}{3}Dp^3.$$

[See equation (27) of the Appendix, and H. Jones and A. R. Miller, *Proc. Roy. Soc.*, A, Vol. 194, p. 484 (1948).]

4. A gas at constant temperature is allowed to expand slowly so that its volume increases from V_1 to V_2. Calculate the amount of work done if the gas obeys Van der Waals' equation of state and also if it obeys Dieterici's equation of state.

Find the amount of work done when one gram-molecule of each of helium and oxygen is allowed to expand isothermally from standard pressure and temperature to twice its volume.

5. From the data given in Table I (p. 108), calculate the constants of Van der Waals' equation for hydrogen, oxygen, and helium.

6. Show that for a gas which satisfies Dieterici's equation of state the critical point is given in terms of the constants of the equation by

$$p_c = a/29·56b^2, \quad V_c = 2b, \quad T_c = a/4Rb.$$

[The locus of the maxima and minima of the isotherms is obtained by equating $(\partial p/\partial V)_T$ to zero. This gives a quadratic equation in V. At the maximum of this curve, that is, the critical point, the two roots of this equation are equal. The results given follow immediately.]

7. Find the constants of Dieterici's equation of state for hydrogen, oxygen, and helium.

CHAPTER V

The Production and Measurement of Low Temperatures

1. The production of very low temperatures was due originally to attempts to liquefy all the known gases. With liquid helium Kammerlingh Onnes reached temperatures lower than one degree above the absolute zero; and using adiabatic demagnetization, temperatures of a few millidegrees have been reached.

We shall deal in this chapter with the various methods that can be used to produce these low temperatures and with the methods of measuring them.

2. The Pictet or Cascade Process.

We have already seen that a gas cannot be liquefied until it is cooled below its critical temperature, but that once this temperature has been reached it is only necessary to apply sufficient pressure and the gas will liquefy.

In the Pictet process, which has been used by Dewar and by Onnes, the low temperature is reached step by step; on this account it is sometimes called the cascade process. We start with methyl chloride, which can be liquefied by compression at ordinary temperatures. The methyl chloride is allowed to evaporate, thus cooling itself—its boiling-point under normal pressure is −24° C.

At the temperatures that can be reached in this way ethylene— critical point +10° C.—can be easily liquefied. The cooled liquid methyl chloride is circulated round a compressor containing ethylene, which is in its turn liquefied. Ethylene boils under normal pressure at −103° C., and it remains liquid down to −169° C. Ethylene boiling under reduced pressure can be used to cool a compressor containing oxygen to such a temperature that the oxygen—critical point −118° C.—can be liquefied. Oxygen boiling under reduced pressure reaches a temperature low enough for the liquefaction of air at atmospheric pressure.

The cascade process cannot be carried further because no substance can be found which remains liquid down to the critical point of hydrogen, −240° C. For the liquefaction of hydrogen and helium the Linde process must be used.

3. The Linde Method—The Joule Effect and the Joule-Kelvin Effect.

We shall first consider the so-called Joule effect. This effect is due to the attractive forces which the molecules of a gas exert on one another. The result of these attractive forces is that, when the gas expands, the potential energy due to these forces is increased, and, if no heat is supplied from outside, the gas is cooled. Joule first attempted to detect this effect with the apparatus shown in fig. 5.1. Compressed gas was contained in the vessel A, which was connected by a stopcock C with the empty vessel B. The whole was contained in a water bath as shown. When the stopcock was opened the gas expanded so as to fill the two vessels, and in doing so did no external work. Applying the first law of thermodynamics, we see that, if there were any increase in the potential energy of the molecules, it would take place at the expense of the kinetic energy, so that the temperature would fall. Joule could detect no such fall of temperature in the water of the bath; and on this basis he propounded his law that the internal energy of a perfect gas is independent of its volume. Later experiments with Kelvin, in which the Joule effect *plus* the effect of departure from Boyle's law was measured, showed

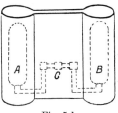

Fig. 5.1

that the reason Joule failed to detect any change in temperature in his earlier experiments was that his methods were not sufficiently sensitive. The heat capacity of the calorimeter and the water in the constant-temperature bath was about a thousand times that of the air, and this masked the change in temperature when the air was allowed to expand. The same difficulty has arisen in later experiments, and to test Joule's law it is necessary to proceed indirectly. Washburn * gave the theory of a calorimetric method of determining the internal energy of a gas as a function of the pressure. He made a detailed analysis of the various factors involved and the precision with which each measurement had to be carried out to obtain a result of the necessary accuracy.

Experiments on oxygen, air, and mixtures of oxygen and carbon dioxide were carried out by Rossini and Fransden.† A mass m gm. of gas was pumped into a bomb until the pressure was p atm. This was placed in a calorimeter of water, and when the whole system was at temperature $T°$ K. the gas was allowed to escape from the bomb to the atmosphere (pressure p_a) through a coil of tubing immersed in the water. During this process, electrical energy was supplied at such a rate that the temperature of the calorimeter and its contents was maintained

---

* E. W. Washburn, *Journ. Res. Bur. Stand.*, Washington, Vol. 9. p. 521 (1932).

† F. D. Rossini and M. Fransden, *Journ. Res. Bur. Stand.*. Washington. Vol. 9, p. 733 (1932).

sensibly constant at T. This electrical energy (corrected for the change in the internal energy of the material of the bomb as the pressure inside it falls), E joules, is equal to the work done by the escaping gas as it pushes back the atmosphere together with the change in the internal energy of the gas as its pressure falls. Thus

$$E = U_a - U_i + m(p\mathrm{v})_a - p_a V_b$$

where $(p\mathrm{v})_a$ is the product of the pressure and the volume of one gram of the gas at atmospheric pressure and V_b is the volume of the bomb. When $(E + p_a V_b)/m$ is plotted against the initial pressure, the ordinate at p_a is the value of $(p\mathrm{v})_a$ which at any temperature is a constant for the given gas. For different initial pressures in the bomb, the change $(U_a - U_i)/m$ in the internal energy of one gram of the gas can be plotted as a function of the initial pressure. For each gas and gas mixture at a particular temperature, Rossini and Fransden found that the internal energy depended linearly on the pressure. Thus, if $g(T)$ is the gradient of the straight-line graph obtained, we can write

$$(\partial U/\partial p)_T = g(T) \quad \text{and} \quad U = g(T) \cdot p + f(T)$$

where the constant of integration can be a function of T alone. This equation for the internal energy represents the results of the experiments of Rossini and Fransden. We have seen that in the limit as $p \to 0$, the behaviour of actual gases approaches that of an ideal gas, so that the preceding equation leads to the conclusion that the internal energy of an ideal gas depends only on the temperature.

The method used by Joule and Kelvin was to allow the gas to stream slowly through a porous plug of cotton-wool or some similar material, as indicated in fig. 5.2. The pressures on the two sides of the plug are p_1 and p_2, and, if the gas is streaming in the direction shown

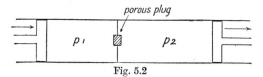

Fig. 5.2

by the arrows, p_1 is greater than p_2. We shall suppose that on the right-hand side of the plug there is an arrangement for supplying heat to the gas streaming out (or if necessary of absorbing heat from it), and that we adjust this arrangement so that the temperature of the stream of gas is exactly the same on the two sides of the plug. Further, we shall suppose that there is no loss of heat.

Let us consider what happens when a gas, which obeys the equation of Van der Waals, passes through the apparatus, the temperature being T. Let V_1 be the volume occupied by 1 gram-molecule at the pressure p_1, and V_2 the volume occupied by 1 gram-molecule at the pressure p_2.

The theory of the Joule-Kelvin effect is given in Chapter XIII, but we can usefully give now the following simple if not rigorous treatment. The net external work done *by the gas* per gram-molecule in passing through the apparatus is $(p_2V_2 - p_1V_1)$. The work done *by the gas* against the attractive forces of the molecules is equal to

$$\int_{V_1}^{V_2} \frac{a}{V^2} dV.$$

The total work done *by the gas* is therefore

$$p_2V_2 - p_1V_1 - \frac{a}{V_2} + \frac{a}{V_1}. \quad \ldots \ldots \quad (1)$$

For the temperature to be the same on the two sides, this work must not be done at the expense of the molecular translational energy. Thus, this is the amount of energy that must be supplied by the arrangement for that purpose.

To the first order of small quantities Van der Waals' equation may be written (see equation (18), Chapter IV)

$$pV = RT - \frac{ap}{RT} + bp.$$

Using this relation in equation (1) and also substituting the approximate value RT/p for V in the terms a/V_1 and a/V_2, we obtain, for the energy that must be supplied,

$$\left(\frac{2a}{RT} - b\right)(p_1 - p_2). \quad \ldots \ldots \quad (2)$$

Since $(p_1 - p_2)$ is necessarily positive, the heat supplied is positive if $2a/RT$ is greater than b; and, therefore, if no heat is supplied, there will be a cooling in this case.

The experiments of Joule and Kelvin showed that there is a cooling effect at ordinary temperatures in all gases except hydrogen, in which there is a slight rise of temperature. If the hydrogen is cooled below —80° C. before it passes through the apparatus, there is a cooling effect in it also. The temperature at which the sign of the Joule-Kelvin effect changes is called the *inversion temperature*, and if the gas obeys Van der Waals' equation it is given by T in the relation

$$2a/RT = b.$$

If ΔT is the cooling effect, the heat that must be supplied to restore the original temperature is $C_p\Delta T$ (see Chapter VI, Section 2). Equating this to the expression (2), we obtain ΔT. The Joule-Kelvin effect is dealt with in a more general and satisfactory way in Chapter XIII.

The Joule-Kelvin cooling effect was applied by Linde to the problem of liquefying gases as follows. Compressed gas passes along the inner copper tube as indicated diagrammatically in fig. 5.3. It then expands through the valve, and the expanded, and therefore cooled, gas passes back through the tube which surrounds that containing the incoming gas, which it cools, so that the gas arriving at the expansion valve gets progressively cooler and cooler. Finally a temperature is reached at which the gas is liquefied and it collects as shown. Actually the tubes are arranged in the form of a spiral, and the whole apparatus must be very well lagged. In liquefying hydrogen it must first be cooled below the inversion point (cf. example at end of this chapter).

The Linde method was used by Dewar, who first succeeded in liquefying hydrogen in 1898. It is also the principle used in the liquid hydrogen plant recently installed at the Clarendon Laboratory, Oxford.*

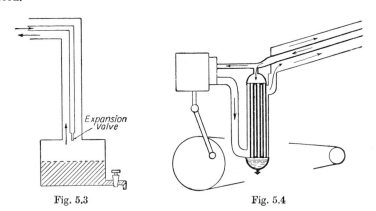

Fig. 5.3   Fig. 5.4

4. The Claude Method.

The cooling effect of a sudden expansion of gas was first observed by Clement and Désormes,† and the first expansion engine using this principle was built by Gorrie ‡ in the middle of the nineteenth century. The principle was applied to the liquefaction of gases by Claude,§ who used it to produce liquid air. In essence, refrigeration is achieved by the adiabatic expansion of a gas with the performance of external work. The final form of apparatus used by Claude is shown diagrammatically in fig. 5.4. The gas expands in the cylinder, doing work, which may be used to help drive the compressor. It is thus cooled, and, after

---

* Jones, Larsen and Simon, *Research*, Vol. 1, p. 420 (1948).

† Clement and Désormes, *Journ. Phys. Chem. Hist. Nat.*, Vol. 89, p. 321 (1819).

‡ Gorrie, United States of America Patent 8080, 6 May, 1851.

§ Claude, *C. R. Acad. Sci.*, Paris, Vol. 134, p. 1568 (1902).

being ejected from the cylinder, it passes back as shown and cools the oncoming gas. It also passes round the condenser shown, in which, as will be seen, the gas is at a high pressure and is consequently easily liquefied.   In developing this apparatus, Claude at first had great difficulty in finding a suitable lubricant, as at these low temperatures ordinary lubricants solidify. Once the gas has begun to liquefy, it acts as its own lubricant.

5. The Liquefaction of Helium.

In 1908 the last of the " permanent " gases, helium, was liquefied by Onnes * at Leiden. From the equation of state of helium Onnes saw that it was possible to cool it below its inversion point (50·5° K.) in hydrogen boiling under reduced pressure. The apparatus with which

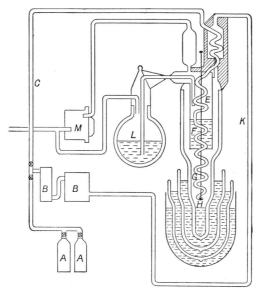

Fig. 5.5

he finally liquefied helium is illustrated diagrammatically in fig. 5.5. The apparatus is similar to but smaller than that used for the liquefaction of hydrogen.

Two hundred litres of pure helium (under atmospheric pressure) were contained in the cylinders A. The gas, compressed to 100 atmospheres in the compressor B, circulates through the tube CEFG, and

* Onnes, *Leiden. Comm.*, 108 (1908); Meissner, *Phys. Zeits.*, Vol. 29, p. 610 (1928); Kapitza, *Proc. Roy. Soc.*, A, Vol. ¹47, p. 189 (1934); for a simple helium liquefier, see Rollin, *Proc. Phys. Soc.*, Vol. 48, p. 18 (1936).

expands through the valve H into the vacuum flask. The expanded gas passes over the spiral G and cools the oncoming gas, thence it passes through the tube K to the compressor B and again through the cycle. The liquid helium collects in the vessel as shown. The spirals E and F are arranged in a vessel in which hydrogen boils at —258° C. The vapour pressure, and hence the boiling-point of the hydrogen, is regulated by the pump M. L contains liquid hydrogen.

In order to be able to see the liquid helium it is necessary that the vacuum vessel containing it and also the surrounding vessels should have a clear unsilvered strip. The vessel in which the liquid helium collects is surrounded by another vacuum vessel containing liquid hydrogen, and this in turn by a vacuum vessel containing liquid air. The flask containing the liquid hydrogen should not come into contact with the outside air, as the solid air makes the hydrogen cloudy.

The critical temperature of helium is —268° C., or only a fraction over five degrees above the absolute zero. With helium boiling under reduced pressure in a vacuum vessel surrounded by liquid helium, Onnes reached a temperature as low as 0·83° absolute.[*] More recently,[†] a temperature of 0·73° absolute has been reached by pumping off helium. Even at such temperatures helium does not solidify.

6. Helium Liquefiers.

The Kapitza [‡] and Collins [§] liquefiers make use of the cooling effect of the adiabatic expansion of a gas with the performance of external work.

In the Kapitza liquefier, helium at a pressure of 30 atmospheres is cooled by liquid nitrogen and then further cooled to 19° K. in a counter-flow heat exchanger. Part of the gas is passed through an expansion engine doing external work; this cools it to 10° K. It is then expanded through a valve, and the liquefied gas is collected in a container at the bottom of the liquefier. There is a gap of 0·05 mm. between the piston and the cylinder of the expansion engine, and the piston is made to move sufficiently rapidly for the loss of gas to be negligible. The gas itself acts as a lubricant as it escapes past the piston. A great advantage of the Kapitza liquefier is that it obviates the intermediate stage of hydrogen. The Kapitza liquefier in use at the Royal Society Mond Laboratory produces about 1·8 litres of liquid helium per hour, the first helium being produced after three-quarters of an hour.

[*] Onnes, *Leiden Comm.*, No. 159 (1922); *Trans. Faraday Soc.*, Vol. 18, p. 145 (1922).

[†] Lasarew and Esselson, *Journ. Phys. U.S.S.R.*, Vol. 5, p. 15 (1941).

[‡] Kapitza, *Nature*, Vol. 133, p. 708 (1934); *Proc. Roy. Soc.*, A, Vol. 147, p. 189 (1934); Cockroft, *Actes du 7e Congrès intern. du Froid*, Vol. 1, p. 373 (1936).

[§] Collins, *Rev. Sci. Instr.*, Vol. 18, p. 157 (1947).

In the Collins liquefier, which has been designed so that it can also serve as a cryostat in which to carry out experiments, the expansion cylinders and the counter-flow heat exchangers are suspended from a steel plate which serves as a cover for the cryostat. At the top, the temperature is substantially the same as atmospheric temperature, and at the bottom, it can be as low as the boiling-point of helium under the existing pressure. It also makes use of a close-fitting piston and cylinder. In the Collins liquefier, neither nitrogen nor hydrogen is used as an intermediate stage. The helium, or other gas to be liquefied, is fed directly to the expansion cylinders and, after passing through heat exchangers, is eventually passed through a Joule-Thomson expansion valve, to be collected in a receptacle at the bottom of the cryostat. The amount of helium processed by the expander is small at first because of the high initial temperature. When a steady state has been reached, the Collins liquefier produces between 0·7 and 1·3 litres of liquid helium per hour, or 2·0 litres per hour of liquid hydrogen or liquid nitrogen. Another idea for a liquefier which depends on the performance of external work by the gas was put forward by Simon * and was later developed by him and Long.† In it, an elastic metal bellows replaces the piston and cylinder of the Kapitza and Collins liquefiers. This bellows engine forms a gas-tight unit and it can be suspended in a high vacuum to give good thermal insulation. Such an engine operates with a high degree of reversibility. With a consumption of 1400 c.c. of liquid air an hour for pre-cooling it produced 600 c.c. of liquid helium per hour.

The Simon expansion method ‡ has also been used with considerable success to liquefy helium. The principle of the method is very simple. The gas to be liquefied is compressed isothermally in a container which is pre-cooled to the lowest temperature possible in a low-temperature bath. The container is then thermally isolated, and the compressed gas is allowed to expand slowly through a valve which consists of a pin-hole in a thin copper diaphragm. The method is feasible only with gases which have low boiling-points, because otherwise the heat capacity of the container is too great in comparison with that of the gas. For a steel container of 150 c.c. capacity, which is built to stand a pressure of 100 atmospheres, the ratio of the heat capacity of the container to that of the helium it contains varies by a factor of 5000 between room temperature and 10° K. This great difference arises because at a constant pressure a given container holds more gas at low temperatures than at

* F. E. Simon, Deutsches Reichspatent, Nr. 508233, 3 January 1928.

† H. M. Long and F. E. Simon, *Nature*, London, Vol. 172, p. 581 (1953); *Appl. Sc. Res.*, A, Vol. 14, p. 237 (1954).

‡ Simon, *Z. ges. Kaelte-Ind.*, Vol. 39, p. 89 (1932); *Phys. Zeits.*, Vol. 34, p. 232 (1932); *Actes du 7e Congrès intern. du Froid*, Vol. 1, p. 367 (1936); *Physica*, Vol. 4, p. 886 (1937); Simon and Ahlberg, *Z. Phys.*, Vol. 81, p. 817 (1933); Cooke, Rollin and Simon, *Rev. Sci. Instr.*, Vol. 10, p. 251 (1939); Scott and Cooke, *Phys. Rev.*, Vol. 72, p. 161 (1947).

high, and also because the specific heat of solid bodies approaches zero
rapidly as the temperature falls. Pickard and Simon * have given a
quantitative study of the performance of an expansion liquefier.

A helium liquefier which uses the Joule-Thomson expansion method
of liquefaction with hydrogen as an intermediate stage has been developed † at the cryogenic laboratory at the Ohio State University.
It has a very large capacity and delivers 7·5 litres of liquid helium per
hour when conditions are steady. It is similar to other small liquefiers,
making use of this principle, which had been developed earlier at
Columbus and at Oxford.‡

A helium liquefier which makes use of the cooling effect of the
Joule-Thomson expansion of a gas, and which uses hydrogen for an
intermediate stage, has been constructed at the Royal Society Mond
Laboratory to the design of Dr. J. Ashmead. This liquefier was designed to have an output of about 4 litres per hour, to be simple to
operate and to service, to have a short starting-time, and to be as safe as
possible. To meet these requirements, it was decided to use the Joule-
Thomson expansion of helium pre-cooled by liquid hydrogen. The dis-
advantages usually met with in helium liquefiers which use hydrogen as
an intermediate stage were overcome in the following way.§

The hydrogen and helium liquefiers were combined in the same
container. The liquid hydrogen produced is never decanted from the
machine, but serves only to cool the helium below its inversion temperature. The hydrogen circuit is completely closed; this ensures that
the explosion hazard is considerably reduced and that the hydrogen
needs to be purified only very infrequently. Furthermore, the combination of the two liquefiers in a single container makes it possible
to get a very good starting-time.

Hydrogen at 150 atmospheres and helium at 25 atmospheres are
cooled in an exchanger by returning hydrogen, returning helium and
liquid nitrogen under reduced pressure. The hydrogen is then expanded through a Joule-Thomson valve to a pressure of 1·5 atmospheres; this yields some liquid hydrogen. It passes into a container
in which it boils at a pressure of 6 cm. of mercury, giving a temperature of 14° K. The high-pressure helium is cooled by passage in
contact with the hydrogen containers and thus enters the final exchanger at 14° K. After passing through it, the helium is expanded
through a Joule-Thomson valve and some of it liquefies.

This liquefier has been in use since the summer of 1949. Liquid
hydrogen is produced 30 minutes after the machine has started, and

* Pickard and Simon, *Proc. Phys. Soc.*, Vol. 60, p. 405 (1948).

† Daunt and Johnston, *Rev. Sci. Inst.*, Vol. 20, p. 122 (1949).

‡ Daunt and Johnston, *Phys. Rev.*, Vol. 72, p. 161 (1947); Daunt and Mendelssohn
Journ. Sci. Inst., Vol. 25, p. 318 (1948).

§ Ashmead, *Proc. Phys. Soc.*, B, Vol. 63, p. 504 (1950).

after a further 40 minutes the liquefier has reached equilibrium and is yielding liquid helium. The consumption of liquid nitrogen is 8 Kg./hour and the output of liquid helium is 3·8 litres per hour. Operated as a hydrogen liquefier, it yields 5 litres per hour.

Practical details about the liquefaction of gases by various methods have been given by Wenner.* He examines the input and output temperatures and pressures to give the maximum yield in various liquefaction processes.

The Measurement of Low Temperatures

7. The International Scale and the Gas Scale from 0° to —182·97° C.

The temperature scale between 0° and —182·97° C. (Int. 1948) fixed by international agreement for legal purposes is defined as follows (Chapter I, Section 22). The temperature t is deduced from the resistance R_t of a standard platinum thermometer by means of the formula

$$R = R_0[1 + at + bt^2 + c(t - 100)t^3].$$

R_0 is the resistance of the thermometer at the ice point; the constants a and b are determined by calibration experiments at the steam and sulphur points, and the additional constant c is determined by calibration at the temperature of equilibrium between liquid and gaseous oxygen at the pressure of one standard atmosphere. This temperature is to be taken as —182·97° C. on the gas scale.† The platinum thermometer must fulfil the requirements set out in Chapter I, Section 23, and in addition R_t/R_0 must be less than 0·250 for $t = -183°$ C.

In the same way as in using a platinum resistance thermometer above the ice point, we introduce the platinum temperature defined by

$$R = R_0(1 + \alpha t_{pt}),$$

where α is determined by measurements at the ice and steam points. Thus, the relation between the platinum temperature and the temperature on the international scale is

$$t_{pt} = \{at + bt^2 + ct^3(t - 100)\}/(a + 100b).$$

This leads to the difference formula

$$t - t_{pt} = t(t - 100)10^{-4}\delta + t^3(t - 100)10^{-8}\beta, \quad \cdot \ \cdot \ \cdot \quad (3)$$

where δ is given by the same formula as in Chapter I, Section 23, and

$$\beta = - 10^8 c/(a + 100b).$$

The procedure, again, is to calculate the platinum temperature and to use its value in the difference formula to obtain the correction by a method of successive approximations.

* R. R. Wenner, *Thermochemical Calculations*, McGraw-Hill Book Co. Inc., New York (1941), Chapter XVI.

† If the pressure p mm. of mercury differs from one standard atmosphere, the temperature t_p is given by

$$t_p = -182 \cdot 970 + 1 \cdot 254 \times 10^{-2}(p - 760) + 6 \cdot 44 \times 10^{-6}(p - 760)^2 + 5 \cdot 01 \times 10^{-9}(p - 760)^3.$$

This is the scale that is accepted for legal purposes, but it must be realized that the object of the specifications is to reproduce the gas scale as accurately as our present knowledge permits. Heuse and Otto,* and later workers, have carried out a very accurate series of experiments to test how closely the international scale agrees with the gas scale. They placed a helium gas thermometer side by side with standard platinum thermometers (from which the legal temperature was obtained) in baths maintained at the temperature of equilibrium between oxygen vapour and liquid oxygen at a pressure of one atmosphere, at the temperature of equilibrium between solid carbon dioxide and carbon dioxide vapour at a pressure of one atmosphere, and at the temperature of freezing mercury. In addition the temperature of equilibrium between liquid hydrogen and hydrogen vapour at a pressure of one atmosphere was determined on the gas scale. The results were corrected for the departure of helium from the ideal gas (see Chapter I, Section 14), and, in addition to testing the agreement between the gas scale and the international scale, the experiments give a series of reliable fixed points which can be used for calibrating any given thermometer. The results are given in Table I.†

TABLE I

Fixed point	Gas scale temperature	$t_{gas} - t_{legal}$
Freezing-point mercury	−38·832 C.	+0·033
Carbon dioxide point ..	−78·483	+0·046
Oxygen point	−182·962	+0·008
Hydrogen point ..	−252·780	—

8. The Measurement of Temperatures down to −190° C.

In practice the most accurate method of measuring temperatures down to −190° C. is to use a platinum thermometer in the way described in the previous section. If the constants of the thermometer cannot conveniently be determined by calibration at the steam and sulphur points, results which are sufficiently accurate for most purposes will be obtained if the thermometer is calibrated at the ice point, the freezing-point of mercury, the carbon dioxide point, and the oxygen point.

* Heuse and Otto, *Ann. d. Physik*, Vol. 9, p. 486 (1931); Keesom and Dammers, *Physica*, Vol. 2, p. 1080 (1935); Yost, Garner, Osborne, Rubin and Russel, *Journ. Amer. Chem. Soc.*, Vol. 63, p. 3488 (1941).

† The constant-temperature bath at the hydrogen point was a closed Dewar flask containing liquid hydrogen. The temperature of boiling was controlled by regulating the pressure. The pressure at which liquid hydrogen and hydrogen vapour were in equilibrium at the temperature of the bath was determined with a vapour pressure thermometer containing *pure* hydrogen (see Chapter VIII, Section 2). At the oxygen point a similar arrangement was used with oxygen instead of hydrogen. At the carbon dioxide point the bath was of petrol and ether cooled with liquid air and the vapour pressure thermometer contained pure carbon dioxide. For the melting-point of mercury a mass of 3·5 kg. mercury contained in a double-walled glass vessel (with air between the walls) was placed in a thermostat which was about five degrees below the freezing-point of mercury. The freezing took place so slowly that the temperature was constant to within a few thousandths of a degree for over an hour.

Vapour pressure thermometers are very convenient for use in this range of temperatures, and a considerable number of substances whose boiling-points lie between $+10°$ and $-180°$ C. are available.* The method of measuring the vapour pressures is dealt with in Chapter VIII, Section 2.

Iron-constantan or copper-constantan thermocouples can conveniently be used in this range.†

9. Temperatures between 14° and 80° K.

Henning ‡ has measured the variation of vapour pressure of nitrogen between $60°$ and $80°$ K., and of hydrogen between $14°$ and $20°$ K.§ Within these two ranges vapour pressure thermometers of nitrogen and hydrogen respectively can therefore be used. Justi ‖ and others have established the triple point of oxygen $54.24°$ and the triple point of nitrogen $63.09°$ K. as fixed points.

Onnes ¶ has shown that it is better to use a resistance thermometer of lead than one of platinum. The following procedure is recommended by Nernst.** From the measurements of Onnes, who measured the resistance of a particular sample of lead wire—which we shall, for convenience, call the standard lead wire —at various temperatures on the gas scale, Nernst has drawn up the following table giving the value of r_t or R_t/R_0 for the standard wire at various gas scale temperatures.

TABLE II—RESISTANCE OF LEAD ††

Temperature	r_t	Temperature	r_t
°C.		°C.	
-259	0·01237	-228	0·12678
-257	0·01760	-223	0·14637
-255	0·02335	-218	0·16576
-253	0·02960	-213	0·18496
-251	0·03637	-208	0·20392
-249	0·04362	-203	0·22274
-247	0·05120	-198	0·24142
-245	0·05901	-193	0·26005
-243	0·06694	-188	0·27862
-238	0·08692	-183	0·29713
-233	0·10693	0	1·00000

* See Henning and Stock, *Zeits. f. Physik*, Vol. 4, p. 226 (1921); Henning and Heuse, *Zeits. f. Physik*, Vol. 23, p. 113 (1924).

† Giauque, Buffington, and Schultze, *Journ. Amer. Chem. Soc.*, Vol. 49, pp. 2343, 2367 (1927).

‡ Henning, *Zeits. f. Physik*, Vol. 40, p. 784 (1927); Henning and Otto, *Phys. Zeits.*, Vol. 37, p. 633 (1936).

§ The constant-temperature baths were obtained by using nitrogen and hydrogen boiling under reduced pressure maintained by powerful pumps.

‖ Justi, *Ann. d. Physik*, Vol. 10, p. 983 (1931).

¶ Onnes, *Leiden Comm.*, No. 99 (1907). See; however, Henning and Otto, *Phys. Zeits.*, Vol. 37, pp. 601, 639 (1936).

** Nernst, *Grundlagen des neuen Wärmesatzes*, 2nd edition, p. 31.

†† The Leiden scale on which the above measurements are based is a few hundredths of a degree higher than the Reichsanstalt scale of Henning (see Henning and Heuse, *Zeits. f. Physik*, Vol. 23, pp. 106, 116 (1924)).

Further, Nernst has shown that, if r_t' is the corresponding quantity for another lead wire, the following relation holds:

$$r_t' = \frac{r_t - \alpha}{1 - \alpha}, \quad \cdots \cdots \cdots \quad (4)$$

where α is a constant for the new sample of lead wire. This relation is sometimes for convenience referred to as the α rule. The value of α may be determined by measuring the resistance of the wire under consideration at $0°$ C. and at one other temperature, say the boiling-point of oxygen or of hydrogen. Once α is known we can convert the measured values of r_t' into the values of r_t that would be obtained using the standard wire. These can be converted into temperatures, using Table II.

Thermocouples of copper-constantan or iron-constantan can be used in this region, but couples of gold-silver or of platinum-silver are more sensitive.*

10. Temperatures between 5° and 14° K.

Between 5° and 14° K. no fixed points are available and these temperatures can only be measured satisfactorily by means of a helium gas thermometer or some resistance thermometer or thermocouple that has been directly compared with a helium gas thermometer. Tin resistance thermometers can be used in this temperature range. It is necessary to standardize the readings by taking measurements at a few points in the hydrogen (14 to 20° K.) and helium (below 5° K.) ranges. The advantage of tin is that it can be obtained very pure.

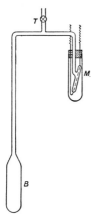

11. Temperatures below 5° K.

Keesom and his co-workers † have determined the vapour pressure of helium between 4·899° and 0·844° K., so that we have a continuous series of fixed points in this range.

The constant-temperature bath was of liquid helium boiling under various reduced pressures produced by very fast condensation pumps. The vapour pressure of the helium was measured on a McLeod gauge and the measurements were corrected for thermo-molecular pressure (see Chapter III, Section 23).

Fig. 5.6

The temperature of the bath was measured by means of helium gas thermometers with the helium at a low pressure. The arrangement of the gas thermometers is shown in fig. 5.6. The bulb B was connected

---

* See Onnes and Crommelin, *Leiden Comm.*, Nos. 95a and 95f; see also Nernst, *Grundlagen neuen Wärmesatzes*, 2nd edition, pp. 37–38; Giauque, Buffington, and Schultze, *Journ. Amer. Chem. Soc.*, Vol. 49, pp. 2343, 2367 (1927).

† W. H. Keesom, Sophus Weber, and Nøgaard, *Leiden Comm.*, No. 202b (1929); W. H. Keesom, Sophus Weber, and G. Schmidt, *Leiden Comm.*, No. 202c (1929); W. H. Keesom, *Leiden Comm. Supp.*, No. 71d (1932); G. Schmidt and W. H. Keesom, *Leiden Comm.*, No. 250a (1937); *Physica*, Vol. 4, p. 971 (1937); J. Kistemaker and W. H. Keesom, *ibid.*, Vol. 12, p. 227 (1946); J. Kistemaker, *ibid.*, Vol. 12, p. 272 (1946).

by a capillary tube to the calibrated hot-wire manometer M which was kept in a mixture of ice and distilled water, and was used to measure the pressure. The tap T was closed except for admitting the helium. The effect of the deviation of helium from the ideal gas was shown by calculation to be negligible at the pressures used. The calculation was carried out using values of the second virial coefficient determined by measuring the isotherms of helium at these temperatures.

The results which were obtained were represented by formulæ which gave the vapour pressure as a function of temperature. The formulæ which are used are based on the Kirchhoff relation for the pressure of the vapour in equilibrium with the liquid (see Chapter VIII, Section 9). For temperatures between 2·19° K. and the boiling-point, the following formula was used:

$$\log_{10} p = -\frac{3·024}{T} + 2·208 \log_{10} T + 1·217, \quad . \quad . \quad (5)$$

where p cm. of mercury at the ice point is the vapour pressure. For temperatures below 2·19° K., Keesom * later derived a formula more nearly corresponding to the theoretical form. It could therefore be extrapolated with greater confidence to temperatures lower than those which had been measured. The constant term was made equal to the theoretical value of the chemical constant (see Chapter VIII). The fourth-power term was introduced to correspond to the variation of the specific heat of liquid helium II (see Section 13 below), and the coefficients were calculated to give the best agreement with the experimental values. The formula which was obtained is

$$\log_{10} p = -\frac{3·018}{T} + 2·484 \log_{10} T - 0·00297 T^4 + 1·197. \quad (6)$$

Equations (5) and (6) together form the 1932 temperature scale.

By 1937, experience of low-pressure measurements and knowledge of the laws of rarefied gases had increased, and more accurate values of the thermomolecular pressure difference were known for helium. Schmidt and Keesom † undertook a new determination of the vapour pressure of helium in order to establish the temperature scale in the helium range more accurately. The results were represented as differences from the 1932 scale. In 1939, Keesom and Lignac ‡ published two formulæ to represent the 1937 scale above 2·19° K. These formulæ with the table of differences from the 1932 scale below 2·19° K. together

* W. H. Keesom, *Leiden Comm.*, No. 219a (1932).
† G. Schmidt and W. H. Keesom, *Leiden Comm.*, No. 250c (1937); *Physica*, Vol. 4, p. 971 (1937).
‡ W. H. Keesom and Lignac, *Leiden Comm. Supp.*, No. 90c (1939).

constitute the 1937 temperature scale. The accuracy of the measurements on which the 1937 scale is based probably far exceeds that of any of the earlier measurements. These formulæ are

$$\log_{10} p = -\frac{4{\cdot}7921}{T} + 0{\cdot}00783T + 0{\cdot}017601T^2 + 2{\cdot}6730,$$

$$\log_{10} p = -\frac{4{\cdot}7948}{T} + 0{\cdot}0343 \log_{10} T + 0{\cdot}018024T^2 + 2{\cdot}6775.$$

Subsequently, Lignac also derived a formula (unpublished) to represent the 1937 measurements in the temperature range between $1{\cdot}6°$ and $2{\cdot}19°$ K. It is

$$\log_{10} p = -\frac{3{\cdot}1189}{T} + 2{\cdot}5 \log_{10} T - 5{\cdot}981 \cdot 10^{-5}T^8 + 1{\cdot}1958.$$

Below $1{\cdot}6°$ K., the 1937 scale depended on only three points in the neighbourhood of $1{\cdot}2°$ K. The calibration of paramagnetic salts against the vapour pressure suggested that the 1937 scale was several hundredths of a degree too low at $1°$ K. Furthermore, it was shown * that the 1937 scale was thermodynamically inconsistent. Different values were obtained for the variation with temperature of the latent heat of vaporization of helium according as it was calculated (a) by integrating the equation for dL/dT using the specific heat data of Keesom and Keesom † and of Pickard and Simon,‡ or (b) using the values of the entropy calculated by Kaischew and Simon.§ Magnetic measurements had shown that the 1937 scale was substantially correct at $1{\cdot}6°$ K. Bleaney and Simon therefore adjusted the two latent-heat curves to fit at this temperature, and then used the values of the latent heat obtained from the integration of dL/dT to calculate the vapour pressures for temperatures below $1{\cdot}6°$ K. In this way they obtained the following formula for temperatures below $1{\cdot}6°$ K.:

$$\log_{10} p = -\frac{3{\cdot}117}{T} + 2{\cdot}5 \log_{10} T + 1{\cdot}196 + \Delta, \qquad . \quad (7)$$

in which p cm. of mercury at the ice point is the pressure of the vapour in equilibrium with the liquid. The appropriate theoretical values have been used for the constants in the second and third terms in this expression. The quantity Δ is a small correction term; its value is

* Bleaney and Simon, *Trans. Faraday Soc.*, Vol. 35, p. 1205 (1939).

† W. H. Keesom and A. P. Keesom, *Physica*, Vol. 2, p. 557 (1935).

‡ Pickard and Simon, Abstracts of papers communicated to the Royal Society, S 21 (1939).

§ Kaischew and Simon, *Nature*, Vol. 133, p. 460 (1934).

given by the graph which is reproduced in fig. 5.7. This scale was verified experimentally using a magnetic thermometer.*

More recently, new measurements of the vapour pressure have been made by Kistemaker † for temperatures below the boiling-point. These measurements suggested that further small corrections were required to the 1937 scale.

There is only one set of measurements ‡ of the vapour pressure at temperatures between the boiling and critical temperatures. These results were later recalculated § by applying a correction for the

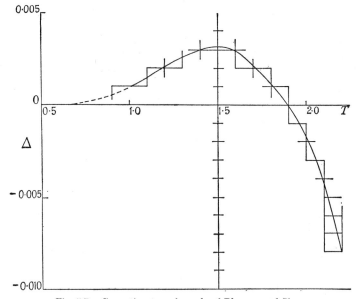

Fig. 5.7.—Correction term formula of Bleaney and Simon

thermomolecular pressure difference. An interpolation formula has been fitted to these results so that it joins smoothly to the results for temperatures below the boiling-point. The interpolation formula gives T as a quadratic function of p:

$$T = 2 \cdot 967 + 1 \cdot 905 \, . \, 10^{-2} p - 3 \cdot 521 \, . \, 10^{-5} p^2. \quad . \quad . \quad (8)$$

It should be noted, however, that there are apparent discrepancies, amounting to several hundredths of a degree, in the experimental

* B. Bleaney and R. A. Hull, *Proc. Roy. Soc.*, A, Vol. 178, p. 74 (1941).

† Kistemaker, *Physica*, Vol. 12, p. 272 (1946).

‡ Onnes, *Leiden Comm.*, No. 124b (1911).

§ Onnes and Weber, *ibid.*, No. 147b (1915).

values in this region, and the interpolation formula cannot be more reliable than the experimental data on which it is based.

The temperature scale in the helium range was discussed at a conference held at the Van der Waals Laboratorium, Amsterdam, in 1948. As a result of this conference, a temperature scale in terms of the equilibrium vapour pressure of the helium isotope of mass 4 was agreed upon for use in cryogenic laboratories. It is based on the Bleaney and Simon formula, equation (7), for temperatures below 1·6° K.; the Leiden 1937 scale formulæ for temperatures from 1·6 to 2·19° K. and from 2·19° K. to the boiling-point (4·2° K.); the interpolation formula, equation (8), for temperatures between the boiling-point and critical point. This temperature scale is given in the form of a detailed table of values of temperature and vapour pressure. In the table, the vapour pressure is given in millimetres of mercury at 20° C. A few values of temperature and pressure are reproduced from it in Table III.

TABLE III.—VAPOUR PRESSURE OF HELIUM (ISOTOPE OF MASS 4)
AT DIFFERENT TEMPERATURES

(The pressure is given as millimetres of mercury at 20° C.)

T° K.	p	T° K.	p
0·10	$3\cdot4 \times 10^{-32}$	2·50	76·92
0·20	$7\cdot3 \times 10^{-16}$	3·00	181·2
0·50	$1\cdot6 \times 10^{-5}$	3·50	353·4
0·726 *	$3\cdot6 \times 10^{-3}$	4·00	615·6
1·00	0·121	4·212 ‡	760
1·50	3·593	4·50	980·0
2·00	23·45	5·00	1432
2·186 †	38·36	5·20 §	1720

* Lowest temperature reached by pumping from a bath of helium 4.
† Lambda point.   ‡ Boiling-point.   § Critical point.

In experiments on the polarization of nuclei in manganese ammonium sulphate, irregularities were observed ‖ in the variation of susceptibility with temperature. On further investigation it was shown that these irregularities were to be attributed to errors in the temperature scale, amounting to 12 millidegrees at the lambda point. These results are substantially in agreement with Kistemaker's measurements of the vapour pressure of helium between 1·6° K. and the lambda point

‖ R. A. Erickson and L. D. Roberts, *Phys. Rev.*, Vol. 93, p. 957 (1954).

and also indicate that there are small errors in the 1948 scale above the lambda point.

Two modifications * of the 1948 scale have been proposed, one by J. R. Clement and the other by H. van Dijk and M. Durieux. The former is based on gas-thermometer measurements, using carbon resistors and paramagnetic salts as interpolation thermometers. Values of the latent heat and of the entropy calculated from this scale fall within the limits of error of the measurements on which the scale of van Dijk and Durieux is based. It is therefore possible to re-write Clement's scale in thermodynamic form. These differences were examined in 1958 by the Comité Consultatif de Thermométrie of the Comité International des Poid et Mesures. A practical scale in terms of the vapour pressure of helium (isotope 4) was agreed upon.† It is called the 1958 scale and designated as T_{58}.

In addition to helium gas and vapour-pressure thermometers, resistance thermometers can be used at liquid helium temperatures. Keesom and Van den Ende ‡ have tried various alloys and have found unannealed phosphor bronze the most suitable. Constantan and manganin were used formerly, but they show ice point changes and also marked resistance changes in a comparatively small magnetic field. Unannealed phosphor bronze is free from these defects, and gives a reproducible and reasonably linear variation of resistance with temperature between 0·994° and 4·218°K. Any given resistance thermometer must be calibrated by means of a helium vapour pressure thermometer.

12. Constant-temperature Baths.

References to constant-temperature baths produced by boiling suitable substances under fixed pressures have been made in the preceding sections.

Between 0° C. and liquid air temperatures baths of suitable organic liquids cooled by liquid air and automatically controlled can be constructed.§

Ruhemann ‖ has devised a method for obtaining a constant-temperature enclosure which is similar in principle to that used with air by Griffiths and Griffiths (see Chapter VII, Section 4). Using the Joule-Kelvin effect in hydrogen, temperatures between those of liquid air and liquid hydrogen can be produced and maintained. For lower temperatures liquid hydrogen must be used to precool helium and, provided sufficient compressed helium is available, this is the

---

* W. E. Keller, *Nature*, London, Vol. 178, p. 883 (1956).

† H. van Dijk, M. Durieux, J. R. Clement, and J. K. Logan, *Physica*, Supplement to Vol. 24, p. 129 (1958).

‡ Keesom and Van den Ende, *Leiden Comm.*, No. 203c (1929).

§ For details, see Egerton and Ubbelohde, *Trans. Faraday Soc.*, Vol. 26, p. 236 (1930); MacGillivray and Swallow, *Journ. Sci. Inst.*, Vol. 7, p. 257 (1930); Scott and Brickwedde, *B. of Stand. J. of Research*, Vol. 6, p. 401 (1931). The last-named authors give suitable non-inflammable liquids where these are available.

‖ Ruhemann, *Zeits. f. Physik*, Vol. 65, p. 67 (1930).

most convenient method to use between liquid hydrogen temperatures and 4° K. With suitable arrangements temperatures down to 1° K. can be produced.

If only comparatively small quantities of helium at only a few atmospheres pressure are available, the method discovered by Simon and developed by Mendelssohn * can be used. In this method the cooling process is the desorption of helium adsorbed on charcoal at liquid hydrogen temperatures. A similar method has also been used by Justi † at higher temperatures, where hydrogen adsorbed on charcoal at liquid nitrogen temperatures is desorbed. By controlling the rate of desorption he has been able to obtain constant-temperature enclosures down to 50° K. He has also obtained enclosures up to 112° K. by controlling the rate of adsorption of hydrogen on cooled degassed charcoal.

The Equilibrium between Different States of Helium and Hydrogen at Low Temperatures

13. The Solidification of Helium.

By boiling helium under reduced pressure Onnes showed that it could be cooled to 0·83° K. but that even at this low temperature it did not solidify. Keesom ‡ succeeded in solidifying helium by working at high pressures.

The helium was compressed in a narrow brass tube which formed a communication between two German silver tubes. The brass tube and part of the two German silver tubes were in a bath of liquid helium. Preliminary observations showed that at a pressure of 130 atmospheres (temperature uncertain) the tube system appeared to be blocked, and when the pressure was diminished by one or two atmospheres it was open again. By diminishing the temperature to 3·2° K. the same phenomena were observed at 86 atmospheres pressure. This method had been used previously by Onnes and von Gulik § in preliminary measurements on the solidification curve of hydrogen. By applying the method systematically the solidification curve of helium was traced from 1·1 to 4·2° K.

These observations were confirmed by compressing helium in a glass tube provided with a magnetic stirrer. When the helium solidified the stirrer could be seen to stick. In one experiment part of the helium was liquid and part solid, and the solid part could be hammered by the stirrer which was in the liquid part. No limiting surface between the solid and liquid could be seen. It is therefore probable that the refractive index of the solid, which is homogeneous and transparent, differs very little from that of the liquid.

In more recent experiments, Simon and Swenson ‖ have made measurements almost to 1° K. The extrapolated melting pressure at absolute zero is 25·00 ± 0·01 atmospheres. They find that the slope of the melting curve is continuous throughout, although it changes very rapidly in the neighbourhood of the lambda point (see Section 14 below). There is a molar volume difference of about 2 c.c. right down

* Mendelssohn, *Zeits. f. Physik*, Vol. 73, p. 482 (1931).

† Justi, *Ann. d. Physik*, Vol. 9, p. 570 (1931).

‡ Keesom, *Leiden Comm.*, No. 184b (1926); see also W. H. Keesom and A. P. Keesom, *ibid.*, No. 224e (1933).

§ Onnes and von Gulik, *Leiden Comm.*, No. 184a (1926).

‖ Simon and Swenson, *Nature*, Vol. 165, p. 829 (1950).

to the absolute zero. Further, the heat of melting calculated from the Clausius-Clapeyron equation approaches zero at the absolute zero, so that there the internal energy of the liquid is less than that of the solid as predicted by Simon.*

The results obtained are shown by the curve in fig. 5.8, from which the very rapid change in the slope at the lambda point is evident. At the lowest temperatures reached the curve is almost parallel to the temperature axis. This indicates that helium has no solid-liquid-gas triple point (see Chapter XVI, Section 12). It should be noted that on the scale of fig. 5.8 the vapour-pressure curve of the liquid would hardly depart appreciably from the temperature axis.

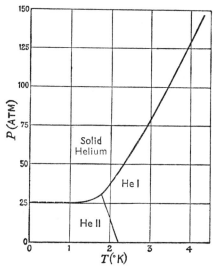

Fig. 5.8.—Liquid-solid equilibrium of helium
(Simon and Swenson)

For temperatures between $1.0°$ K. and $1.4°$ K., the measured melting pressure P atmospheres can be represented by an equation

$$P = 25.00 + 0.053T^8.$$

For temperatures above about $2.5°$ K., the melting pressure varies only as $T^{1.55}$ (see Section 15 below); the high power of T in the equation valid at lower temperatures indicates how rapid is the change of gradient in the neighbourhood of the lambda point. The fact that the melting pressure at the lowest temperatures depends on temperature as a very high power of T is of great theoretical importance in connexion with the third law of thermodynamics. Its theoretical significance is considered in Chapter XIX.

* Simon, *Nature*, Vol. 133, p. 529 (1934).

14. Two States of Liquid Helium.

The rapid change in slope of the curve showing the equilibrium between solid and liquid helium has since been shown to be associated with the existence of two modifications of liquid helium.*

Early experiments of Onnes and his co-workers indicated the possibility of anomalous behaviour in density, surface tension, latent heat of vaporization, and the specific heat of liquid helium at a temperature of about 2·2° K. Experiments by Keesom and Wolfke on the dielectric constant indicated a similar effect.

The existence at this temperature of a transition point between two states of liquid helium was definitely established by taking a cooling curve with a constantan resistance thermometer when the temperature of the helium was steadily lowered by slowly reducing the pressure above it. At 2·2° K. there was a definite small horizontal portion in the otherwise regular temperature-time curve.

The observations were later extended by Keesom and Clusius by taking ordinary cooling curves with helium at various pressures contained in a vessel surrounded by a bath of liquid helium at a temperature lower than the transformation point. In this way the slanting straight line was obtained (fig. 5.8) showing the relation between the pressure and the temperature at which the two types of liquid helium are in equilibrium. It will be seen that it meets the melting curve of solid helium at the point at which the slope of the latter curve changes. This point is a triple point at which liquid helium I, liquid helium II, and solid helium are in equilibrium. This transformation is considered in Chapter XVII, Section 1.†

15. The Extension of the Melting Curves of Helium and Hydrogen to High Pressure.

Simon and his colleagues ‡ have used the blocked-tube method for investigating the melting-points of condensed gases up to pressures of about 8000 atmospheres and have obtained very interesting results. At 7200 kg. cm.⁻² they obtained solid helium at 50° K., which is about ten times the critical temperature. From about 2·5° K. to the highest temperatures reached, the melting-pressure curve can be represented within the accuracy of the experimental data (± 100 atmospheres) by an equation.

$$\frac{p}{16 \cdot 45} = \left(\frac{T}{0 \cdot 992}\right)^{1 \cdot 5544} - 1,$$

—16·45 atmospheres being the internal pressure.

* See Keesom and Clusius, *Leiden Comm.*, No. 216b, where references are given to the earlier work.

† For a summary of the properties of liquid helium II, see J. F. Allen and H. Jones, *Nature*, Vol. 143, p. 227 (1939); H. Jones, *Reports on Progress in Physics*, Vol. 6, p. 280 (1939); W. H. Keesom, *Helium*, Elsevier, Amsterdam (1942), Chapters IV and VI; see also Chapter XVII, Section 2.

‡ Simon, Ruhemann, and Edwards, *Zeits. f. phys. Chem.*, B, Vol. 6, pp. 62, 331 (1929); Vol. 7, p. 86 (1930); Holland, Huggill, Jones and Simon, *Nature*, Vol. 165, p. 147 (1950); F. A. Holland, J. A. W. Huggill, and G. O. Jones, *Proc. Roy. Soc. A*, Vol. 207, p. 268 (1951); see also R. L. Mills and E. R. Grilly, *Phys. Rev.*, Vol. 99, p. 480 (1955); Vol. 101, p. 1246 (1956).

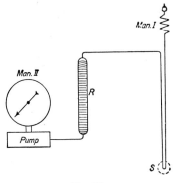

Fig. 5.9

The method used is illustrated in fig. 5.9. By means of subsidiary connexions which are not shown in the figure the gas at a pressure of about 80 atmospheres was introduced into the tube R. A fine steel capillary connected R to the manometer I and the gas was compressed into this capillary by pumping mercury

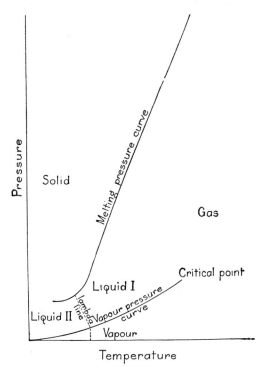

Fig. 5.10.—Phase diagram of helium

into R. The manometer II which measured the pressure in R was of the standard type. The manometer I was constructed by winding the steel capillary tube into a spiral and attaching a small mirror to the straight part at the closed end of the tube. A beam of light was reflected on to a scale from the mirror which, owing to the elastic deformation of the tube, turned when the pressure changed. This instrument was calibrated by comparison with manometer II.

The point S was kept at the temperature to be investigated and the helium was slowly compressed. The two manometers moved together until a certain pressure was reached at which the tube blocked so that manometer I remained steady although the pressure in manometer II was raised considerably higher. This pressure was the melting pressure at the temperature of S.

In addition to helium the method has been applied to hydrogen, in which case the equilibrium temperature and pressure at which the solid breaks down have been traced up to 75° K. or 42 deg. above the critical temperature, and to neon, in which case the existence of the solid has been demonstrated up to 65° K. or 21 deg. above the critical temperature. In view of these results it is interesting to draw pressure temperature diagrams showing the equilibria.

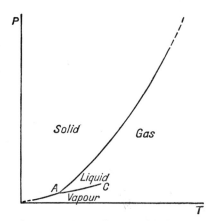

Fig. 5.11.—Phase diagram of hydrogen

The diagram (not drawn to scale) for helium is shown in fig. 5.10. At temperatures below the critical point the solid melts to form a liquid, while at temperatures above the critical point it melts to form a gas. It is important to realize that there is no discontinuity in the melting curve at the critical temperature, and no way of telling whether the state of the melted solid is liquid or gaseous apart from gradually diminishing the pressure at constant temperature and seeing if at any stage there is a separation into two phases.

The diagram (not drawn to scale) for hydrogen is shown in fig. 5.11. At temperatures below the triple point A the solid passes directly to the vapour phase (sublimes), and at temperatures above the critical point C it passes directly to the gas phase (melts to form a gas). The curve showing the latter equilibrium is continuous with the ordinary melting curve, but there is a sharp break in its gradient at A when we pass from the sublimation curve to the ordinary melting curve.

It may be mentioned here that no evidence whatever was found for the existence of a critical temperature for the melting process solid to fluid. Simon estimates that in the absence of a solid-fluid critical temperature, helium would solidify at room temperature under a pressure of 100,000 atmospheres.

Cooling by Adiabatic Demagnetization *

16. Theory of the Method.

The general principle of obtaining low temperatures involves first, a reversible process, by which heat is evolved when it is carried out in one direction, and secondly, a device for establishing or breaking thermal contact with a heat container at a given temperature T_1. Temperatures less than T_1 can then be obtained in the following way.

Start with the system in thermal contact with the heat container at T_1 and let the process be carried out in the direction in which heat is evolved. The heat is carried away to the heat container. Now break the thermal contact, and carry out the process in the reverse direction. A state of lower temperature is thereby obtained. Simon's expansion liquefier (Section 6) is one example of the use of this principle. Cooling by adiabatic demagnetization is another. It makes use of the fact that when a thermally isolated paramagnetic substance is demagnetized its temperature falls. Langevin † pointed out that changes in the magnetization of paramagnetic substances must be generally accompanied by reversible temperature changes. It will be seen below, equation (19), that for an appreciable effect it is necessary that the heat capacity of the salt be small and the temperature-dependence of the magnetic moment be large. As Langevin pointed out, neither of these conditions holds at ambient temperatures, and the effect is therefore small. The discovery by Woltjer and Onnes that the behaviour of some paramagnetic salts could be described by Langevin's elementary theory of paramagnetism down to helium temperatures opened up a new field of investigation, for it was recognized that the conditions for appreciable magneto-caloric effects are fulfilled at these temperatures. This led Debye and Giauque ‡ independently to suggest that very low temperatures might be produced by the adiabatic demagnetization of paramagnetic salts previously cooled to liquid helium temperatures. At this time, the susceptibility of gadolinium sulphate had been determined

---

* These sections should be omitted until after the chapters on thermodynamics have been read. I am indebted to Dr. C. G. B. Garrett for advising me on the revision of Sections 16 to 19 below.

† P. Langevin, *Ann. Chim. Phys.*, Vol. 5, p. 70 (1905).

‡ Debye, *Ann. d. Physik*, Vol. 81, p. 1154 (1926); Giauque, *Journ. Amer. Chem. Soc.*, Vol. 49, pp. 1864, 1870 (1927).

fairly accurately,* and the heat developed could be derived by using a simple thermodynamical argument. Although no precise estimate of the temperature which might be reached in this way could be made at that time, it was evident that it would be far below $1°$ K. The lowest temperatures which can be reached easily will be the temperatures at which Curie's law for the temperature dependence of the magnetic susceptibility begins to break down; of such a failure there is no evidence at the lowest liquid helium temperatures. The first experiments were carried out by Giauque and Macdougall. They showed that the method was feasible by reaching a temperature of $0·53°$ K. by the demagnetization of gadolinium sulphate from an initial temperature of $3·4°$ K.

The theory of the method is as follows.† Consider a magnetic field produced by a coil, the electromotive force being maintained by a battery. If the intensity of magnetization $\mathscr{I}$ changes by $d\mathscr{I}$, an electromotive force is induced in the coil. This decreases the Joule heat developed in the coil by $\mathscr{H}\, d\mathscr{I}$, while the total work done by the battery remains the same. Thus, the work done on the system must be $\mathscr{H}\, d\mathscr{I}$, where $\mathscr{H}$ is the magnetic field and $\mathscr{I}$ is the intensity of magnetization. The first law of thermodynamics can then be written

$$dQ = dU - \mathscr{H}\, d\mathscr{I}, \quad \ldots \ldots \quad (9)$$

where dQ is the heat supplied to the system. The second law of thermodynamics can be written

$$dU = T\, dS + \mathscr{H}\, d\mathscr{I}. \quad \ldots \ldots \quad (10)$$

In these equations, the entropy S and the intensity of magnetization $\mathscr{I}$ are to be regarded as functions of the absolute temperature T and the magnetic field strength $\mathscr{H}$. Thus, we can write

$$dU = T\left\{\left(\frac{\partial S}{\partial T}\right)_{\mathscr{H}} dT + \left(\frac{\partial S}{\partial \mathscr{H}}\right)_{T} d\mathscr{H}\right\} + \mathscr{H}\left\{\left(\frac{\partial \mathscr{I}}{\partial T}\right)_{\mathscr{H}} dT + \left(\frac{\partial \mathscr{I}}{\partial \mathscr{H}}\right)_{T} d\mathscr{H}\right\}, \quad (11)$$

and, since U is a function of the state of the system, dU is a perfect differential, and the latter expression must be identical with

$$dU = \left(\frac{\partial U}{\partial T}\right)_{\mathscr{H}} dT + \left(\frac{\partial U}{\partial \mathscr{H}}\right)_{T} d\mathscr{H}.$$

---

* Woltjer and Onnes, *Versl. Akad.*, Amsterdam, Vol. 32, p. 772 (1923); *Leiden Comm.*, No. 167c (1923).

† It should be noted that the part of the proof given here down to the equation (15) amounts to deducing the appropriate Maxwell relation (Chapter XIII) *ab initio*. It can also be deduced by considering the "magnetic Gibbs function" as in Example 6 at the end of this chapter. The use of the Maxwell relation to study adiabatic demagnetization is given in the text following equation (15). For the theory, the student should also refer to H. B. G. Casimir, *Magnetism and Very Low Temperatures*, Cambridge University Press (1940); and C. G. B. Garrett, *Magnetic Cooling*, Harvard University Press (1954).

It follows from the condition for a perfect differential that

$$\left(\frac{\partial \mathscr{I}}{\partial T}\right)_{\mathscr{H}} = \left(\frac{\partial S}{\partial \mathscr{H}}\right)_{T}, \quad \cdots \quad \cdots \quad (12)$$

and

$$\left(\frac{\partial U}{\partial \mathscr{H}}\right)_{T} = T\left(\frac{\partial \mathscr{I}}{\partial T}\right)_{\mathscr{H}} + \mathscr{H}\left(\frac{\partial \mathscr{I}}{\partial \mathscr{H}}\right)_{T}. \quad \cdots \quad (13)$$

By using equation (13), the internal energy or the entropy in an arbitrary field can be calculated from the internal energy or the entropy in zero field at the same temperature, when the magnetization curves at different temperatures are known. From equations (9) and (13) it follows that

$$dQ = \left\{\left(\frac{\partial U}{\partial T}\right)_{\mathscr{H}} - \mathscr{H}\left(\frac{\partial \mathscr{I}}{\partial T}\right)_{\mathscr{H}}\right\}dT + T\left(\frac{\partial \mathscr{I}}{\partial T}\right)_{\mathscr{H}}d\mathscr{H}.$$

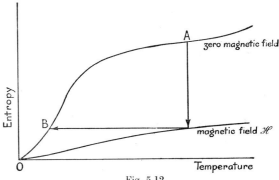

Fig. 5.12

Thus, the total heat supplied to the body during isothermal magnetization is given by

$$\Delta Q = T\int_{0}^{\mathscr{H}}\left(\frac{\partial \mathscr{I}}{\partial T}\right)_{\mathscr{H}}d\mathscr{H}, \quad \cdots \quad (14)$$

and, for the entropy, we have

$$S(\mathscr{H}, T) - S(0, T) = \int_{0}^{\mathscr{H}}\left(\frac{\partial \mathscr{I}}{\partial T}\right)_{\mathscr{H}}d\mathscr{H}. \quad \cdots \quad (15)$$

Equation (15) is illustrated by fig. 5.12, in which the entropy is shown schematically as a function of temperature for two different external fields. The changes which take place in an isothermal magnetization followed by an adiabatic demagnetization (carried out reversibly) are shown by the arrows. This shows clearly the resultant fall in temperature as the paramagnetic salt passes from the state represented by A to the state represented by B.

In the ideal paramagnetic case, the intensity of magnetization is a function of $\mathscr{H}/T$. In this case $(\partial U/\partial \mathscr{H})_T$ is zero and therefore

$$S(\mathscr{H}, T) = S(0, T) - \frac{1}{T} \int \mathscr{H} \, d\mathscr{I}, \quad \ldots \quad (16)$$

since, under these conditions,

$$\left(\frac{\partial \mathscr{I}}{\partial T}\right)_{\mathscr{H}} = - \frac{\mathscr{H}}{T} \left(\frac{\partial \mathscr{I}}{\partial \mathscr{H}}\right)_T.$$

Furthermore, the total amount of heat supplied to the body during isothermal magnetization is

$$\Delta Q = - \int \mathscr{H} \, d\mathscr{I}. \quad \ldots \ldots \quad (17)$$

Thus, heat is liberated during the magnetization process and the entropy is lowered. It follows that, if a paramagnetic salt is at a temperature T and a magnetic field is applied, then heat is evolved during the magnetization process. If the substance is in thermal contact with a heat container, the resulting state is one of lower entropy than the initial state. Now break the thermal contact and switch off the field. No heat is supplied, and the entropy will remain constant. Thus, the adiabatic demagnetization gives a resulting state in zero field with lower entropy than the initial state. It is therefore a state of lower temperature.

Let $S(0, T_1)$ be the entropy of the initial state. After the isothermal magnetization, the entropy will be given by

$$S(\mathscr{H}, T_1) = S(0, T_1) + \int_0^{\mathscr{H}} \left(\frac{\partial \mathscr{I}}{\partial T}\right)_{\mathscr{H}} d\mathscr{H},$$

where $\mathscr{H}$ is the applied field. If the field is now switched off after thermal contact with the heat container has been broken, the resulting state is one at temperature T_2, with $T_2 < T_1$, such that

$$S(0, T_2) = S(\mathscr{H}, T_1).$$

Now, the change in entropy of the substance when its temperature falls from T_1 to T_2 is given by

$$S(0, T_2) = S(0, T_1) - \int_{T_2}^{T_1} \left(\frac{C_{\mathscr{H}}}{T}\right) dT,$$

where $C_{\mathscr{H}}$ is the specific heat. Thus

$$\int_{T_2}^{T_1} \frac{C_{\mathscr{H}}}{T} \, dT = - \int_0^{\mathscr{H}} \left(\frac{\partial \mathscr{I}}{\partial T}\right)_{T=T_1} d\mathscr{H}. \quad \ldots \quad (18)$$

Introducing the molar susceptibility χ, this result can be written as

$$\int_{T_2}^{T_1} \frac{C_{\mathscr{H}}}{T} \, dT = -\int_0^{\mathscr{H}} \mathscr{H} \left(\frac{\partial \chi}{\partial T}\right)_{T=T_1} d\mathscr{H}. \quad \cdot \quad \cdot \quad (19)$$

At normal room temperature the variation with temperature of the susceptibility is small and the specific heat approaches the Dulong and Petit value (see Chapter VII, Sections 6 and 7) so that the change in temperature would be very small. On the other hand, at low temperatures, the temperature variation of the magnetic susceptibility becomes very great. For a substance which obeys Curie's law, it varies as T^{-2}. Also, the specific heat of solids approaches zero very rapidly at low temperatures. Thus, until temperatures are reached at which anomalies in the magnetic susceptibility or in the specific heat are operative, demagnetization from a given field produces a greater temperature change the lower the initial temperature. It is therefore evident that the cooling effect of an adiabatic demagnetization becomes very great at low temperatures.

The initial temperature in demagnetization experiments is usually about $1°$ K. For most salts used in magnetic cooling the lattice entropy at this (and lower temperatures) is negligible compared with the magnetic entropy. At these temperatures it is therefore not valid to attempt to describe the process in terms which equate the increase in the magnetic entropy to the drop in the thermal entropy of the lattice. The process must rather be looked upon as follows.* The absolute temperature is to be regarded as a parameter which determines the distribution of magnetic ions amongst the different quantum states. When the salt is demagnetized adiabatically, the magnetic ions will be redistributed among the available states and the temperature will fall until the various internal constraining forces produce a state in zero field with the same degree of order as that produced by the external magnetic field at the initial temperature. The constraining forces which produce the ordered state in the absence of an external field are (*i*) the electric field due to other ions distributed on crystal sites around each paramagnetic ion, (*ii*) direct interactions between magnetic ions.

The contributions to the entropy which arise from these forces are shown schematically in fig. 5.13 which is reproduced from the report by Ambler and Hudson referred to above. The drop in the entropy to $R \log_e 2$ shows the effect of the crystalline electric field; the further fall is due to the magnetic (or exchange) interactions. The curve for the salt in which the magnetic interactions are weaker lies to the left of the

---

* This was emphasized in a statement on adiabatic demagnetization prepared by R. H. Fowler and J. K. Roberts and circulated in the Cavendish Laboratory before the Second World War. See also, N. Kürti in *Low Temperature Physics, Four Lectures*, Pergamon Press Ltd., London (1952), pp. 33, 40 and E. Ambler and R. P. Hudson, *Reports on Progress in Physics*, Vol. 18, p. 255 (1955).

diagram. Starting from given initial conditions of temperature and external magnetic field, it is therefore possible to reach a lower temperature using the salt in which the magnetic interactions are weaker. Furthermore, this salt has the greater enthalpy (measured by $\int T \, dS$) at low temperatures, so that this low temperature could be maintained for a longer time.

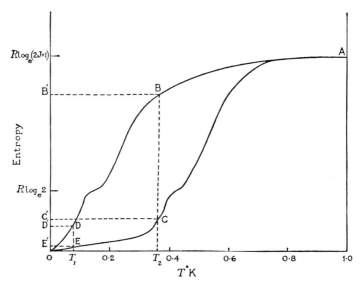

Fig. 5.13.—Representation of the entropy of paramagnetic salts showing the contributions arising from the crystalline field and the exchange forces. [After E. Ambler and R. P. Hudson, *Reports on Progress in Physics*, Vol. 18, p. 255 (1955).]

Giauque and Macdougall * carried out a careful examination of the magnetic properties of gadolinium sulphate, and attempted to establish the thermodynamic scale below 1° K. In the meantime, de Haas, Wiersma and Kramers † adapted the magnetic balance to obtain data on a number of paramagnetic substances. They obtained the important result that potassium chromium alum gives much lower temperatures than the salts of the rare earths. Kürti and Simon ‡ built an apparatus in which the vessel used for making the measurements is attached directly to a liquefier which produces liquid helium

* Giauque and Macdougall, *Phys. Rev.*, Vol. 43, p. 768 (1933); *ibid.*, Vol. 44, p. 235 (1933); *Journ. Amer. Chem. Soc.*, Vol. 57, p. 1175 (1935).

† De Haas, Wiersma and Kramers, *Physica*, Vol. 13, p. 175 (1933); *Nature*, Vol. 131, p. 719 (1933); *Naturwiss.*, Vol. 21, p. 732 (1933).

‡ Kürti and Simon, *Physica*, Vol. 1, p. 1107 (1934); *Nature*, Vol. 133, p. 907 (1934).

by the expansion method. They introduced the method of heating by γ-rays, described in Section 17.

The apparatus used at the Royal Society Mond Laboratory is shown diagrammatically in fig. 5.14*a*. The paramagnetic salt is suspended in a vessel which is surrounded by liquid helium boiling under reduced pressure and which contains some helium gas to establish thermal contact between the salt and the walls.
When the magnetic field is switched on the temperature of the salt rises, but the heat is rapidly conducted away by the helium gas, so that the salt is left in the magnetic field and at the temperature of the helium bath. The helium gas is now pumped away, so that the salt is thermally isolated, and the magnetic field is removed. The temperature of the salt then falls.

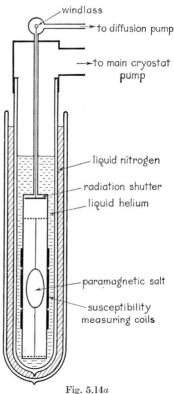

To detect the fall in temperature the magnetic susceptibility of the salt is measured by the magnetic thermometer shown in the diagram, which consists of a primary and secondary coil. The mutual inductance between these is measured by means of an alternating current bridge and from this the susceptibility is obtained. From these measurements an empirical temperature T^* on the magnetic scale can be obtained, based on the assumption that the substance continues to obey Curie's law ($\chi T =$ constant) down to the low temperatures attained.† Thus, if χ_1 is the susceptibility at the known temperature T_1 of the helium bath and χ_2 the susceptibility after the cooling process, T^* is defined by the equation

$$T^* = \frac{\chi_1}{\chi_2} T_1. \quad \ldots \ldots \quad (20)$$

Fig. 5.14*a*

Details of the magnetic cooling technique used at the Clarendon Laboratory, Oxford, have been given by Hull ‡ and of the magnetic

† For a discussion of the effect of the shape of the specimen used on the value of χ see Kürti and Simon, *Phil. Mag.*, Vol. 26, p. 849 (1938).

‡ R. A. Hull, *Report of Cambridge Conference on Low Temperature Physics*, Physical Society, London (1947), p. 72.

cooling installation at the United States National Bureau of Standards have been given by de Klerk and Hudson.†

Since the magnetic interactions between the paramagnetic ions will be weakened if the paramagnetic salt is diluted with a non-paramagnetic material, a lower temperature can be reached in this way. A

Fig. 5.14b.—Apparatus for adiabatic demagnetization used in the Royal Society Mond Laboratory, Cambridge

more complicated compound containing the paramagnetic ions can be prepared so that they are distributed regularly throughout the material.‡ Alternatively, a mixed crystal can be used.

17. Relation between T* and the Thermodynamic Temperature.

It is important to determine the relation between the magnetic temperature T^* and the thermodynamic temperature T because, pro-

† D. de Klerk and R. P. Hudson, *Journ. Res. Bur. Stand.*, Washington, Vol. 53, p. 73 (1954).

‡ See Casimir, *Magnetism and Very Low Temperatures* (Cambridge Physical Tracts), 1940.

vided this relation is known, measurements of magnetic and thermal properties in this region give tests of the theory of magnetism, elucidate the thermal and magnetic properties of paramagnetic salts, and give information about the physical properties at very low temperatures of other materials which may be cooled in contact with the salt.* There are considerable difficulties in the way of doing this and we shall discuss the various methods that have been proposed.

We shall first indicate a magnetic method of determining the absolute temperature. In equation (10), we may regard $\mathscr{H}$ and S as the state variables so that T and $\mathscr{I}$ are to be treated as functions of $\mathscr{H}$ and S. Equation (10) then becomes

$$dU = T(S, \mathscr{H})dS + \mathscr{H}\left[\left(\frac{\partial \mathscr{I}}{\partial S}\right)_{\mathscr{H}} dS + \left(\frac{\partial \mathscr{I}}{\partial \mathscr{H}}\right)_{S} d\mathscr{H}\right].$$

Since U is a function of state of the system, dU is a perfect differential and the latter expression must be identical with

$$dU = \left(\frac{\partial U}{\partial S}\right)_{\mathscr{H}} dS + \left(\frac{\partial U}{\partial \mathscr{H}}\right)_{S} d\mathscr{H}.$$

From the condition for a perfect differential, it then follows that

$$\left(\frac{\partial T}{\partial \mathscr{H}}\right)_{S} = -\left(\frac{\partial \mathscr{I}}{\partial S}\right)_{\mathscr{H}}.$$

This gives the integral expression

$$[\Delta T]_{S} = -\int_{\mathscr{H}_i}^{\mathscr{H}_f} \left(\frac{\partial \mathscr{I}}{\partial S}\right)_{\mathscr{H}} d\mathscr{H}.$$

Values of the intensity of magnetization and the magnetic field strength must then be determined at various entropies. The range of entropies must be such that the lattice of intensity-field curves will range from known high temperatures (that is, temperatures which can be determined by, say, gas thermometer, vapour pressure, or resistance measurements) to low unknown temperatures. Starting from a known temperature and a given initial field, the final temperature which is reached when the field is varied adiabatically can then be determined from the intensity-field curves. This is essentially the method proposed by

---

* See, for example, Kürti and Simon, *Proc. Roy. Soc.*, A, Vol. 152, p. 21 (1935); Ashmead, *Nature*, Vol. 143, p. 853 (1939). In this connexion reference should also be made to Casimir, de Haas and de Klerk, *Physica*, Vol. 6, p. 255 (1939).

Giauque † and used by him and Macdougall ‡ in 1933 and 1934. In this method, ΔT is the small difference between two large quantities. Very accurate magnetic measurements are required for the successful use of the method. This has militated against its wide adoption. The important point, however, is that such a method is available, that is, determinations of absolute temperature may be made in this temperature region without it being necessary to introduce heat deliberately into the salt system.

Another method which involves making very precise magnetic measurements was introduced by de Haas and Wiersma.§ An analysis of the errors in this method was made by Casimir and de Haas ‖ who showed how the errors can be estimated from a fairly rough determination of adiabatic intensity-field curves.

Both of these methods provide an independent check on the thermodynamical methods which are generally used. We shall now describe these latter methods.

The various thermodynamical methods which have been used to determine the absolute temperature in the demagnetization range differ in the method by which heat is supplied to the sample. All involve the following four steps.

(1) Plot the entropy S as a function of the magnetic field $\mathscr{H}$ at a fixed liquid helium temperature T_0, using equation (12) and measurements of susceptibility.

(2) Demagnetize adiabatically from this temperature with various initial fields, that is, various initial values of S, to zero field and measure T^*. Thus plot S as a function of T^* for $\mathscr{H} = 0$.

(3) Measure the heat required at $\mathscr{H} = 0$ to raise the temperature from T^* to T_0. Thus plot the internal energy U as a function of T^* for $\mathscr{H} = 0$. This measurement can be carried out by heating the substance in various ways which are referred to below.

(4) The absolute temperature T corresponding to T^* may be deduced as follows. For $\mathscr{H} = 0$ we have

$$dQ = dU = T\,dS,$$

since the $p\,dV$ term is negligible. Therefore

$$T = \frac{dU}{dS} = \frac{(\partial U/\partial T^*)_{\mathscr{H}=0}}{(\partial S/\partial T^*)_{\mathscr{H}=0}} = \frac{(\partial Q/\partial T^*)_{\mathscr{H}=0}}{(\partial S/\partial T^*)_{\mathscr{H}=0}}. \quad . \quad . \quad (21)$$

† W. F. Giauque, *Industr. Eng. Chem.*, Vol. 28, p. 743 (1936); see also *Phys. Rev.*, Vol. 92, p. 1339 (1953).

‡ W. F. Giauque and D. P. Macdougall, *Journ. Amer. Chem. Soc.*, Vol. 60, p. 376 (1938).

§ W. J. de Haas and E. C. Wiersma, *Physica*, Vol. 3, p. 491 (1936).

‖ H. B. G. Casimir and W. J. de Haas, *Physica*, Vol. 7. p. 70 (1940); *Leiden Comm.*, No. 258d (1940).

The various methods which have been proposed † for supplying energy to the paramagnetic salt are

    (i) radiation from a heated filament,
    (ii) radiation from a body at normal temperature,
    (iii) radiation from radioactive material, for example, gamma rays,
    (iv) the addition of a small amount of a solid of known energy content,
    (v) the condensation of small measured amounts of helium gas on the salt,
    (vi) the use of an induction heater,
    (vii) resistance heaters, for example, carbon resistors,
    (viii) paramagnetic relaxation and hysteresis.

Of these methods, Giauque and his colleagues ‡ have used induction heating, the condensation of helium gas, and resistance heaters, while the use of paramagnetic relaxation and hysteresis was introduced at Leiden.§

The method of heating the salt by irradiating it with γ-rays was first used by Kürti and Simon,‖ who applied it to iron ammonium sulphate. It has also been used by Bleaney working with potassium chrome alum, and by Cooke and Hull working with manganous ammonium sulphate.¶ The main difficulty in applying the method is in determining the absolute value of the heat supplied by the γ-rays. If this absolute rate is not known, we can determine from (21) a quantity bT, in which the constant of proportionality b depends on the absolute rate, as a function of T^*. If the measurements are carried up into the region of higher temperatures, the fact that here T and T^* must agree enables us to determine the value of b and therefore that of the absolute rate at which heat is supplied. In this region it is difficult to isolate the specimen thermally owing to the slow but appreciable evaporation of adsorbed helium from it. Having determined the heat input to the salt in this way as a function of the magnetic temperature, the entropy was determined, also as a function of magnetic temperature, by a

† W. F. Giauque and D. P. Macdougall, *Phys. Rev.*, Vol. 47, p. 885 (1935); W. F. Giauque, *ibid.*, Vol. 92, p. 1339 (1953); F. E. Simon, *Nature*, London, Vol. 135, p. 763 (1935); H. B. G. Casimir, W. J. de Haas, and D. de Klerk, *Leiden Comm.*, 256b (1939); *Physica.* Vol. 6, p. 255 (1939).

‡ W. F. Giauque and J. W. Stout, *Journ. Amer. Chem. Soc.*, Vol. 60, p. 358 (1938); W. F. Giauque and D. P. Macdougall, *ibid.*, Vol. 60, p. 376 (1938); W. F. Giauque, J. W. Stout, and C. W. Clark, *ibid.*, Vol. 60, p. 1053 (1938).

§ H. B. G. Casimir, W. J. de Haas, and D. de Klerk, *Physica*, Vol. 6, p. 255 (1939); D. de Klerk, M. J. Steenland, and C. J. Gorter, *ibid.*, Vol. 15, p. 649 (1949).

‖ Kürti and Simon, *Proc. Roy. Soc.*, A, Vol. 149, p. 161 (1935).

¶ Hull, Report of the Physical Society Conference at Cambridge, Vol. 2, p. 72 (1947); Cooke, *Proc. Phys. Soc.*, A, Vol. 62, p. 269 (1949); A. H. Cooke, H. Meyer. and W. P. Wolf, *Proc. Roy. Soc.*, A, Vol. 237, pp. 395, 404 (1956).

series of experiments in which a specimen of the salt was magnetized at a known field and temperature, producing a change of entropy which can be calculated, followed by adiabatic demagnetization. The measurement of the temperature after demagnetization, on the magnetic scale, was made by comparing the magnetic moment in a field of a few gauss with its moment in the same field at the known initial temperature. The graph of entropy as a function of magnetic temperature is obtained by plotting this temperature against the calculated change of entropy during the isothermal magnetization. In fig. 5.15

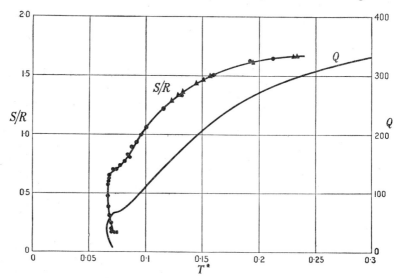

Fig. 5.15.—S and Q as functions of T^* for iron ammonium alum (Kürti and Simon)

we reproduce from Cooke's paper typical curves of entropy and heat content as functions of magnetic temperature. These are Kürti and Simon's results for iron ammonium alum. From equation (21) it then follows that the ratio of the slopes of these two curves at a given magnetic temperature gives the thermodynamical temperature. In this way, the curve shown in fig. 5.16, relating the thermodynamical temperature to the magnetic temperature, is obtained. Once this has been done, other quantities, such as the true specific heat dQ/dT, can be evaluated. In addition, the comparison of these experimental results with the theories of Onsager[*] and van Vleck[†] makes it possible to calculate the splitting of the energy levels of the magnetic ions

[*] Onsager, *Journ. Amer. Chem. Soc.*, Vol. 58, p. 1486 (1936).

[†] Van Vleck, *Journ. Chem. Phys.*, Vol. 5, p. 320 (1937); van Vleck and Penney, *Phil. Mag.*, Vol. 17, p. 961 (1934).

in these salts.   In this way, information can be obtained about the level splitting due to the Stark effect, dipole-dipole interactions, exchange interactions, and hyperfine structure.

Both theories fit the experimental results on chrome alum well over the temperature range investigated.   The Curie temperature, below which remanence occurs, was found at 0·042° K. for iron ammonium alum and at 0·15° K. for manganous ammonium sulphate.

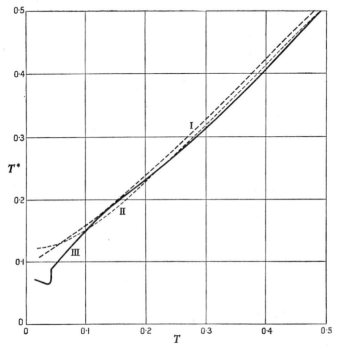

Fig. 5.16.—T^* as a function of T from experiments of Kürti and Simon on iron ammonium alum (curve III).   Curve I, Onsager's theory; curve II, van Vleck's theory.

Neither theory predicts the existence of a Curie point, nor the existence of a maximum value in susceptibility (minimum of T^*).   It is clear that, although the effect of a crystalline field is treated successfully, there must be other interaction effects which have still to be explained.

Experiments have also been carried out at Leiden.   Working with a spherical single crystal of chromium potassium alum, de Klerk, Steenland and Gorter † have also found that the susceptibility has a

† De Klerk, Steenland and Gorter, *Nature*, Vol. 161, p. 678 (1948); *Physica*, Vol. 15. p. 649 (1949).

maximum value below which a feeble magnetic hysteresis occurs; the minimum value of T^*, which corresponds to this maximum in the susceptibility for chromium potassium alum, is 32 millidegrees. At these lowest temperatures, it was found that the width of the hysteresis loop provided a useful thermometer. For values of T^* below about $0.06°$, paramagnetic losses in an alternating field were measured; frequencies in the range 225 to 525 cycles per second were used, and the losses varied somewhat more slowly than as the square of the frequency. In this temperature range (of T^*) these paramagnetic losses were used as a thermometer. The paramagnetic losses provided the means of heating the specimen, and made it possible to determine ΔQ accurately. The width of the hysteresis loop was used as a secondary thermometer. It was calibrated against the thermodynamic temperature,† which could be determined from the amount of heat supplied and the change in entropy. The lowest temperature which they observed was about 3 millidegrees absolute. At the lowest temperatures, the amount of heat supplied to the salt was measured, using a ballistic method, by describing a number of hysteresis loops; the results were in reasonable agreement with those obtained using the paramagnetic losses in an alternating field to heat the salt. From the entropy-temperature curve, the specific heat can be calculated; there is a flat minimum in the specific heat corresponding to an entropy of $0.4R$, which is noteworthy in being so much lower than $R \log_e 2$. These results disagree with those on the same salt using irradiation by γ-rays to heat the salt. It has been claimed ‡ that with the latter method a part of the energy which is absorbed may be stored instead of being transmitted as heat to the spin system, but Kürti and Simon § have advanced reasons which show that the method of heating by γ-rays as practised at Oxford is unexceptionable. This is supported by the concordance of measurements by Gardner and Kürti ‖ on chromium methyl ammonium sulphate with those obtained by Ambler and Hudson;¶ and by the fact that later measurements at Leiden ** suggest that the earlier (1948) measurements made there were in error.

The results which have been described in the preceding paragraphs are to be regarded as illustrative of the measurements which are made in magnetic-cooling experiments. For a critical examination of the results which have been obtained for particular paramagnetic salts,

† W. H. Keesom, *Physica*, Vol. 2, p. 805 (1935); *Leiden Comm. Supp.*, 77c (1935); Kürti, Lainé and Simon, *C. R. Acad. Sci. Paris*, Vol. 204, pp. 675, 754 (1937); Casimir, de Haas and de Klerk, *Physica*, Vol. 6, p. 255 (1939); *Leiden Comm.*, 256b.

‡ R. L. Platzmann, *Phil. Mag.*, Vol. 44, p. 497 (1953).

§ N. Kürti and F. E. Simon, *ibid.*, Vol. 44, p. 501 (1953).

‖ W. E. Gardner and N. Kürti, *Proc. Roy. Soc.*, A, Vol. 223, p. 542 (1954).

¶ E. Ambler and R. P. Hudson, *Journ. Chem. Phys.*, Vol. 27, p. 378 (1957).

** J. A. Beun, A. R. Miedema, and M. J. Steenland, *Physica*, Vol. 23, p. 1 (1957).

the student should consult specialized monographs and reviews.*
The processes which have been described in the preceding sections
have two aims. First, the properties of paramagnetic salts are of interest and of very great theoretical importance in themselves. Secondly,
the processes which have been considered can be used to cool other
substances, for example liquid helium or metals, to these very low
temperatures, so that their properties in this temperature region can
be studied.

18. Two-stage Demagnetization.

It has been suggested † that low temperatures could be reached
by carrying out the demagnetization in two stages. The idea is illustrated schematically in fig. 5.17. A and B are two
samples of paramagnetic salt which are connected
by a rod C which initially has to provide thermal
contact between the two samples of salt. These
are suspended from a cage, in a container from
which the gas can be pumped off. The whole is
immersed in a helium bath, placed in the gap of a
magnet. A suitable material for the container is
German silver, as it provides good thermal contact
with the helium bath. Starting with the whole
system in a magnetic field at a temperature in the
helium range (about 1·5° K.), the salt A is demagnetized adiabatically. It is thus cooled in the
way described in the preceding sections. By conduction along the rod C, the salt B is also cooled to
a temperature of the order of a few hundredths of a
degree. The thermal contact between A and B is
then broken, and, starting at this much lower tem-

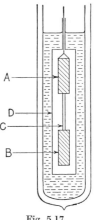

Fig. 5.17

perature, the second salt is then demagnetized. An important condition
for the success of the process is that the thermal contact between A and
B shall be established and broken at will. This is a matter of considerable technical difficulty.

The thermal conductivity of tin in the superconducting state is very
much less than it is in the normal state at the same temperature. This
fact has led to the suggestion ‡ that a tin wire could be used as a thermal
switch which can be made and broken by switching a magnetic field on
and off.

* See the books already referred to by H. B. G. Casimir and C. G. B. Garrett and the
article by E. Ambler and R. P. Hudson, *Reports on Progress in Physics*, Vol. 18, p. 255
(1955).

† Simon, Report of Strasbourg Conference, 1939, " Le Magnétisme ", Vol. 3, p. 13.

‡ C. J. Gorter, *Les phénomènes cryomagnétiques*, Paris: Cérémonies Langevin-
Perrin (1948); C. V. Heer and J. G. Daunt, *Phys. Rev.*, Vol. 76, p. 854 (1949).

It has also been suggested * that exchange gas in a high-vacuum system could be used as a thermal switch. The two parts of the system which, at different times, are to be connected thermally and insulated from one another, are connected one to a copper rod and the other to a copper tube which forms a sheath around the rod. The exchange gas can be admitted to, or pumped from, the space between the copper rod and tube to make or break thermal connexion between the two parts of the equipment.

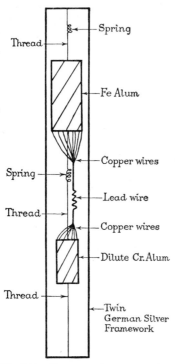

Fig. 5.18.—Two-stage demagnetization cryostat used at Oxford

A two-stage demagnetization has been carried out at Oxford.† The salt system that was used is shown in fig. 5.18. The thermal switch between the two stages consisted of a lead wire. A final temperature in the region of 0·003° K. was obtained using an initial field of 4200 gauss. In subsequent experiments a final temperature of 10^{-3} °K. was reached on demagnetization from an initial field of 9000 gauss. The temperature remained below 0·01° K. for forty minutes. It should be noted that not only is it possible to reach much lower temperatures with the two-stage process but this can be achieved with smaller initial magnetic fields than in a conventional magnetic-cooling experiment.

19. Nuclear Demagnetization.

It has been pointed out in Section 16 that one way in which lower temperatures have been attained is to use a diluted salt. When a paramagnetic salt is diluted with a substance that is not paramagnetic, the magnetic interactions are very much weaker, and this makes it possible to reach lower temperatures by demagnetization. Gorter and Kürti and Simon ‡ have indicated that since the nuclear moments are about a thousand times smaller than the electronic moments, still lower temperatures could be reached by using the nuclear spins instead

* G. O. Jones, *Journ. Sci. Instr.*, Vol. 28, p. 181 (1951).

† J. Darby, J. Hatton, B. V. Rollin, E. F. W. Seymour, and H. B. Silsbee, *Proc. Phys. Soc.*, A, Vol. 64, p. 861 (1951).

‡ Gorter, *Phys. Z.*, Vol. 35, p. 923 (1934); Kürti and Simon, *Proc. Roy. Soc.*, A, Vol. 149, p. 152 (1935).

of the electronic spins of a paramagnetic salt. To use the nuclear spins in the same way as the electronic paramagnetism is used in an ordinary adiabatic demagnetization, it would be necessary to carry out a two-stage demagnetization, as described in Section 18. The first stage would consist of the demagnetization of a paramagnetic salt, and the second of a nuclear demagnetization. Simon * has given detailed calculations from which he concludes that, using 10 c.c. of copper for the second stage, and with a rate of heating of 1 erg per minute, it would be possible to reach a temperature of 5 Θ_n, and to maintain a temperature between 5 Θ_n and 10 Θ_n for $10^7 \Theta_n$ minutes, where Θ_n is the nuclear spin degeneracy temperature. Θ_n has been calculated to be of the order of 10^{-6} °K.

The first successful nuclear demagnetization was carried out † at the Clarendon Laboratory, Oxford. About 0·75 gm. of copper in the form of fine wires was cooled from about 0·01° K. to 2×10^{-5} °K. using a magnetization field of 28 kG. After demagnetization, the copper warmed up in a few minutes. From the results obtained, it was estimated that the characteristic temperature of the nuclear inter-actions is $2·3 \times 10^{-6}$ °K. Kittel ‡ has shown that, under the con-ditions of the experiment, the conduction electrons and the lattice cool to almost the same temperature in about 1 second. This is so even though the relevant relaxation time at 10^{-5} °K. is about 10^5 seconds; the very small specific heat of the electrons ensures that equilibrium is reached when only a minute fraction of the spins have relaxed.

EXAMPLES

1. For a gas which obeys Dieterici's equation of state, show that the inversion temperature is eight times the critical temperature.

2. Show that for a gas which obeys Van der Waals' equation the ratio of the inversion temperature to the critical temperature is 27/4, so that much less pre-liminary cooling is necessary to liquefy a gas by the Linde method than by the cascade process.

3. According to the measurements of Clark and Keesom,§ the specific heat of a gram mole of gadolinium sulphate in the temperature range 1·5 to 20° K. is given fairly accurately by

$$C_p = \frac{2·34}{T^2} + 1·21 \cdot 10^{-3}T^3 \text{ joule/degree.}$$

Show that the change in entropy due to magnetization in a field which does not produce saturation is

$$\Delta S = 3·91 \cdot 10^{-7}\mathcal{H}^2/T^2 \text{ joule/degree.}$$

---

* Simon, Report of Strasbourg Conference, 1939, " Le Magnétisme ", Vol. 3, p. 14.

† N. Kürti, F. N. H. Robinson, F. E. Simon, and D. A. Spohr, *Nature*, London, Vol. 178, p. 450 (1956).

‡ C. Kittel, *Phys. Rev.*, Vol. 104, p. 1807 (1956).

§ Clark and W. H. Keesom, *Leiden Comm.*, No. 240a (1935); *Physica*, Vol. 2, p. 1075 (1935).

Hence show that, starting with the salt at $10°$ K. in a field of 12,000 gauss, the temperature after adiabatic demagnetization is $2·6°$ K. With what initial field would it be necessary to start in order to produce a final temperature of $1·5°$ K.? (The nuclear spin of the gadolinium ion is 7/2.)

4. Introducing the Gibbs free energy

$$G' = U - TS - \mathscr{H}\,\mathscr{I},$$

show that

$$\left(\frac{\partial G'}{\partial T}\right)_{\mathscr{H}} = -S \quad \text{and} \quad \left(\frac{\partial G'}{\partial \mathscr{H}}\right)_{T} = -\mathscr{I}.$$

Hence show that

$$\left(\frac{\partial T}{\partial \mathscr{H}}\right)_{S} = -T\mathscr{H}\left(\frac{\partial \chi}{\partial T}\right)_{\mathscr{H}} \Big/ C_{\mathscr{H}},$$

where $C_{\mathscr{H}}$ is the molar specific heat in constant magnetic field and χ is the molar susceptibility. Thus show that under adiabatic conditions there is a fall in the temperature of a paramagnetic salt when the magnetic field in which it is placed is reduced. (This provides an alternative deduction of the result obtained in Section 16.)

5. The specific heat in zero magnetic field can be determined by measurements of the magnetic moment in adiabatic demagnetization to a final non-zero field. In the absence of saturation

$$\mathscr{I} = \chi(T)\mathscr{H},$$

so that

$$dS(\mathscr{H},\,T) = \frac{\partial S(0,\,T)}{\partial T}\,dT + \tfrac{1}{2}\chi''\mathscr{H}^{2}\,dT + \chi'\mathscr{H}\,d\mathscr{H},$$

where χ' has been written for $d\chi/dT$. Hence, by finding an expression for $(\partial \mathscr{I}/\partial \mathscr{H})_{S}$ in terms of $\partial S(0,\,T)/\partial T$, show that the specific heat in zero field can be calculated.

6. By considering the magnetic Gibbs function

$$G' = U - TS - \mathscr{H}\,\mathscr{I},$$

find dG' and show that

$$\left(\frac{\partial S}{\partial \mathscr{H}}\right)_{T} = \left(\frac{\partial \mathscr{I}}{\partial T}\right)_{\mathscr{H}}.$$

This is a Maxwell relation (Chapter XIII). Show that it leads immediately to equation (15) of the text.

7. Between $0·2°$ and $1°$ K., potassium chrome alum $[\text{K}_2\text{SO}_4\cdot\text{Cr}_2(\text{SO}_4)_3\cdot24\text{H}_2\text{O}]$ obeys a Curie law, and the specific heat of the spin system in the absence of a magnetic field is inversely proportional to the square of the temperature. Construct a Mollier diagram * for the salt, and show that for small applied fields the curves of constant field are parabolæ and those of constant temperature are straight lines.

If H is the enthalpy and $\mathscr{H}$ is the applied magnetic field, show that

$$\left(\frac{\partial \mathscr{H}}{\partial S}\right)_{H} = -\left(\frac{\partial \mathscr{H}}{\partial S}\right)_{T}, \quad \text{and that} \quad \left(\frac{\partial H}{\partial S}\right)_{T} = 2\left(\frac{\partial H}{\partial S}\right)_{\mathscr{H}}.$$

The salt is cooled in a helium bath to $1°$ K. while in a field of 5000 gauss. Find the temperature reached by the salt when the magnetic field is removed, assuming the spin-lattice relaxation time to be so short that equilibrium is maintained.

The specific heat of the spin system at $1°$ K. in the absence of a field is $1·37 \times 10^{6}$ ergs per gm.-ion of salt, the lattice specific heat is $100\ T^{3}$ ergs per gm., and the constant of the Curie law is $1·86$ e.m.u. per gm.-ion.

* C. G. B. Garrett, *Phil. Mag.*, Vol. 41, p 621 (1950).

CHAPTER VI

The Specific Heats of Gases

1. The specific heat of a substance (see Chapter II) is defined as the amount of energy required to raise the temperature of 1 gm. of the substance through one degree.

In the case of a gas, the conditions under which the heating is carried out must be carefully specified. There are two important cases: (1) when the gas is heated at constant volume, (2) when it is heated at constant pressure. In the latter case heating the gas causes an increase in its *internal energy* and also causes the gas to do *external work* by expanding against the external pressure. In the former case no external work is done, and all the energy supplied goes to increase the internal energy.

We shall consider 1 gm. of any gas. Let c_v be the amount of energy required to heat the gas through one degree when the volume is kept constant; c_v is called the *specific heat at constant volume*.

Now let us heat the 1 gm. of gas through one degree keeping the pressure constant. Let us suppose for example that the gas is enclosed in a vessel with a moving piston at one end, the external pressure on which remains constant. Let c_p be the amount of energy required in this case; c_p is called the *specific heat at constant pressure*. As the gas is heated it expands and pushes out the piston, thus doing work against the external applied pressure. Let L cm. be the distance through which the piston moves. If p is the pressure and A is the area of the piston, the force acting on the piston is pA and the work done on the surroundings against this force is equal to

$$pAL.$$

AL is the change in the volume of the gas; that is, it is equal to $(v_2 - v_1)$, where v_1 is the initial and v_2 the final volume of the gas. The work done by the gas in expanding is, therefore,

$$\left. \begin{array}{l} p(v_2 - v_1) \\ p\,\delta v. \end{array} \right\} \quad . \quad . \quad . \quad . \quad . \quad . \quad (1)$$

or

This amount of energy must be supplied as well as the amount required to increase the internal energy of the gas.

Difference between the Specific Heats at Constant Pressure and at Constant Volume

2. Perfect Gases.

A perfect gas obeys Joule's law; that is, at constant temperature, the internal energy (Chapter II, Section 18) is independent of the volume. If then the gas is heated through the same range of temperature at constant pressure and at constant volume the increase in the internal energy is the same in the two cases. If the rise of temperature is one degree, it is equal to c_v.

From equation (1) it follows that c_p is given by

$$c_p = c_v + p(v_2 - v_1). \quad \ldots \ldots \ldots \quad (2)$$

Since the gas is perfect, we may write

$$pv_1 = \frac{R}{M} T_1, \quad \text{and} \quad pv_2 = \frac{R}{M} T_2,$$

or

$$p(v_2 - v_1) = \frac{R}{M} (T_2 - T_1),$$

where R is the gas constant and M is the molecular weight. Using this relation in equation (2), and remembering that

$$T_2 - T_1 = 1,$$

we obtain

$$c_p - c_v = \frac{R}{M}. \quad \ldots \ldots \ldots \quad (3)$$

The molecular heats, C_p and C_v, are defined as the amounts of energy required to raise the temperature of 1 gram-molecule of the gas through one degree at constant pressure and at constant volume respectively. Thus,

$$C_p = Mc_p \quad \text{and} \quad C_v = Mc_v.$$

From equation (3) we have for any perfect gas

$$C_p - C_v = R. \quad \ldots \ldots \ldots \quad (4)$$

The difference between the molecular heats at constant pressure and at constant volume of any perfect gas is, therefore, equal to

8·314 joules per degree,

and for actual gases it is approximately equal to this.*

---

* Assuming that the internal energy of a gas was independent of its volume, Mayer suggested that a value for the mechanical equivalent of heat could be obtained from the ratio of the value of R in ergs determined by the method described in Chapter I, Section 38, to its value in calories deduced from the measured molecular heats at constant pressure and at constant volume. The calculation was of no actual value, until Joule showed later that the internal energy of a gas was to a close approximation independent of its volume.

3. Actual Gases.

We can calculate the difference between C_p and C_v for any gas provided we know its equation of state. The calculation is important because it enables us to deduce C_v, if C_p has been measured, and *vice versa*. The calculation of the difference in this case requires the application of the second law of thermodynamics.

The simplest method of obtaining the result is an indirect one. The second law of thermodynamics gives the following relations (see end of Chapter XIII, Examples 3 and 4).

$$\left(\frac{\partial C_v}{\partial V}\right)_T = T\left(\frac{\partial^2 p}{\partial T^2}\right)_V,^*$$

$$\left(\frac{\partial C_p}{\partial p}\right)_T = -T\left(\frac{\partial^2 V}{\partial T^2}\right)_p.^*$$

Integrating these expressions, we obtain

$$\left.\begin{aligned}
C_v &= (C_v)_0 + T\int_\infty^V \left(\frac{\partial^2 p}{\partial T^2}\right)_V dV, \\
C_p &= (C_p)_0 - T\int_0^p \left(\frac{\partial^2 V}{\partial T^2}\right)_p dp,
\end{aligned}\right\} \quad \ldots \ldots \quad (5)$$

where $(C_v)_0$ and $(C_p)_0$ are the limiting values, at zero pressure or density, for the molecular heats.

Provided the pressures are not too high, so that we need only take into account the second virial coefficient (see Chapter IV, Section 1), we may write

$$pV = RT + Bp, \quad \ldots \ldots \ldots \quad (6)$$

where B is the second virial coefficient and is a function of the temperature but not of the pressure. From this equation we obtain

$$p = \frac{RT}{V} + \frac{B}{V}p.$$

In the second term on the right, which is a small correction term, we may put $p = RT/V$, thus obtaining

$$\left.\begin{aligned}
p &= \frac{RT}{V} + B\frac{RT}{V^2}. \\
\end{aligned}\right.$$

From equation (6) we obtain also

$$\left.\begin{aligned}
V &= \frac{RT}{p} + B.
\end{aligned}\right\} \quad \ldots \ldots \ldots \quad (7)$$

Differentiating these two equations, we obtain respectively

$$\left(\frac{\partial^2 p}{\partial T^2}\right)_V = \frac{2R}{V^2}\frac{dB}{dT} + \frac{RT}{V^2}\frac{d^2B}{dT^2},$$

$$\left(\frac{\partial^2 V}{\partial T^2}\right)_p = \frac{d^2B}{dT^2}.$$

---

* For the application of these two equations to measurements of specific heats at high pressures, see Partington and Shilling, *The Specific Heats of Gases*, pp. 151–167 (Benn, 1924); Hoxton, *Phys. Rev.*, Vol. 36, p. 1091 (1930); Workman, *Phys. Rev.*, Vol. 37, p. 1345 (1931).

Substituting these values in equation (5), we obtain

$$C_v = (C_v)_0 + \int_{\infty}^{V} \frac{RT}{V^2}\left(2\frac{dB}{dT} + T\frac{d^2B}{dT^2}\right)dV,$$

$$C_p = (C_p)_0 - \int_0^p T\frac{d^2B}{dT^2}\,dp.$$

And by integration

$$C_v = (C_v)_0 - \left(2\frac{dB}{dT} + T\frac{d^2B}{dT^2}\right)p, \qquad \ldots \ldots \quad (8)$$

and

$$C_p = (C_p)_0 - T\frac{d^2B}{dT^2}p. \qquad \ldots \ldots \ldots \quad (9)$$

In equation (8) we have substituted p for RT/V in the correction term.

Since $(C_p)_0$ and $(C_v)_0$ refer to the gas in the " perfect " condition, we may write

$$(C_p)_0 - (C_v)_0 = R.$$

We obtain, therefore, from equations (8) and (9)

$$C_p - C_v = R + 2\frac{dB}{dT}p. \qquad \ldots \ldots \ldots \quad (10)$$

We shall now consider the form which equations (8), (9), and (10) take when we use the value of B given by Berthelot's equation in both its original (equation (10), Chapter IV) and its special (equation (16), Chapter IV) form. We have for the two forms (see equations (22) and (21) of Chapter IV)

$$B = \left(b - \frac{a'}{RT^2}\right) \qquad \ldots \ldots \ldots \quad (11)$$

and

$$B = \frac{9}{128}\frac{RT_c}{p_c}\left(1 - \frac{6T_c^2}{T^2}\right). \qquad \ldots \ldots \quad (11a)$$

From equations (11) and (11a) we obtain respectively for dB/dT,

$$\frac{dB}{dT} = \frac{2a'}{RT^3}, \qquad \ldots \ldots \ldots \quad (12)$$

and

$$\frac{dB}{dT} = \frac{27}{32}\frac{RT_c^3}{p_c}\frac{1}{T^3}. \qquad \ldots \ldots \quad (12a)$$

For $\frac{d^2B}{dT^2}$,

$$\frac{d^2B}{dT^2} = -\frac{6a'}{RT^4}, \qquad \ldots \ldots \quad (13)$$

and

$$\frac{d^2B}{dT^2} = -\frac{81}{32}\frac{RT_c^3}{p_c}\frac{1}{T^4}. \qquad \ldots \ldots \quad (13a)$$

Substituting these results in equations (8), (9), and (10), we obtain

$$C_v = (C_v)_0 + \frac{2a'}{R} \frac{p}{T^3}, \qquad \ldots \ldots \quad (14)$$

$$= (C_v)_0 + \frac{27}{32} \frac{RT_c^3}{p_c} \frac{p}{T^3}; \qquad \ldots \ldots \quad (14a)$$

$$C_p = (C_p)_0 + \frac{6a'}{R} \frac{p}{T^3}, \qquad \ldots \ldots \quad (15)$$

$$= (C_p)_0 + \frac{81}{32} \frac{RT_c^3}{p_c} \frac{p}{T^3}; \qquad \ldots \ldots \quad (15a)$$

$$C_p - C_v = R + \frac{4a'}{R} \frac{p}{T^3}, \qquad \ldots \ldots \quad (16)$$

$$= R + \frac{27}{16} \frac{RT_c^3}{p_c} \frac{p}{T^3}. \qquad \ldots \ldots \quad (16a)$$

The equations giving the corrections in terms of the critical constants should be used only in cases where direct compressibility results, from which the value of a' can be calculated, are not available. In such cases they are extremely useful.*

The Measurement of the Specific Heat at Constant Volume

We shall now consider the experimental methods by which the specific heat at constant volume can be measured directly.

4. The Joly Steam Calorimeter.

Joly † was the first to determine accurately the specific heat of gases at constant volume. He used the steam calorimeter which is shown in fig. 6.1. A front view is shown on the left and a side view on the right. Two equal copper spheres hang in a closed chamber from the two arms of a balance. One of the spheres is exhausted and the other contains the gas under investigation. When the spheres have come into temperature equilibrium with the chamber, steam is admitted to it. The heat required to raise the temperatures of the two spheres to that of the steam is provided by the condensation of steam on the spheres, which are provided with pans to catch the water so condensed. More water is condensed on the sphere which is full of gas than on the empty one, and the difference is measured by adding weights until balance is restored. If m is the difference in the mass of water condensed, $m\lambda$ is the amount of heat required to raise the mass of gas contained in the full sphere from its initial temperature

---

* See, for example, Eucken and Bartels, *Zeits. f. phys. Chem.*, Vol. 98 p. 75 (1921); see also the calculation in Chapter VIII, Section 25.

† Joly, *Proc. Roy. Soc.*, A, Vol. 48, p. 440 (1890).

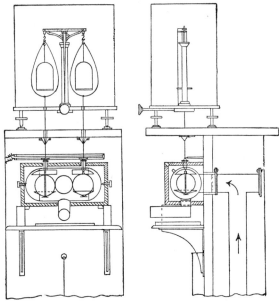

Fig. 6.1

to that of the steam, where λ is the latent heat of vaporization of water (see Chapter VIII).

Corrections must be made for:

(1) Thermal expansion of the sphere and the consequent work done by the gas in expanding.

(2) Distension of the sphere under the increased pressure of the gas as the temperature rises.

(3) Buoyancy effects due to slightly unequal volumes of the spheres, owing to one being distended and the other not.

(4) Unequal thermal capacities of the two spheres.

(5) Reduction of the weight of the water precipitated to its weight *in vacuo*.*

5. Eucken's Experiments on Hydrogen at Low Temperatures.

Eucken † has determined the specific heat at constant volume of hydrogen at low temperatures by a method which is essentially similar

---

* For a modern application of the Joly steam calorimeter, see Chapter VIII, Section 21.

† Eucken, *Berl. Ber.*, p. 141 (1912); p. 682 (1914); *Verh. d. deut. phys. Ges.*, Vol. 18, p. 4 (1916). Eucken and Hiller, *Zeits. f. phys. Chem.*, B, Vol. 4, p. 142 (1929), have used a similar method to investigate the specific heats of para- and ortho-hydrogen (see Section 28).

to that used by Nernst for solids (see Chapter VII, Section 2). The method can only be applied at low temperatures where the thermal capacity of the metal calorimeter falls off (Chapter VII, Section 7), so that the thermal capacity of the gas is not small compared with that of the container. The hydrogen was contained in a thin-walled steel flask with a constantan wire wound round it. Heat was supplied by passing an electric current through the wire, and the temperature rise corresponding to a given amount of electrical energy supplied was measured by a resistance thermometer of lead or platinum.

6. The Explosion Method.

The gas to be investigated and a known amount of an explosive mixture are placed in a steel bomb. The explosion is started by an electric spark. If Q is the heat of reaction, w_1 the thermal capacity of the gas, w_2 that of the products of combusion, t_1 the initial temperature, and t_2 the maximum temperature reached, we have, neglecting the effects of heat loss,

$$Q = (w_1 + w_2)(t_2 - t_1).$$

The maximum temperature reached by the gas is measured by measuring its maximum pressure. The apparatus used by Pier is shown in fig. 6.2.

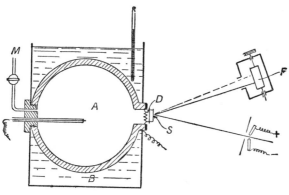

Fig. 6.2

The vessel A was contained in a large water-bath B. Through the tube M the vessel was evacuated and the desired gases were introduced. The maximum pressure reached was measured by the deflection of a beam of light reflected on to the film F from the mirror S which was attached to a corrugated steel membrane D. The latter was clamped securely to the vessel. It was calibrated by applying a measured static pressure to the inside of the bomb and measuring the deflection.

Assuming that the laws of a perfect gas may be applied to the gaseous mixture, we have

$$t_2 = \left(\frac{P}{e} - 1\right)(273 + t_1) + t_1,$$

where

    P = ratio of explosion pressure to initial pressure,
    e = ratio of final number of molecules to initial number (the number
        is in general changed by the explosion),
    t_2 = explosion temperature, and t_1 = initial temperature.

Corrections * are necessary for:

(1) Heat loss.
(2) Lag in the manometer.
(3) Incomplete combustion.

The best check that the corrections have been satisfactorily made is to carry out some experiments with a gas such as argon, for which it is highly probable, both from theoretical and experimental considerations, that the specific heat does not vary with the temperature.

The explosion method is very valuable, since it enables us to determine specific heats up to very high temperatures—about 3000°.

The method has been modified by Womersley,† so as to determine directly the heat loss to the walls. The inside of the bomb (a cylinder 1 ft. in length and 1 ft. in diameter) was lined with teak. A continuous strip of pure copper $\frac{1}{16}$ in. thick and $\frac{1}{4}$ in. wide was wound so that the inside of the vessel was completely covered—only $\frac{1}{20}$ in. space was left between the successive coils. The ends of the vessel were similarly covered with copper strips. The whole of the copper was connected in series and formed one arm of a Wheatstone's Bridge so that its temperature changes could be followed. The deflection of the galvanometer in the bridge was photographed on the same film as the deflection of the manometer.

This method has been used by Fenning and Whiffen ‡ to measure the molecular heats at constant volume of carbon monoxide, nitrogen, carbon dioxide, and water vapour. Their results are in good agreement with those deduced from spectroscopic data.

---

* See Bjerrum, *Zeits. f. Elektrochemie*, Vol. 17, p. 731 (1911); Vol. 18, p. 101 (1912); Siegel, *Zeits. f. phys. Chemie*, Vol. 87, p. 641 (1914); Wohl and v. Elbe, *Zeits. f. Elektrochemie*, Vol. 35, p. 644 (1929).

† Womersley, *Proc. Roy. Soc.*, A, Vol. 100, p. 483 (1921).

‡ Fenning and Whiffen, *Phil. Trans.*, A, Vol. 238, p. 149 (1939).

The Measurement of the Specific Heat at Constant Pressure

7. There are two methods of determining the specific heat at constant pressure. In both cases a continuous stream of gas is used. In the first method, which we may call the *method of mixtures*, a heated stream of gas gives up its heat in a calorimeter and the amount of heat so given up is measured. In the second method, which we may call the *continuous-flow method* on account of its similarity to that used by Callendar and Barnes in their experiments on liquids, a steady stream of the gas is heated electrically, and the rise in temperature, the rate of flow and the rate of supply of electrical energy are measured. Alternatively the cooling of an electrically heated tube is measured.

8. Regnault's Experiments.

The principle of the method of mixtures is simply illustrated by the experiments of Regnault,[*] whose apparatus is shown in fig. 6.3.

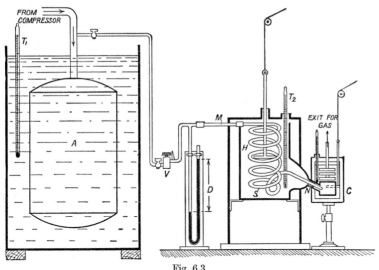

Fig. 6.3

The gas is compressed into the cylinder A, whence it flows through the valve V and the capillary tube M into the copper spiral S, where it is practically at atmospheric pressure. S is immersed in the constant-temperature bath H, and when the gas leaves S it is at the temperature of H, which is measured by the thermometer T_2. The gas at the temperature of H enters the copper spiral immersed in the calorimeter C, which is filled with water. As it passes through this spiral it heats up the water in the calorimeter, and is itself cooled down until, when it leaves the spiral, it is at the same temperature as the calorimeter.

[*] Regnault, *Mém. de l'Acad.*, Vol. 26, p. 1 (1862).

Let t_1 be the initial and t_2 the final temperature of the calorimeter, and let W be its thermal capacity.

Let t be the temperature of the gas when it enters the calorimeter, and let m be the mass of gas which flows while the calorimeter temperature rises from t_1 to t_2. If c_p is the specific heat of the gas, we have, assuming that the rate of flow is constant,

$$mc_p\left(t - \frac{t_1 + t_2}{2}\right) = W(t_2 - t_1).$$

Corrections must be made for heat loss from the calorimeter and for the conduction of heat along the copper tube connecting the spiral in H to that in C. The latter correction can be determined by carrying out an experiment with no gas flowing.

Experiments were carried out by Regnault up to a pressure of 10 atmospheres by allowing the gas to escape from the apparatus through a fine capillary.

A detailed theory of this method which applies to all flow methods has been given by Searle.*

9. Holborn and Henning's Experiments.

A similar method has been used by Holborn and Henning † to determine specific heats up to 1400° C. Their apparatus is shown in fig. 6.4.

The gas is heated by passing through the spiral in the oven X, and then through the tube RR which is also electrically heated. It then enters the double-walled platinum tube P, which is heated by passing a heavy current through the tube itself; the current leads for this current are shown at Z_1Z_1.

The temperature of the gas, as it leaves the tube P and just before it enters the calorimeter, is measured by the thermocouple L (see inset right-hand top corner). Errors in the thermocouple reading due to radiation to the cold parts of the apparatus E are prevented by the baffle plates D.

After leaving D the gas passes into the calorimeter M. This consists of a vessel of silver foil filled with paraffin oil, and provided with an electric heating coil B, a stirrer, and thermometers. The gas passes through three cylinders of silver, L_1, L_2, and L_3, connected in series. These cylinders are packed with silver filings so as to give good thermal contact between the gas and the calorimeter. In passing through these cylinders the gas is cooled down to the temperature of the calorimeter, and the consequent rise of temperature of the calorimeter is measured. To minimize heat loss the calorimeter is surrounded by a large vessel which is filled with a vegetable oil and is heated to a constant temperature.

The corrections in this type of apparatus are difficult.‡

Nernst § has used a similar method to determine the specific heat of ammonia up to 600° C.

---

* Searle, *Proc. Camb. Phil. Soc.*, Vol. 13, p. 241 (1906).

† Holborn and Henning, *Ann. d. Physik*, Vol. 23, p. 809 (1907).

‡ See Callendar, *B. A. Report*, p. 334 (1908).

§ Nernst, *Zeits. f. Elektrochemie*, Vol. 16, p. 96 (1910).

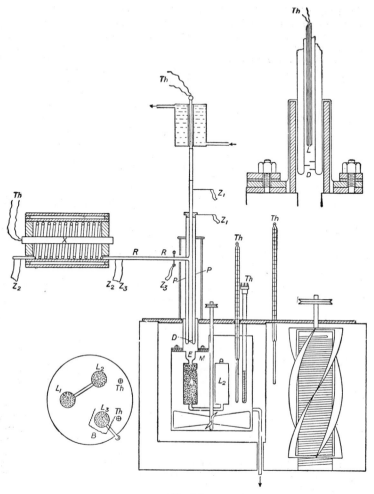

Fig. 6.4

10. The Continuous-flow Method.

The continuous-flow method or that of stationary electric heating was first applied to gases by Swann.* The most accurate work using this method is that of Scheel and Heuse,† who used the method between room temperature and −180° C. Their calorimeter is shown in fig. 6.5.

* Swann, *Proc. Roy. Soc.*, A, Vol. 82, p. 147 (1909).
† Scheel and Heuse, *Ann. d. Physik*, Vol. 37, p. 79 (1912); Vol. 40, p. 473 (1913); Vol. 95, p. 86 (1919).

The calorimeter is of glass and is sealed inside the tube M which is evacuated to reduce heat loss. The whole calorimeter is immersed in a constant-temperature bath. After passing through a long tube which is immersed in this bath, the gas enters the calorimeter at the bottom and flows past the platinum thermometer P_1, which measures the inlet temperature. To reach the heater K, which is of constantan wire, it has to flow up between the walls C and B, and then down between the walls B and A. By this arrangement any heat escaping from the heater is brought back by the stream of oncoming gas. The copper gauze G serves to mix the gas thoroughly before it reaches the thermometer P_2. The difference between the readings of P_1 and P_2 gives the rise of temperature of the gas stream.

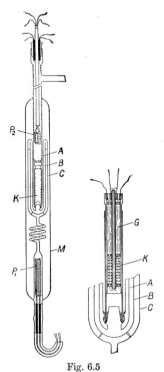

Fig. 6.5

The method has been used by Knoblauch and his co-workers * in experiments on steam between 110° and 350° C. and up to pressures of 30 atmospheres; and by Haber † for ammonia.

11. Experiments of Blackett, Henry, and Rideal.

An accurate flow method in which the difficult problems of measuring the temperature of the gas and of determining heat losses are avoided has been devised by Blackett, Henry, and Rideal.‡ It has been used up to 370° C. and with suitable modifications can be used up to considerably higher temperatures.

One form of the apparatus is shown in fig. 6.6. The fine iron tube AA about 11 cm. long through which the gas flowed had an internal diameter of 1·4 mm. and an external diameter of 2 mm. It was surrounded by a massive iron tube BB which had conical holes at the ends in which the conical steel plugs CC fitted. These were held in place by the screwed collars DD and were electrically insulated from B by thin mica sheets shown black in the figure. The conical plugs carried cylindrical plugs EE in which the experimental tube fitted tightly. Fine constantan wires were attached to the tube and with it formed thermocouples. The two outer wires were accurately symmetrical about the middle one. The temperature of the jacket B was measured by a calibrated thermocouple.

The whole apparatus was placed inside a nichrome-wound furnace and the

* Knoblauch and Jacob, *Zeits. d. Ver. deuts. Ing.*, Vol. 51, p. 81 (1917); Knoblauch and Mollier, Vol. 55, p. 665 (1911); Knoblauch and Winkhaus, Vol. 59, p. 376 (1915); Knoblauch and Raisch, Vol. 66, p. 418 (1922).

† Haber, *Zeits. f. Elektrochemie*, Vol. 21, p. 228 (1915); see also Osborne, Stimson, Sligh, and Cragoe, *Refrig. Eng.*, Vol. 10, p. 145 (1923).

‡ Blackett, Henry, and Rideal, *Proc. Roy. Soc.*, A, Vol. 126, p. 319 (1930); Henry, *Proc. Roy. Soc.*, A, Vol. 133, p. 492 (1931); see also Chapman, *Proc. Roy. Soc.*, A, Vol. 126, p. 675 (1930).

jacket B was thus brought to the temperature at which the specific heat was required. The ends of the tube AA were at the same temperature as B, but the tube itself was heated by passing an alternating current through it so that the temperature of the centre was in general about 5 degrees above that of B. The tube was accurately centred using the screws SS, the adjustment being carried out by observing when the two outer thermocouple wires connected through a galvanometer gave no deflection.

Gas was then passed slowly at a measured rate through the tube and caused the temperature of the thermocouple on the inlet side of the middle to fall and that of the other one to rise. The difference Δ between the temperatures of the outer thermocouples was measured directly by opposing them and measuring the resultant E.M.F. The temperature excess θ_m of the middle of the tube above B (that is, above the ends) was also measured.

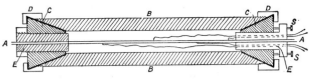

Fig. 6.6

For a given value of θ_m and a given gas the value of Δ will depend on the rate of flow q (measured in c.c. per second). The detailed theory of the method shows that the limiting value when $q = 0$ of the slope of the curve connecting Δ/θ_m and q is proportional to σ, the specific heat per unit volume of the gas; that is, that

$$\underset{q \to 0}{\mathrm{Lim}} \frac{d}{dq}\left(\frac{\Delta}{\theta_m}\right) = A\sigma,$$

where A is a constant that depends on the tube and not on the gas.

To compare the specific heats at constant pressure per unit volume of two gases at a given temperature all that is necessary is to pass first one gas and then the other at varying rates through the tube and to plot Δ/θ_m (both of which are measured directly) against q. The ratio of the slopes of the two curves extrapolated to $q = 0$ gives the ratio of the specific heats.*

An experimental test of the method at ordinary temperatures was obtained by using air, helium, hydrogen and carbon dioxide at 20° C., and the actual results for air, hydrogen, and carbon dioxide are plotted in fig. 6.7 with Δ/θ_m measured in arbitrary units. It will be seen that the slopes of the curves at $q = 0$ can be accurately determined. The specific heats of all these gases are in fact accurately known at this temperature, and the following results were obtained for the ratio (C_p of gas/C_p of air).

Gas	Flow method	Accepted value
Helium	0·717	0·716
Hydrogen	0·986	0·987
Carbon dioxide ..	1·264	1·268

These gases have widely different properties and the agreement in all cases with

* For two ideal gases at a given temperature and pressure the ratio of the specific heats at constant pressure per unit volume is equal to the ratio of the molecular heats at constant pressure. This follows from Avogadro's law.

the accepted values is satisfactory. It was shown also that values of θ_m varying from 3 to 20 degrees could be used without affecting the results.

At higher temperatures a monatomic gas must be used as the standard (compare Sections 6, 25 and 26) and the validity of the method up to 370° C. has been established experimentally by Henry by using both argon and helium (which differ widely in their properties—thermal conductivity, density, &c.) as standards and showing that concordant results were obtained.

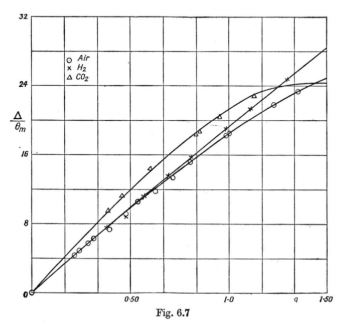

Fig. 6.7

THE RATIO OF THE SPECIFIC HEATS OF A GAS

In addition to the above methods of measuring specific heats there is an important group of methods which depend on the measurement of the *ratio* of the specific heats. From this measurement the individual values of C_p and C_v can be deduced by using equation (16) (or for a perfect gas, equation (4)), which gives their difference.

To understand these methods we must consider some further points in the theory of gases.

Adiabatic Changes

12. So far we have considered two types of change in a gas: (1) the volume of the gas remains constant, and energy is supplied, causing a change in the pressure and in the temperature; (2) the pressure remains constant, and energy is supplied, causing a change in the volume and

in the temperature. In both of these cases heat is supplied from out-side.

We shall now consider a type of change of which the characteristic feature is that *there is no exchange of heat between the gas and its sur-roundings*. This is, of course, the case in which the system under in-vestigation is enclosed by an adiabatic wall (Chapter I, Section 2). The corresponding change is called an *adiabatic change*.*

Applying the first law of thermodynamics, we have for such a change

Decrease of internal energy $=$ External work performed.

If we call U the internal energy, we may write

$$dU = -p\,dV, \quad \ldots \ldots \ldots \quad (17)$$

where dU is the *increase* in the internal energy. The general equation applies to all such changes.

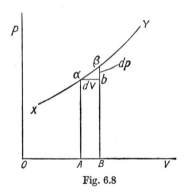

Fig. 6.8

Let us suppose that we have 1 gram-molecule of a gas contained in a cylinder fitted with a moving piston, both the cylinder and the piston being made of some material which is impermeable to heat. Let the changes in the gas be represented in fig. 6.8, in which pressures are plotted as ordinates and volumes as abscissæ. The relation between the pressure and the volume will be represented by a curve $X\alpha\beta Y$; our object is to find the equation of this curve.

13. Perfect Gases.

Let us first consider a perfect gas. Let the pressure, volume, and temperature at the point α be respectively p, V, and T, and at the

---

* For a fuller discussion of adiabatic changes, see Chapter XII, Sections 2 and **3**.

point β let them be $p + dp$, $V + dV$, and $T + dT$. For a perfect gas we have

$$pV = RT,$$

and $$(p + dp)(V + dV) = R(T + dT);$$

that is, neglecting products of the small quantities dp and dV,

$$p\,dV + V\,dp = R\,dT. \quad \ldots \ldots \quad (18)$$

By equation (17) $$dU = -p\,dV,$$

and for a perfect gas the increase in the internal energy is equal to the molecular heat at constant volume multiplied by the rise of temperature; that is,

$$dU = C_v\,dT. \quad \ldots \ldots \ldots \quad (19)$$

Using this result, the preceding equation becomes

$$C_v\,dT = -p\,dV. \quad \ldots \ldots \quad (20)$$

Eliminating dT between equation (18) and (20), and using the result expressed in equation (4) that

$$C_p - C_v = R, \quad \ldots \ldots \ldots \quad (4)$$

we obtain $$\frac{dp}{p} = -\frac{C_p}{C_v}\frac{dV}{V}.$$

Writing $$\frac{C_p}{C_v} = \gamma,$$

this equation becomes $$\frac{dp}{p} = -\gamma\frac{dV}{V}. \quad \ldots \ldots \ldots \quad (21)$$

This is the differential equation of the curve XY in fig. 6.8.

We may obtain the following further differential equations from equations (18), (20), and (4).

To obtain the relation between dV and dT: substitute RT/V for p in equation (20) and substitute for R from (4), and we have

$$(\gamma - 1)\frac{dV}{V} = -\frac{dT}{T}. \quad \ldots \ldots \quad (22)$$

To obtain the relation between dp and dT, eliminate dV between equations (18) and (20) and substitute for R from (4), and we have

$$\frac{\gamma - 1}{\gamma}\frac{dp}{p} = \frac{dT}{T}. \quad \ldots \ldots \quad (23)$$

If we wish to integrate equations (21), (22), and (23) in terms of elementary functions, we must make the assumption that C_v, and therefore also C_p and γ, are independent of the temperature. It is important to realize that this constancy is not implied in the definition of a perfect gas. Making this assumption and integrating, we obtain

$$\log p + \gamma \log V = constant, \text{ or } pV^\gamma = constant; \quad (21a)$$

$$(\gamma - 1) \log V + \log T = constant, \text{ or } TV^{\gamma-1} = constant; \quad (22a)$$

$$\left(\frac{\gamma-1}{\gamma}\right) \log p - \log T = constant, \text{ or } \frac{p^{(\gamma-1)/\gamma}}{T} = constant. \quad (23a)$$

If we start from an arbitrary zero condition in which $p = p_0$, $V = V_0$, $T = T_0$, we have

$$\frac{p}{p_0} = \left(\frac{V_0}{V}\right)^\gamma = \left(\frac{T}{T_0}\right)^{\gamma/(\gamma-1)}. \quad \ldots \quad (24)$$

Even if C_v is not independent of the temperature, the integrated equations will hold over a small range of temperatures for which C_v is sensibly constant.

14. Actual Gases.

Consider two states of a system which are such that it is possible to pass from state A to state B by an adiabatic change. Let the pressure and the volume of the system when it is in these two states be $p + \Delta p$ and $V + \Delta V$, and p and V, respectively. Consider also a state C which is such that it is possible to pass from A to C by a constant-pressure change and from B to C by a constant-volume change. Thus, C is the state of the system in which the pressure and the volume of the system are $p + \Delta p$ and V. Let the temperatures of the states A, B, and C be $T + \delta T_1$, $T + \delta T_2$, and T respectively. Then Δp and ΔV are the changes in pressure and volume, and

$$\Delta T = \delta T_1 - \delta T_2 \quad \ldots \quad \ldots \quad (25)$$

is the change in temperature in passing *adiabatically* from A to B. The internal energy is a function of the state of the system, so that the change in internal energy in passing from A to B is independent of the path by which the change is effected. Using appropriate suffixes to denote the internal energy of the various states, the change in internal energy in an adiabatic change from state A to state B is

$$U_B - U_A = p\Delta V. \quad \ldots \quad \ldots \quad (26)$$

Now consider the same change carried out in two steps. First, take the system from state A to state C by a constant-pressure process, and then from state C to state B by a constant-volume process. In the first step, external work of amount $p\Delta V$ is expended. Thus, introducing the specific heats at constant pressure and constant volume, we have

$$U_o - U_A = -C_p \delta T_1 + p\Delta V,$$

and

$$U_B - U_o = C_v \delta T_2.$$

Thus, we obtain another expression for the change in internal energy in going from state A to state B,

$$U_B - U_A = p\Delta V - C_p \delta T_1 + C_v \delta T_2. \qquad . \ . \ . \quad (27)$$

Equations (26) and (27) yield the relation

$$C_p \delta T_1 - C_v \delta T_2 = 0. \qquad . \ . \ . \ . \ . \ . \quad (28)$$

Since the system passes from state A to state C by a constant-pressure process, the difference in temperature of these two states is given by

$$\delta T_1 = \left(\frac{\partial T}{\partial V}\right)_p \Delta V; \qquad . \ . \ . \ . \ . \ . \quad (29)$$

likewise, since the system passes from state C to state B by a constant-volume process, the difference in temperature between these two states is given by

$$\delta T_2 = -\left(\frac{\partial T}{\partial p}\right)_V \Delta p. \qquad . \ . \ . \ . \ . \quad (30)$$

Substituting equations (29) and (30) in equation (28), we obtain

$$C_p \left(\frac{\partial T}{\partial V}\right)_p \Delta V + C_v \left(\frac{\partial T}{\partial p}\right)_V \Delta p = 0, \qquad . \ . \ . \quad (31)$$

and the Δp and ΔV which occur in this equation are the changes in pressure and volume in the *adiabatic* change from A to B. Furthermore,[*]

$$\left(\frac{\partial T}{\partial V}\right)_p \bigg/ \left(\frac{\partial T}{\partial p}\right)_V = -\left(\frac{\partial p}{\partial V}\right)_T.$$

---

[*] This is simply an application of the fact that if there is a functional relationship

$$f(x, y, z) = 0$$

between three variables, so that any one of them is given implicitly as a function of the other two, then

$$\left(\frac{\partial x}{\partial y}\right)_z \left(\frac{\partial y}{\partial z}\right)_x \left(\frac{\partial z}{\partial x}\right)_y = -1.$$

This result follows from a consideration of the partial derivatives of f with respect to the three variables.

Thus, if we use a subscript S to denote an adiabatic change, and a subscript T to denote an isothermal change, the ratio of the slopes of the adiabatic and isothermal lines in the pV-diagram is given by

$$\left(\frac{\partial p}{\partial V}\right)_S = \gamma \left(\frac{\partial p}{\partial V}\right)_T, \quad \cdots \cdots \quad (32)$$

where γ is the ratio of the specific heat at constant pressure to that at constant volume.

Further, equation (28) can be written as

$$(C_p - C_v)\delta T_1 - C_v(\delta T_2 - \delta T_1) = 0,$$

and, using equations (25) and (29), this leads to

$$(C_p - C_v)\left(\frac{\partial T}{\partial V}\right)_p \Delta V + C_v \Delta T = 0.$$

Thus, it follows that the ratio of the adiabatic to the constant pressure coefficient of expansion is given by

$$\left(\frac{\partial V}{\partial T}\right)_S = -\frac{1}{\gamma - 1}\left(\frac{\partial V}{\partial T}\right)_p. \quad \cdots \cdots \quad (33)$$

Again, equation (28) can be written as

$$(C_p - C_v)\delta T_2 - C_p(\delta T_2 - \delta T_1) = 0,$$

and, using equations (25) and (30), this leads to

$$(C_p - C_v)\left(\frac{\partial T}{\partial p}\right)_V \Delta p - C_p \Delta T = 0.$$

Thus, the ratio of the adiabatic to the constant volume pressure coefficient is given by

$$\left(\frac{\partial p}{\partial T}\right)_S = \frac{\gamma}{\gamma - 1}\left(\frac{\partial p}{\partial T}\right)_V. \quad \cdots \cdots \quad (34)$$

These formulæ are used in deriving the equation for an actual gas which corresponds to equation (24) for an ideal gas.

If the gases are not too highly compressed we may use the expansion in a power series for the equation of state as far as the term in p. Thus

$$pV = RT + Bp.$$

Differentiating this equation, we have

$$\left(\frac{\partial p}{\partial V}\right)_T = -\frac{p}{V-B};$$

$$\left(\frac{\partial V}{\partial T}\right)_p = \frac{V-B}{T} + \frac{dB}{dT};$$

$$\left(\frac{\partial p}{\partial T}\right)_V = \frac{p}{T}\left(1 + \frac{p}{R}\frac{dB}{dT}\right);$$

and, using these values in equations (32), (33), and (34), we have for infinitesimal adiabatic changes

$$\gamma\frac{dV}{V-B} = -\frac{dp}{p}; \quad \dots \quad (35)$$

$$(\gamma-1)\frac{dV}{V-B} = -\frac{dT}{T}\left(1 + \frac{T}{V-B}\frac{dB}{dT}\right); \quad \dots \quad (36)$$

$$\left(\frac{\gamma-1}{\gamma}\right)\frac{dp}{p} = \frac{dT}{T}\left(1 + \frac{p}{R}\frac{dB}{dT}\right). \quad \dots \quad (37)$$

The last equation, (30), is the most important of the three. It cannot be integrated in terms of elementary functions, but for *small* changes of pressure, and assuming that γ is a constant, Nernst has deduced from Berthelot's equation the approximate integral relation *

$$\left(\frac{p}{p_0}\right)^{\frac{\gamma-1}{\gamma}} = \frac{T}{T_0}\left(1 + \frac{27}{32}\frac{\pi}{\theta^3}\right), \quad \dots \quad (38)$$

where $\quad \pi = \dfrac{p+p_0}{2p_c}, \quad$ and $\quad \theta = \dfrac{T+T_0}{2T_c}.$

Equation (38) may be used to deduce the value of γ from experimental measurements.

15. Experimental Methods.

The earliest experimental work on adiabatic processes is that of Clement and Désormes (1819). The gas is contained in a large vessel provided with a stopcock and a pressure gauge. The initial pressure p_1 is slightly above that of the atmosphere. The stopcock is opened and rapidly closed again. While it is open the pressure falls to p, the pressure of the atmosphere. The expansion of the gas is adiabatic, and during the expansion the gas is cooled. After the stopcock is closed

---

* See Nernst, *Theoretical Chemistry*, p. 259 (English trans., 5th edition, 1923).

again the gas takes up heat from its surroundings until it reaches its initial temperature, and in doing so its pressure increases. Let the final pressure reached be p_2.

From a measurement of p_1, p, p_2 the value of γ for the gas can be calculated.

We will assume that the gas is perfect. Let the volume originally occupied by the mass of gas, which after the stopcock is opened fills the vessel, be $\mathbf{V}_1$; and let the volume of the vessel be $\mathbf{V}$.

For the adiabatic process we have

$$p_1\mathbf{V}_1{}^\gamma = p\mathbf{V}^\gamma;$$

and, remembering that the initial and final temperatures are equal,

$$p_1\mathbf{V}_1 = p_2\mathbf{V}.$$

Eliminating $\mathbf{V}_1$ and $\mathbf{V}$ from these two equations, we have

$$\left(\frac{p_1}{p_2}\right)^\gamma = \frac{p_1}{p},$$

or
$$\gamma = \frac{\log p_1 - \log p}{\log p_1 - \log p_2}. \qquad \ldots \ldots \quad (39)$$

A most serious difficulty in using the method of Clement and Désormes is that, when the stopcock is opened, oscillations occur and it is impossible to know exactly the right moment at which to close the stopcock. Lummer and Pringsheim (1894) overcame this difficulty by measuring the change in the temperature of the gas after adiabatic expansion, in which case it is not necessary to close the stopcock.

A modern form of Lummer and Pringsheim's apparatus used by Partington * is shown in fig. 6.9. The gas was contained in the vessel A, and its temperature change after expansion was measured by the change in the resistance of the fine platinum wire B, which was at its centre. We shall call B the *bolometer*.

In order to obtain accurate results by this method the following conditions must be satisfied:

(1) A galvanometer of very rapid period must be used so that a detailed record of the temperature changes in the bolometer, during and after expansion, can be made. Partington used an Einthoven string galvanometer G, capable of recording changes in 0·01 sec.

(2) The bolometer must have a very small heat capacity, must be as free as possible from lag, and must be so constructed that the effect of conduction of heat along the leads is eliminated. Partington used

* Partington, *Phys. Zeits.*, Vol. 14, p. 969 (1913); *Proc. Roy. Soc.*, A, Vol. 100, p. 27 (1921); see also Eucken, Lüde, and Hoffman, *Zeits. f. phys. Chem.*, B, Vol. 5, pp. 413, 442 (1929).

a bolometer B (shown separately in the figure) of platinum wire 0·001 to 0·002 mm. in diameter, with compensating leads, so that the effect of conduction along the leads was eliminated. The amount of wire attached to the compensating leads was found by trial.

(3) A large expansion vessel must be used, so as to reduce the effects of conduction and convection in the gas. Partington used a spherical copper vessel A of 130 litres capacity. With this large vessel and with proper compensation in the bolometer, the galvanometer deflection occurred instantaneously, remained perfectly steady for some seconds, and then changed in the opposite direction.

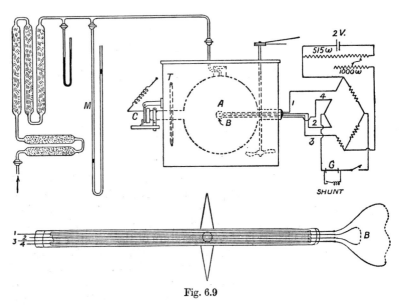

Fig. 6.9

The initial excess pressure above the atmosphere was read on an oil manometer M, and the atmospheric pressure on a Fortin barometer. The size of the expansion valve C could be varied by inserting diaphragms of brass plate. The actual expansion orifice was made gradually smaller by means of these diaphragms until no overshooting took place when the gas was released. When overshooting is eliminated the galvanometer deflection is instantaneous and steady. With too large an aperture the gas surges backwards and forwards, and on this account the galvanometer deflection is not steady, the initial deflection being slightly greater than the true value. With too small an aperture the expansion is prolonged and not adiabatic.

The actual method of experimenting was to lower the resistance in the arm of the bridge opposite to the bolometer by an arbitrary amount. The initial excess pressure was then varied until the galvano-meter showed no deflection if its circuit was closed immediately the expansion had taken place. The temperature change corresponding to this fixed lowering of resistance was afterwards determined by adding iced water to the bath containing the expansion vessel until the gal-vanometer again showed no deflection. Both this temperature and the temperature before expansion were measured on a standardized thermometer T. The results were deduced using equation (38).

A further modification of Lummer and Pringsheim's method has been used by Kistiakowsky and Rice.* They have used a new design of the expansion chamber and incorporated a means of measuring the pressure accurately and rapidly. They have also found that if a wol-laston wire is subjected to extensive heat treatment, the electrical properties of the wire are stabilized. Using such wollaston wires as a resistance thermometer, they have found that the changes in resis-tance which follow changes in the pressure of the gas, as a result of the expansion of the gas, can be turned into temperature changes directly by means of coefficients of resistance which are determined separately. Their experimental data on air and carbon dioxide can be compared with the theoretical values (see Section 25). They have also made measurements on ethane and deutero-ethane.

Assmann † showed that the oscillations of a mercury column en-closing a quantity of gas can be used to study adiabatic changes in a gas. Rüchardt ‡ has improved the accuracy of the method by replac-ing the mercury column by a steel ball in an accurately ground tube. Clark and Katz § have also used a modification of Assmann's method in which the gas is enclosed in two chambers formed by the ends of a cylinder with a steel piston in the middle of it. The piston is caused to oscillate by an alternating electromotive force applied in coils out-side the cylinder, thus subjecting the gas to alternate compressions and rarefactions. The system has a natural frequency of oscillation depending on the constants of the apparatus and the value of γ for the gas. The frequency of the alternating electromotive force is varied. The amplitude of the oscillation of the piston is varied, and the frequency for which resonance occurs is measured. The method yields results of great reproducibility and accuracy. The results which have been obtained for some of the gases which Clark and Katz have meas-ured are given below, where they are compared with the theoretical values.

---

* Kistiakowsky and Rice, *Journ. Chem. Phys.*, Vol. 7, p. 281 (1939).

† Assmann, *Ann. Phys.*, Vol. 85, p. 1 (1852); see also M. Aubert-Heutz, *C. R. Acad. Sci.*, Paris, Vol. 235, p. 25 (1952).

‡ Rüchardt, *Phys. Zeit.*, Vol. 30, p. 58 (1929); see also Brodersen, *Zeits. f. Physik*, Vol. 62, p. 180 (1930).

§ Clark and Katz, *Can. Journ. Res.*, A, Vol. 18, p. 23 (1940); *ibid.*, Vol. 19, p. 111 (1941); *ibid.*, Vol. 21, p. 1 (1943).

Gas	Temperature, °C.	Experimental value (extrapolated to zero pressure)	Theoretical value
Helium	23·0	1·666$_9$	1·6667
Argon	24·2	1·666$_7$	1·6667
Hydrogen	24·4	1·404$_5$	1·4000
Nitrogen	23·0	1·400$_6$	1·4000

Clark and Katz made measurements at different pressures and report values of γ for pressures up to about 25 atmospheres. They found that for simple gases γ varied linearly with pressure for moderate pressures. They showed that this behaviour was consistent * with that of a gas which has an equation of state

$$pV = RT + Bp.$$

The Velocity of Sound

16. The sound vibrations in a gas are so slow † that the changes accompanying them are adiabatic. From this it follows (see Example 2 at the end of Chapter XIII) that the velocity of sound Υ is given by the relation

$$\Upsilon^2 = \gamma \left(\frac{\partial p}{\partial \rho} \right)_T, \quad \ldots \ldots \quad (40)$$

where ρ is the density. The value of $(\partial p/\partial \rho)_T$ can be deduced from the equation of state of the gas. Thus from a measurement of Υ the value of γ can be determined. This furnishes one of the most convenient and accurate methods of measuring specific heats. For a perfect gas, equation (40) gives

$$\Upsilon^2 = \gamma RT/M.$$

For an actual gas the value of $(\partial p/\partial \rho)_T$ can be deduced from the equation of state as follows. We write the equation in the usual form,

$$pV = RT + Bp.$$

We have
$$\left(\frac{\partial p}{\partial \rho} \right)_T = \left(\frac{\partial p}{\partial V} \right)_T \frac{\partial V}{\partial v} \frac{\partial v}{\partial \rho};$$

* See also Example 7 at the end of Chapter XIII; compare Rundle, *Journ. Amer. Chem. Soc.*, Vol. 66, p. 1797 (1944).

† Wood, Alex., *Acoustics*, Blackie (1940), p. 123.

V refers to 1 gram-molecule and v to 1 gm. We have, therefore,

$$V = Mv, \text{ and } v = 1/\rho,$$

from which

$$\frac{\partial V}{\partial v} = M, \text{ and } \frac{\partial v}{\partial \rho} = -\frac{V^2}{M^2};$$

where M is the molecular weight. The value of $\left(\dfrac{\partial p}{\partial V}\right)_T$ is given by

$$\left(\frac{\partial p}{\partial V}\right)_T = -\frac{p}{V - B}.$$

We have, therefore,

$$\left(\frac{\partial p}{\partial \rho}\right)_T = \frac{1}{M}\frac{pV^2}{V - B}$$

$$= \frac{RT}{M}\left(1 + \frac{Bp}{RT}\right)^2$$

$$= \frac{RT}{M}\left(1 + 2\frac{Bp}{RT}\right).$$

The last expression is a first approximation.

Using the value of B given by Berthelot's equation (see equation (21), Chapter IV), and substituting the result in equation (40), we obtain

$$\Upsilon^2 = \gamma\frac{RT}{M}\left\{1 + \frac{9}{64}\frac{p}{p_c}\frac{T_c}{T}\left(1 - 6\frac{T_c^2}{T^2}\right)\right\}. \quad \cdot \quad \cdot \quad (41)$$

From the measured value of Υ at temperature T and pressure p the value of γ can be deduced, using this equation.

An alternative method which involves the deduction of equation (40) in a particular case can be given as follows. For a perfect gas, the equation of state can be written in the form

$$p = RT\rho/M,$$

where ρ is the density and M is the molecular weight. For an adiabatic process, the first law of thermodynamics can be written

$$C_v\Delta T - (pM/\rho^2)\Delta\rho = 0.$$

Thus, for the re-establishment of equilibrium following the passage of a sound wave, we have

$$C_v\frac{\partial T}{\partial t} - \frac{pM}{\rho^2}\frac{\partial\rho}{\partial t} = 0. \quad \cdot \quad \cdot \quad \cdot \quad \cdot \quad \cdot \quad \cdot \quad (42)$$

where t measures the time. If u is the velocity of a molecule in the gas, and x is its displacement, the equation of motion is

$$\frac{\partial u}{\partial t} = \frac{1}{\rho}\frac{\partial p}{\partial x} = -\frac{RT}{M}\left(\frac{\partial \log T}{\partial x} + \frac{\partial \log \rho}{\partial x}\right), \quad \cdot \quad \cdot \quad \cdot \quad (43)$$

and the equation of continuity is

$$\frac{\partial \rho}{\partial t} + \frac{\partial(\rho u)}{\partial x} = 0. \qquad \ldots \ldots \ldots \ldots \quad (44)$$

The equation of a plane sound wave, propagated in the x-direction, can be written as

$$P = P_0 \exp i(\omega t - kx), \qquad \ldots \ldots \ldots \quad (45)$$

where P is the local pressure in the gas, $\omega/2\pi$ is the frequency, $2\pi/k$ is the wavelength and k is the wave vector. If the condensation s and the relative excess temperature θ are defined by

$$T = T_0(1 + \theta),$$
$$\rho = \rho_0(1 + s),$$

where T_0 and ρ_0 are the temperature and the density respectively in the unperturbed state, and θ, s, and u are also of the form (45), these equations reduce to

$$\omega u - \frac{RT_0}{M} k(\theta + s) = 0, \qquad \ldots \ldots \ldots \quad (42')$$

$$\omega s - ku = 0, \qquad \ldots \ldots \ldots \quad (43')$$

and

$$\omega C_v T_0 \theta - \frac{pM}{\rho} \omega s = 0. \qquad \ldots \ldots \ldots \quad (44')$$

These equations have a non-trivial solution only if the determinant formed by the coefficients vanishes, that is, if

$$k^2 = \frac{M}{\gamma RT} \omega^2. \qquad \ldots \ldots \ldots \ldots \quad (46)$$

In this case, the wave vector is real, and the velocity of propagation of the sound wave is given by

$$\Upsilon^2 = \gamma RT/M. \qquad \ldots \ldots \ldots \ldots \quad (47)$$

It should be noted that the velocity of sound propagation in a gas is of the same order of magnitude as the root-mean-square velocity of the gas molecules. The method which we have just presented will be used when we consider the dispersion of ultrasonic waves in a gas (Section 30).

17. The Velocity of Sound in Free Air.

Most of the earlier determinations of the velocity of sound were made in the open and over long distances. Such determinations are affected to an unknown extent by wind and by the presence of moisture and are of little use for the present purpose.

An accurate determination has been made by Hebb * by a method depending on the reflection of the sound between two paraboloids

* Hebb, *Phys. Rev.*, Vol. 20, p. 89 (1905); Vol. 14, p. 74 (1919).

15 in. in diameter and placed 5 ft. apart. The value obtained by Hebb after correction for the amount of moisture present is *

Velocity in dry air at 0° C. $= 331 \cdot 41$ metre sec^{-1}.

There have been several determinations of the velocity of sound in recent years. Lenihan † gives

$$331 \cdot 45 \pm 0 \cdot 04 \text{ metre sec.}^{-1}$$

for the velocity of sound in dry air at 0° C. Hardy ‡ and his colleagues give

$$343 \cdot 42 \pm 0 \cdot 07 \text{ metre sec.}^{-1}$$

for the velocity of sound in dry air at 20° C. Caro and Martin § measured the time of transit of a sinusoidal pulse between two condenser microphones placed about four metres apart. They made measurements at 250 c/s and 1000 c/s over a range of pressures extending down to 5 mm. of mercury. They give

$$343 \cdot 40 \pm 0 \cdot 02 \text{ metre sec.}^{-1}$$

for the velocity of sound in dry air at 20° C. These recent determinations agree amongst themselves (allowing for the different temperatures at which the results are stated) and are also practically the same as Hebb's value.

The value of γ deduced from this value of the velocity of sound is

$$\gamma = 1 \cdot 4031.$$

As we shall see in the next section, all measurements of specific heats using the velocity of sound method ultimately depend on the accuracy of Hebb's result.

The measurements by Caro and Martin § provide no evidence for supposing that the velocity of sound increases at low pressures as had been reported by Abbey and Barlow ‖ and by Maulard.¶ There was in

---

* See Partington and Shilling, *The Specific Heats of Gases*, p. 80 (Benn, 1924).

† J. M. A. Lenihan, *Acustica*, Vol. 2, p. 205 (1952).

‡ H. C. Hardy, D. Telfair, and W. H. Pielemeier, *Journ. Acous. Sci. Amer.*, Vol. 13, p. 226 (1942).

§ D. E. Caro and L. H. Martin, *Nature*, London, Vol. 172, p. 363 (1953); *Proc. Phys. Soc.*, Vol. 66, p. 760 (1953).

‖ R. L. Abbey and G. E. Barlow, *Aust. Journ. Sci. Res.*, A, Vol. 1, p. 175 (1948); R. L. Abbey, *ibid.*, Vol. 5, p. 233 (1952).

¶ J. Maulard, *C. R. Acad. Sci.*, Paris, Vol. 229, p. 1 (1949).

any case no acceptable explanation of the pressure effect reported in these latter observations, and the experiments carried out by Caro and Martin appear to be conclusive that the free-space velocity of sound is independent of pressure.

18. The Velocity in a Tube.

Equation (47) refers to the velocity of sound in a gas in an unconfined space. All of the determinations of the velocity other than those in air at ordinary temperatures have been made in tubes, the velocity in a tube differs appreciably from that in an open space. A correction must be made for this fact.

The correction depends on three factors: (1) the gas, (2) the tube, and (3) the frequency of the sound. The most satisfactory way of dealing with the correction appears to be to write

$$\Upsilon' = \Upsilon(1 - kc),$$

where Υ' is the observed velocity in the tube and Υ is the true velocity in the free gas.

c depends on the coefficient of viscosity, the thermal conductivity, the density, and the specific heat (or the value of γ *) of the gas. The way in which c varies with these various quantities has been calculated from theoretical considerations by Kirchhoff.† His result can be written in the form

$$c = \sqrt{\frac{\eta}{\rho}} \left\{ 1 + \sqrt{\epsilon} \left(\frac{\gamma - 1}{\sqrt{\gamma}} \right) \right\},$$

where

$$\epsilon = \frac{\kappa}{\eta C_v},$$

and η is the coefficient of viscosity and κ is the thermal conductivity According to Eucken, $\epsilon = \frac{1}{4}(9\gamma - 5)$.

k depends on the tube (radius, thickness, surface, thermal conductivity, etc.) and on the frequency of the sound. We assume that k remains constant when the tube is filled with various gases or when

---

* The object of the experiments is to determine γ, which is not known. We are only considering a correction term, however, and it is sufficient in this to use an approximate value of γ which can be deduced without making the correction.

† Kirchhoff, *Ann. d. Physik*, Vol. 134, p. 177 (1868).

its temperature is changed, provided that the frequency of the sound remains constant. With this assumption the value of k is determined by filling the tube with dry air free from carbon dioxide for which Υ, the true velocity at $0°$ C., is known as a result of Hebb's experiments, and determining Υ', the velocity of sound in the tube. The value of c can be calculated from the above formula of Kirchhoff, and thus k is determined.*

19. Experimental Methods.

We shall now consider the various experimental methods by which the velocity of sound in a tube can be determined. All the methods except that of Dixon depend on the determination of the wave-length λ of sound of known frequency n. The velocity follows from the relation

$$\Upsilon = n\lambda.$$

The value of λ is determined by setting up stationary vibrations in the gas in the tube and determining the distance between nodes.

20. Dust Figure Methods.

The earliest method is that of Kundt, whose apparatus is illustrated in fig. 6.10. Two tubes A and B are connected by a sounding-rod S, which passes through the indiarubber sheets m_1 and m_2 which close the ends of the tubes. One of the tubes is kept filled with air and the other with the gas in question. When the sounding-rod is made to

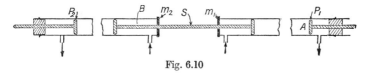

Fig. 6.10

vibrate by stroking it, the gas in the tubes is set into vibration. The motion of the gas may be followed by observing the motion of fine powder (lycopodium or fine silica dust) scattered lightly along the tube. The powder collects in small heaps at the nodes, where the movement is a minimum. The positions of the pistons P_1 and P_2 are adjusted until the vibration is stationary, which means that the distance between the pistons and the ends of the sounding-rods is equal to an exact number of half wave-lengths of the sound in the gas. The wavelength is determined by measuring the distance between the successive heaps of powder at the nodes and multiplying by 2.

* For a fuller discussion of this question, see Partington and Shilling, *The Specific Heats of Gases*, pp. 52–53; Dixon, *Proc. Roy. Soc.*, A, Vol. 100, p. 1 (1921); and Vol. 105, p. 199 (1924); P. S. H. Henry, *Proc. Phys. Soc.*, Vol. 43, p. 340 (1931).

This method gives a direct comparison between the velocity of sound in the gas and that in air, so that the actual frequency of the sounding-rod need not be known. Apart from small corrections dealt with above, if λ_g and λ_a are the measured wave-lengths in the gas and in the air tubes, and if Υ_g and Υ_a are the velocities, we have

$$\frac{\Upsilon_g}{\Upsilon_a} = \frac{\lambda_g}{\lambda_a}.$$

Interesting applications of the method of Kundt are found in the work of Kundt and Warburg * on mercury vapour, and in the work of Ramsay † on argon and helium. All these gases were found to be monatomic (see Section 25).

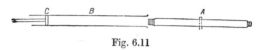

Fig. 6.11

Kundt's method has been improved by Behn and Geiger,‡ whose apparatus is shown in fig. 6.11. The gas is contained in a closed tube, which is held at the central point by the clamp A. The tube itself is used as the source of sound and it projects into the end of the air comparison tube B. The latter is brought into resonance with it by adjusting the piston C. To bring the tube itself into resonance with the gas inside it, so that an exact number of half wave-lengths occupies the length of the tube, small weights in the form of metal discs are added to the ends as required. The tube correction is determined by filling the tube with air. The method has been used by Partington and Shilling § and others.

21. The Method of Partington and Shilling.

A method has been developed by Partington and Shilling ‖ in which the use of dust in the tube is avoided. The method is particularly suitable for work at high temperatures and has been applied up to 1000° C. The apparatus is shown in fig. 6.12.

A silica tube FF, 4 cm. bore and 230 cm. long, is wound for 200 cm. of its length with heating coils so arranged that a uniform temperature can be obtained over the whole length. At X a glass tube of similar diameter and 150 cm. long is attached by means of the screwed joint. Inside the silica tube F is a piston,

* Kundt and Warburg, *Ann. d. Physik*, Vol. 157, p. 353 (1876).

† Ramsay, *J. C. S.*, Vol. 67, p. 684 (1895); *Phil. Trans.*, A, Vol. 186, p. 228 (1895).

‡ Behn and Geiger, *Verh. d. deuts. phys. Ges.*, Vol. 9, p. 657 (1907).

§ Partington and Shilling, *Phil. Mag.*, Vol. 45, p. 416 (1923).

‖ Partington and Shilling, *Trans. Faraday Soc.*, Vol. 18, p. 386 (1923); Shilling, *Phil. Mag.*, Vol. 3, p. 273 (1927).

also of silica, and carried by the silica tube A. The disc forming the piston has a diameter about 4 mm. less than that of the tube F, and is prevented from touching it by the mica plates m, which are strapped on by stout platinum wire. If the disc scrapes along the tube the resultant squeak is sufficient to render measurements impossible. At X is placed an asbestos disc a to prevent radiation and convection into the tube M with resultant irregularity in the furnace temperature. Joined to A by means of a cork is a steel tube B. By its uniformity of cross-section and diameter, and the fact that it is always quite cool, the steel tube enables a gas-tight gland to be made through which B slides. To the free end of B is attached a saddle having glass sides which ride along the edge of the millimetre scale S. Throughout the tubes A and B run the leads to a platinum platinum-

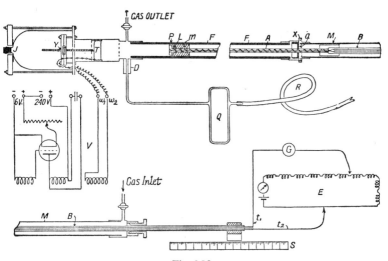

Fig. 6.12

rhodium thermocouple, having its junction at L immediately behind the piston P. The E.M.F. of this thermocouple is measured on the bridge E. The temperature can thus be measured at all points along the furnace tube.

To set up the sound waves a telephone T is attached to the end of the tube FF, and is excited at a constant accurately known frequency of about 3000 vibrations per second by means of the valve oscillator V. A rubber tube to the ear from the side tube D enables the experimenter to hear the points of resonance as the piston is moved along the tube. These points are accurately measured, the zero point being chosen well within the uniformly heated portion of the tube. A series of 10 to 25 half wave-lengths is measured. A screw adjustment enables the telephone diaphragm, which forms the reflecting surface at this end, to be moved relative to the side tube D. A bell-jar J fits over the end and renders it gas-tight. The adjustment of the telephone must be carefully made by trial and error, as the success of the measurement depends entirely on the accommodation of the distance of the diaphragm from the side tube D to the sound wave-length, which increases with temperature. The temperature slope from the zero point to the telephone diaphragm varies with each temperature, but this slope need not be known, since no measurements are taken within its range; it is only necessary to be sure that a state of equilibrium has been attained.

22. The Method of Dixon.

Dixon * measured the velocity of sound directly in a tube of metal or of fused silica about 15 m. long and 2·5 cm. in diameter. The tubes were coiled up to make them fit into a reasonable space. A lead tube in a water bath was used for temperatures up to 100° C. For the higher temperatures a silica tube with a platinum heating coil wound in sections was used. The heating coil was also used as a thermometer. Determinations of the velocity in nitrogen were made in the silica tube. For other gases a steel tube heated in a gas oven was used and the temperature was determined by rapidly filling the tube with nitrogen after the experiment with the gas under consideration was finished. From the measured velocity in nitrogen and the results obtained with this gas in the silica tube the temperature of the steel tube could be deduced.

The end of the tube was closed by a steel diaphragm. This was struck a blow from the outside by an electrically controlled hammer and the sound impulse given out travelled along the tube. Near each end of the tube was a circular hole in the wall, which was closed by a thin sheet of platinum foil; to the platinum foil was attached a fine platinum wire. When the sound impulse passed the part of the tube to which the foil was attached, the latter was pushed slightly outwards, and this caused the platinum wire to break a contact. The times at which the sound impulse passed each of the two platinum diaphragms was thus recorded on a chronograph together with the movements of a standard tuning fork. From the chronograph record the time taken for the sound impulse to travel along the tube could be deduced.

Experiments were carried out up to 1000° C., and the results obtained are in agreement with those obtained later by Partington and Shilling, using the entirely different method described in the preceding section.

RESULTS

23. The presentation of the results of experiments on the specific heats of gases will be simplified by first considering some theoretical questions which will give us a simple scheme according to which the experimental values can be classified.

24. Degrees of Freedom.

We shall define *the number of degrees of freedom of a thermodynamical system as the number of independent squared terms which enter into the expression for the energy of the system.*† Let us take some examples.

* Dixon, *Proc. Roy. Soc.*, A, Vol. p. 1 (1921); Dixon and Greenwood, Vol. 105, p. 199 (1924).
† This differs from the number of mechanical degrees of freedom used to specify a dynamical system.

(1) *A Monatomic Gas.*—We shall suppose that a certain mass of a monatomic gas contains N similar molecules. Each molecule is a particle of mass m, which is capable of translation but not of rotation.* The kinetic energy of any one such molecule is given by

$$\tfrac{1}{2}mu^2 + \tfrac{1}{2}mv^2 + \tfrac{1}{2}mw^2,$$

where u, v, w are its components of velocity parallel to three mutually perpendicular axes; u, v, and w can be varied independently. In this case for each molecule there are three independent squared terms in the expression for the energy, and each molecule therefore has three degrees of freedom. The N molecules have $3N$ degrees of freedom.

(2) *A Diatomic Gas.*—We shall suppose that the molecules of a diatomic gas consist of two particles at a fixed distance apart, and that such a molecule can rotate about any axis at right angles to the line joining the two particles but not about the line itself; this last assumption is similar to that which we made about a monatomic molecule not being capable of rotation. In this case the expression for the kinetic energy of a molecule contains three squared terms depending on the components of translational velocity parallel to three mutually perpendicular axes, and also two squared terms depending on the components of rotational velocity about two axes at right angles to each other and to the line joining the centres of the two atoms of which the molecule is made up. In all, therefore, each molecule possesses 5 degrees of freedom, and N molecules possess $5N$ degrees of freedom.

(3) *A Polyatomic Gas.*—The same considerations show that each molecule of a gas, whose molecules contain three or more atoms arranged in space at fixed distances apart, has in all 6 degrees of freedom, 3 for translation and 3 for rotation. N such molecules have $6N$ degrees of freedom.

(4) *Relative Movement of Atoms in a Molecule.*—Consider a diatomic molecule in which the distance between the atoms is not fixed, so that the atoms can vibrate relative to each other. This adds two extra squared terms in the expression for the energy—one depending on the kinetic and one on the potential energy. Such a molecule possesses 7 degrees of freedom, and N molecules possess $7N$ degrees of freedom. In general each possible vibration adds 2 degrees of freedom.

25. The Equipartition of Energy.

Maxwell showed that, if in their motion the molecules obey the ordinary laws of mechanics, *the total energy of a system is equally divided among the different degrees of freedom.*† This is called the principle of the *equipartition of energy.*

* For a qualitative theoretical explanation of why a monatomic gas molecule can-not be set into rotation, see Section 28.

† See Jeans, *Dynamical Theory of Gases,* 3rd edition, Sections 99 and 100.

We have already seen that for a perfect gas at temperature T (see equations (2a) and (8) of Chapter III)

$$\tfrac{1}{2}m\overline{u^2} + \tfrac{1}{2}m\overline{v^2} + \tfrac{1}{2}m\overline{w^2} = \frac{3}{2}\frac{R}{N_0}\,T,$$

where R is the gas constant and N_0 is Avogadro's number. The energy of the 3 degrees of freedom (see Section 24 (1)) of translation is therefore on the average equal to $\tfrac{3}{2}RT/N_0$ for each molecule. Using this result together with the principle of the equipartition of energy, it follows that in a system at temperature T each degree of freedom contributes

$$\frac{1}{2}\frac{R}{N_0}\,T$$

to the total energy.

If each molecule has n degrees of freedom, and we consider the N_0 molecules in a gram-molecule, we obtain for the total internal energy U of a gram-molecule of a perfect gas at temperature T

$$U = \tfrac{1}{2}nRT. \quad \ldots \ldots \ldots \quad (48)$$

The molecular heat at constant volume C_v is equal to $(\partial U/\partial T)_v$, and is therefore given by

$$C_v = \tfrac{1}{2}nR. \quad \ldots \ldots \ldots \quad (49)$$

For a perfect gas $C_p - C_v = R$, and therefore

$$C_p = (n + 2)\frac{R}{2},$$

and

$$\gamma = 1 + \frac{2}{n}. \quad \ldots \ldots \ldots \quad (50)$$

In Table I we give the values for C_v and γ predicted for various types of molecules by this theory.

TABLE I

Type of molecule	Degrees of freedom	C_v (calories per deg. C.)	γ
Monatomic	3	$\tfrac{3}{2}R = 2\cdot980$	1·667
Diatomic	5	$\tfrac{5}{2}R = 4\cdot967$	1·400
Polyatomic	6	$3R = 5\cdot961$	1·333
Diatomic with vibrating atoms	7	$\tfrac{7}{2}R = 6\cdot954$	1·286
Polyatomic ,, ,,	8	$4R = 7\cdot948$	1·250
,, ,, ,,	10	$5R = 9\cdot930$	1·200
&c.	&c.	&c.	&c.

26. Experimental Values.

The experimental values of C_v and γ for various gases at 15° C. and at atmospheric pressure are given in Table II.*

TABLE II

Gas	Number of atoms in molecule	C_v		γ	
		Experimental	Theoretical, Table I	Experimental	Theoretical, Table I
Argon	1	2·98	} 2·98	1·667	} 1·667
Helium	1	2·98		1·667	
Air (dry, free CO_2) ..	2	4·95		1·403	
Carbon monoxide ..	2	4·94		1·404	
Hydrogen	2	4·87		1·405	
Hydrochloric acid ..	2	5·11	4·97	1·400	1·400
Nitrogen	2	4·93		1·401	
Nitric oxide	2	5·00		1·400	
Oxygen	2	5·04		1·396	
Chlorine	2	5·93		1·355	
Sulphuretted hydrogen	3	6·08		1·340	
Carbon dioxide ..	3	6·75		1·300	
Carbon disulphide ..	3	9·77		1·235	
Nitrous oxide.. ..	3	6·81		1·300	
Sulphur dioxide ..	3	7·49	>5·96	1·264	<1·33
Acetylene	4	6·83		1·280	
Methane	5	6·48		1·310	
Ethylene	6	8·20		1·250	
Ethane	8	9·40		1·220	

The values for monatomic and diatomic gases (except chlorine) agree with the theory of equipartition of energy, assuming no internal vibrations. Hydrogen has a slightly low value for C_v (see Section 27).

The polyatomic gases fit in qualitatively but not quantitatively. The explanation of this must be deferred till later (see Section 29). In connexion with this the following Table III † is of interest. In all the molecules the total number of atoms is the same, but, as we go down the table, chlorine atoms are successively substituted for hydrogen.

---

* From Partington and Shilling, *The Specific Heats of Gases,* who give a critical summary of results. For further summaries, see Schmidt and Schnell, *Zeits. f. techn. Physik.* Vol. 9, p. 81 (1928); Nernst and Wohl, *ibid.,* Vol. 10, p. 608 (1929); and Eucken, *Grundriss der Physikalischen Chemie,* fourth edition, Leipzig (1934), p. 91.

† From Partington and Shilling, *loc. cit.*

TABLE III

Gas or vapour

CH_4	....	1·313
CH_3Cl	....	1·279
CH_2Cl_2	....	1·219
$CHCl_3$	....	1·154
CCl_4	....	1·130

The values collected in these tables indicate that at audiofrequencies the velocity of sound is independent of the frequency, and the measurements lead to values of γ in agreement with the simple theory given in Section 25.

The values given in Tables II and III refer to gases at atmospheric pressure. Strictly speaking, for purposes of comparison with the theory of equipartition of energy, we should use values extrapolated to zero pressure, but the changes that would be made in the figures would be small and would make no appreciable difference to the agreement with the theory. In the following section we consider results obtained at low temperatures. Here the corrections to zero pressure become much more important, and we use the extrapolated values.

27. Hydrogen at Low Temperatures.

In Table IV we give the values obtained by Eucken [*] for the molecular heat at constant volume of hydrogen in the ideal condition at various absolute temperatures. The results are independently confirmed by the work of Scheel and Heuse (see Section 10) and by that of Brinkworth.[†] We have the remarkable result that *at temperatures below about 60° K. hydrogen behaves as a monatomic gas.*

TABLE IV

Temperature (° Abs.)		$(C_v)_0$	Temperature (° Abs.)		$(C_v)_0$
35	....	2·98	80	....	3·14
45	....	3·00	100	....	3·42
60	....	2·99	196·5	....	4·39

The experiments of Eucken suggest the possibility that below 20° K. the molecular heats of hydrogen and helium may fall below $\frac{3}{2}R$. This result is referred to as the degeneration of gases.[‡]

[*] See Section 5.

[†] Brinkworth, *Proc. Roy. Soc.*, A, Vol. 107, 510 (1925).

[‡] The theory of the degeneration of a perfect gas is based on the application of the quantum theory to the translation of the molecules. See Fermi, *Zeits. f. Physik*, Vol. 36, p. 902 (1926); and Dirac, *Proc. Roy. Soc.*, A, Vol. 112, p. 661 (1926).

28. Rotation.

According to Bohr's theory the angular momentum of a rotating body is quantized according to the law

$$I\omega = j(h/2\pi), \quad \ldots \ldots \quad (51)$$

where I is the moment of inertia, ω the angular velocity in radians per second, h is Planck's constant and is equal to $6.56 \cdot 10^{-27}$ erg-sec., and $j = 1, 2, 3, \ldots$. The rotational energy E_r is given by

$$E_r = \tfrac{1}{2}I\omega^2 = j^2h^2/(8\pi^2 I).$$

According to quantum mechanics the rotational energy E_r is given by

$$E_r = j(j+1)h^2/(8\pi^2 I), \quad \ldots \ldots \quad (52)$$

which differs only in detail from the previous equation. From equation (52) the smallest value apart from zero that E_r can assume is

$$(E_r)_{\min} = h^2/(4\pi^2 I). \quad \ldots \ldots \quad (53)$$

We see that the minimum value above zero that the rotational energy can assume is inversely proportional to the moment of inertia of the molecule.

Let us consider the hydrogen molecule. Measurements of the ultra-violet band spectrum of hydrogen indicate that the moment of inertia † is

$$4.67 \cdot 10^{-41}.$$

Using this value and the value of h given above in equation (53), we obtain

$$(E_r)_{\min} \simeq 2 \cdot 10^{-14} \text{ ergs.} \quad \ldots \ldots \quad (54)$$

The energy of translation of a gas molecule at temperature T is given by

$$E_t = \frac{3}{2}\frac{R}{N_0}T \simeq 2 \cdot 10^{-16}T. \quad \ldots \ldots \quad (55)$$

Comparing equations (54) and (55), it can be seen that below 60° abs. the mean energy of translation of a molecule is small compared with the minimum rotational energy above zero that a hydrogen molecule can

---

* The reading of the following sections should be postponed until after Chapters XXI and XXII have been read.

† See Hori, *Zeits. f. Physik*, Vol. 44, p. 850 (1927); and for the theory, see Born, *The Mechanics of the Atom*, Bell (1927), § 12.

possess. It follows that only a very small fraction of the molecules will possess any rotational energy at all and that the gas will therefore behave as if it were monatomic.

The reason why monatomic gases cannot be set into rotation is that for the atom I is extremely small, and therefore by equation (40) the minimum rotational energy is very high, and compared with it the translational energy of gas molecules is small even at the highest temperatures to which investigations have been carried.

The above considerations account qualitatively for the experimental results. Actually quantum mechanics has accounted quantitatively for them and, further, has predicted effects which have since been shown to be realizable experimentally.

Analysis of the band spectrum of hydrogen shows that a distinction must be drawn between hydrogen molecules for which the rotational quantum number j of equation (46) is even and those for which it is odd. The two types are called para- and ortho-hydrogen respectively. Lines corresponding to transitions from states in which j is even to states in which j is odd, and from states in which j is odd to states in which it is even, are not observed.* Further, the lines corresponding to odd values of j are three times as intense as those corresponding to even values of j, which shows that at ordinary and high temperatures ortho-hydrogen molecules are three times as numerous as para-hydrogen molecules.

The application of Boltzmann's law shows that at low temperatures the equilibrium mixture should approach more and more nearly to pure para-hydrogen with $j = 0$. If, however, the theoretical curve for the specific heat is worked out on the assumption that true equilibrium is established at all temperatures, the results obtained do not agree with the experimental values. On the basis of the result that lines in the spectrum corresponding to transitions from ortho- to para-hydrogen (or from para- to ortho-hydrogen) do not occur, Dennison † therefore suggested that, in the time taken for specific heat measurements, the change in the direction of true temperature equilibrium between ortho- and para-hydrogen takes place to a negligible extent. Thus the measured specific heat is that of a stable mixture of three parts of ortho-hydrogen and one part of para-hydrogen. The actual value of the specific heat can be calculated from equation (52), if the moment of inertia is assumed known from the analysis of the band spectrum.

Let us first consider pure para-hydrogen. The number N_j of molecules in the jth rotational state is by Boltzmann's law given by

$$N_j = N_0 g_j \exp \{-j(j+1)h^2/(8\pi^2 IkT)\},$$

where N_0 is the number for which $j = 0$, and g_j is the statistical weight of the jth state. The factor g_j must be included because of the multiplicity of the rotational states, each state of quantum number j consisting of g_j states of practically identical energy. In his analysis of the band spectrum of hydrogen Hund ‡ showed that $g_j = 2j + 1$. Using these relations, it can be shown that C_P, the rotational molecular heat of pure para-hydrogen, is given by

$$C_P = Rx^2 \frac{d^2}{dx^2} Q_P,$$

* Fowler, *Statistical Mechanics*, 2nd edition, Cambridge (1936).

† Dennison, *Proc. Roy. Soc.*, A, Vol. 115, p. 483 (1927). For detailed numerical calculations, see Däumichen, *Zeits. f. Physik*, Vol. 62, p. 414 (1930). See also Villars and Schultze, *Phys. Rev.*, Vol. 38, p. 998 (1931), for calculations on methane.

‡ Hund, *Zeits. f. Physik*, Vol. 42, p. 119 (1927).

where $\quad\quad\quad Q_P = \sum\limits_{j=0, 2, 4, \ldots} (2j + 1)e^{-j(j+1)x}$, and $x = \dfrac{h^2}{8\pi^2 I k T}.$

Similarly, C_O, the rotational molecular heat of pure ortho-hydrogen, is given by

$$C_O = Rx^2 \frac{d^2}{dx^2} Q_O,$$

where $\quad\quad\quad Q_O = \sum\limits_{j=1, 3, 5, \ldots} (2j + 1)e^{-j(j+1)x}.$

If a fraction σ of the total number of molecules in the mixture are para-hydrogen molecules, the rotational molecular heat of the mixture is given by $\{\sigma C_P + (1 - \sigma)C_O\}$. For ordinary hydrogen $\sigma = \frac{1}{4}$ and the calculated curve and observed values are shown by the curve marked 25% in fig. 6.13.

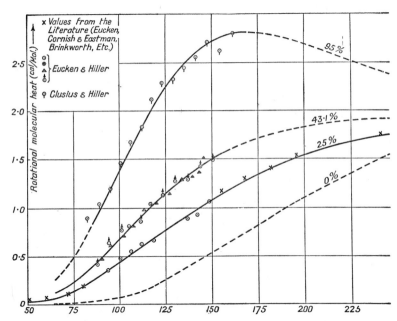

Fig. 6.13.—Specific heat of hydrogen for different ortho- and para-hydrogen fractions

Eucken and Hiller and also Clusius and Hiller * have prepared mixtures containing varying proportions of para-hydrogen by leaving hydrogen in contact with active charcoal (which acts as a catalyst for the transformation) at the temperature of liquid hydrogen, or by compressing hydrogen to pressures up to

* Eucken and Hiller, *Zeits. f. phys. Chem.*, B, Vol. 4, p. 142 (1929); Clusius and Hiller, *Zeits. f. phys. Chem.*, B, Vol. 4, p. 158 (1929). For an account of similar work with D_2, see Eucken, *J. de Physique*, Vol. 7, p. 281 (1936).

180 atmospheres and keeping it at the temperature of liquid air.* Some equilibrium percentages calculated from Boltzmann's equation are given in Table V. It will be seen from the table that at the temperature of liquid hydrogen a high

TABLE V

Temperature (° K.)	Percentage para-hydrogen
21·2	99·7
42·5	85·8
85	48·0
170	25·3

percentage of para-hydrogen is obtained. From the theoretical specific heats for pure ortho- and para-hydrogen and the measured value at one temperature they calculated the percentage of para-hydrogen in any given mixture. They then constructed the theoretical curve and showed that the experimental values for the mixture in question followed the theoretical curve closely (see fig. 6.13). Further, with the sample containing 95 per cent para-hydrogen they verified the prediction of the theory that for pure para-hydrogen the rotational specific heat rises considerably above the equipartition value of 2 calories per gram-molecule per degree.

The heat of reaction in the conversion of ortho- to para-hydrogen at low temperatures causes evaporation of liquid hydrogen. This is of importance in cryogenic experiments at temperatures in the hydrogen range. The rate of evaporation, as a function of the ortho-hydrogen concentration, has been measured by Larsen, Simon and Swenson,† who give methods by which the loss can be minimized.

29. Internal Vibrations.

Referring to Table II, it will be seen that the molecular heat of chlorine at constant volume is higher than would be expected from the equipartition theory for a non-vibrating diatomic molecule. This suggests internal vibrations of the atoms in the molecule. According to Table I a diatomic molecule with vibrating atoms should have 7 degrees of freedom and the molecular heat at constant volume should be equal to 6·95 compared with the observed value 5·93. It will be seen that the observed value corresponds to a fraction of a degree of freedom.

* Bonhoeffer and Harteck have shown that in the latter case the transformation takes place at the walls of the containing vessel. They also showed that in the presence of active charcoal the equilibrium between ortho- and para-hydrogen corresponding to the temperature of the charcoal is established quickly. They measured the change in thermal conductivity, which is proportional to the change in the specific heat. These workers have made a detailed study of the transformation: see Bonhoeffer and Harteck, *Zeits. f. phys. Chem.*, B, Vol. 4, p. 113 (1929); Bonhoeffer and Farkas, Vol. 12, p. 231 (1931); Farkas, Vol. 14, p. 371 (1931). For the application of the change in conductivity to the analysis of the gases, see Bolland and Melville, and Twigg, *Trans. Faraday Soc.*, Vol. 33, pp. 1316, 1329 (1937).

† Larsen, Simon and Swenson, *Rev. Sci. Instr.*, Vol. 19, p. 266 (1948).

Such an effect is by no means confined to chlorine, but is shown by all the polyatomic gases in the table, as comparison with Table I shows. Further, a similar effect is shown by all the diatomic gases if measurements are made at higher temperatures. As the temperature is raised, the molecular heat gradually rises above the equipartition value.

The presence of such partial degrees of freedom cannot be explained on the basis of classical mechanics, but is satisfactorily accounted for if the quantum theory is applied to the internal vibrations of the atoms in the molecule.

The result obtained in Chapter XXII, Section 4, can be applied immediately to this case. From equation (13a) there we see that each vibration of frequency ν contributes

$$\frac{R(h\nu/kT)^2 e^{h\nu/kT}}{(e^{h\nu/kT} - 1)^2} = R\left\{\frac{h\nu}{2kT} \operatorname{cosech} \frac{h\nu}{2kT}\right\}^2$$

to the molecular heat (the result given in equation (13a), Chapter XXII, refers to *three* independent vibrations of frequency ν). We may therefore write

$$(C_v)_{\text{vib.}} = R\Sigma \frac{(h\nu/kT)^2 e^{h\nu/kT}}{(e^{h\nu/kT} - 1)^2}, \quad \cdot \quad \cdot \quad \cdot \quad \cdot \quad (56)$$

where $(C_v)_{\text{vib.}}$ is the contribution of the internal vibrations to the molecular heat, and the sum is to be taken for all the different possible vibrations of the atoms in the molecule, each having its appropriate value of ν. The values of ν can be determined by measurements on the infra-red spectrum, or, for homopolar molecules, from the visible and ultra-violet bands (see the paper of Hori cited in Section 28).

In comparing equation (56) with experiment it is assumed that the translational motion and the rotational motion contribute their equipartition values to the molecular heat. The observed value of the vibrational molecular heat is, therefore, given by

$$(C_v)_{\text{vib.}} = C_v - \tfrac{3}{2}R\,(\text{trans.}) - \tfrac{3}{2}R\,(\text{rotat.})$$

for a polyatomic molecule; and by

$$(C_v)_{\text{vib.}} = C_v - \tfrac{3}{2}R\,(\text{trans.}) - R\,(\text{rotat.})$$

for a diatomic molecule.

For numerical comparisons between observed values of $(C_v)_{\text{vib.}}$ and those deduced from spectroscopic data, reference must be made to the original papers.*

* See Bjerrum, *Zeits. f. Elektrochemie*, Vol. 17, p. 732 (1911); Vol. 18, p. 103 (1912); Hettner, *Zeits. f. Physik*, Vol. 1, p. 351 (1920); Kemble and van Vleck, *Phys. Rev.*, Vol. 21, p. 653 (1923); McCrea, *Proc. Camb. Phil. Soc.*, Vol. 24, p. 80 (1928), who extends the theory.

Pierce, Kneser * and others have obtained interesting results using ultrasonic waves produced by a crystal oscillator. The waves were reflected from a reflector at distance x from the crystal source. When $x = n\lambda/2$, the oscillation in the gas builds up and reacts on the crystal. This affects an ammeter placed in the anode circuit of the valve in the circuit which supplies energy to the crystal. Thus if we plot current against x we get a curve with equally spaced peaks in it. The distance between the peaks gives $\lambda/2$. Kneser concentrated on the variation of velocity with the frequency ν in carbon dioxide. To ensure that the measurement of ν itself should not introduce an error into the velocity, he measured the ratio of the velocity in carbon dioxide, and the velocity in argon, by comparing the wave-lengths at the same frequency. Measurements with an ultrasonic interferometer up to frequencies of 200 kc/s show that there is no dispersion in monatomic and diatomic gases. This indicates that they do not have any vibrational degrees of freedom. Since they show no anomalies, it is possible to use one of them, such as argon, as a standard for comparison. The results obtained

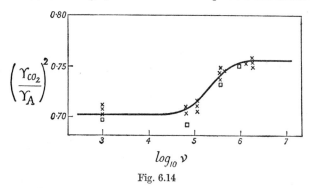

Fig. 6.14

are plotted in fig. 6.14, in which the ratio of the squares of the velocities is given as a function of $\log_{10}\nu$. These, and similar results which have been obtained for other polyatomic molecules, indicate that there is dispersion of the sound wave at high frequencies. There is a change in the velocity of the wave, and in the effective value of γ (see below); corresponding to this, there is a high attenuation of the wave, which drops again at higher frequencies.

The probable explanation of the behaviour is that there is a time-lag in the establishment of equilibrium between the translational energy and the internal energy of the molecules. Adiabatic compression (or rarefaction) in the sound wave first alters the translational energy. As a result of collisions this additional translational energy is converted into rotational and vibrational energy until the energies of all the different types of motion have their equilibrium values.

If the time of oscillation in the sound wave is large compared with the time taken for this equilibrium to be established, the gas is in equilibrium at any instant and the appropriate value of γ in the formula for the velocity, equation (40), is the ordinary value γ at room temperature.

For carbon dioxide at room temperature the translational molecular heat is $1.5R$, the rotational R, and the vibrational $0.85R$. Thus, if the time of oscillation

* Pierce, Proc. Amer. Acad. Arts and Sciences, Vol. 60, p. 271 (1925); Kneser, Ann. d. Physik, Vol. 11, pp. 761, 777 (1931); Vol. 12, p. 1015 (1932). For a general summary and bibliography, see W. T. Richards, Rev. Mod. Phys., Vol. 11, p. 36 (1939); Kittel, Reports on Progress in Physics, Vol 11, p. 205 (1946–47); see also Bergmann, Der Ultraschall, 3rd edition, Berlin (1942), Edwards Bros., Michigan (1944), pp. 171, 206.

in the sound wave is large compared with the time required to establish equilibrium between the translational and the internal degrees of freedom, the value of γ is $\gamma = (1\cdot5 + 1 + 0\cdot85 + 1)/(1\cdot5 + 1 + 0\cdot85) = 1\cdot30$. Let the sound velocity for such slow oscillations be Υ_0. On the other hand, if equilibrium between translational and rotational motion is established almost instantaneously, but if the time of oscillation of the sound waves is small compared with the time taken to establish equilibrium with the vibrational motion, this will be unaffected by the passage of the waves and the effective value of γ will be $3\cdot5/2\cdot5$ or $1\cdot40$. Thus the velocity Υ at these frequencies will be given by $\Upsilon^2 = \Upsilon_0^2(1\cdot40/1\cdot30) = 1\cdot08\Upsilon_0^2$. The ratio of the ordinates of the two horizontal parts of the curve drawn in fig. 6.14 has this value $1\cdot08$. The view that the oscillations of the sound waves at the higher frequencies are so rapid that the vibrational energy of the molecules is practically unaffected is thus seen to be in accord with the experimental facts.

Henry,[*] using the heated tube method (see Section 11), has obtained results which agree better with the theoretical values than those obtained earlier by the sound velocity method. He has suggested that the reason for the discrepancy between his results and those given by the sound velocity method is due to the fact that in the latter the time-lag in establishing equilibrium is not negligible compared with the period of oscillation in the waves. Sherratt and E. Griffiths [†] have carried out a very careful determination using the sound velocity method and ultrasonic waves; by using different frequencies it is possible to correct for this effect, and the corrected values are in good agreement with theory. They have also shown with carbon dioxide that, in conformity with Kneser's earlier results, there is a considerable absorption in carbon dioxide above a certain frequency.

In the foregoing description, it has been assumed that equilibrium between the translational and rotational degrees of freedom is established in a time negligible with the period of the sound wave. This may not always be so. Recent measurements of ultrasonic absorption in hydrogen and deuterium [‡] can be interpreted as indicating the existence of rotational relaxation frequencies of the order of magnitude of 10 Mc/sec. Subsequently, the velocity dispersion which would be expected to be associated with this absorption peak was detected.[§] This provides conclusive evidence that, in some cases, the rotational degrees of freedom can also lag behind the translational degrees of freedom and that there is a corresponding relaxation process. There is also evidence that different vibrational modes of a molecule may have different relaxation times.[||]

30. Theory of Dispersion of Sound in Gases.

An account of the process which takes place in a gas, when the equilibrium between different degrees of freedom is recovered, can be given in the following way.[¶] The internal and external degrees of freedom are treated as independent thermodynamical systems only loosely coupled together. It should be noted that this model, in which

[*] Henry, *Proc. Roy. Soc.*, A, Vol. 133, p. 492 (1931); *Nature*, Vol. 129, p. 200 (1932).

[†] Sherratt and E. Griffiths, *Proc. Roy. Soc.*, A, Vol. 147, p. 292 (1934); Vol. 156, p. 504 (1936).

[‡] Van Itterbeek and Vermaelen, *Physica*, Vol. 9, p. 345 (1942).

[§] Stewart, Stewart and Hubbard, *Phys. Rev.*, Vol. 68, p. 231 (1945); Stewart, *Phys. Rev.*, Vol. 69, p. 632 (1946).

[||] Alexander and Lambert, *Proc. Roy. Soc.*, A, Vol. 179, p. 499 (1942); Pielemeier, *Journ. Acoust. Soc. Amer.*, Vol. 15, p. 22 (1943).

[¶] Herzfeld and Rice, *Phys. Rev.*, Vol. 31, p. 691 (1928).

the effects are ascribed to a relaxation process, implies a system in which all the parts (degrees of freedom of different types) are not all at the same temperature. There is therefore a dissipation of energy which becomes particularly pronounced when the period of the heating and cooling cycle (in this case, the period of the ultrasonic wave) is comparable with the time required for the exchange of heat between the parts of the system. The time lag in the establishment of equilibrium produces velocity dispersion and anomalous absorption or attenuation of the wave. We now consider the mathematical details of the treatment.

If the internal and external degrees of freedom are treated separately, the first law of thermodynamics can be written

$$C_i \Delta T_i + C_e \Delta T_e - (pM/\rho^2)\Delta\rho = 0$$

for an adiabatic process. Subscripts i and e will be used to specify the thermodynamical functions for the internal and external degrees of freedom respectively. For a periodic wave, equation (45), this becomes

$$\omega C_i T_0 \theta_i + \omega C_e T_0 \theta_e - (pM/\rho)\omega s = 0, \qquad . \ . \quad (57)$$

where the various symbols have the same meaning as in Section 16. The exchange of energy between the external and internal degrees of freedom is assumed to be characterized by a single relaxation time τ such that

$$\frac{\partial T_i}{\partial t} = -\frac{T_i - T}{\tau}, \qquad . \ . \ . \ . \ . \ . \quad (58)$$

where T is the equilibrium temperature to which all the degrees of freedom would approach exponentially, that is,

$$T = (n_e T_e + n_i T_i)/(n_e + n_i),$$

where n_e and n_i respectively are the numbers of external and internal degrees of freedom per molecule. For a periodic wave, equation (58) becomes

$$i\omega\theta_i = -f(\theta_i - \theta_e)/\tau, \qquad . \ . \ . \ . \ . \quad (58')$$

where f has been written for $n_e/(n_e + n_i)$. Equation (58′) provides an additional condition which has to be satisfied. The determinantal equation analogous to equation (46) is

$$k^2 = \omega^2 \frac{M}{RT_0} \frac{C_v{}^0 + i\omega\tau C_v{}^\infty}{C_p{}^0 + i\omega\tau C_p{}^\infty}, \qquad . \ . \ . \ . \quad (59)$$

where $$C^0 = C_e + C_i,$$

and is the effective heat capacity in the limit of zero frequency;

$$C^\infty = C_e,$$

and is the effective heat capacity in the limit of infinite frequency. The velocity of propagation is given by

$$\Upsilon^2 = \frac{RT_0}{M} \frac{C_p{}^0 + i\omega\tau C_p^\infty}{C_v{}^0 + i\omega\tau C_v^\infty}. \quad \cdots \quad (60)$$

In general, for $\omega\tau \sim 1$, γ is complex and its value is given by

$$\gamma = \frac{C_p{}^0 + i\omega\tau C_p^\infty}{C_v{}^0 + i\omega\tau C_v^\infty}. \quad \cdots \quad (61)$$

Consider the two limiting cases. For $\omega\tau \ll 1$, equation (61) leads to

$$\gamma^0 = C_p{}^0/C_v{}^0 = 1 + 2/(n_e + n_i).$$

For $\omega\tau \gg 1$, equation (61) leads to

$$\gamma^\infty = C_p^\infty/C_v^\infty = 1 + 2/n_e.$$

These two effective values of γ are in agreement with the experimental results which have been considered in Section 29.

The fact that the value of γ in the general case, given by equation (61), is complex implies that the pressure and volume changes are out of phase. Thus, for $\omega\tau \sim 1$ the gas passes through a hysteresis cycle in the pV-plane. This represents an energy loss which we have already seen is shown by an attenuation of the ultrasonic wave. The theory indicates that the intensity should fall to $1/e$ of its initial value in six wave-lengths; the experimental results * for measurements on carbon dioxide at the relaxation frequency of about 20 kc/sec. show that the intensity falls to $1/e$ of its value in about four wave-lengths.

Ultrasonic dispersion in gases provides a typical example of a whole class of processes which are known as relaxation phenomena. The essence of all relaxation phenomena is that a particular property of a system shall be shared between different parts of the system, but that the time required for the sharing between the different parts be comparable with the periodic time of the cyclical process which perturbs the equilibrium. For systems which can be characterized by a single relaxation time τ, the equilibrium is restored as $\exp(-t/\tau)$. For the case of ultrasonic absorption in gases, the property of the system is the energy, the different parts of the system are the degrees of freedom of the different types, and the perturbing process is the passage of the ultrasonic wave with its attendant periodic pressure changes.

*Fricke, *Journ. Acoust. Soc Amer.*, Vol. 12, p. 245 (1940).

EXAMPLE

Show that

$$\left[\left(\frac{\partial V}{\partial p}\right)_{T} - \frac{T}{C_{v}}\left(\frac{\partial V}{\partial T}\right)_{p}^{2}\right]\left[\left(\frac{\partial p}{\partial V}\right)_{T} + \frac{T}{C_{p}}\left(\frac{\partial p}{\partial T}\right)_{V}^{2}\right] = 1.$$

CHAPTER VII

The Specific Heats of Solids and Liquids

1. The determination of the specific heats of solids has occupied attention for many years. The earliest method used was the method of mixtures, which is briefly mentioned in Chapter II, Section 4. Modern applications of the method are described in Section 8, and in Chapter IX, Section 5. Other workers have employed the Bunsen ice calorimeter (see Chapter IX, Section 3).

For work at ordinary and low temperatures the method of electrical heating is the most convenient way of determining the specific heats of solids and liquids. In this method the rise of temperature of the solid is measured when a given amount of heat in the form of electrical energy is supplied to it. The method was first applied to solids by Gaede,* and has been developed by Nernst and others for work at low temperatures. In principle the method is similar to that employed by Jaeger and Steinwehr for determining the mechanical equivalent of heat (see Chapter II, Section 14).

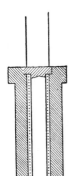

Fig. 7.1

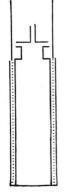

Fig. 7.2

2. The Nernst Calorimeter.

If the substance of which the specific heat is required is a metal, the calorimeter has the form shown in fig. 7.1, and is made of the metal itself. The heating coil is wound on a cylinder which fits inside a hole bored in another cylindrical block of the same metal. The winding is insulated by thin paraffined paper and the small space between the two pieces of metal is filled with paraffin wax. The heating coil of platinum is itself used as the thermometer.

If the substance is not a metal, it is contained in a silver vessel as shown in fig. 7.2. The heating coil is wound on the outside of the vessel, and silver foil is wrapped round it in order to diminish heat losses from the heating coil itself and to improve the thermal contact between the heating coil and the flask. As shown in the figure, the lid of

---

* See also Simon and Ruhemann, *Zeits. f. phys. Chem.*, Vol. 129, p. 321 (1927).

the vessel has a small capillary tube of silver fitted to it. For work at moderately low temperatures (down to the boiling-point of air) the vessel remains full of air, and the capillary tube is closed with a drop of solder so as to be gas-tight. For work at low temperatures the vessel is first filled with hydrogen and then the tube is quickly closed. It is most important that the vessel should be gas-tight, because, as we shall see below, it is suspended in a vacuum, and if it were not gas-tight the gas would be pumped out of it. The presence of the gas inside the vessel is very necessary in order that thermal equilibrium may be rapidly established throughout the contents of the vessel. In the absence of gas, radiation is the only means of thermal transfer (see Chapter XX).

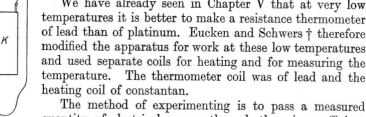

If the substance is a gas at ordinary temperatures, the containing vessel must have a capillary tube attached through which it can be filled. The method of filling is described in connexion with the work of Simon and Lange in Chapter VIII, Section 16.*

We have already seen in Chapter V that at very low temperatures it is better to make a resistance thermometer of lead than of platinum. Eucken and Schwers † therefore modified the apparatus for work at these low temperatures and used separate coils for heating and for measuring the temperature. The thermometer coil was of lead and the heating coil of constantan.

The method of experimenting is to pass a measured quantity of electrical energy through the wire, sufficient to raise the temperature of the calorimeter through a small amount, usually about one degree. It takes a short time for temperature equilibrium to be established after the current has been passed through the heater. If accurate results are to be obtained, it is essential that the loss of heat in this time be very small. This condition can be satisfactorily fulfilled only if the calorimeter is surrounded by a high vacuum. It is therefore arranged as shown in fig. 7.3. K is the calorimeter. It is suspended by two wires, which also serve as leads, inside a glass flask. This flask is connected to a vacuum pump and to a tube containing charcoal cooled in liquid air or hydrogen.

Fig. 7.3

In carrying out an experiment, the glass flask containing the calorimeter is placed in a constant-temperature bath, e.g. of ice, liquid air, or liquid hydrogen, according to the temperature required. Air (or, for the lower temperatures, hydrogen) is allowed to remain in the flask until the calorimeter has reached the temperature of the bath.

The flask is then completely evacuated and readings of the resistance

* See also Eucken, *Verh. d. deuts. phys. Ges.*, Vol. 14, p. 4 (1916).

† Eucken and Schwers, *Verh. d. deuts. phys. Ges.*, Vol. 15, p. 578.

of the thermometer in the calorimeter are taken at short intervals. The resistance should be steady. A known amount of electrical energy (measured on an ammeter and a voltmeter) sufficient to raise the temperature of the calorimeter about one degree is then passed through the heating coil. After the heating is finished, resistance measurements are again taken at short intervals of time. These measurements show that equilibrium is established quickly, and from them the rise in the temperature of the calorimeter can be determined.

The small correction for loss of heat during the time occupied in heating and in reaching equilibrium is made in the following way. In Table I we give the

Table I

Time		Temperature (arbitrary units)
19 min.	....	185·8
20 ,,	....	185·7
21 ,,	....	185·8
21 min. 10 sec. to 21 min. 50 sec.	....	heating current on
22 min.	....	201·8
23 ,,	....	200·0
24 ,,	....	199·0
25 ,,	....	198·0
26 ,,	....	197·0
27 ,,	....	196·1

temperature record of a typical experiment. It will be noticed that after 23 min. the temperature changes at a uniform rate. This means that equilibrium is established, and that this change is due to loss of heat. In correcting for heat loss we assume that from the moment the heating is finished the rate of change of temperature due to heat loss is the same as the rate measured from 23 min. onwards, or 1 temperature unit per minute. To obtain the equilibrium temperature at 21 min. 50 sec., the time when the heating finished, we extrapolate back from 23 min. and add on to the reading at that time, 200, the change that would occur in 1 min. 10 sec. at the rate of 1 temperature unit per minute, thus obtaining 201·17. We have to make a further correction for the loss of heat which takes place while the heating is in progress. At the beginning of the heating there is no loss, and at the end the rate of loss is that given above, namely 1 unit per minute. The mean rate of loss is therefore equal to half the rate of loss at the end, i.e. to 0·5 temperature units per minute. The temperature change due to loss of heat while the heating current is flowing is therefore the change that takes place in 40 sec. at the rate of 0·5 units per minute, which is 0·33 units. The corrected temperature at the end of the heating is therefore 201·5 units, and the rise of temperature produced by the given amount of electrical energy is

$$201·5 - 185·8 = 15·7 \text{ units.}$$

3. The " Adiabatic Vacuum Calorimeter " of Simon and Lange.

Improvements have been introduced by Simon and Lange,* whose apparatus is shown in fig. 7.4. The idea of the apparatus is to eliminate heat losses by surrounding the calorimeter with an enclosure which is always maintained at the same temperature as that of the calorimeter itself.

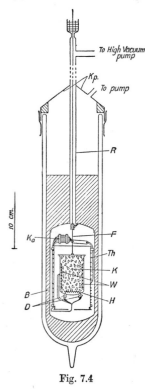

Fig. 7.4

The substance to be investigated is contained inside the calorimeter K, which is made of copper foil 0·1 mm. thick. The constantan heating coil H and the lead resistance thermometer W are also contained inside the calorimeter. The platinum leads to the thermometer and the heater pass out vacuum-tight through lead glass at D. The leads are attached to the frame Ka, where they are soldered on to the external leads. The calorimeter is suspended freely inside the thermostat Th by the wire F. The thermostat consists of a brass cylinder wound with a heating coil. One junction of a copper-constantan thermocouple is attached to the thermostat and the other junction to the outside of the calorimeter. The current through the thermostat heating coil is adjusted so that the thermostat is always at the same temperature as the calorimeter. The thermostat is surrounded by the copper vessel B, which can be removed by opening the solder joint at the top of B. The leads pass up through the thin-walled German-silver tube R. The whole apparatus can be evacuated and is immersed in liquid hydrogen (shown shaded) contained in a Dewar flask. The top of the flask is closed vacuum-tight by a brass lid Kp attached to the flask by wax. By varying the pressure in the Dewar flask above the surface of the hydrogen, the temperature of the liquid can be varied as described in Chapter VIII, Section 17.

4. Other Methods.

It is not possible to deal in detail with all the variations of these methods that have been used by various workers. That used by Griffiths and Griffiths † is of interest on account of the method of controlling the temperature. The calorimeter was surrounded by a copper vessel which had a spiral tube wound round it. Through this tube a current of air was passed. This air had previously been cooled

---

* See Lange, *Zeits. f. phys. Chem.*, Vol. 110, p. 343 (1924).

† Griffiths (E. H.) and Griffiths (Ezer), *Phil. Trans.*, A, Vol. 213, p. 119 (1913), and Vol. 214, p. 319 (1914); *Proc. Roy. Soc.*, A, Vol. 89, p. 561 (1914).

by expansion through a nozzle. By controlling the flow of air it was possible to hold the temperature of the copper vessel constant to one-hundredth of a degree at temperatures down to −180° C.

5. Specific Heats at Constant Pressure and at Constant Volume.

We have seen in dealing with gases that the distinction between the specific heat at constant volume and that at constant pressure is of great importance. This also applies to solids, and before giving the results of the experiments we have just described we must consider this difference briefly. The expansion of solids when they are heated is so small that the work done against the external pressure is negligible compared with the amounts of energy involved in specific heat measurements, so that we directly measure changes in internal energy, even though all our experiments are necessarily carried out at constant pressure. In the case of solids, however, the cohesive forces between the atoms are so large that a considerable amount of work is done against them in the small expansion that does take place, and this work is of course included in the change of internal energy measured in our specific heat determinations. Our consideration of the interpretation of the specific heats of gases has indicated that the most important knowledge gained from specific heat measurements is that which concerns the laws governing the motion of the constituent atoms or molecules; the same applies to solids, and we must therefore attempt to eliminate from our results the effects of changes in potential energy which accompany thermal expansion.

We shall see in equation (14), Chapter XIII, that the difference in joules between c_p and c_v is given by

$$c_p - c_v = \frac{9\alpha^2 v}{\kappa} T,$$

where α is the coefficient of linear expansion, v is the volume of 1 gm., and κ is the isothermal compressibility.

In general, we have not the data to use the above correction formula directly. We can, however, use the result established experimentally and theoretically by Grüneisen (see Chapter X, Section 5) that the coefficient of expansion is proportional to the specific heat at constant pressure, and that the specific volume and the compressibility vary little with temperature. The above formula, which is a correction to be subtracted from the measured value of c_p to give c_v, then becomes

$$c_p - c_v = A c_p^2 T,$$

in which the constant A can be determined by measurement of the coefficient of expansion, the specific volume, and the compressibility at any one temperature, using the measured value of c_p.

Nernst and Lindemann * have shown that there is a close con-nexion between the value of A in the above formula and the melting-point T_s of the solid, and that A is given by

$$A = \frac{0 \cdot 0051}{T_s}.$$

The truth of this last experimental law can be judged by the fol-lowing table given by Schrödinger,† in which the ratio of the specific heats at constant pressure and at constant volume deduced from the thermodynamic formula is compared with that deduced using the formula

$$c_p - c_v = \frac{0 \cdot 0051}{T_s} c_p{}^2 T.$$

Table II

Comparison of the ratio c_p/c_v given by the thermodynamic formula with that given by the approximate formula of Nernst and Lindemann

	Al	Cu	Ag	Pb	Pt	NaCl	KCl
Thermodynamic ..	1·042	1·025	1·047	1·055	1·019	1·051	1·038
Approximate	1·040	1·027	1·032	1·068	1·019	1·036	1.039

Nernst has also shown that an even simpler form of correction term can be used, viz.

$$c_p - c_v = aT^{3/2}.$$

Applying one or other of these corrections, we can reduce the measured specific heats at constant pressure to specific heats at constant volume.

Experimental Results

6. Dulong and Petit's Law.

In dealing with the experimental results, it is convenient to com-mence by stating a law discovered by Dulong and Petit in 1819. It deals with the results at ordinary temperatures and applies to solid elements. It may be stated as follows:

The product of the specific heat at constant volume and the atomic weight, that is, the atomic heat, is the same for all substances, and is equal to 24·94 joules per gram-atom per degree.

As was shown later, this law can be deduced from the principle of

* Nernst and Lindemann, *Zeits. f. Elektrochemie*, Vol. 17, p. 817 (1911).
† Schrödinger, *Phys. Zeits.*, Vol. 20, p. 452 (1919).

equipartition of energy which has been applied to gases in the previous chapter. Each atom of a solid is to be regarded as an oscillator vibrating about its mean position. The total motion is made up of three vibrations parallel to three mutually perpendicular axes. The amount of energy of each of these three vibrations can be varied independently of the others, and the expression for the energy of each vibration consists of two squared terms, one depending on the potential and the other on the kinetic energy. Each atom then has 6 degrees of freedom, and the N_0 atoms in a gram-atom have $6N_0$ degrees of freedom. The theorem of equipartition of energy states that at temperature T the energy associated with each degree of freedom is equal to $0.5(R/N_0)T$. The energy E of the $6N_0$ degrees of freedom of a gram-atom is therefore equal to $3RT$. The atomic heat at constant volume is equal to dE/dT; that is,

$$C_v = 3R = 24.94 \text{ joules per degree.}$$

A law analogous to Dulong and Petit's law has been shown by Kopp and Neumann to be approximately true for chemical compounds. The law states that the molecular heat of a solid chemical compound is equal to the sum of the atomic heats of the constituent atoms.

7. General Results.

The results of the experiments of many investigators can be summarized as follows. The generalization applies only to a certain number of substances which are specified in detail in Table III (p. 226). These substances are generally described as " simple substances "; they all crystallize in the regular or other simple systems.

(1) At ordinary and higher temperatures the atomic heat at constant volume converges towards the value $3R$ given by the Dulong-Petit law.

(2) At low temperatures the atomic heat at constant volume falls below the value given by the Dulong-Petit law, and converges towards the value zero as the absolute zero is approached.

(3) From the absolute zero up to a certain limiting temperature (see Chapter XXII) the atomic heat at constant volume is accurately proportional to the cube of the absolute temperature. It applies not only to simple substances but to all substances. Recent investigations have shown, however, that the true T^3 region only holds at much lower temperatures than had previously been thought, and certainly only at temperatures much lower than would be expected from the elementary theory given by Debye (see Chapter XXII, Section 5).

(4) The curves showing the relation between atomic heat at constant volume and absolute temperature (see fig. 7.5 *) for various substances

---

* From Jeans, *Report on Radiation and the Quantum Theory*.

are all exactly similar in shape. They can be made to coincide exactly merely by altering the scale of the temperature axis.

This last most important result can be expressed as follows: The atomic heats at constant volume of simple substances are given by an expression of the form

$$C_v = F\left(\frac{T}{\Theta}\right),$$

where the function F is the same for all the substances, and Θ is a constant characteristic of each substance. The exact meaning of the

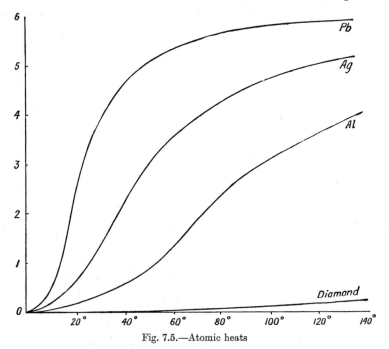

Fig. 7.5.—Atomic heats

constant Θ will appear later (see Chapter XXII); for the present its meaning may be taken as follows. Let Θ_1 be the value of the constant for substance 1, and Θ_2 its value for substance 2; further, let T_1 and T_2 be any two temperatures at which the respective values of C_v for the two substances are equal; then we have

$$\frac{T_1}{\Theta_1} = \frac{T_2}{\Theta_2}.$$

In accordance with this law it should be possible to represent the variation of the atomic heat at constant volume with temperature for all substances on the same curve, and Schrödinger * has shown that this can be done. We give Schrödinger's curves in fig. 7.6. Values of T/Θ are plotted as abscissæ and atomic heats at constant volume as ordinates. The curve marked II is the complete one. It is not possible without confusion to show all the points on the one curve, so portions of the curve have been reproduced, and the results for some of the substances plotted on these separate portions. The group of curves marked I have been displaced horizontally, and the curve marked III has been displaced both horizontally and vertically. It will be seen

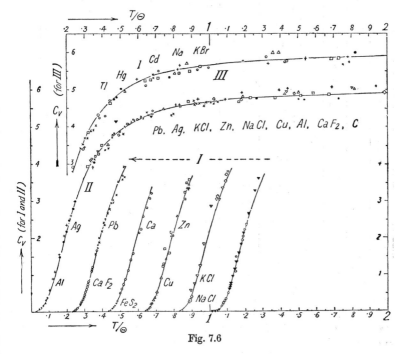

Fig. 7.6

that the experimental results for all the substances considered follow the same curve remarkably closely. Table III gives a list of most of the substances which can be represented on this curve; it also gives the sign used in plotting each substance, and the value of Θ.†

The case of diamond with its very high value of Θ is interesting. Diamond was long regarded as an exceptional substance, its specific

---

* Schrödinger, *Phys. Zeits.*, Vol. 20, p. 452 (1919); see also Chapter XXII, Section 9.

† For references, see Schrödinger's paper. For later work, see Keesom and van den Ende, *Leiden Comm.*, No. 203 (d); Lange and Simon, *Zeits. f. phys. Chem.*, Vol. 134, p. 374 (1928); Clusius and Harteck, *ibid.*, Vol. 134, p. 243 (1928); Clusius, *ibid.*, B, Vol. 3, p. 41 (1929); Clusius and Vaughan, *Journ. Amer. Chem. Soc.*, Vol. 52, p. 4686 (1930).

Table III

Sign in fig.			Substance		Crystal system	Temp. interval (° Abs.)	$(C_p - C_v) . 10^5$	Θ
Curve								
I	II	III						
$\times$	$\times$		Lead	Pb	Regular	14–573	$3 \cdot 2\, C_p^2 T$	88
		$\bigcirc$	Thallium	Tl	?	23–301	$2 \cdot 7\, C_p^2 T$	96
		$\square$	Mercury	Hg	Regular	31–232	$21\, T^{3/2}$	97
		$\times$	Iodine	I	Rhombic	22–298	$10\, T^{3/2}$	106
		$+$	Cadmium	Cd	Regular	50–380	$3 \cdot 2\, C_p^2 T$	168
		$\triangle$	Sodium	Na † {	Regular quadr. }	50–240	$3 \cdot 8\, C_p^2 T$	172
		$\bullet$	Potassium bromide }	KBr	Regular	79–417	$2 \cdot 7\, C_p^2 T$	177
	$\bullet$		Silver	Ag	Regular	35–873	$2 \cdot 5\, C_p^2 T$	215
$\bigcirc$			Calcium	Ca	?	22–62	0	226
$\triangledown$	$\triangledown$		Sylvin	KCl	Regular	23–550	$2 \cdot 0\, C_p^2 T$	230
$\square$	$\square$		Zinc	Zn {	Rhombic Hexagonal }	33–673	$2 \cdot 6\, C_p^2 T$	235
$\diamondsuit$	$\diamondsuit$		Rock salt	NaCl	Regular	25–664	$2 \cdot 7\, C_p^2 T$	281
$\triangle$	$\triangle$		Copper	Cu †	Regular	14–773	$1 \cdot 3\, C_p^2 T$	315
		$+$	Aluminium	Al	Regular	19–773	$2 \cdot 2\, C_p^2 T$	398
$\bigcirc$			Iron	Fe †	Regular	32–95	0	453
$\bigcirc$	$\bigcirc$		Fluorspar	CaF_2	Regular	17–328	$A\, C_p^2 T$ *	474
$+$			Pyrites	FeS_2 †	Regular	22–57	$A\, C_p^2 T$ *	645
$\blacktriangledown$	$\blacktriangledown$		Diamond	C	Regular	30–1169	$0 \cdot 6\, C_p^2 T$	1860

heat being much lower than predicted by the Dulong-Petit law. The results considered here bring it into line with other substances.

Other substances not included in the table, which are mostly substances that do not crystallize in the regular system, obey Dulong and Petit's law at ordinary temperatures, but at low temperatures the specific heats fall off according to a different law from that obeyed by the substances in Table III. In the light of the theory given in Chapter XXII, Section 4, they can be classified to a certain extent.

Experiments at High Temperatures

8. The experiments at high temperatures indicate specific heats considerably in excess of those predicted by the law of Dulong and Petit. Special methods must be used in these experiments.

* The constant A reckoned from the thermodynamic formula by the investigator.
† Na, Cu, Fe, FeS$_2$, lie above the curve at higher temperatures; see also Chapter XXII.

Magnus * has measured the specific heat of metals up to temperatures of about 900° C. He used a modification of the method of mixtures in which copper replaces water as the standard substance. This method was first employed by Nernst and his co-workers. The apparatus is illustrated in fig. 7.7.

The essential feature of the apparatus is the copper block K, which is attached to the inside of the Dewar flask D by Wood's metal, and the temperature of which is measured by thermocouples. The specimen of metal G, of which the specific heat is to be measured, is heated in the oven O as shown, to a measured temperature. It is then allowed to fall into K, the specific heat of which at ordinary temperatures is accurately known. The ordinary method of mixtures is used to determine the heat given up by the specimen in cooling from the oven temperature to the final temperature. Actually the specimen in falling first reaches the small copper vessel F, which is held in position only by the spring in a piece of stiff paper, and which is torn away immediately the specimen reaches it. This vessel F serves the purpose of protecting the falling specimen from the air during the last part of its fall and, further, it has two projections soldered to it, which enable it and the specimen to be easily removed from K, in which they stick firmly after the fall. The specimen G, the vessel F, and the hole in K all have the same taper, and when the fall is complete the cover KV of the hole in K can be quickly released by an electric contact.

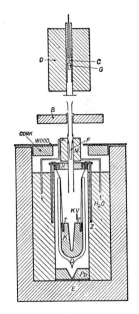

The other parts of the apparatus, such as the vessels Z and M with their water circulations, the wooden box E, and the wooden cover H, serve to keep the heat losses small and definite.

Magnus and his co-workers † have applied the same method to a considerable number of substances.

Fig. **7.7**

A different method, which is capable of being used up to very high temperatures, has been used by Corbino ‡ and others. The metal to be investigated is in the form of a fine wire suspended in a vacuum. The wire is heated by the passage of an electric current. One modification of the method, due to Worthing, is as follows. If the heating current through a filament is changed, we

    * Magnus, *Ann. d. Physik*, Vol. 48, p. 983 (1915).

    † See Magnus and Holzmann, *Ann. d. Physik*, Vol. 3, p. 585 (1929); see also F. M. Jaeger and Rosenbohm, *Proc. K. Akad. Amsterdam*, Vol. 33, p. 457 (1930); Vol. 34, p. 808 (1931).

    ‡ Corbino, *Phys. Zeits.*, Vol. 11, p. 413 (1910); Vol. 12, p. 292 (1911); Vol. 13, p. 375 (1912); Vol. 14, p. 915 (1913). See also Pirani, *Verh. d. deuts phys. Ges.*, Vol. 14, p. 1037 (1912); Worthing, *Phys. Rev.*, Vol. 5, p. 340 (1915); Zwikker, *Zeits. f. Physik*, Vol. 52, p. 668 (1929).

have at any instant while it is reaching its new state of equilibrium

$$iV = f(T) + c_p m \frac{dT}{dt},$$

in which i, V, and T represent the instantaneous values of the current, potential, and temperature respectively, t is the time, m is the mass of the filament, and c_p its specific heat. The three terms represent respectively the rate of heat production in the filament, the rate of heat loss by radiation, and the rate of change of the heat energy of the filament. T is determined from the resistance, and $f(T)$ from the energy supplied to the filament when its temperature remains steady. Correction can be made for losses to the leads due to their changing temperature by using filaments of the same cross-section but of different lengths.

Klinkhardt * used another method and heated the metal under investigation by bombarding it with cathode rays from a hot filament. The metal was made the anode and the heat supplied was obtained by measuring the potential difference between anode and cathode, and the electron current flowing to the anode. If the substance was a non-metal it was enclosed in a metal box. The method can be used up to about 1000° C.

THE SPECIFIC HEATS OF LIQUIDS

9. The methods for measuring the specific heats of liquids are the same as those used for solids. For the most accurate experiments the precautions described in Chapter II, where we have dealt with the measurements on water, must be taken. For work with molten metals the methods described in Chapter IX, Section 5, may be used.

Ferguson and J. T. Miller † have shown that an accurate value for the specific heat of a liquid may be obtained (a) by measuring electrically the heat required to maintain the liquid and calorimeter containing it at a given temperature, and (b) by measuring the rate of cooling when no energy is supplied.

The theory of the specific heats of liquids has not been developed to any considerable extent on account of the meagreness of our knowledge of the liquid state. It is, however, interesting to compare the specific heat of a liquid just above the melting-point with that of the solid just below the melting-point. It is found in general that, if the specific heat of the solid has reached the Dulong-Petit value, the difference between the values for the liquid and for the solid is small. If it has not, there is in general a large difference. Water may be taken as an example of the latter case. The molecular heat of ice (specific heat multiplied by 18) just below the melting-point is approximately equal to 36, and that of water is approximately 72 joules per gram.

---

* Klinkhardt, *Zeits. f. Elektrochemie*, Vol. 32, p. 534 (1926).

† Ferguson and J. T. Miller, *Proc. Phys. Soc.*, Vol. 45, p. 194 (1933).

CHAPTER VIII

Vaporization

1. If a liquid is placed in a vacuum, it evaporates. For example, when a drop of liquid is allowed to rise through the mercury in a barometer, it evaporates on reaching the vacuum at the top, and the level of the mercury is depressed owing to the pressure exerted by the vapour. If more liquid is added, it continues to evaporate until a certain definite pressure of the vapour is reached at which equilibrium is established between the liquid and the vapour. The pressure at which equilibrium occurs depends on the temperature; it is called the *vapour pressure* at the given temperature. The equilibrium is a dynamic and not a static one. A certain number of the molecules which reach the surface have velocities sufficiently in excess of the average to enable them to escape from the attraction of the neighbouring molecules into the space occupied by the vapour; on the other hand, the molecules of the vapour which reach the surface of the liquid are attracted by the liquid molecules and are captured, thus increasing the amount of the liquid. The number of such captures depends on the vapour pressure. The state of equilibrium is reached when these two opposing effects balance one another, so that on the whole there is no net gain or loss of either liquid or vapour.

If the space above the liquid is not a vacuum but is occupied by another gas, equilibrium is established when the partial pressure of the vapour is equal to the vapour pressure of the liquid at the given temperature (for the very small effect of a change in the total pressure on the vapour pressure of a liquid, see examples 1, 2, 3, and 4, end of Chapter XVI).

As the temperature rises the vapour pressure increases. If the heating is carried out under such conditions that the external pressure remains constant—for example, if the liquid is open to the atmosphere —a temperature is finally reached at which bubbles of vapour are formed throughout the volume of the liquid; this temperature is called the *boiling-point*. If further heat is supplied, it does not cause a further rise of temperature, but is used in producing more vapour. The energy so absorbed is used up in doing work against the attractive forces of the molecules and against the external pressure. The amount of heat required to convert 1 gm. of liquid into vapour at the same temperature is called *the latent heat of vaporization*. It is found experimentally that

229

at the boiling-point the vapour pressure is equal to the external pressure. This fact gives an accurate and convenient method of determining vapour pressures by determining the boiling-point under various external pressures.

Solids also have a definite vapour pressure, but in many cases it is small; sometimes, however, the vapour pressure of a solid becomes equal to the atmospheric pressure before the melting-point is reached. In such cases the solid is completely vaporized without melting, and the only way to reach the melting-point is to heat the solid under pressure. When a solid passes directly into the vapour state, the process is usually called *sublimation*. We also speak of sublimation pressure and of heat of sublimation.

Determinations of vapour pressures and of latent heats of vaporization are of considerable theoretical and practical interest, and we shall now consider the methods used to measure them in various cases.

THE MEASUREMENT OF VAPOUR PRESSURE

Non-metals

2. Direct or Static Methods.

The most simple and direct method of measuring vapour pressures is that which is used for pressures of the order of a few to about 100 cm. of mercury at temperatures below the ordinary atmospheric temper-

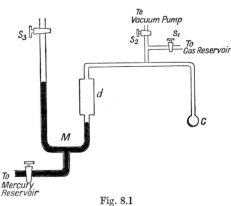

Fig. 8.1

ature. Such methods are used to measure the vapour pressures of the permanent gases at temperatures between their freezing- and boiling-points.[*]

The general principle of the apparatus is shown in fig. 8.1. The mercury manometer is shown at M. The space between the top of the left-hand column of mercury and the tap s_3 can be evacuated, or the tap s_3 can be left open to the atmosphere, according to the magnitude of the pressure which is to be measured. In carrying out an experiment, the whole of the apparatus above the right-hand column of mercury

---

[*] See, for example, Henning and Heuse, *Zeits. f. Physik*, Vol. 23, p. 113 (1924); Heuse and Otto, *Ann. d. Physik*, Vol. 9, p. 493 (1931).

in M is evacuated through the tap s_2, which is then closed. The purified gas is then admitted from a reservoir through the tap s_1. c is the condensation tube which is surrounded by a bath at a constant low temperature. In this tube the gas is liquefied or solidified, and after

Fig. 8.2

a sufficient amount of liquid or solid has formed the tap s_1 is closed. When the apparatus has become steady, the pressure is read on the manometer. This gives the vapour pressure at the temperature of the bath. After the reading has been taken, more mercury is admitted into the apparatus so that the tube d is filled with mercury, and the manometer is again read. If the gas is pure, the pressure should not be changed by this procedure. If necessary, a cathetometer can be used to measure the difference between the levels of the mercury in the two arms of the manometer. For lower pressures a manometer designed by Lord Rayleigh * is often convenient.†

For measurements with substances which are liquids at ordinary temperatures, a small quantity of the liquid may be introduced into the vacuum at the top of a barometric column and the depression of the column measured. The portion of the barometer tube which contains the liquid and vapour must of course be kept at a constant temperature in a suitable bath. Correction must be made for the fact that the surface tension in the ordinary barometer tube differs from that in the tube when the mercury is in contact with another liquid. This correction can be determined by using two tubes connected together at the top as shown in fig. 8.2. The space at the top is evacuated and some of the liquid is introduced into one of the tubes. The difference in the level in the two tubes corrected for the weight of the drop of liquid in one of them gives the correction.

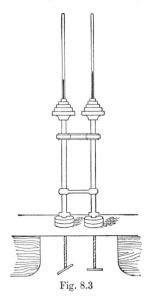

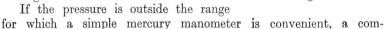

Fig. 8.3

If the pressure is outside the range for which a simple mercury manometer is convenient, a compressed air or nitrogen manometer,‡ and for high pressures an

* Rayleigh, *Phil. Trans.*, A, Vol. 196, p. 208 (1901).

† See Scheel and Heuse, *Ann. d. Physik*, Vol. 29, p. 723 (1909).

‡ For different types of absolute manometer, see Chapter IV, Section 9.

apparatus of the type used by Andrews * in his investigations on carbon dioxide, can be used. The vapour is contained in a thick-walled glass tube with a capillary at its upper end. The lower end is closed by mercury. This tube is placed in a heavy metal tube filled with water, which has a steel screw plunger at the bottom. The capillary projects from the top of the metal vessel, and all the joints are made tight with leather washers. The glass tube and capillary are carefully calibrated. An exactly similar arrangement containing the manometric gas is placed beside the former one, and communication between the two is established by connecting the two metal tubes by a side tube, so that the pressures in the two tubes are always the same. The pressure is determined from the volume occupied by the manometric gas, for which the relation between pressure, volume, and temperature is accurately known (see Chapter IV, Section 5). The pressure is controlled by screwing the steel plungers in or out. For any given temperature the pressure at which liquid and vapour are in equilibrium can be determined. The apparatus is illustrated in fig. 8.3. Measurements on water at high temperatures and pressures have been carried out by Holborn and Baumann.†

3. Boiling-point Method.

Another type of method for determining vapour pressures depends on the fact mentioned in Section 1 that at the boiling-point the vapour

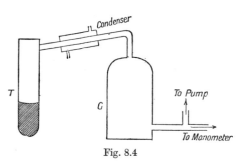

Fig. 8.4

pressure is equal to the external pressure.‡ The principle of this method is shown in fig. 8.4. The liquid is heated in the tube T, and the vapour is condensed by the condenser. The vessel G is a large gas reservoir, the object of which is to avoid fluctuations of pressure. The pressure in G can be varied by a pump and is measured by a manometer of a type suitable to the pressure used. When the liquid boils the temperature of the vapour in T is measured. At this temperature the vapour pressure is equal to the external pressure, which is measured by the manometer. This method can be used over a wide range of pressures and temperatures.

* Andrews, *Phil. Trans.*, p. 575 (1869), Part II.

† Holborn and Baumann, *Ann. d. Physik*, Vol. 31, p. 945 (1910).

‡ For a modification of this method, see Rodebush and Dixon, *Phys. Rev.*, Vol. 26, p. 851 (1925); Fiock and Rodebush, *Journ. Amer. Chem. Soc.*, Vol. 48, p. 2522 (1926), who have applied the method to alkali halides.

Metals *

4. Most determinations of the vapour pressures of metals at temperatures such that they are not very low have been made by the boiling-point method. The direct or statical method has also been used. Ingold † has devised an accurate form of this method in which a Bourdon gauge of fused silica is employed. His results on lead are consistent with those of Egerton determined at much lower temperatures by the method described in Section 5. Jenkins ‡ has applied a simple direct method to determine the vapour pressures of zinc, cadmium, and mercury with an accuracy of about 1 mm. of mercury. The metal is contained in a V-tube of fused silica, one end of which is closed. The open end is connected to a long condenser tube and thence to an ordinary mercury manometer, a pump, and a supply of nitrogen. The V-tube is so mounted in a furnace that it can be rotated and the closed end filled completely with the molten metal. On restoring the V-tube to its original position the closed end is filled only with the metallic vapour. The pressure of the nitrogen is adjusted until the level of the molten metal in the two limbs of the V-tube is the same. The measurement of this pressure on the manometer gives the vapour pressure of the metal.

5. Knudsen's Method.

From the theoretical point of view the quantity which it is usually important to determine is the vapour pressure at the freezing-point of a metal. The above methods can be used only at temperatures considerably higher than the freezing-point. Extrapolation over this wide range is liable to lead to serious error.

Knudsen § devised a method which depends on the rate of effusion of the vapour through a small opening. Using this method, vapour pressures as low as a few ten-thousandths of a millimetre of mercury can be measured accurately. He used it to determine the vapour pressure of mercury at temperatures down to 0° C., at which the vapour pressure is only 0·0001846 mm. of mercury.

A slight modification of the method has been used by Egerton ‖ to determine the vapour pressures of various metals. We shall describe Egerton's apparatus. The general arrangement is indicated in fig. 8.5.

---

* See Egerton, *Phil. Mag.*, Vol. 48, p. 1053 (1924); for the work on mercury, see Laby, *Phil. Mag.*, Nov., 1908, and Egerton, *Phil. Mag.*, Vol. 39, p. 1 (1920).

† Ingold, *Journ. Chem. Soc.*, Vol. 121, p. 2419 (1922).

‡ Jenkins, *Proc. Roy. Soc.*, A, Vol. 110, p. 456 (1926).

§ Knudsen, *Ann. d. Physik*, Vol. 29, p. 179 (1909).

‖ Egerton, *Proc. Roy. Soc*, A, Vol. 103, p. 469 (1923); Edmondson and Egerton, *Proc. Roy. Soc.*, A, Vol. 113, p. 520 (1927); see also Harteck, *Zeits. f. phys. Chem.*, Vol. 134, p. 1 (1928); and for another method Mayer, *Zeits. f. Phys.*, Vol. 67, p. 240 (1931). Mayer and Wintner (*J. Chem. Phys.*, Vol. 6, p. 301 (1938)) have used the method with alkali halide crystals.

The metal is contained in a small silica pot with a circular hole about 2 mm. in diameter in the lid; the latter is ground so as to fit closely. The pot is placed at the bottom of a silica tube 3 cm. in diameter. This tube fits into a hole about 8 cm. deep in a large block of copper weighing about 35 lb. The mass of this block and its high thermal conductivity tend to maintain the tube at a constant and uniform temperature. The block is surrounded by 3 in. of magnesia powder contained in a polished tin.

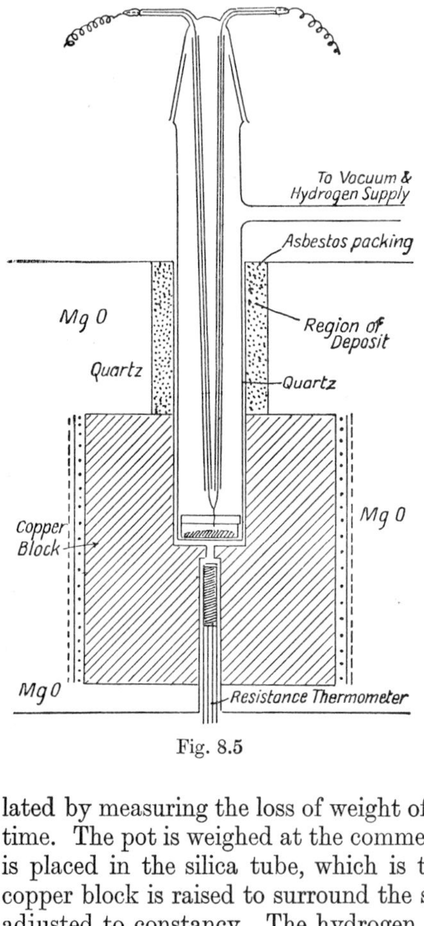

The copper block is heated by two separate windings and its temperature is automatically controlled as follows: The current through the first winding is so adjusted that it is just not sufficient to maintain the block at the temperature at which it is desired to carry out an experiment. The other smaller winding is in circuit so long as a relay makes contact. The current is then sufficient to heat the block above the desired temperature. The relay is operated by a sensitive resistance thermometer at the centre of the copper block. The galvanometer mirror throws the light from a 100-c.p. pointolite lamp on to a selenium cell which is connected to a sensitive relay; this in turn operates the main relay. At 700° C. the temperature of the block can be maintained constant with a maximum variation of $\frac{1}{3}$ deg. from the mean, the probable error of the mean temperature being less than $\frac{1}{20}$ deg. for a 6-hr. run. The temperature of the metal being vaporized is measured by a thermocouple as shown.

To Vacuum & Hydrogen Supply

Asbestos packing

Region of Deposit

Quartz

Mg O

Quartz

Mg O

Copper Block

Mg O

Resistance Thermometer

Fig. 8.5

As we shall see below, the vapour pressure can be calculated by measuring the loss of weight of the metal in the pot in a given time. The pot is weighed at the commencement of the experiment, and is placed in the silica tube, which is then filled with hydrogen. The copper block is raised to surround the silica tube, and the temperature adjusted to constancy. The hydrogen is rapidly pumped out, and the time of commencement is taken when the pressure reaches about 0·05 mm.; the pressure is quickly reduced further to about 0·00001 mm. of mercury. During the experiment the highest possible vacuum is maintained in the apparatus, so that there is no interference by gas molecules with the motion of the molecules of vapour which stream out of the hole in the silica pot, up the tube, and finally condense in the cooler parts of the tube as shown in the figure. An experiment is stopped by letting in pure hydrogen. The pot is reweighed at the end of an experiment to determine the loss. In the case of Egerton's experiments on lead the time of an experiment varied from three to fifty hours. The theory of the method is as follows.

Combining the results of equations (38) and (40) of Chapter III, we have that the mass M of a gas which in unit time streams through a tube in which a plate with an opening is placed is given by

$$M = \sqrt{\rho_1} \, \frac{p' - p''}{W_1 + W_2},$$

where ρ_1 is the density of the gas at a pressure of 1 dyne per square centimetre and at the temperature of the system. $(p' - p'')$ is the pressure difference between two points between which the resistance is W_2 in the tube itself and W_1 in the opening in the plate. This assumes that the mean free path of the gas molecules is large compared with the dimensions of the opening or of those of the cross-section of the tube.

The resistance of the opening is given by

$$W_1 = \frac{\sqrt{2\pi}}{A},$$

where A is the area of the opening (see equation (40), Chapter III); that of the tube, if it is circular, of radius R and length L, by

$$W_2 = \frac{3}{8} \sqrt{\frac{2}{\pi}} \frac{L}{R^3} \text{ (see equation (39), Chapter III).}$$

In the case of Egerton's apparatus L is the length of the tube from the top of the silica pot to the point at which the condensation occurs. Actually the temperature over the whole length of the tube is not quite constant, but since the resistance of the tube is only 1 per cent of the resistance of the hole, ρ_1 can be taken as the density of the vapour at a pressure of 1 dyne per square centimetre and at the temperature inside the pot. The density of a vapour of atomic weight A at 0° C. can be taken as $A/32$ times that of oxygen, which is accurately known. The density at temperature T can be taken as $273 \cdot 2/T$ times that at 0° C. The pressure p' is the pressure inside the silica box, that is, the vapour pressure which we wish to measure, while p'' is the pressure at the point at which the deposit occurs and may be neglected.

p' can thus be determined from the measured loss of weight in a given time. from the resistances which can be calculated from the measured dimensions, and from the calculated value of the density of the vapour at a pressure of 1 dyne per square centimetre at the temperature of the experiment.

6. Methods depending on the Rate of Vaporization: Langmuir's Work.

Langmuir * has used an ingenious dynamical method for measuring the vapour pressures of some metals, such as solid tungsten and platinum. The method depends on the rate of loss of weight of a fila-

---

* Langmuir, *Phys. Zeits.*, Vol. 14, p. 1273 (1913); Langmuir and Mackay, *Phys. Rev.*, Vol. 4, p. 377 (1914); H. A. Jones, Langmuir, and Mackay, *Phys. Rev.*, Vol. 30, p. 201 (1927).

ment heated in a vacuum. A somewhat similar method has been used by v. Wartenberg,[*] who determined the vapour pressures of lead, thallium, and silver by passing a slow stream of an inert gas over the heated metal and measuring the concentration of the vapour in the gas.

As we have said at the beginning of this chapter, the equilibrium between a liquid and its vapour is a dynamic one, and is established when the number of molecules of vapour which leave the surface of the liquid per second is equal to the number of vapour molecules which in 1 sec. strike the surface of the liquid and do not escape again. The latter number depends on the pressure of the vapour and on its temperature; the former is the number of molecules at the surface which have sufficient kinetic energy to escape from the attractions of their neighbours; this number depends on the temperature of the liquid. At temperatures at which the vapour pressure is only a small fraction of a millimetre of mercury, we assume that the number of molecules escaping from the liquid in 1 sec. is independent of whether the liquid is in equilibrium with its vapour or whether the molecules escape into a vacuum; the rate of condensation depends only on the pressure of the vapour. The same considerations apply to the equilibrium of a solid with its vapour.

The number of molecules of vapour which strike the surface of the solid in 1 sec. can be calculated if we know the vapour pressure and the area of the solid. The number of condensed molecules formed per second cannot be greater than this number, which is equal to

$$\tfrac{1}{4}n\bar{c}$$

per unit area of the solid. n is the number of molecules per cubic centimetre of the vapour and $\bar{c}$ is their mean velocity (see expression (31a), Chapter III). The total mass μ of the vapour molecules which strike unit area of the solid surface in 1 sec. is given by

$$\mu = \tfrac{1}{4}\rho\bar{c},$$

where ρ is the density of the vapour.

We can write the gas law $$pV = RT$$

in the form $$\rho = \frac{pM}{RT},$$

where M is the molecular weight.

We have further, from equations (6) and (21), Chapter III,

$$p = \frac{\pi}{8}\rho(\bar{c})^2.$$

Combining the last two equations, we obtain

$$\bar{c} = \sqrt{\frac{8RT}{\pi M}},$$

and using this value the total mass of the vapour molecules which strike unit area of the solid surface in unit time becomes

$$\mu = p\sqrt{\frac{M}{2\pi RT}}. \qquad \cdots \cdots \cdots (1)$$

[*] v. Wartenberg, *Zeits. f. Elektrochemie*, Vol. 19, p. 482 (1913); see also Melville and Gray, *Trans. Faraday Soc.*, Vol. 32, p. 1026 (1936).

If we can assume that each atom of the vapour which strikes the solid surface is condensed, this equation must give the relation between the vapour pressure p and the mass μ lost per unit area per second when the solid is heated to a temperature T in a vacuum. Langmuir, Jones and Mackay support this assumption by showing that the values of Λ_0 (see Section 24) deduced from the observations at different temperatures agree,* and that the results are therefore consistent among themselves. On the other hand, Harteck † has pointed out that the values of Λ_0 so obtained in some cases show a drift with temperature. Further, using Knudsen's method, Harteck has shown that for silver and copper, where the temperature ranges of his experiments and Langmuir's overlap, the values given by Langmuir's method are too low, which appears to be definite evidence against the assumption. For a further discussion of this point, see Section 7.

The method of determining μ used by Langmuir was to heat the filament in a high vaccum by the passage of an electric current as in an ordinary incandescent lamp. At these low pressures the mean free path of the vapour molecules is large compared with the size of the bulb containing the filament, so that all the atoms which leave the filament reach the wall, which is at such a comparatively low temperature that they stick there.

Langmuir determined the temperature T of the filament optically (see Chapter XX, Section 22). Apart from p, which we wish to determine, the only other unknown in the last equation is μ. This Langmuir determined by direct weighing as follows.

Let W_0 be the weight of the wire per unit length at the beginning of the experiment. Let W_1 be the weight of the wire per unit length at the end of the experiment. Further, let

ρ be the density of the wire;
r_0 be the radius of the wire at the beginning of the experiment;
r_1 be the radius of the wire at the end of the experiment.

We have $\qquad\qquad W = \pi r^2 \rho,$ or $r = \sqrt{(W/\pi\rho)}.$

If, as before, μ is the mass lost in unit time from unit area of the surface, the mass lost from unit length of the filament in unit time is $\mu 2\pi r$; we have therefore

$$-2\pi r \rho (dr/dt) = \mu\, 2\pi r,$$

or, in other words, $-dr/dt$ is constant and equal to μ/ρ. We have therefore

$$\frac{\mu}{\rho} = \frac{r_0 - r_1}{t} = \frac{\sqrt{W_0} - \sqrt{W_1}}{t}\, \frac{1}{\sqrt{\pi\rho}},$$

or

$$\mu = \sqrt{\frac{\rho}{\pi}}\, \frac{\sqrt{W_0} - \sqrt{W_1}}{t}, \qquad \ldots \ldots \quad (2)$$

t being the time of duration of an experiment. Thus μ was determined by weighing the filament at the beginning and end of an experiment.

The results obtained were extrapolated by Jones, Langmuir, and Mackay, right up to the boiling-point of the liquid. The method of carrying out the calculations will be understood from Sections 11 and 12, and the footnote below. Reasonable assumptions were made about the specific heats of the solid and

---

* The value of Λ_0 was determined from each observation using equation (7), the vapour being assumed monatomic. The atomic heat of the solid was known from experimental results, and the value of the constant i was obtained from the theoretical relation between i and the atomic weight. This relation is well supported experimentally (see Section 24).

† Harteck, *Zeits. f. phys. Chem.*, Vol. 134, p. 1 (1928).

liquid metals and the latent heats of fusion were known. In this way the following boiling-points * were obtained.

Metal		Boiling-point
Tungsten	....	6970° K.
Molybdenum	....	5960
Platinum	....	4800
Nickel	....	3650
Iron	....	3475
Copper	....	3110
Silver	....	2740

These results are interesting, but in view of Harteck's criticism they must be accepted only tentatively.

7. The Coefficient of Condensation.

Equation (1) gives the *maximum* rate of vaporization per unit area of surface of solid or liquid at temperature T in terms of the vapour pressure p and the molecular weight of the vapour M. The actual rate of vaporization (measured in grams per second per unit area) may be less than this, so we write

$$\mu = \alpha p \sqrt{\frac{M}{2\pi RT}},$$

where α is necessarily less than unity. α is called the *coefficient of condensation*.

α can be determined by measurements on the rate of vaporization at temperatures at which the vapour pressure is known.† The method used is similar to that used by Brønsted and Hevesy for the separation of the isotopes of mercury (see Section 26). Volmer and Estermann ‡ have measured rates of evaporation and have come to the conclusion that in the case of some solids α is considerably less than unity.

Bennewitz § has criticized the result and considers that α is always equal to unity, and that the effect observed by Volmer and Estermann occurs only when the rate of vaporization is so great that, on account of the latent heat of vaporization, the surface temperature of the solid falls below the mean temperature. Strong support for this view is found in the fact that the effect occurs to a marked extent with substances that are poor conductors of heat.

On the other hand, careful experiments by Alty ‖ with water, in which the temperature difference between the surface and bulk of the liquid was measured, suggest that in this case the coefficient may be of the order 0·01.

Results of Vapour-pressure Measurements

8. The formulæ used to express the results of vapour-pressure measurements are all based on the Clausius-Clapeyron equation (see equation (23), Chapter XVI):

$$\Lambda = (V^g - V^l)T \frac{dp}{dT},$$

* For references to attempts to determine the boiling-point (and melting-point) of carbon, see Herbst, *Zeits. f. techn. Physik*, Vol. 7, p. 467 (1926).

† See Knudsen, *Ann. d. Physik*, Vol. 47, p. 697 (1915); Vol. 50, p. 472 (1916).

‡ Volmer and Estermann, *Zeits. f. Physik*, Vol. 7, p. 1 (1921).

§ Bennewitz, *Zeits. f. Physik*, Vol. 10, p. 169 (1922).

‖ Alty, *Proc. Roy. Soc.*, A, Vol. 131, p. 554 (1931); *Phil. Mag.*, Vol. 15, p. 82 (1933).

where V^g is the volume of 1 gram-molecule of the vapour, V^l that of 1 gram-molecule of the liquid, Λ is the molecular latent heat of vaporization, and p is the vapour pressure at temperature T.

The equation as it stands is exact. In order to integrate it we must make some assumptions. We shall assume that the pressure of the vapour is not high, so that we may apply the perfect gas laws to it; further, we shall assume that V^l can be neglected in comparison with V^g. Under these conditons we may write $V^g = RT/p$, and the equation becomes

$$\Lambda = RT^2 \frac{d \log p}{dT}, \quad \ldots \ldots \ldots \quad (3)$$

which leads to

$$\frac{dp}{dT} = \frac{\Lambda p}{RT^2}. \quad \ldots \ldots \ldots \quad (3')$$

Also, under these conditions, we have

$$\left[\frac{\partial(V^g - V^l)}{\partial T} \right]_p = \frac{R}{p}. \quad \ldots \ldots \quad (4)$$

From the definition of entropy (Chapter XII, Sections 8 and 10), we have

$$\frac{\Lambda}{T} = S^g - S^l$$

where S^g and S^l are the entropies of one gram-molecule of the vapour and the liquid respectively. Differentiating along the saturation curve (indicated by d/dT) we get *

$$\frac{d}{dT}\left(\frac{\Lambda}{T}\right) = \frac{d}{dT}(S^g - S^l)$$

$$= \left(\frac{\partial S^g}{\partial T}\right)_p + \left(\frac{\partial S^g}{\partial p}\right)_T \frac{dp}{dT} - \left(\frac{\partial S^l}{\partial T}\right)_p - \left(\frac{\partial S^l}{\partial p}\right)_T \frac{dp}{dT}$$

$$= \frac{C_p{}^g - C_p{}^l}{T} - \left[\frac{\partial(V^g - V^l)}{\partial T}\right]_p \frac{dp}{dT},$$

if we make use of the Maxwell relation (5) of Chapter XIII. With the help of equation (4), this reduces to

$$\frac{d}{dT}\left(\frac{\Lambda}{T}\right) = \frac{C_p{}^g - C_p{}^l}{T} - \frac{\Lambda}{T^2},$$

whence

$$\frac{d\Lambda}{dT} = C_p{}^g - C_p{}^l.$$

* In this differentiation we are concerned with the change in S for a change along the saturation curve. If we consider p and T as the state variables the changes in p and T along the saturation curve are not independent. Thus, we have

$$dS = \left(\frac{\partial S}{\partial T}\right)_p dT + \left(\frac{\partial S}{\partial p}\right)_T \frac{dp}{dT} dT$$

for the change in S along the saturation curve.

Integrating this equation, and making use of equation (3'), we get

$$RT^2 \frac{d \log p}{dT} = \Lambda = \Lambda_{T_1} + \int_{T_1}^{T} (C_p{}^g - C_p{}^l) \, dT, \qquad . \quad (5)$$

where

$$\Lambda_{T_1} = \left[RT^2 \frac{d \log p}{dT} \right]_{T = T_1}$$

is the constant of integration.

It is left as an exercise to the reader to show that an alternative expression is

$$RT^2 \frac{d \log p}{dT} = \Lambda_{T_1} + R \int_{T_1}^{T} \frac{d \log p}{d \log T} \, dT + \int_{T_1}^{T} (C_{\text{sat}}^g - C_{\text{sat}}^l) \, dT, \quad (5')$$

where C_{sat} is the heat capacity measured along the saturation curve.

9. The Kirchhoff Formula.

If we suppose that the range of temperature from T_1 to T is sufficiently small for $C_p{}^g$ and $C_p{}^l$ to remain appreciably constant, equation (5) can be written

$$\frac{d \log p}{dT} = \frac{\Lambda_{T_1} + (C_p{}^l - C_p{}^g)T_1}{RT^2} - \frac{(C_p{}^l - C_p{}^g)}{RT}.$$

$C_p{}^l$ is in general greater than $C_p{}^g$, so that $(C_p{}^l - C_p{}^g)$ is positive. Integrating this equation, we obtain

$$\log p = - \frac{\Lambda_{T_1} + (C_p{}^l - C_p{}^g)T_1}{R} \frac{1}{T} - \frac{(C_p{}^l - C_p{}^g)}{R} \log T + A,$$

where A is a constant of integration. This equation is of the form

$$\log p = A - \frac{B}{T} - C \log T, \qquad . \quad . \quad . \quad . \quad . \quad (6)$$

where A, B, and C are constants. This is Kirchhoff's equation, which has been widely used to represent the results of vapour-pressure measurements. For example, Knudsen and Wenman and Volker * have shown that the results of a large number of determinations of the vapour pressure of mercury can be expressed as follows:

From 15° C. to 270° C.,

$$\log_{10} p = 10 \cdot 5724 - \frac{3342 \cdot 26}{T} - 0 \cdot 847 \log_{10} T;$$

and from 270° C. to 450° C.,

$$\log_{10} p = 10 \cdot 530 - \frac{3328}{T} - 0 \cdot 848 \log_{10} T.$$

---

* Knudsen, *Ann. Physik*, Vol. 29, p. 179 (1909); Wenman and Volker, *Z. physikal Chem.*, A, Vol. 161, p. 40 (1932); see also Egerton, *Phil. Mag.*, Vol. 39, p. 1 (1920).

10. The General Equation.

To obtain the general equation for the vapour pressure, we put $T_1 = 0$ and write $C_p{}^g = \frac{5}{2}R + C_{int.}$, where $C_{int.}$ is the internal molecular heat due to rotations and vibrations. Equation (5) becomes

$$RT^2 \frac{d \log p}{dT} = \Lambda_0 + 2 \cdot 5RT + \int_0^T C_{int.} \, dT - \int_0^T C_p{}^s dT.$$

Λ_0 is a constant which is discussed in Section 12. The equation applies to the vapour pressure of a solid * of which the molecular heat is $C_p{}^s$. Integrating, we obtain

$$\log p = -\frac{\Lambda_0}{RT} + 2 \cdot 5 \log T + \int_0^T \frac{dT}{RT^2} \int_0^T (C_{int.} - C_p{}^s) \, dT + i, \quad (7)$$

where i is a constant of integration. Experiment and theory indicate that near absolute zero $\int_0^T C_{int.} \, dT$ and $\int_0^T C_p{}^s dT$ are at least proportional to T^2 (Chapter VI, Sections 28–29; Chapter VII, Section 7), so that the integral in (7) is finite.

11. The Chemical Constant.

The integration constant i in the vapour-pressure equation of a substance is much more fundamental than would be supposed (see Chapter XVIII, Section 3). It is usually called the *chemical constant*; its value is determined by measuring all the other quantities in equation (7). The measurement of the specific heats has been dealt with in Chapters VI and VII; the measurement of vapour pressures has been dealt with in the earlier part of this chapter. It remains to consider the measurement of Λ_0.

12. The Latent Heat of Vaporization at the Absolute Zero.

We cannot conceive of any method by which we could vaporize a solid at the absolute zero and so measure the value of Λ_0 directly.

---

* If we are dealing with a liquid, it is only necessary to use, instead of the last term $\int_0^T C_p{}^s dT$ in the above equation, the expression

$$\int_0^{T_m} C_p{}^s dT + F_m + \int_{T_m}^T C_p{}^l dT,$$

where T_m is the melting-point, and F_m the molecular latent heat of fusion. This quantity is known as the difference of enthalpy of the liquid at temperature T and the solid at absolute zero.

It is quite sufficient for our present purpose to regard Λ_0 as a constant defined by the equation *

$$\Lambda_T{}^s = \Lambda_0 + \int_0^T C_p{}^g dT - \int_0^T C_p{}^s dT, \quad \ldots \quad (8)$$

where $\Lambda_T{}^s$ is the measured molecular latent heat of vaporization of the solid at temperature T; or, what amounts to the same thing, by the equation

$$\Lambda_T{}^l = \Lambda_0 + \int_0^T C_p{}^g dT - \int_0^{T_m} C_p{}^s dT - F_m - \int_{T_m}^T C_p{}^l dT, \quad (9)$$

where $\Lambda_T{}^l$ is the measured molecular latent heat of vaporization of the liquid at temperature T, T_m is the melting-point, and F_m is the molecular latent heat of fusion.

To determine Λ_0 from equation (9) we must measure, in addition to the specific heats, F_m and the latent heat of vaporization of the liquid. The values of Λ_0 deduced from measurements of the latent heat of vaporization of the liquid at different temperatures should agree.

The measurement of F_m is dealt with in Chapter IX. We now proceed to consider the measurement of the latent heat of vaporization of liquids.

THE MEASUREMENT OF LATENT HEAT OF VAPORIZATION

13. The methods used to determine the latent heat of vaporization may be divided into three main groups:

(a) Those in which the heat required to vaporize a given mass of liquid is measured directly; in practically every case the heat is measured electrically, but we must also include under this head determinations using the Bunsen ice calorimeter.

(b) Those in which the heat given up by a given mass of vapour in condensing is measured by allowing it to heat up a given mass of water the rise of temperature of which is measured.

(c) Indirect methods in which the latent heat is deduced from the variation of the vapour pressure with temperature, using the Clausius-Clapeyron equation.

We need not consider (c) further. Of the other two groups (a) is capable of use over a much wider range of temperatures and is the more important; (b) is the older.

Evaporation Methods

14. We cannot describe in detail all the modifications of the evaporation method that have been used. It will be sufficient to describe the accurate work of Henning on water, the results of which are used in

---

* The meaning of Λ_0 is discussed in Chapter XXIII, Section 12.

a direct test of the second law of thermodynamics (see Chapter XVI, Section 8); and also some typical experiments at low temperatures on the vaporization of the so-called permanent gases, whose chemical constants are of considerable importance.

15. Henning's Experiments.

Henning * has determined the latent heat of vaporization of steam at temperatures from 30° to 180° C. by a method similar in some respects to that used earlier by Griffiths.† His apparatus is shown in fig. 8.6.

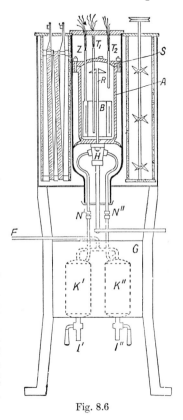

The water is contained in a bronze cylinder A, with a bronze lid S screwed on air-tight. This lid has three nickel tubes screwed air-tight into it. Two of these, T_1 and T_2, are closed and contain thermometers which give the temperature of the liquid and vapour (we may here note that this apparatus can be and has been used to determine the vapour pressure at various temperatures—see Holborn and Henning, *Ann. d. Physik*, Vol. 26, p. 833 (1908)); the third one, Z, carries current and potential leads to an electric heater made up of constantan strips. The heater is contained in a metal cylinder B, which is ring-shaped and air-tight. The steam passes down through the tube R, which has an umbrella-shaped top to prevent drops of water being splashed down it, to the two-way tap H. By altering this tap the steam may be made to pass down N′ or N″ to either of the condensation vessels K′ or K″ which are contained in a vessel G through which water circulates. Until conditions are steady the steam is condensed in K″; at a given instant it is switched over to condense in K′, and during the time that it is condensing in K′ the supply of electric energy is measured; at the end of the experiment it is switched back to K″. The amount of water condensed in K′ is determined by running it off through the tap I′ and weighing it. The temperature of boiling is ad-

Fig. 8.6

justed by altering the pressure inside the whole system. The pressure is trans-mitted through the tube F which leads to a cylinder of compressed air (or to an exhaust pump) and to an open mercury or other manometer.

In order to prevent heat loss from the cylinder A it is contained in an air space in the centre of a ring-shaped oil bath which is electrically

---

* Henning, *Ann. d. Physik*, Vol. 21, p. 849 (1906); Vol. 29, p. 441 (1909).

† Griffiths, *Phil. Trans.*, A, p. 261 (1895); Awbery, *Proc. Phys. Soc.*, Vol. 39, p. 417 (1927).

heated so that it is as nearly as possible at the temperature of the boiling water. The small residual loss is determined by carrying out two experiments with all the temperatures the same. The two experiments last the same time, but the rate of supply of electrical energy to B is different. The heat gained by A by conduction in the two experiments is the same: call this q. Let Q_1 and Q_2 be the heats supplied electrically in the two experiments, and let m_1 and m_2 be the masses of steam condensed. If λ is the latent heat of vaporization at the particular temperature, we have

$$Q_1 + q = m_1\lambda,$$
$$Q_2 + q = m_2\lambda.$$

q, which may be positive or negative, can be eliminated by subtracting these two equations, and thus λ may be determined.

16. Experiments at Low Temperatures.

The experiments of Simon and Lange * to determine the latent heat of vaporization of hydrogen may be taken as typical of the methods used at low temperatures. The apparatus is shown in fig. 8.7.

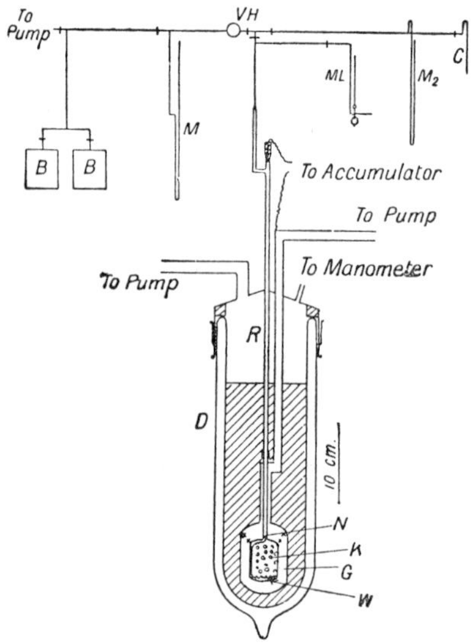

Fig. 8.7

The calorimeter K (capacity about 60 c.c., mass about 8 gm.) is made of copper foil about 0·1 mm. thick. The tubes N and R which lead into it are of German silver. N is a capillary 1·5 mm. in diameter with walls 0·06 mm. thick, R is 3 mm. in diameter with walls 0·2 mm. thick. K is contained inside a copper vessel G from which it is separated by a distance of about 1 cm. G is connected to a mercury pump by a tube about 1 cm. in diameter. Up to the bend this tube is of copper and above it of German silver. By pumping the gas out of G the calorimeter is surrounded by a vacuum. The apparatus is assembled by soldering K and then G at the points marked with crosses.

G is pumped out, cooled down in liquid air, and then immersed in liquid hydrogen contained in the Dewar flask D—the shading indicates the liquid hydrogen.

The calorimeter is now placed in communication with the hydrogen gas contained in B, by opening the tap H. If the pressure above the hydrogen in the

* Simon and Lange, *Zeits. f. Physik,* Vol. 15, p. 312 (1923).

Dewar flask is lowered, it boils and the temperature falls—in general it is best to maintain the pressure in the flask equal to that of saturated hydrogen vapour at the triple point * (13·93° absolute, vapour pressure = 5·38 cm. of mercury); hydrogen is condensed in the tube R and drops into K.

When enough has condensed the taps on B are closed. The temperature of the condensed hydrogen can be further reduced if necessary by pumping out the space above it with a mercury pump and with carbon in the tube C immersed in liquid air.

K contains a constantan heating coil W of resistance about 3300 ohms.

The temperature of the hydrogen can be determined by measuring the vapour pressure, using the MacLeod gauge ML for the lowest pressures, and for pressures above 6 cm. of mercury the mercury manometer M_2.

The transfer of heat along the capillary N and through the vacuum is very small.

In measuring the latent heat of vaporization, heat is supplied to the coil W, and the evaporated gas is collected in B. From the rise in pressure (measured by the manometer M), the volume of B, and the equation of state of hydrogen, the mass evaporated can be calculated; B is immersed in a water-bath to keep its temperature constant. It is necessary for the evaporation to take place at constant pressure. This is effected by adjusting the valve V and thus keeping the reading of the manometer M_2 constant. The latent heat of evaporation is determined by measuring the mass evaporated when a given amount of energy is supplied to the heating coil. Correction is made for leakage of heat to the calorimeter by measuring the rate of evaporation with no current flowing through the coil.

17. Dieterici's Experiments.†

Dieterici has used a Bunsen ice calorimeter (see Chapter IX, Section 3) to measure the latent heat of vaporization at 0° C. The water is contained in the inner tube of the calorimeter, and the vaporization which absorbs heat causes more ice to form, so that the volume of ice *plus* water in the calorimeter is increased and mercury is forced out.

Condensation Methods

18. Berthelot's Apparatus.

In Berthelot's apparatus (fig. 8.8) the flask containing the liquid under examination is heated by a circular gas-burner *l*, burning under a metallic disc *m*. The centre of the flask is traversed by a wide tube TT, through which the vapour descends into the calorimeter, where it condenses in the spiral SS and collects in the reservoir R. The calorimeter is placed inside a water-jacket, and is protected from the radiation of the burner by a slab of wood covered by a sheet of wire gauze. By means of this arrangement partial condensation is avoided before the vapour enters the calorimeter, and the error arising from conductivity is corrected by observation of the motion of the thermometer placed in the calorimeter before the distillation commences and after it is

* See Chapter XVI, Section 12.   † Dieterici, *Wied. Ann.*, Vol. 37, p. 506 (1889).

completed. The weight of liquid condensed is about 20 to 30 gm. at most and the time occupied is only from 2 to 4 min. The mass of vapour condensing in the tube is measured, and the heat given up is determined by measuring the rise of temperature of the water in the calorimeter. By this method we measure the heat of vaporization *plus* the heat given up by the condensed liquid in cooling from the condensation point to the final temperature of the calorimeter. A correction must be made for the latter quantity of heat.

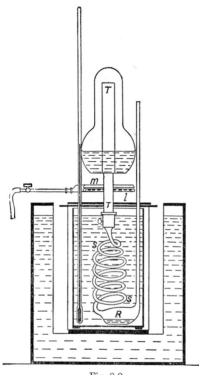

Fig. 8.8

Errors are likely to arise in apparatus of this type owing to superheating of the vapour as it passes down the central tube past the gas ring. Further, in this as in all the other methods the carrying over by the vapour of minute drops of liquid tends to give low values for the latent heat of vaporization. It is very difficult to remove this last source of error with a boiling liquid, but it is probable that the faster the rate of boiling the more of these minute drops are produced, so that by varying the rate of boiling an estimate can probably be made of the extent to which the results are affected by this source of error.

Harker * has made some improvements in the apparatus of Berthelot by lagging the down tube with asbestos surrounded by a steam pipe and paying attention to the rate of boiling. He also introduced a valve by which the liquid could at will be made to pass into the condenser or allowed to escape; disturbance at the beginning and end of the experiment was thus avoided.

* Harker, *Manchester Lit. and Phil. Soc.* (1896).

19. Awbery and Griffiths' Apparatus.*

These workers introduced the use of the method of continuous flow, which in this case possesses many advantages. Their apparatus is shown in fig. 8.9.

The boiling vessel at the top was electrically heated, and through the top projected a thermocouple which measured the temperature of the vapour. To diminish any radiation transfer between the liquid or vapour and the top of the

boiler, the conical radiation shield shown in the figure was placed inside. This was perforated with holes to allow free circulation of the vapour, and supported on a sheet-metal cylinder. The vessel was well lagged with asbestos wool. Through the base passed a re-entrant tube of such length that it projected above the surface of the liquid. Through this tube was carried a silica tube which extended to about 20 in. below the base. This tube was surrounded by a jacket through which a stream of water flowed at a constant rate. As shown in the figure, the stream flowed up an outer jacket, when its temperature was approximately that of the air, and down the inner jacket, during which time it took up heat from the condensing vapour and from the liquid, and was almost completely shielded

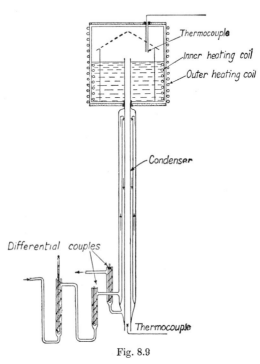

Fig. 8.9

from radiation by the surrounding stream of incoming water. As an additional precaution against loss of heat the tube was heavily lagged with cotton-wool. A set of copper-constantan thermocouples arranged differentially gave the rise of temperature of the water stream. A thermocouple inserted in the mouth of the silica tube gave the temperature of the condensed liquid on leaving the apparatus.

In this experiment it was essential that the vapour should be produced at a steady rate; this was ensured by the use of electrical heating. If, after a steady state has been reached, M is the mass of water flowing per second, θ its rise of temperature (measured by the differential couples), t_2 the boiling-point of the liquid, t_1 the temperature of the liquid leaving the apparatus, λ its latent heat of vaporization,

* Awbery and Ezer Griffiths, *Proc. Phys. Soc. Lond.*, Vol. 36, p. 305 (1924).

s its mean specific heat over the range t_1 to t_2, and m the mass of liquid condensed per second, we have

$$M\theta = m[\lambda + s(t_2 - t_1)].$$

s must be determined by a separate experiment, using one of the methods described in Chapter VII. M and m are easily determined by collecting the amounts of water and condensed liquid which leave the apparatus in a given time, and weighing them.

20. The Joly Steam Calorimeter.

The latent heat of vaporization of water can be measured directly in terms of its mean specific heat by using the steam calorimeter * described in Chapter VI, Section 4. The temperature of the empty bulb of thermal capacity K is raised from the freezing-point to the boiling-point of water by surrounding it with steam, a mass m of steam being condensed on the bulb, where

$$100K = m\lambda,$$

λ being the latent heat of vaporization.

The bulb is then filled with a mass M of water and the process repeated, a mass m' of steam being condensed, where

$$100(K + Ms) = m'\lambda,$$

s being the mean specific heat of water from $0°$ to $100°$ C.

Taking the difference between these equations, we obtain

$$\lambda = 100\,\frac{Ms}{(m' - m)}.$$

A comparison of the latent heat so determined with that determined using an electrical method such as Henning's would probably furnish the most accurate method of determining the ratio of the mean specific heat to that at a given temperature, say $15°$ C.

Results

21. Trouton's Rule.

The only important generalization concerning latent heats of vaporization is Trouton's rule, which states that *the ratio of the molecular latent heat of vaporization to the boiling-point is a constant for all substances*; that is, if Λ is the molecular latent heat of vaporization and T_b is the boiling-point on the absolute scale at atmospheric pressure,

$$\frac{\Lambda}{T_b} = \text{constant.}$$

* Carlton-Sutton, *Proc. Roy. Soc.*, A, Vol. 93, p. 155 (1917).

The rule does not apply to substances whose vapours are associated. For many substances the value of the constant is about 88 if the latent heat is given in joules. Table I illustrates its applicability.

It will be seen that the rule is only approximately true. Attempts have been made to improve it and in particular to express the Trouton constant as a function of the temperature. Such attempts are practically useful but of small theoretical importance.* The formula of v. Wartenberg,

$$\frac{\Lambda}{T_b} = 31 \log_{10} T_b + 8\cdot 3,$$

represents roughly the experimental values for substances with non-associated vapours, if Λ is measured in absolute joules.

TABLE I

Substance	Λ (Joules)	T_b (°Abs.)	$\dfrac{\Lambda}{T_b}$	
			Experiment	v. Wartenberg
Normal Vapours: He	92	4·22	21·3	28·0
H$_2$	917	20·4	45·2	49·0
N$_2$	5,610	77·3	72·4	67·0
O$_2$	6,820	90·1	75·8	69·1
HCl	16,300	188·1	86·6	78·7
Cl$_2$	19,300	239·5	80·4	82·0
Pentane	25,500	309·0	82·9	85·4
CS$_2$	27,200	319·3	87·9	85·8
C$_6$H$_6$	30,800	353	87·1	87·1
Aniline	42,000	457	91·7	90·8
Hg	59,400	630	94·6	95·0
Cs	65·300	858	76·2	99·2
Rb	78,300	942	83·3	100·4
Na	97,500	1155	84·5	103·4
Zn	116,100	1180	98·4	103·4
Pb	193,000	1887	102·1	109·7
Associated Vapours: NO	13,600	122	111·8	72·8
NH$_3$	23,300	239·8	97·9	82·0
C$_2$H$_5$OH	40,000	351	113·8	87·1
H$_2$O	40,600	373	108·8	87·9
Formic acid	23,200	374	61·9	87·9
Acetic acid	24,400	391	62·4	88·7

* See for a summary, Kendall, *Journ. Amer. Chem. Soc.*, Vol. 36, p. 1620 (1914); also v. Wartenberg, *Z. f. Elektrochem.*, Vol. 20, p. 444 (1914); Forcrand, *C. R.*, Vol. 156, pp. 1439, 1648 (1913); Hildebrandt, *Journ. Amer. Chem. Soc.*, Vol. 37, p. 970 (1915); Wagner, *Z. f. Elektrochem.*, Vol. 31, p. 308 (1925).

THE DETERMINATION OF VAPOUR DENSITY

22. The density of a saturated vapour can be accurately determined by the method of Fairbairn and Tate,* the principle of which is shown diagrammatically in fig. 8.10. Communication between the tubes A and B is broken only by mercury. After both tubes have been evacuated a small amount of the liquid under investigation, the mass m of which is known, is introduced into A, and a considerable amount of the same liquid into B. The whole apparatus is then slowly heated. As long as any liquid remains in A the level of mercury in A and B remains constant—that in A is slightly higher on account of the greater amount of liquid in B. Immediately all the liquid in A is evaporated the level of the mercury column in A begins to rise rapidly. The temperature at which this occurs is measured. At this temperature the mass of vapour m occupies the volume cut off by the mercury in A. Thus the density of the saturated vapour at this temperature can be determined.

Fig. 8.10

Another accurate method is to take a calibrated tube, and after evacuation to introduce a mass m of the substance under investigation. Some of the liquid is vaporized and the volumes v_1 and v_2 occupied by the liquid and vapour respectively can be observed. A similar observation is made at the same temperature when the mass of substance present is m', the volumes in this case being v_1' and v_2'. If ρ_g is the density of the vapour, and ρ_l that of the liquid, we have

$$v_1\rho_l + v_2\rho_g = m,$$

$$v_1'\rho_l + v_2'\rho_g = m',$$

from which

$$\rho_g = \frac{mv_1' - m'v_1}{v_1'v_2 - v_1v_2'},$$

$$\rho_l = \frac{mv_2' - m'v_2}{v_1v_2' - v_1'v_2}.$$

This method has been used by Mathias and Onnes † in connexion with an investigation on oxygen.

* Fairbairn and Tate, *Phil. Trans.*, Vol. 150, p. 185 (1860); *Phil. Mag.*, Vol. 21, p. 230 (1861).

† See Mathias and Onnes, *Leiden Comm.*, No. 117 (1911).

NUMERICAL VALUES FOR THE CHEMICAL CONSTANT

23. Agreement between Theoretical and Experimental Values.*

Stern † and Tetrode ‡ have studied the equilibrium between a solid and its vapour from the point of view of statistical mechanics. In the case of a monatomic vapour they show that the integration constant i of equation (7), which we have called the chemical constant, is given by

$$i = \log \frac{(2\pi m)^{3/2} k^{5/2}}{h^3},$$

where m is the mass of one atom of the vapour, k is Boltzmann's constant, and h is Planck's constant. This may be written

$$i = i_0 + 1{\cdot}5 \log M,$$

where M is the molecular weight, and where

$$i_0 = \log \frac{(2\pi)^{3/2} R^{5/2}}{N_0{}^4 h^3} = 10{\cdot}17,$$

where natural logarithms are used and where all quantities are measured in c.g.s. units.

If pressures are measured in atmospheres, and logarithms to the base 10 are used, we shall denote the integration constant in equation (7) by C, keeping i for the case in which c.g.s. units and natural logarithms are used. The value of C is obtained by multiplying i by a numerical factor. We have

$$C = C_0 + 1{\cdot}5 \log_{10} M,$$

where

$$C_0 = -1{\cdot}589.$$

C_0 is a universal constant.

This theoretical value of C_0 can be compared with the values determined by subtracting $1{\cdot}5 \log_{10} M$ from the measured values of C for various substances. The measured value of C is obtained by substituting in equation (7) experimental values for all the quantities in the equation except the integration constant. Values of C_0 obtained in this way are given in Table II.

Except in the case of sodium and potassium, the theoretical and experimental values agree to within the probable experimental error. The differences in the case of sodium and potassium may be due to the

---

* The reading of this section should be postponed until Chapters XXI and XXII have been read.

† Stern, *Phys. Zeits.*, Vol. 14, p. 629 (1913); *Zeits. f. Elektrochemie*, Vol. 25, p. 66 (1919).

‡ Tetrode, *Amsterdam Proc.*, Vol. 17, p. 1167 (1915); for a short account, see Born, *Atomtheorie des festen Zustandes*, p. 703 (1923).

Table II

Substance		Value of C_0 (experimental)	Substance		Value of C_0 (experimental)
Neon *	..	-1.56 ± 0.04	Zinc ‖	..	-1.5 ± 0.3
Argon †	..	-1.61	Cadmium ¶	..	-1.51 ± 0.13
Xenon ‡	..	-1.58 ± 0.02	Mercury ‖	..	-1.63 ± 0.03
Sodium §	..	-1.41 ± 0.03	Lead **	..	-1.7 ± 0.2
Potassium §	..	-1.47 ± 0.04	Hydrogen ††	..	-1.57

presence of a small proportion of diatomic molecules in the vapours. On the other hand, as suggested by Schottky, it may show that the statistical weights of an atom in the solid and vapour states are not the same. The matter is of considerable importance, and a full discussion of the weights to be assigned in the vapour and crystal states has been given by Fowler.‡‡

The statistical theory has been extended by Ehrenfest and Trkal [1] to the case of a vapour whose molecules are not monatomic. A considerable amount of experimental evidence on the question has been collected by Eucken.[2] It is not possible to deal with this question without going into the details of the statistical theory.[3]

NOTE ON THE APPLICABILITY OF THE GAS LAWS TO VAPOURS

24. In the development of the theory of the chemical constant we have assumed that the gas laws are applicable to vapours. It is desirable to do this because the meanings of the equations are much clearer when not complicated by a large number of small correction terms of numerical interest only.

The assumption of the perfect gas laws leads in general to numerical errors of a few per cent. Since such errors are of importance in the accurate determination of chemical constants, we shall consider how they are avoided. We shall follow Simon [4] in his calculation of the chemical constant of hydrogen.

* Clusius, *Zeits. f. phys. Chem.*, B, Vol. 4, p. 1 (1929).

† Born, *Ann. d. Physik*, Vol. 69, p. 473 (1922).

‡ Clusius and Riccoboni, *Zeits. f. phys. Chem.*, B, Vol. 38, p. 81 (1938); Clusius, Kruis and Konnertz, *Ann. d. Physik*, Vol. 33, p. 642 (1938), obtained -1.59 ± 0.02 from measurements with krypton.

§ Edmondson and Egerton, *Proc. Roy. Soc.*, A, Vol. 113, pp. 520, 533 (1927); see also Rodebush and Walters, *Journ. Amer. Chem. Soc.*, Vol. 52, p. 2654 (1930).

‖ Egerton, *Phil. Mag.*, Vol. 39, p. 15 (1920).

¶ Lange and Simon, *Zeits. f. phys. Chem.*, Vol. 134, p. 378 (1928).

** Egerton, *Proc. Roy. Soc.*, A, Vol. 103, p. 485 (1923).

†† Simon, *Zeits. f. Physik*, Vol. 15, p. 307 (1923). The measurements must all be made in the region where hydrogen behaves as a monatomic gas. See also Stern, *Proc. Roy. Soc.*, A, Vol. 130, p. 367 (1931); Vol. 131, p. 339 (1931).

‡‡ Fowler, *Statistical Mechanics*, 2nd edition, Cambridge (1936), Section 7.2.

[1] Ehrenfest and Trkal, *Proc. Amst. Akad.*, Vol. 23, p. 162 (1920).

[2] Eucken, *Phys. Zeits.*, Vol. 30, p. 818 (1929); Vol. 31, p. 361 (1930).

[3] See Fowler, *Statistical Mechanics*, 2nd edition, Section 7.3.

[4] Simon, *Zeits. f. Physik*, Vol. 15, p. 307 (1923); see also Eucken, Karwat, and Fried, *Zeits. f. Physik*, Vol. 29, p. 1 (1925).

(a) Berthelot's equation for hydrogen vapour is (see equation (16), Chapter IV)

$$\frac{pV}{RT} = 1 + \frac{9}{128}\frac{T_c}{p_c}\frac{p}{T}\left(1 - \frac{6T_c^2}{T^2}\right).$$

We are going to apply the equation at temperatures below the triple point, that is, $T < 13\cdot94°$ absolute. At such temperatures 1 is small compared with $6T_c^2/T^2$, which is equal to $6600/T^2$. We therefore neglect it and write the above equation

$$\frac{pV}{RT} = 1 - 688\frac{p}{T^3}. \quad \ldots \ldots \ldots \quad (10a)$$

The numerical factor 688 agrees better with the results of compressibility experiments than does the factor deduced from the critical constants. p is measured in atmospheres. It must be remembered that we are only calculating small correction terms, and that for such purposes approximations like the above are sufficiently accurate.

(b) We require further an approximate expression for the variation of vapour pressure with temperature in order to determine the specific heat of the vapour at a given temperature. The approximate expression

$$p = 2\cdot63 \,.\, 10^{-13}T^{10} \text{ atmospheres} \quad \ldots \ldots \quad (10b)$$

represents the results between the triple point (vapour pressure, 5·38 cm.) and 11° absolute (vapour pressure, 0·516 cm.) with an error not greater than 3 per cent. For vapour pressures smaller than 0·5 cm. the difference between the specific heat in the actual condition and in the ideal condition ($p = 0$) is negligible.

(c) The thermodynamic equation for the variation of Λ (equation (24), Chapter XVI) is

$$\frac{d\Lambda}{dT} = C_p^g - C_p^s + \Lambda\left[\frac{1}{T} - \frac{1}{(V_g - V_s)}\left(\frac{\partial(V_g - V_s)}{\partial T}\right)_p\right]. \quad . \quad (10c)$$

Neglecting V_s and using equations (10a) and (10b), this becomes, to the first order of small terms,

$$\frac{d\Lambda}{dT} = C_p^g - C_p^s - \Lambda\,.\,5\cdot43\,.\,10^{-10}T^6. \quad \ldots \ldots \quad (10d)$$

In the correction term we may put $\Lambda = 1000$ (the measured value at the triple point is 1029 joules). We obtain

$$\frac{d\Lambda}{dT} = C_p^g - C_p^s - 5\cdot43\,.\,10^{-7}T^6. \quad \ldots \ldots \quad (10e)$$

The measurements of Eucken * (see Chapter VI, Section 27) show that at these temperatures hydrogen behaves as a monatomic gas. $(C_p)_0$, the molecular heat at $p = 0$, is therefore equal to $\frac{5}{2}R$. In order to obtain the actual molecular heat of the vapour we use the relation in Chapter XIII, Example (4),

$$\left(\frac{\partial C_p}{\partial p}\right)_T = -T\left(\frac{\partial^2 V}{\partial T^2}\right)_p.$$

Integrating and using equations (10a) and (10b), we obtain for the molecular heat of the vapour at the pressure at which it is in equilibrium with the liquid at temperature T

$$C_p - (C_p)_0 = 1\cdot09\,.\,10^{-9}RT^7.$$

* Eucken, *Sitz. d. preuss. Akad. d. Wiss.*, p. 141 (1912).

Using this relation in (10e), we have

$$\frac{d\Lambda}{dT} = 2 \cdot 5R - C_p{}^s - 5 \cdot 43 \cdot 10^{-7}T^6 + 1 \cdot 09 \cdot 10^{-9}RT^7.$$

And by integration

$$\Lambda = \Lambda_0 + 2 \cdot 5RT - \int_0^T C_p{}^s dT - 7 \cdot 76 \cdot 10^{-8}T^7 + 1 \cdot 36 \cdot 10^{-10}RT^8. \quad (10f)$$

The molecular latent heat of vaporization of the liquid at the triple point is 912 joules, and the latent heat of fusion is 117 joules. Adding the two, we obtain for the latent heat of vaporization of the solid at the triple point

$$\Lambda_{13 \cdot 94} = 1029 \text{ joules,}$$

and using this value in the above equation we obtain, assuming that $C_p{}^s$ is a Debye function (see Chapter XXII, Sections 1 and 2) with $\Theta = 91$,

$$\Lambda_0 = 767 \cdot 6 \text{ joules.} \quad \dotfill \quad (10g)$$

(d) We write the Clausius-Clapeyron equation in the form

$$\frac{d \log p}{dT} = \frac{\Lambda}{RT^2} \frac{RT}{pV},$$

that is, we neglect the volume of the solid, but do not assume that the vapour obeys the laws of a perfect gas.

Using equations (10a), (10b), and (10f), and neglecting terms less than 0·05 per cent of the total value, this becomes

$$\frac{d \log p}{dT} = \frac{\Lambda_0}{RT^2} + \frac{2 \cdot 5}{T} - \frac{1}{RT^2} \int_0^T C_p{}^s dT + \frac{8 \cdot 94 \cdot 10^{-8}}{R} T^5 + 5 \cdot 89 \cdot 10^{-10}T^6.$$

Integrating this and introducing logarithms to the base 10, we obtain

$$\log_{10} p = - \frac{767 \cdot 6}{19 \cdot 13T} + 2 \cdot 5 \log_{10} T - \frac{1}{19 \cdot 13} \int_0^T \frac{dT}{T^2} \int_0^T C_p{}^s dT *$$
$$+ 5 \cdot 30 \cdot 10^{-10}T^6 + 3 \cdot 67 \cdot 10^{-11}T^7 + C. \quad (10h)$$

We have written C for the constant of integration when logarithms to the base 10 are used and pressures are measured in atmospheres, retaining i for the constant with natural logarithms and c.g.s. units.

Substituting in this equation the numerical values for the triple point, we have

$$0 \cdot 8503 - 2 = -2 \cdot 8783 + 2 \cdot 8607 - 0 \cdot 0292 + 0 \cdot 0039 + 0 \cdot 0038 + C,$$

giving

$$C = -1 \cdot 11_1,$$

and

$$C_0 = C - 1 \cdot 5 \log_{10} M$$
$$= -1 \cdot 56_7.$$

Note the order of magnitude of the correction terms. If we had assumed that the ideal gas equations were applicable to the vapour, we should have obtained

$$\Lambda_0 = 761 \cdot 3 \text{ joules,} \quad C = -1 \cdot 12_7, \quad C_0 = -1 \cdot 58_3.$$

---

* For this integral, see Chapter XXII, Section 6.

THE SEPARATION OF ISOTOPES *

25. The experiments of Aston have shown that many of the chemical elements are made up of atoms of identical chemical properties but of different atomic weights. Such atoms are called isotopes. The separation of isotopes is a matter of considerable difficulty owing to the fact that chemical methods are not ordinarily available.† Of the physical methods that have been used, that depending on the varying rates of evaporation of atoms of different mass is one of the most successful.‡

The method is similar in principle to that used by Langmuir to determine the vapour pressures of tungsten and other elements of high melting-point (see Section 6). In equation (1) it is shown that the total mass μ of vapour molecules leaving unit area of a liquid or solid surface in unit time is given by

$$\mu = p\sqrt{\frac{M}{2\pi RT}},$$

where p is the vapour pressure at temperature T, and M is the molecular weight. The total number of molecules which leave unit area of the surface in unit time is equal to $N_0\mu/M$ or to

$$N_0 p\sqrt{\frac{1}{2\pi RTM}}.$$

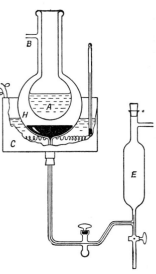

Fig. 8.11

If at a given temperature the vapour pressures of two isotopes are equal, p will be the same for them, and the rates of vaporization will be inversely proportional to the square roots of the atomic weights.§

It should, however, be noted that for isotopes of *light* elements, for which the *relative* atomic masses differ appreciably, this is no longer true. For instance, at 1·2° K. the vapour pressure of helium 3 is 35 times as great ‖ as that of helium 4.

The experimental arrangement used by Brønsted and Hevesy in their brilliant work on the separation of the isotopes of mercury is shown in fig. 8.11. The space

---

* The rest of the matter in this chapter on the separation of isotopes and on adsorption is included here as it illustrates the principles of Section 6.

† It should be noted, however, that the different masses of isotopes do cause their thermodynamical functions to have slightly different values. By using suitable reactions, this can be used to separate them. Such fractionation, occurring in natural processes, is the reason that isotopic abundance varies with samples of material from different sources. See Urey, *J. Chem. Soc.*, p. 562 (1947); Thode, *Research*, Vol. 2, p. 154 (1949). See also Chapter XVIII, Section 8.

‡ See Brønsted and Hevesy, *Phil. Mag.*, Vol. 43, p. 31 (1922); see also Mulliken and Harkins, *Journ. Amer. Chem. Soc.*, Vol. 44, pp. 37, 1033 (1922); Egerton and Lee, *Proc. Roy. Soc.*, A, Vol. 103, p. 499 (1923).

§ See, for example, Grimm, *Zeits. f. phys. Chem.*, B, Vol. 2, p. 181 (1929).

‖ Sydoriak, Hammel and Grilly, *Phys. Rev.*, Vol. 75, p. 303 (1949).

between the two walls of the double-walled vessel is highly evacuated by a pump attached at B. A is filled with liquid air, and the mercury in H is heated by standing in an oil bath C to a temperature of about 40° to 60° C. Evaporation takes place from the mercury in H and the vapour condenses to a solid on the surface of A. The vapour pressure at this low temperature is quite negligible, so that there is no re-evaporation of the condensed solid. The distance between A and H is comparable with the mean free path of the mercury atoms, so that very few collisions occur in the vapour, and atoms, once they have left the surface of H, do not return to it.

After the evaporation has proceeded for some time it is stopped, and the mercury remaining in H is run off into E and removed. The liquid air is removed from A, so that the mercury attached to it melts and can likewise be run off into E and examined.

Since the rate of evaporation is inversely proportional to the square root of the atomic weight, we should expect the atomic weight of the residue in H to increase progressively as the distillation goes on. If the atomic volume is the same for all isotopes,* the density will be proportional to the atomic weight, so that the density of the residue should also increase progressively as the distillation proceeds. That this is what actually happens is shown by the results given in Table III. We commence with 2700 c.c. of ordinary mercury, the density of which we take as unity. The distillation proceeds until about 640 c.c. have distilled off, leaving a residue R_1 of volume 2062 c.c. This residue is further evaporated until about 460 c.c. have passed off, leaving a residue R_2 of 1601 c.c. After determining the density of R_2 it is reintroduced into the apparatus and distilled further; the process can be continued as long as is desired. For the smaller fractions a smaller apparatus is used.

TABLE III

Sample	Volume	Density
Ordinary mercury	2700·0	1·000000
R_1	2062·0	—
R_2	1601·0	1·000016
R_3	1283·0	—
R_4	1030·0	1·000024
R_6	585·0	1·000034
R_8	382·0	1·000053
R_{12}	128·0	1·000079
R_{14}	10·3	1·000134
R_{15}	5·5	1·000153
R_{18}	0·2	1·00023

In order to obtain mercury of low density, the first distillate D_1 of volume 642 c.c. was further distilled until 154 c.c. had passed off. This 154 c.c., which we call D_2, was distilled, giving a distillate D_3 of volume 50 c.c., and so on. The results are shown in Table IV.

* According to the Rutherford-Bohr theory of the atom, the atomic volume to a very close approximation depends only on the nuclear charge and not on the nuclear mass. The nuclear charge is the same for isotopes.

TABLE IV

Sample	Volume	Density
Ordinary mercury	2700·0	1·000000
D_1	642·0	0·999977
D_2	154·0	0·999953
D_3	50·0	0·999933
D_4	13·5	0·999911
D_5	3·3	0·999881
D_{14}	0·2	0·99974

Comparing the densest mercury, R_{18} (density $= 1\cdot00023$), with the lightest, D_{14} (density $= 0\cdot99974$), we see that they differ in density by about five parts in ten thousand.

For the detailed theory of the separation the original paper must be consulted.

ADSORPTION

26. It has been known for a considerable time that porous substances like wood-charcoal can take up considerable quantities of gases, particularly at low temperatures. Gas so taken up is said to be *adsorbed*, and the charcoal or other substance is called the *adsorbent*. At liquid-air temperatures the adsorption of gases by wood-charcoal is almost complete, and Dewar used this fact to produce very high vacua by placing charcoal, cooled to the temperature of liquid air, in an already partially evacuated space. At higher temperatures, however, a definite equilibrium is set up between the adsorbed substance and the gas, and for a given mass of adsorbent at a given temperature, the mass of adsorbed gas depends on the pressure. If the pressure is increased, the amount of adsorbed gas is increased and vice versa. The adsorbed substance is supposed to be held on the surface of the adsorbent, but, in the case of a porous substance like charcoal, the quantitative study of the phenomenon cannot be carried far because the actual extent of the surface is not known. Langmuir was the first to carry out experiments on adsorption on the surfaces of smooth substances like polished metals or glass which have a definite area of surface. This was a great advance. We shall deal only with the adsorption of gases by such substances from the elementary kinetic point of view, and shall not touch on adsorption from solutions or on the surface of liquids.*

The most direct method of studying adsorption phenomena is the following. The adsorbent is arranged in the form of a very large number of thin plates separated from each other so as to expose a large area to the gas. These plates are placed in a vessel and, after having been heated *in vacuo* to a high temperature so as to remove surface impurities, are allowed to come into equilibrium with the gas, the pressure of which is measured accurately on a low-pressure gauge. A tap is now opened connecting to an evacuated space, and, when equilibrium is again established, the pressure is measured. It is found that the pressure is greater than that calculated from Boyle's law using the known ratio of the volumes before and after opening the tap. This is due to the fact that at the lower pressure there is less gas adsorbed on the surface of the plates, and from

---

* For a discussion of adsorption on liquid surfaces, see Burdon, *Surface Tension and the Spreading of Liquids* (Cambridge Monographs on Physics), Cambridge University Press (1949).

the departure from Boyle's law the difference between the masses adsorbed at the two pressures can be calculated. By this method it is possible to obtain the adsorption isotherm, which is simply the relation between adsorbed mass and pressure at a given temperature.

In this way the following results are obtained:

(1) At very low pressures the mass adsorbed is proportional to the pressure. At this stage the adsorption is usually described as *weak*.

(2) As the pressure is increased, the straight line representing the relation between adsorbed mass (ordinate) and pressure (abscissa) bends over and becomes horizontal, at which stage the adsorption is usually described as *strong*.

The horizontal straight line representing the relation between adsorbed mass and pressure indicates that a state of saturation is reached, and that further increase of pressure does not appreciably affect the mass adsorbed. From our knowledge of the dimensions of atomic lattices it is possible to calculate the number of atoms of the adsorbent which lie in unit area of the surface. Langmuir discovered that in general at saturation the number of adsorbed molecules per unit area of the surface is less than the number of molecules of the adsorbent per unit area. This indicates that adsorbed films are only one molecule thick; they are therefore often spoken of as *monomolecular films*.

27. Elementary Kinetic Theory.

The considerations of Sections 6 and 7 apply to the equilibrium between an adsorbed film and gas. We shall suppose that there is an actual layer of gas molecules on the surface and that it is monomolecular. If m is the mass adsorbed per unit area, the amount "evaporated" per second per unit area is proportional to m * and may be put equal to km, where k is a constant.

The phenomenon of saturation with a monomolecular film indicates that, if m_0 is the adsorbed mass per unit area at saturation, and if m is the actual mass per unit area, only a fraction $(m_0 - m)/m_0$ of the total area is able to retain the gaseous molecules which strike it. The number of molecules striking unit area per second is proportional to p, the pressure. We may therefore write for the total number of molecules deposited on unit area per second

$$k' \frac{m_0 - m}{m_0} p,$$

where k' is a constant.

In the state of equilibrium the number of molecules leaving unit area of the surface per second is equal to the number deposited. We have therefore

$$km = k' \frac{m_0 - m}{m_0} p,$$

and thus

$$m = \frac{p}{A + p/m_0},$$

where A is a constant. When p is very small, m is proportional to p, being equal to p/A, corresponding to weak adsorption; and, when p is large, m is constant

---

* This is true for weak adsorption, where the adsorbed molecules are so far apart that they exert no forces on one another. When the molecules become more closely packed, they may exert an influence on one another so that there is a departure from strict proportionality. For the sake of simplicity we shall assume proportionality in all cases.

and equal to m_0, corresponding to strong adsorption. This equation is therefore qualitatively in agreement with the facts. It is also in good quantitative agreement.

The theory outlined in the preceding paragraphs implies that the forces holding the film on the surface may be roughly classified as chemical in nature; for, roughly speaking, the difference between a chemical and a physical force is that a chemical force is satisfied by or expended on one atom, while a physical force is more of the nature of a field of force, the influence of which extends over a considerable region. This view is supported by the values obtained for the heat of adsorption of monomolecular films on a clean surface. In recent years much experimental work has been carried out on the structure of adsorbed films. It has been found that the building up of successive layers of adsorbed molecules can be followed by studying the changes in, for example, the accommodation coefficient of the surface. Studies on adsorbed monolayers have also done much to elucidate the nature of the reactions which take place at surfaces and of heterogeneous catalysis.*

EXAMPLES

1. Show that the heat capacity C_{sat} measured along the saturation curve is given by

$$C_{\text{sat}} = C_p - T\left(\frac{\partial V}{\partial T}\right)_p \frac{dp}{dT}$$

$$= C_v + T\left(\frac{\partial p}{\partial T}\right)_V \frac{dV}{dT}$$

$$= C_v + T\left(\frac{\partial V}{\partial T}\right)_p \left[\left(\frac{\partial p}{\partial T}\right)_V - \frac{dp}{dT}\right].$$

2. Show that the compressibility k_{sat} and the volume coefficient of expansion β_{sat} measured along the saturation curve are given by

$$k_{\text{sat}} = k - \beta \Big/ \frac{dp}{dT}$$

and

$$\beta_{\text{sat}} = \beta - k \frac{dp}{dT},$$

where k is the isothermal compressibility and β is the isobaric volume coefficient of expansion.

* For the early work on monomolecular films reference should be made to Langmuir: *Journ. Amer. Chem. Soc.*, Vol. 38, p. 2221 (1916); Vol. 39, p. 1848 (1917); Vol. 40, p. 1361 (1918). For an account of further interesting properties of monomolecular films, see Langmuir and Kingdon, *Proc. Roy. Soc.*, A, Vol. 107, p. 61 (1925). For later developments, see the reports of the discussions on adsorption by the Faraday Society (1932 and 1950), J. K. Roberts, *Some Problems in Adsorption* (Cambridge Physical Tracts), Cambridge University Press (1939), and A. R. Miller, *The Adsorption of Gases on Solids* (Cambridge Monographs on Physics), Cambridge University Press (1949).

CHAPTER IX

Fusion

1. When a solid is heated above a certain temperature, it melts and forms a liquid. With a pure crystalline solid, such as ice, for example, the temperature at which it is in equilibrium with the liquid under a given external pressure is perfectly definite—in fact such equilibrium points are used as fixed points in thermometry. On the other hand, when an amorphous solid like glass is heated it gradually softens and there is no definite melting-point.

If we take a solution of, say, salt and water, and freeze it, the composition of the solid which separates is in general different from that of the liquid, so that as the freezing proceeds the strength of the solution changes, and with it the freezing-point. On this account a solution or alloy does not in general show a definite freezing-point. The study of the freezing or melting of alloys forms a special branch of physical chemistry. We shall concern ourselves only with pure crystalline substances.

We have seen (Chapter II, Section 3) that the early experiments of Black showed that during fusion heat is absorbed by a substance without any change of temperature occurring. The amount of heat required to change 1 gm. of solid into liquid at the same temperature is called the *latent heat of fusion* of the substance. The same amount of heat is given out when 1 gm. of the liquid changes to solid at the same temperature.

The Measurement of the Latent Heat of Fusion of Ice

2. The Method of Mixtures.

Many determinations have been made of the latent heat of fusion of ice; most of the earlier workers used the method of mixtures. If we take M gm. of ice at $0°$ C., the melting-point, and mix it with m gm. of water at temperature t_1, and if the final temperature of the mixture is t_2, we have

$$M(L + t_2) = m(t_1 - t_2),$$

where L is the latent heat of fusion, and where we neglect the effect of losses of heat and of the variation of the specific heat of water.

In some of the later experiments by this method the ice was cooled some degrees below 0° C. in order to be sure that there was no moisture adhering to it. In such experiments it is necessary to determine the specific heat of ice. The method of doing this will be made clear later when we consider the measurements of the latent heat of fusion of metals.

3. The Bunsen Ice Calorimeter.

The use of the Bunsen ice calorimeter * depends on the fact that a change of volume occurs during fusion; ice, bismuth, and antimony contract on fusion, while most other substances expand. The basis of the ice calorimeter is as follows. The sample under test is introduced into a calorimeter which is sheathed in a mantle of ice. As thermal equilibrium is established, the ice melts and its volume changes. The change in volume is determined by measuring the mass of mercury it displaces in a closed system.

In recent years, the ice calorimeter has been developed † at the United States Bureau of Standards as a high-precision instrument to make accurate measurements of enthalpy. This calorimeter is shown in fig. 9.1.

The material of which the change in enthalpy is to be measured is introduced to the calorimeter through the central well, A, which tapers towards the bottom. The lower part of the well is surrounded by two coaxial glass vessels, P, which provide an insulating space between the inner ice-water system and the surrounding ice bath, E. The change in volume when the ice mantle, I, melts is transmitted to the mercury reservoir, M. The displaced mercury passes through the mercury tempering coil, T, and thence through a needle valve, V, to the beaker, B. The change in the mass of this beaker and its contents gives the change in the amount of mercury in the calorimeter system. A constant flow of dry carbon dioxide or helium gas up the central well prevents the diffusion of water vapour from above and its condensation. It has been found that helium reduces the lag in the establishment of thermal equilibrium between the sample and the inner wall of the well. The sample, of which the thermal properties are to be determined, is heated in a furnace situated above the central well, A. The gate, G, was specially designed to prevent the transfer of heat from the furnace to the calorimeter along the central well. To minimize heat leak, the calorimeter is immersed in the ice bath, E, up to the level L.

* R. Bunsen, *Pogg. Ann.*, Vol. 141, p. 1 (1870).

† D. C. Ginnings and R. J. Corruccini, *Journ. Res. Nat. Bur. Standards*, Washington, Vol. 38, p. 583 (1947). For an account of a similar precision instrument in use at the laboratories of the British Iron and Steel Research Association, see L. E. Leake and E. T. Turkdogan, *Journ. Sci. Instr.*, Vol. 31, p. 447 (1954).

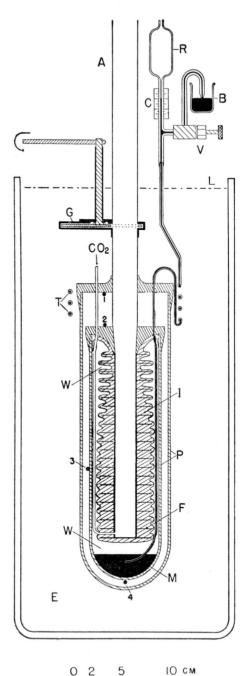

Fig. 9.1.—The Ice Calorimeter used at the United States Bureau of Standards. [After D. C. Ginnings, T. B. Douglas, and A. F. Ball, *Journ. Res. Nat. Bur. Standards*, Washington, Vol. 45, p. 23 (1950)].

The calorimeter is calibrated by means of an electrical heater which fits around the calorimeter well. In the apparatus shown in fig. 9.1, the heater is removed after the calibration. The amount of mercury which is transferred to the beaker is determined when measured amounts of electrical energy are dissipated. The calibration factor, K, of the calorimeter is the amount of energy supplied per gram of mercury displaced from the reservoir. The calibration factor of the apparatus at the Bureau of Standards * is

$$K = 270 \cdot 47 \pm 0 \cdot 03 \text{ absolute joule per gram of mercury.}$$

Once the calibration factor has been determined, the energy transferred to the calorimeter in any other experiment can be calculated immediately from the mass of mercury displaced from the reservoir to the beaker. It should also be noted that the calibration factor determines the latent heat of fusion of ice. If v_m, v_i, and v_w respectively are the specific volumes of mercury, ice, and water at $0°$ C., then the latent heat of fusion of ice, L joules per gram, is given by

$$L = K(v_i - v_w)/v_m.$$

Typical of the measurements which have been made in recent years with the ice calorimeter are the following. The change in the enthalpy of corundum † between the ice point and various temperatures to $900°$ C. has been determined. The heat capacity and the entropy were calculated from these measurements. The heat capacities of sodium,‡ of lead,§ and of lithium ‖ and their heats of fusion have been measured. Thermodynamic properties of certain alloys and eutectic mixtures have also been determined.¶

A Bunsen-type calorimeter which uses diphenyl ether ** instead of water has also been constructed. The melting-point of diphenyl ether is $26 \cdot 9°$ C. so that this calorimeter operates at very nearly the standard thermochemical reference temperature of $27°$ C.

4. Electrical Method.

An accurate determination using the electrical method has been made by Dickinson, Harper, and Osborne.†† The ice, cooled below 0°C.,

---

* Private communication from Dr. Ginnings.

† D. C. Ginnings and R. J. Corruccini, *Journ. Res. Nat. Bur. Standards*, Washington, Vol. 38, p. 393 (1947).

‡ D. C. Ginnings, T. B. Douglas, and A. F. Ball, *ibid.*, Vol. 45, p. 23 (1950).

§ T. B. Douglas and J. L. Dever, *National Bureau of Standards*, Report 2302 (1953).

‖ T. B. Douglas, L. F. Epstein, J. L. Dever, and W. H. Howland, *ibid.*, Report 2879 (1953).

¶ T. B. Douglas and J. L. Dever, *National Bureau of Standards*, Reports 2302, 2303 (1953).

** P. A. Giguere, B. G. Morissette, and W. A. Olmos, *Canadian Journ. Chem.*, Vol. 33, p. 657 (1955).

†† Dickinson, Harper, and Osborne, *Sci. Paper of Bur. of Standards*, No. 209 (1913).

was heated in a calorimeter which was a slight variation of the calorimeters used by Nernst for his specific heat work. The heat required to raise the temperature of the ice to 0° C., to melt it, and to heat the water formed to just above 0° C. was determined. A very careful study of the specific heat of ice was made, so that the correction could be made accurately for the heat required to raise the temperature of the ice from its initial value to 0° C.

As the temperature of the solid approaches the melting-point the presence of a minute quantity of impurity is sufficient to cause a slight amount of the solid to melt prematurely. The latent heat required affects the apparent specific heat of the solid. This effect must be carefully looked for, and the excess above the normal specific heat must be reckoned as part of the latent heat (for details, see Dickinson, Harper, and Osborne, *loc. cit.*).

The value of the latent heat of fusion of ice * at 0° C. is

333·5 international joules per gram.

The Measurement of the Latent Heat of Fusion of Metals

5. The electrical method can be employed for the measurement of the latent heat of fusion of metals, but the most accurate and convenient method is the method of mixtures. The metal, heated to a measured temperature in a furnace, is dropped into water or into an ice calorimeter. In using this method, Awbery and Ezer Griffiths † have introduced several important improvements.

In their experiments the metal was heated in a crucible suspended in an electric furnace to a steady temperature measured by a carefully calibrated thermocouple of platinum and platinum-rhodium. The thermal capacity of the crucible was determined by making a blank experiment in which the empty crucible was used.

The heated metal was transferred from the furnace to the calorimeter, which stood alongside it, but which was carefully shielded from it. Fig. 9.2 shows a section of the calorimeter with the lid closed and a plan with the lid open. The main vessel was 12 in. in diameter by 19 in. in depth. The dimensions were so proportioned that the average temperature rise of the water on dropping in the heated metal would be about five degrees.

The calorimeter was made as shown in the figure in order to ensure thorough mixing of the water. Alongside the main calorimeter was a

---

* N. S. Osborne, *Journ. Res. Nat. Bur. Standards*, Washington, Vol. 23, p. 643 (1939).

† Awbery and Ezer Griffiths, *Proc. Phys. Soc. London*, Vol. 38, p. 378 (1926) (gives summary of previous work); see also Umino, *Tôhoku Univ. Sci. Rep.*, Vol. 15, p. 597 (1926).

smaller vessel, 4 in. in diameter, connected to it by two wide pipes. The stirrer consisted of two propellers on a shaft running the length of this chamber, arranged so that the water in the smaller chamber was lifted and thrown through the upper pipe into the larger chamber. The thermometer was inserted as shown. The hole in the top of the calorimeter could be quickly closed by a well-fitting rotating lid. The calorimeter was constructed entirely of copper, with soldered joints. The water equivalent was calculated from the mass and the specific heat.

An important source of error in experiments employing the method of mixtures is always the loss of heat in transferring the specimen from the furnace to the calorimeter. Different workers have employed various methods to overcome this trouble, such for example as mounting the furnace directly over the calorimeter and dropping the crucible containing the heated metal directly into the water. The difficulty which then arises is to eliminate heat transfer from the furnace to the calorimeter. Awbery and Griffiths reduced the error by using a large mass of metal, 1 to 5 Kgm. (of the order of a hundredfold that employed by previous investigators). Doubling the dimensions of the specimen increases the heat capacity eightfold, while the heat loss in transfer, being proportional to the area, is only multiplied four-

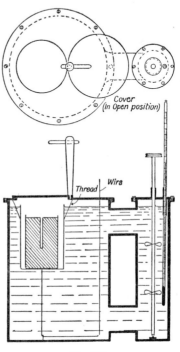

Fig. 9.2

fold. Similarly the actual calorimetry is simplified, since a large mass of water (28 Kgm.) may be used without the temperature rise becoming too small to be measured accurately. In addition the metal, whether solid or liquid, was always contained in a crucible, and a blank test was carried out with the empty crucible. It is reasonable to suppose that the same heat loss would occur with the crucible full or empty, since the actual magnitude of the temperature drop is small, and the cooling area is the same in the two cases. The error is thus eliminated.

Another source of error in working with metals at high temperatures is the formation of steam when the metal strikes the water. This difficulty can be overcome by using an ice calorimeter, but this introduces other difficulties, for example, small specimens must be used.   Awbery and Griffiths overcame the difficulty by completely enclosing the specimen in the calorimeter before the water had access to it, so that any steam formed could not escape from the calorimeter. A sheet-metal vessel (shown in the figure with the crucible in it) was suspended by three threads from the top of the calorimeter with the open mouth just above the surface of the water.   The crucible was placed in this vessel in the first place and the lid of the calorimeter was quickly closed.   The vessel was then drawn under the water by means of a wire attached to its base and passing through eyelets in the

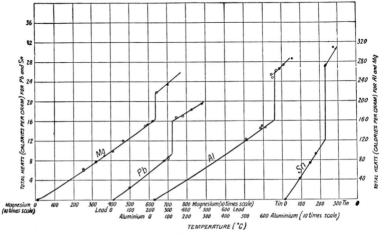

Fig. 9.3

bottom of the calorimeter.   That the use of the inner vessel did not introduce serious error was proved by varying the time that the crucible remained in it before it was submerged.   In one case it was allowed to remain 22 min., and the value obtained from this experiment for the total heat was only 3 per cent low as compared with a normal experiment.

Each experiment of this sort gave the difference between the total heat * of the metal at the temperature of the furnace and at the final temperature of the calorimeter.   This final temperature varied on account of the variable temperature rise.   The small correction necessary to reduce the total heats to a common final temperature (20° C.) was obtained using the known value of the specific heat at ordinary temperatures.   The total heats for some metals so obtained are plotted against temperatures in fig. 9.3.   The melting-point of a metal was

* See footnote to Chapter VIII, Section 10.

determined by taking a cooling curve * using the same thermocouple. The latent heat is the difference between the total heats of solid and liquid at the melting-point, and the specific heats of solid and liquid are given by the slopes of the respective curves. In the case of aluminium there are experimental points on the liquid curve below the observed melting-point; these obviously correspond to supercooled liquid. The following results were obtained by Awbery and Griffiths.

TABLE I

Metal	Melting-point (°C.)	Latent heat (joules per gm.)
Tin	232	61·1
Bismuth	269	54·4
Lead	327	26·4
Zinc	420	111·3
Antimony ..	630	101·7
Magnesium ..	644	194·6
Aluminium ..	657	386·7

The Measurement of Latent Heats of Fusion at Low Temperatures

6. For the measurement of latent heats of fusion at low temperatures the electrical method is used. The apparatus is the same as is used for the measurement of specific heats at low temperatures. Similar methods are used to determine heats of transformation between different modifications of the same substance in the solid state.†

The Relation between the Latent Heat of Fusion and the
Melting-point

7. Attempts have been made to find a relation for metals between the atomic latent heat of fusion L_m and the melting-point on the absolute scale T_m, corresponding to Trouton's rule for the latent heat of vaporization.

Clusius and his co-workers ‡ have measured the latent heats of fusion of the solids of the rare gases. The results of all these measurements are summarized in Table II.

---

* See Chapter I, Section 20.

† See, for example, Eucken, *Verh. d. deuts. phys. Ges.*, Vol. 14, p. 4 (1916); Simon and Lange, *Zeits. f. Physik*, Vol. 15, p. 312 (1923).

‡ See Clusius and Riccoboni, *Zeits. f. phys. Chem.*, Vol. 38, p. 81 (1938).

Table II

The Increase in Entropy attending Fusion at the Melting-point *

Substance	Melting-point (° Abs.) T_m	Latent heat of fusion (joule./g.-mol.) L_m	$\Delta S_m = L_m/T_m$	Lattice type
Na	370·7	2550	6·91 ⎫	
K	336·1	2300	6·74 ⎬	B.c. cube
Rb	312	2180	6·99 ⎭	
Cu	1356	11,300	8·33 ⎫	F.c. cube
Ag	1235	11,300	9·17 ⎭	
Zn	692·5	7500	10·9 ⎫	Hex. c.p.
Cd	594·0	6300	10·6 ⎭	
Hg	234·1	2340	10·0	Hex.
Al	931·5	10,500	11·2	—
Tl	563	6150	10·9	Hex. c.p.
Ne	24·5	335	13·7 ⎫	F.c. cube
A	83·8	1120	13·4 ⎬	
Kr	116	1630	14·1 ⎭	
H_2	13·95	117	8·4	—
D_2	18·65	197	10·5	—
H_2O	273·1	6020	22·0	—
D_2O	276·92	—	—	—

*Taken from Moelwyn-Hughes, *Physical Chemistry*, Pergamon Press (1957), p. 267.

CHAPTER X

Thermal Expansion

1. As the temperature of a body changes, its dimensions change. In the case of an isotropic solid, whose properties are the same in all directions, the expansion of a line of unit length for a given change in the temperature is the same in whatever direction the line is drawn in the solid. Substances which crystallize in the cubic system are truly isotropic, and metals are quasi-isotropic. By this we mean that metals, being composed of a very large number of small crystals orientated entirely at random, have the same average properties in all directions. The change of length of a solid with temperature can in general be represented by an equation of the form

$$l_t = l_0(1 + at + bt^2 + ct^3 + \ldots),$$

where l_t is the length at temperature $t°$ C. of a specimen whose length at $0°$ C. is l_0, and a, b, c are constants. Such an equation is of course entirely empirical.

The quantity
$$\frac{1}{l_{t_1}} \frac{l_{t_2} - l_{t_1}}{(t_2 - t_1)}$$

is called the mean coefficient of linear expansion for the temperature range t_1 to t_2.

The quantity
$$\frac{1}{l} \frac{dl}{dt}$$

is the true coefficient of linear expansion at the temperature t. In general, for reasonably small temperature ranges the mean coefficient of expansion over a temperature range may be taken as equal to the true coefficient of expansion at the mean temperature.

EXAMPLE

Show that for an isotropic solid the coefficient of cubical expansion is to a first approximation equal to three times the coefficient of linear expansion.

THE MEASUREMENT OF THE LINEAR EXPANSION
OF SOLIDS

2. The coefficient of linear expansion of solids can be measured either by comparator or by optical methods.

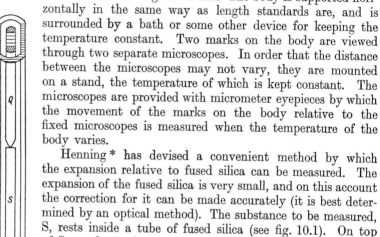

Fig. 10.1

The comparator method can be used only when the substance is available in the form of a long rod or bar. The body is supported horizontally in the same way as length standards are, and is surrounded by a bath or some other device for keeping the temperature constant. Two marks on the body are viewed through two separate microscopes. In order that the distance between the microscopes may not vary, they are mounted on a stand, the temperature of which is kept constant. The microscopes are provided with micrometer eyepieces by which the movement of the marks on the body relative to the fixed microscopes is measured when the temperature of the body varies.

Henning * has devised a convenient method by which the expansion relative to fused silica can be measured. The expansion of the fused silica is very small, and on this account the correction for it can be made accurately (it is best determined by an optical method). The substance to be measured, S, rests inside a tube of fused silica (see fig. 10.1). On top of S stands another rod of fused silica, Q, which has a scale engraved on its upper end. The movement of this scale relative to the scale engraved on the top of the tube is observed in a microscope. The tube is immersed in the constant-temperature bath up to half the height of the rod Q. Assuming that the tube and the rods are at the same temperature at the same horizontal level, we measure the relative change of length of the rod S and an equal length of fused silica tube.

Optical Methods

Optical methods can be used even when only small specimens are available. They are of two kinds: (a) Fizeau's method, and (b) the optical lever method.

3. Fizeau's Method.†

In this method the substance to be examined is cut into a plate with parallel faces, and from 1 to 10 mm. thick. This plate P (see

* Henning, *Ann. d. Physik*, Vol. 22, p. 631 (1907); see also Holborn and Henning, *Zeits. f. Instk.*, Vol. 32, p. 122 (1912); Braun, *Zeits. f. techn. Physik*, Vol. 7, p. 505 (1926); Simon and Bergmann, *Zeits f. phys. Chem.*, B, Vol. 8, p. 255 (1930).

† Fizeau, *Ann. d. Chimie et de Phys.*, Vol. 2 (1864); and Vol. 8, p. 335 (1866).

fig. 10.2) rests on a plane metal disc AB, which is supported by three metal screws passing through it near the circumference. On the top of these screws rests a glass plate CD which is brought very close to the top of P by adjusting the lengths of the screws. A beam of light falls perpendicularly on the system and interference fringes are produced by the beams reflected from the lower surface of CD and the upper surface of P. When the temperature changes the thickness of the air film changes by an amount equal to the difference between the expansion of the plate P and the projecting parts of the screws. The change in thickness can be measured by the displacement of the fringes relative to marks ruled on the lower surface of the glass plate. If the centre of one band is displaced through a distance equal to the distance between two bright bands, this corresponds to a change in the thickness of the air film of one-half a wave-length of light; for sodium light the wave-length is 0·000059 cm., and changes of a tenth of the distance between two bright bands can be observed, which means that changes of thickness of 0·000003 cm. can be measured easily. The expansion of the screws is determined by making observations with the plate P absent. The apparatus has been improved in many respects by Tutton.*

Fig. 10.2

In general, it is more convenient, if possible, to use the substance under test in the form of a hollow cylinder resting on a polished flat base with a glass plate resting on the top of it, and to observe the fringes formed by the light reflected from the base and from the lower surface of the glass plate. In this way the expansion of the substance is measured directly and no correction is necessary for the expansion of the screws.†

This method has been used by Nix and MacNair ‡ to measure the thermal expansion of several pure metals over a wide temperature range.

4. The Optical Lever Method.

Unless automatic photographic recording is used, § the interference method has the disadvantage that it is necessary to observe and count the fringes during the whole time that the temperature is changing. It has the advantage of being an absolute method.

Provided there is available a standard substance, whose expansion over the required temperature range is known, an optical lever

---

* Tutton, *Phil. Trans.*, Vol. 191, p. 313 (1898).

† See, for example, Dorsey, *Phys. Rev.*, Vol. 25, p. 88 (1907); Merritt, *Journ. Res. Bur. Stand.*, Washington, Vol. 10, p. 59 (1932).

‡ Nix and MacNair, *Phys. Rev.*, Vol. 60, p. 597 (1941); *ibid.*, Vol. 61, p. 74 (1942).

§ See Sinden, *Journ. Opt. Soc. Amer.*, Vol. 15, p. 171 (1927).

method can be used to measure the expansion relative to the standard substance. The method does not require continuous observation, as it is only necessary to take readings when the temperature is steady.

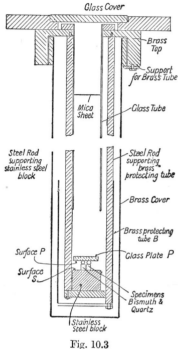

Fig. 10.3

Such a method has been used by Roberts * to measure the expansion of crystals of metallic bismuth from ordinary temperatures up to the melting-point, crystalline quartz being taken as the standard substance. The apparatus is shown in fig. 10.3.

The bismuth and quartz specimens, which were the same size (5 to 10 mm.) and which were optically flat, were placed side by side on the polished surface of the stainless steel block S. A glass plate P, which was slightly wedge-shaped, rested on three $\frac{3}{32}$-in. steel spheres, which were firmly set in a phosphor-bronze plate. The spheres rested on pieces of thin microscope cover-glass placed on the top of the specimens. These prevented the spheres from pressing into the bismuth at the higher temperatures.

The different expansions of the bismuth and quartz specimens caused the angle between the lower surface of P and the surface of S to vary with temperature. This variation was determined by measuring the angle between the reflections of a parallel beam of light from these surfaces. Any effect due to the unequal expansion of the supports was eliminated as it affected both surfaces equally.

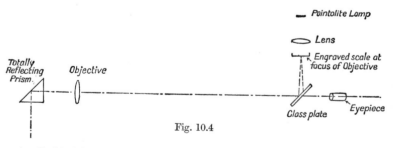

Fig. 10.4

A cylindrical brass tube closed at the bottom served as container. This tube was carried on supports attached to the brass top. A heating coil was wound over the whole length of the container.

    * Roberts, *Proc. Roy. Soc.*, A, Vol. 106, p. 385 (1924); see also Cohn, *Zeits. f. techn. Physik*, Vol. 11, p. 118 (1930).

In all experiments of this kind, whether the interference method or the optical lever method is employed, convection currents are a serious source of trouble, as they spoil the definition. They were eliminated by surrounding the specimens by a brass tube B, and by passing the light down to the reflecting surfaces through a glass tube as shown in the figure.

The arrangement of the optical system is shown in fig. 10.4. A pointolite lamp was used as the source of light. It illuminated a scale consisting of fine lines 5 mm. apart ruled on the surface of a platinized glass plate. The light from the scale was reflected through 90° at the surface of a plane glass plate. The scale was placed at the focus of a telescope objective, which rendered the beam of light parallel before it was reflected by a totally reflecting prism down into the part of the apparatus shown in fig. 10.3. On its return it was observed by a micrometer eyepiece.

A short-focus lens was placed between the pointolite lamp and the scale in order to form an image of the lamp on the surfaces P and S. This increased the intensity of the light and enabled the whole aperture of P and S to be used.

The focal length of the objective lens was 112 cm. The arm of the optical lever was about 0·5 cm.; this gave a very steady support for the plate P, and it was possible to use an arm considerably smaller than this if desired. With such an arrangement a relative change of length of the specimens of $3 . 10^{-6}$ cm. could be measured; this is about the same as can be done with an interference method.

Results

5. The Grüneisen Law.

The results of the measurements of the thermal expansion of isotropic metals can be summed up in the law of Grüneisen,[*] which states that *the ratio of the coefficient of expansion of a metal to its specific heat at constant pressure is constant at all temperatures.* This law can best be tested at low temperatures, where both the specific heat and the coefficient of expansion vary considerably with temperature. Some results illustrating the truth of the law are collected in Table I. They also indicate the order of magnitude of the coefficients of expansion, α. The Grüneisen law is of great importance,[†] and any tenable theory of the solid state must lead to it (see Chapter XXIII). Its practical use has been discussed by Hume-Rothery.[‡]

The coefficients of expansion of certain nickel steel alloys are negative, and that of one of these alloys, invar, is at ordinary temperatures very nearly, or actually, zero, according to the temperature. For this reason invar is used for making secondary standards of length, and also in the manufacture of clocks and watches.

[*] Grüneisen, *Ann. d. Physik*, Vol. 26, p. 211 (1908).
[†] For an application, see Chapter XXII, Section 9.
[‡] Hume-Rothery, *Proc. Phys. Soc.*, Vol. 57, p. 209 (1945).

TABLE I *

Temperature (°C.)	$\alpha \cdot 10^6$	$\dfrac{\alpha \cdot 10^6}{C_p}$	Temperature (°C.)	$\alpha \cdot 10^6$	$\dfrac{\alpha \cdot 10^6}{C_p}$
Aluminium			*Silver*		
−173	13·6	(107)	−167	15·0	(319)
−100	18·2	109	−87	17·1	329
0	23·0	110	0	18·3	327
100	24·9	112	100	19·2	331
300	29·0	119	500	23·1	350
438	29·8	112	800	26·0	342
Copper			*Iridium*		
−87	14·1	174	0	6·36	205
0	16·1	177	100	7·0	212
100	16·9	180	1200	9·5	207
400	19·3	179			
600	20·9	182	*Platinum*		
			−150	7·4	269
Palladium			−100	7·9	268
−150	9·2	192	0	8·9	280
−100	10·1	191	100	9·2	277
0	11·5	198	875	11·2	267
100	12·2	197			
875	15·5	204			

6. Anisotropic Bodies.

In the case of anisotropic crystals the expansion is different in different directions. The result of this is that, if a cube is cut from such a crystal and is heated, the different sides become unequal in length and also the angles between them cease to be right angles. This change in the angles of a crystal with temperature seems to have been first noticed by Mitscherlich (about 1820), who gave the correct interpretation of the effect.

There are, however, for any crystal three mutually perpendicular directions such that, if a cube is cut with its sides parallel to them and heated, the angles all remain right angles, although the lengths of the sides change by different amounts. These three directions are called the *principal* axes of dilation, and the coefficients of expansion parallel to these axes are called the *principal* coefficients of expansion. If the principal coefficients of expansion are known, the coefficient of expansion in any other direction can be calculated. In the case of uniaxial crystals there is an axis of crystalline symmetry perpendicular to which the physical properties are the same in all directions, and there are only two principal coefficients of expansion, that parallel to the axis

* See also Ebert, *Zeits. f. Physik*, Vol. 47, p. 712 (1928).

of symmetry and that perpendicular to it. In the case of crystals which do not possess an axis of symmetry the principal axes of dilation do not necessarily coincide with the crystallographic axes.*

It is interesting to note that in the case of some crystals rise of temperature causes a contraction in certain directions; for Iceland spar, for example, Benoit found an expansion parallel to the axis but a contraction perpendicular to the axis.

EXAMPLES

1. If α_1, α_2, α_3 are the three principal coefficients of expansion of a crystal, show that the coefficient of cubical expansion is ($\alpha_1 + \alpha_2 + \alpha_3$).

2. Show that the coefficient of expansion of a line, whose direction cosines relative to the principal axes of dilation are l, m, n, is $l^2\alpha_1 + m^2\alpha_2 + n^2\alpha_3$.

THE EXPANSION OF LIQUIDS AND GASES

7. The expansion of gases has already been dealt with in Chapters III and IV. The volume coefficient of expansion of liquids is usually considerably greater than that of solids, a fact which is illustrated by the ordinary mercury-in-glass thermometer, and in general the simplest way of determining the coefficient of expansion of a liquid is to measure its coefficient of expansion relative to a solid and to make a correction for the expansion of the solid. The latter can be determined by one of the methods described above.

One way of determining the relative expansion is to suspend the solid in the liquid and to determine its loss in weight, using Archimedes' principle to deduce the results. Another way is to use a weight thermometer.

8. The Weight Thermometer.

This instrument consists of a vessel, usually of glass or silica, of the shape shown in fig. 10.5. The vessel is completely filled with the liquid under investigation by alternately heating and cooling it with its open end dipping under the surface of the liquid contained in the vessel shown. Great care must be taken to exclude all air; for this purpose it is necessary to boil the liquid after filling until almost half of it is boiled away, and then to allow the instrument to refill.

Fig. 10.5

The weight of the empty tube being known, the experiment consists in determining the weight of the full tube at two different temperatures t_1 and t_2, and thus by subtracting the weight of the empty tube the weights w_1 and w_2 of liquid filling the tube at temperatures t_1 and t_2 are determined.

* For the X-ray method of measurement, see Becker, *Zeits. f. Physik*, Vol. 40, p. 37 (1927); Goetz and Hergenrother, *Phys. Rev.*, Vol. 38, p. 2075 (1931); Vol. 40, p. 643 (1932); Owen and T. L. Richards, *Phil. Mag.*, Vol. 24, p. 304 (1936).

The expansion of a liquid can be represented by an expression of the form

$$v_t = v_0(1 + at + bt^2 + \ldots),$$

or approximately

$$v_t = v_0(1 + at);$$

and if ρ_t is the density of the liquid at temperature t,

$$\frac{\rho_t}{\rho_0} = \frac{1}{1 + at}.$$

We have

$$w_1 = V_1\rho_1, \quad w_2 = V_2\rho_2, \quad \text{or} \quad \frac{w_1}{w_2} = \frac{V_1\rho_1}{V_2\rho_2},$$

where V_1 and V_2 are the volumes of the container, and ρ_1 and ρ_2 are the densities of the liquid, at temperatures t_1 and t_2 respectively. If the expansion of the solid is represented by the expression

$$V_t = V_0(1 + \gamma t),$$

we have

$$\frac{w_1}{w_2} = \frac{(1 + \gamma t_1)(1 + at_2)}{(1 + \gamma t_2)(1 + at_1)}.$$

If γ, the coefficient of expansion of the solid of which the container is made. is known, the coefficient of expansion of the liquid can be determined.

To a first approximation the last equation can be written

$$\frac{w_1}{w_2} = \frac{1 + a(t_2 - t_1)}{1 + \gamma(t_2 - t_1)} = 1 + (a - \gamma)(t_2 - t_1) \text{ approximately,}$$

which shows that the behaviour is approximately the same as if the volume remained constant and the coefficient of expansion of the liquid were $(a - \gamma)$. For this reason $(a - \gamma)$ is called the *apparent coefficient of expansion of the liquid.*

The necessity of knowing γ, the coefficient of expansion of the solid, is a considerable disadvantage, since it cannot be determined on the vessel itself, but must be measured on a specimen of the material of which the vessel is made. The question thus arises whether the treatment that the material receives during the making of the vessel does not alter its physical properties. For this reason it is desirable to use vessels of fused silica, which has a very low coefficient of expansion (volume coefficient about $0{\cdot}0000015$ deg.$^{-1}$), so that any variations are of less importance. Fused silica has the further advantage of not being easily cracked by the rapid temperature changes which occur during the filling.

The weight thermometer can be used to determine the volume coefficient of a solid immersed in the liquid with which it is filled; this method is convenient for powders.

For volatile liquids it is better to determine the volume change of the liquid in a calibrated closed tube like a mercury-in-glass thermometer.

9. The Absolute Expansion of Liquids.

There is one method of determining the coefficient of expansion of a liquid directly and without the necessity of knowing the coefficient of expansion of the containing vessel. This method was first used by Dulong and Petit and was improved by Regnault and later by Callendar and Moss * and by Chappuis.†

The principle of the apparatus which depends on the hydrostatic balancing of two columns at different temperatures is shown diagrammatically in fig. 10.6.

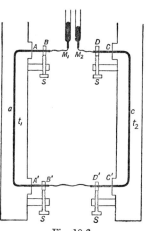

Fig. 10.6

$BAaA'B'$ and $DCcC'D'$ are steel capillary tubes the ends of which project as shown from the sides of constant-temperature baths maintained at temperatures t_1 and t_2 respectively. The ends of the tubes at B and D are joined by flexible connexions to the manometer tubes M_1 and M_2, and the lower ends of the tubes at B' and D' are joined by a flexible connexion. B, B', D and D' are copper blocks soldered to the tubes and are all water-cooled and kept at the same temperature as the room, which is the temperature of the flexible connecting tubes. The portions AB, A'B', CD, C'D' of the tubes are the only parts in which there is a temperature gradient and they must be adjusted to be accurately horizontal. If they were not so adjusted it would be necessary to know the temperature distribution in the liquid in the capillary accurately. The adjustment is made at any temperature by means of the four levelling screws S.

In writing down the conditions for hydrostatic balance let us for simplicity suppose at first that the vertical widths of the capillary tubes AB, &c., are negligible compared with the vertical distance H between the points AA'. The distance between the points CC' is made as nearly as possible equal to H, and we shall denote it by $H + \Delta$. Let h be the difference between the levels of the mercury in the two sides of the manometer (left minus right). If ρ_t is the density of the liquid at temperature t, and ρ_0 the density at 0° C., $\rho_t = \rho_0/(1 + \alpha t)$, where α is the mean coefficient of expansion from 0° to t° C. The condition for hydrostatic equilibrium is

$$\frac{H}{1 + \alpha_1 t_1} = \frac{H + \Delta}{1 + \alpha_2 t_2} - \frac{\Delta}{1 + \alpha_a t_a} - \frac{h}{1 + \alpha_a t_a},$$

or

$$\frac{H}{1 + \alpha_1 t_1} = \frac{H}{1 + \alpha_2 t_2} + \Delta\left(\frac{1}{1 + \alpha_2 t_2} - \frac{1}{1 + \alpha_a t_a}\right) - \frac{h}{1 + \alpha_a t_a}.$$

where α_1 is the mean coefficient of expansion from 0° to t_1° C., and so on, and t_a is the air temperature.

This equation shows us which quantities must be measured accurately. The lengths H and h must each be measured with the accuracy required in the value of α; that is, if we assume for the sake of definiteness that an accuracy of one part

* Callendar and Moss, *Phil. Trans.*, A, Vol. 211, p. 1 (1911).

† Chappuis, *Trav. et Mém. du Bur. Int.*, Vol. 16 (1917).

in ten thousand is required, H must be measured when the tube is at temperature t_1 to one part in ten thousand and so must h. The temperatures t_1 and t_2 must also be accurately measured so that the error in their difference $(t_1 - t_2)$ is not greater than one part in ten thousand.

On account of its occurrence in the last term t_a need only be known with such accuracy that α_a (which for mercury is approximately $0 \cdot 00018$) multiplied by the error in t_a is less than one ten-thousandth. The temperature t_2 is made as nearly as possible equal to t_a, so that the second factor in the second term on the right is small and Δ must be known only with such accuracy that the uncertainty in the whole term is less than one ten-thousandth part of h; the whole term is in fact very small since Δ is also small.

The temperature t_2 is kept constant while t_1 is varied from $0°$ C. to the highest temperature t for which the mean coefficient from 0 to t is required.*

We have supposed that the vertical widths of the capillary tubes AB, &c., are negligible compared with H. This condition is not realizable in practice and in fact each infinitesimal horizontal strip of each of the tubes AB, &c., will strive,

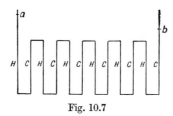

Fig. 10.7

as it were, to set up the value of h appropriate to its own position. The resulting height h will be a compromise and will correspond to the heights between the centres of the tubes at A and A' and at B and B'.

Instead of single hot and cold columns Callendar and Moss in their work on mercury used six hot and cold columns each 2 m. long connected in series as shown diagrammatically in fig. 10.7. The hot columns are marked H and the cold ones C. With this arrangement the difference between the level of the mercury surfaces at a and b was six times what it would have been with a single pair of columns.† Chappuis used seven tubes 1 metre long. All the hot columns were arranged side by side in a constant-temperature oil bath and similarly all the cold columns.

Using the weight thermometer method, Chappuis with a glass weight thermometer ($0°$ to $100°$ C.) and Harlow ‡ in a series of very careful measurements with various silica weight thermometers ($0°$ to $300°$ C.) had obtained concordant results, but these differed considerably from those obtained by Callendar and Moss by the absolute method. At the higher temperatures the results of Harlow and of Callendar and Moss agreed. For this reason Chappuis carried out his absolute determination and his results agreed with those given by the weight

---

* If $t_1 = 0$, and if we assume as a first approximation that $t_a = t$, we obtain from the measurements a first approximation to the value of α_2. This approximate value of α_2 may then be used in the last two terms on the right-hand side (assuming $\alpha_a = \alpha_2$ but not $t_a = t_2$) and thus a more accurate value of α_2 is obtained. A second approximation can be obtained if necessary by using the more accurate value of α_2 to make the corrections. The final value of α_2 so obtained can then be used in reducing the results of measurements for other values of t_1.

† See footnote opposite.

‡ Harlow, *Proc. Phys. Soc. Lond.*, Vol. 24, p. 30 (1911).

thermometer method. Chappuis pointed out the importance in determinations by the absolute method of using reasonably wide capillary tubes so that viscous effects may not appreciably affect the attainment of equilibrium. He suggested that effects of this kind may have been present in the experiments of Callendar and Moss. For a full summary of the experimental results for mercury, reference should be made to a paper by Harlow.‡

10. The Expansion of Water.

The behaviour of water is interesting. From 0° to 4° C. it behaves in an anomalous manner, in that it contracts as the temperature rises. At 4° C. there is a point of maximum density, and above this temperature it expands with rising temperature.

† Similar increased expansion could be obtained by using a single pair of columns of great length, but in this case difficulties would arise in maintaining a uniform temperature, and also the pressure of the mercury would be very different at different points. The coefficient of expansion varies with pressure, so that another variable is introduced. Even in the actual experiment as carried out by Callendar and Moss the mean pressure was $2\frac{1}{2}$ atmospheres. The theory of the influence of pressure is as follows. Consider unit volume of the substance at a given temperature and pressure. Any small change of volume brought about jointly by change of pressure and change of temperature can be written

$$dv = \alpha \, dT - b \, dp,$$

where α is the coefficient of expansion and b is the compressibility. Assuming that the volume always returns to the same value when T and p do so, it follows that dv must be a perfect differential, and therefore

$$\left(\frac{\partial \alpha}{\partial p}\right)_T = - \left(\frac{\partial b}{\partial T}\right)_p.$$

That is, if the compressibility increases with temperature, it follows that the coefficient of expansion falls with increase in pressure.

According to Bridgman (*Proc. Amer. Acad.*, Vol. 47, p. 432) the change of compressibility of mercury between 0° and 22° C. is about $7 \cdot 10^{-9}$ atmos. per degree. We may deduce from this that the change in α is equal to $7 \cdot 10^{-9}$ per atmosphere. For $1\frac{1}{2}$ atmospheres pressure excess as in Callendar and Moss's experiments the effect would be about $1 \cdot 10^{-8}$; that is, only the fifth significant figure would be affected. With ten times this pressure the fourth figure would begin to be affected. Values of the coefficient are usually given to at least five significant figures. When the determination of the coefficient is so perfected as to justify the retention of the fifth figure, it will be necessary to specify the pressure to which the value refers (see Porter, *A Dict. of Applied Physics*, Vol. I, p. 880).

‡ Harlow, *Phil. Mag.*, Vol. 7, p. 674 (1929). It may be mentioned here that Thatte (*Phil. Mag.*, Vol. 7, p. 887 (1929)) has collected data to show that the coefficients of expansion of a considerable number of liquids with widely differing properties can be correlated by means of a simple expression, the form of which is deduced from Var der Waals' equation.

CHAPTER XI

The Transfer of Heat by Conduction and Convection

1. There are three ways in which heat may pass from one body to another: conduction, convection, and radiation.

In the process of conduction the heat energy diffuses through a body by the action of molecules possessing greater kinetic energy on those possessing less. In solids that are electric insulators this action can take place by means of the elastic binding forces between the atoms; in liquids and gases by collisions of molecules possessing greater kinetic energy with those possessing less; the latter process also probably takes place in the case of the so-called free electrons in solid electrical conductors.

In the process of convection there is a streaming motion of the matter as a whole caused by the differences in density of the parts which are at different temperatures; or in some cases the streaming motion is maintained by an external agency. This of course can occur only in the case of liquids or gases.

The transmission of heat by radiation occurs independently of the presence of matter and is similar to the transmission of light.

Radiation is dealt with in Chapter XX. In this chapter we deal with A, Conduction, and B, Convection.

A. CONDUCTION *

2. The quantitative study of conduction involves a determination of *thermal conductivity*, which, as proposed by Fourier in 1822, is defined as follows: Consider a small area dA inside a body. If $\partial T/\partial n$ is the temperature gradient normal to dA, the quantity of heat dQ which flows through dA in an infinitesimal time dt is assumed to be proportional to dA, to $\partial T/\partial n$, and to dt, and is written

$$dQ = -K\,dA(\partial T/\partial n)\,dt. \quad . \quad . \quad . \quad . \quad (1)$$

* For a general survey of experimental methods, see Griffiths, *Proc. Phys. Soc.*, Vol. 41, p. 151 (1928).

The negative sign shows the direction of the heat flow, and K, the constant of proportionality, is called the thermal conductivity of the body at temperature T. If Q is measured in joules, K is measured in joules cm.$^{-1}$ sec.$^{-1}$ deg.$^{-1}$. The deduction of the general equation of propagation of heat by conduction is given at the end of this chapter.

In order to test experimentally the assumptions on which (1) is based, we consider a finite case. Take a cylinder whose ends are perpendicular to the axis and are maintained at definite temperatures. If heat losses from the sides are negligible and if a steady state has been attained, planes perpendicular to the axis are planes of equal temperature. Let A be the area of cross-section, T_1 the temperature at one such plane in the body, T_2 that at another plane, and Δx the distance between the planes (see fig. 11.1). The results of many experiments show that the

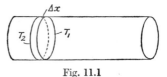

Fig. 11.1

heat flowing from the hot to the cold plane is proportional to the time, to the area A, and, for a given difference of temperature $(T_1 - T_2)$, inversely proportional to the thickness Δx.* We may therefore write for Q, the quantity of heat which flows in unit time,

$$Q = KA(T_1 - T_2)/\Delta x. \quad \cdots \cdots \quad (2)$$

Equation (2), the result of experiment, leads to equation (1) as a limiting case.

3. Thermal Resistivity and Resistance.

By analogy with the electrical case we define the thermal resistivity as the reciprocal of the thermal conductivity. In the case considered in equation (2) we call $\Delta x/KA$ the thermal resistance. The flow of heat is equal to the temperature difference divided by the thermal resistance. The thermal resistances of bodies in series are additive.

4. Practical Methods.

The methods used to determine thermal conductivities vary considerably with the nature of the substance to be investigated, according as it is a metal, a solid non-metal, a gas, or a liquid. The thermal conductivities of these various types differ widely; roughly speaking, metals have conductivities varying from about unity to 0·02, solid non-metals from 0·03 to 0·0001, and gases from 0·003 to 0·00001.

* The inverse proportionality to the thickness is certainly true to a very close approximation, and is always assumed. A direct experimental test is difficult owing to the variation of K with temperature. See the paper of Hercus and Laby cited in Section 5.

GASES *

5. Hercus and Laby's Method.

The most satisfactory method for measuring the thermal conductivity of gases is that of Hercus and Laby † (see fig. 11.2).

The heat flowed from the plate B to the plate C. B consisted of two sheets of copper screwed together with a heating coil in one of them: C was water-cooled. Their surfaces were ground true and silver-plated. In order that the heat flow from B to C should be linear (that is, that the surfaces of equal temperature should be planes), B was surrounded by a guard ring D. The guard ring contained a separate heating coil, the current through which was adjusted so that D was at the same temperature as B. To prevent any loss of heat from the upper surface of B, another plate A above it was maintained at the same temperature as B itself.‡ In this case all the heat generated in B flowed to C, and

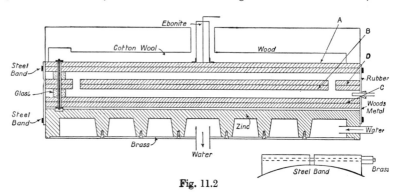

Fig. 11.2

the heat flow was therefore determined by measuring the electrical energy supplied to the heating coil in B. The temperatures of all the copper blocks were measured at various points by attaching constantan wires to them. These formed thermocouples with the plates themselves, each of which had a copper lead attached to it. The plate B was supported from D by three I-shaped ivory buttons. The three plates were held together by three bolts passing through glass distance pieces. The apparatus was made air-tight by a ring of stout rubber clamped to A and C by steel bands. The distance between C and B was 6·28 mm., and a temperature difference of about twenty degrees was used. Heat passed from B to C by radiation as well as by conduction, and a correction was necessary for this effect. The correction amounted to about 5 per cent of the whole transfer. In these experiments it was determined by separate experiments on the loss of

---

* For a bibliography, see Trautz and Zündel, *Zeits. f. techn. Physik*, Vol. 12, p. 273 (1931).

† Hercus and Laby, *Proc. Roy. Soc.*, A, Vol. 95, p. 190 (1919). For improvements, see Hercus and Sutherland, *Proc. Roy. Soc.*, A, Vol. 145, p. 599 (1934).

‡ Actually A was maintained at a temperature slightly above that of B, so that there should be no possibility of convection occurring in the space between these two plates, and a correction was made for the small amount of heat gained by B from A.

heat from a silvered Dewar flask, in which the vacuum was so good that there was no effect due to conduction.

The method of Hercus and Laby has the very great advantage that, since the heat flow is all downwards, there is no convection.

This method has been modified for use at very low temperatures by Ubbink and de Haas.* They have carried out control experiments on hydrogen at 19° K. and on hydrogen and air at 0° C.; these experiments showed that the theory of the method agrees with the experimental results. They have also measured the thermal conductivity of helium gas in the helium range (down to 1·62° K.), the hydrogen range, and the liquid-air range.

6. Hot-wire Method.

In this method a wire surrounded by a coaxial cylinder, which contains the gas, is heated by an electric current.

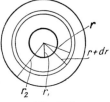

Fig. 11.3

Neglecting end effects the heat flow between coaxial cylinders is as follows. Let r_1 and r_2 be the radii and l the length of the cylinders, a plan of which is shown in fig. 11.3. Consider the flow through the element bounded by cylinders of radius r and $r + dr$, the temperatures at r and $r + dr$ being T and $T + dT$ respectively. The area is $2\pi rl$, and the temperature gradient is dT/dr. Q, the heat flow in unit time, is therefore given by

$$Q = -K\,2\pi rl\frac{dT}{dr}, \qquad \cdots \cdots \cdots \quad (3)$$

K being the thermal conductivity. That is,

$$dT = -\frac{Q}{2\pi l\,K}\frac{dr}{r}.$$

Integrating and remembering that Q is independent of r since there is no flow through the ends of the cylinder, we obtain

$$T = -\frac{Q}{2\pi l\,K}\log r + A, \qquad \cdots \cdots \cdots \quad (4)$$

where A is an integration constant. If T_1 is the temperature at the inner boundary when $r = r_1$, and T_2 the temperature at the outer boundary when $r = r_2$, we have

$$T_1 = -\frac{Q}{2\pi l\,K}\log r_1 + A,$$

$$\left.\vphantom{\frac{Q}{2\pi l K}}\right\} \qquad \cdots \cdots \cdots \quad (5)$$

and

$$T_2 = -\frac{Q}{2\pi l\,K}\log r_2 + A.$$

Eliminating A, we obtain

$$K = \frac{1}{2\pi l}\frac{Q}{(T_1 - T_2)}\log\left(\frac{r_2}{r_1}\right). \qquad \cdots \cdots \cdots \quad (6)$$

The temperature of the wire can be determined from its resistance, and the flow of heat from the energy supplied to it.

* Ubbink and de Haas, *Leiden Comm.*, Nos. 266c, d; *Physica*, Vol. 10, p. 451 (1943).

The method has been used by Schleiermacher * and by Weber,† who has made a special study of the elimination of the effects of convection and of end effects. The latter are determined by using two vessels of different lengths but otherwise similar. The effects of convection are detected by using the tube in both the vertical and horizontal positions, and by varying the pressure of the gas. The general result of such experiments and of earlier ones on the rate of cooling of thermometers ‡ is that at pressures below about 150 mm. of mercury the effects of convection become very small, while in accord with the theory given in Section 7 the conductivity remains constant. This holds until pressures are reached at which the mean free path (see Section 10) becomes comparable with the size of the apparatus (see Section 11). The effects of radiation are determined by exhausting the apparatus completely. Kannuluik and Martin § have used the hot-wire method with a thick wire and other improvements. The advantage of the thick wire is that it minimizes the correction for the temperature discontinuity at the surface (see Section 11). With the thick wire it is necessary to have an accurate theory of the end loss and this has been developed. The results obtained are in agreement with those given by the plate method. || In a modification of the method, Kannuluik ¶ has used two thick nickel wires, contained in a pair of similar metal tubes, as the nearly equal ratio arms of a Kelvin double bridge. The apparatus has been used to determine the thermal conductivity of deuterium relative to that of hydrogen. The thick-wire method has also been used to make an accurate determination of the temperature dependence ** of the thermal conductivity of air between $-183°$ C. and $218°$ C., and of the rare gases between $-183°$ C. and $306°$ C.

7. Elementary Theory of Thermal Conductivity in Gases.

Let us consider the conduction in a gas contained between two infinite parallel plane plates A and B (fig. 11.4), the upper one being at

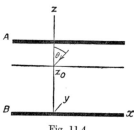

Fig. 11.4

the higher temperature so that there are no convection effects. We shall take the plane of xy parallel to the plates, and shall suppose the gas arranged in planes of equal temperature parallel to the xy plane.

Let us consider a particular plane for which the z co-ordinate is equal to z_0, and let us suppose that the mean energy in ergs of a molecule in this plane is E. The number of molecules which in one second cross unit area of this particular plane in a direction making an angle θ with the axis of z is $\frac{1}{2}n\bar{c}\cos\theta\sin\theta\,d\theta$. The result follows immediately by putting $d\omega = 2\pi\sin\theta\,d\theta$ in equation (32),

* Schleiermacher, *Wied. Ann.*, Vol. 34, p. 623 (1888).

† Weber, *Ann. d. Physik*, Vol. 54, p. 325 (1917); Vol. 82, p. 479 (1927): also Gregory and Archer, *Proc. Roy. Soc.*, A, Vol. 118, p. 594 (1928); Hercus and Laby, *Phil. Mag.*, Vol. 3, p. 1061 (1927); Wilner and Borelius, *Ann. d. Physik*, Vol. 4, p. 316 (1930).

‡ See, for example, Kundt and Warburg, *Pogg. Ann.*, Vol. 156, p. 177 (1875).

§ Kannuluik and Martin, *Proc. Roy. Soc.*, A, Vol. 144, p. 496 (1934); Kannuluik and Law, *Proc. Roy. Soc., Victoria*, Vol. 58, p. 142 (1947).

|| See Laby, *Proc. Roy. Soc.*, A, Vol. 144, p. 494 (1934).

¶ Kannuluik, *Proc. Roy. Soc.*, A, Vol. 175, p. 36 (1940).

** W. G. Kannuluik and E. H. Carman, *Aust. Journ. Sci. Res.*, A, Vol. 4, p. 305 (1951); *Proc. Phys. Soc.*, B, Vol. 65, p. 701 (1952).

Chapter III. If λ is the mean free path (Section 14, Chapter III), these molecules on the average come from a plane whose z co-ordinate is $z_0 + \lambda \cos \theta$. The mean energy of such molecules is therefore

$$E + \lambda \cos \theta \frac{dE}{dz}.$$

The amount of energy carried across the plane by them in the direction of z increasing is

$$-\left(E + \lambda \cos \theta \frac{dE}{dz}\right) \frac{n}{2} \bar{c} \cos \theta \sin \theta \, d\theta. \quad \ldots \quad (7)$$

Integrating for all values of θ from 0 to π, we obtain, for the total flow of energy across the plane in the direction of z increasing,

$$-\tfrac{1}{3}\lambda n \bar{c} \frac{dE}{dz}. \quad \ldots \ldots \ldots \quad (8)$$

If K is the thermal conductivity of the gas in mechanical units, the energy in ergs crossing unit area of the plane is $-K \, dT/dz$, where T is the temperature. We therefore have

$$K \frac{dT}{dz} = \tfrac{1}{3}\lambda n \bar{c} \frac{dE}{dT} \frac{dT}{dz},$$

or

$$K = \frac{\lambda n \bar{c}}{3} \frac{dE}{dT}. \quad \ldots \ldots \ldots \quad (9)$$

If now m is the mass of *one molecule*, the number of molecules in 1 gm. is $1/m$, and the specific heat at constant volume, c_v, is given by

$$c_v = \frac{1}{m} \frac{dE}{dT}.$$

Substituting this in equation (9), we obtain

$$K = \tfrac{1}{3} m \lambda n \bar{c} \, c_v. \quad \ldots \ldots \quad (10)$$

From equation (28), Chapter III, λ is inversely proportional to n, and, therefore, according to equation (10) the thermal conductivity is independent of the pressure. This rather surprising prediction of the theory is confirmed by experiment.

8. Viscosity of Gases.

A quantity that is closely connected with the thermal conductivity of a gas is its coefficient of viscosity. Effects due to viscosity arise when the different parts of a fluid are in motion relative to one another. The shearing stress ϕ across a plane in the fluid is assumed to be proportional to the velocity gradient $\partial u/\partial n$ perpendicular to the plane, so that we may write

$$\phi = \eta \frac{\partial u}{\partial n}. \qquad \ldots \ldots \quad (11)$$

The constant of proportionality η is called the coefficient of viscosity of the fluid. Results deduced from this equation are in agreement with experiment. For example, values of the coefficient of viscosity deduced from experiments on the rate of flow through tubes and from experiments with parallel flat plates agree with one another, provided that it is also assumed that there is no slip between a fluid and a solid boundary.

In a particular case in which the motion is parallel to the xy plane we may write

$$\phi = \eta \frac{\partial u}{\partial z}. \qquad \ldots \ldots \quad (12)$$

Let us consider a plane z_0, and let the motion of the gas be parallel to the xy plane and its velocity in the plane z_0 be u_0. We shall suppose that u_0 is small compared with the translational velocities of the gas molecules.

As in the case of thermal conductivity, the number of molecules crossing unit area of this plane in one second in a direction making an angle θ with the z axis is equal to $\frac{1}{2}n\bar{c} \cos \theta \sin \theta \, d\theta$; and, as in that case also, each such molecule on the average carries momentum $m(u_0 + \lambda \cos \theta \, du/dz)$ across the plane,* where m is the mass of a molecule. The total amount of momentum carried in unit time across unit area of the plane from above to below is, therefore, obtained by integrating the expression

$$m\left(u_0 + \lambda \cos \theta \frac{du}{dz}\right) \frac{n}{2} \bar{c} \cos \theta \sin \theta \, d\theta$$

between the limits $\theta = 0$ and $\theta = \pi$; that is, it is equal to

$$\tfrac{1}{3}m\lambda n\bar{c} \frac{du}{dz}. \qquad \ldots \ldots \ldots \quad (13)$$

This gives the shearing stress across the plane in question. Comparing this expression with (12), we see that the coefficient of viscosity η is given by

$$\eta = \tfrac{1}{3}m\lambda n\bar{c}. \qquad \ldots \ldots \ldots \quad (14)$$

As in the case of the thermal conductivity, it will be seen that the coefficient of viscosity is independent of the pressure. This interesting prediction of the theory was confirmed by experiment, and this fact formed one of the most brilliant successes of the kinetic theory of gases in its earlier history.

* We consider only the additional momentum due to the mass motion of the gas.

9. Ratio of the Thermal Conductivity and the Coefficient of Viscosity.

Comparing equations (14) and (10), we see that the thermal conductivity and the coefficient of viscosity are connected by the relation

$$K = \eta c_v. \qquad \ldots \ldots \ldots \quad (15)$$

The effect of a more detailed analysis is that the formulæ remain the same except that they are multiplied by numerical factors. We used a rather crude method of averaging by assuming that the molecules crossing a given plane all come from the same distance; and also that the molecules in a given plane possess individually the mean energy of the molecules in the plane. Also molecules do not necessarily transfer rotational energy with the same efficiency as they do translational energy. For a detailed treatment of these questions reference should be made to Jeans's *Dynamical Theory of Gases*. The effect of taking these points into account is to multiply the various expressions by numerical factors, and equation (15) becomes

$$K = f\eta c_v, \qquad \ldots \ldots \ldots \quad (16)$$

f being a numerical factor. The experimental values of f are given in Table I which is based on one collected by Hercus and Laby * and on the measurements of Kannuluik and Carman.† The latter measurements were made at a series of temperatures from the oxygen point to the benzophenone point. The values of f were sensibly constant for all temperatures. The values given in Table I are the mean values of those calculated for each temperature.

TABLE I

Gas	K at 0° C.	c_p	γ	c_v	η at 0° C.	f
He ..	$34 \cdot 1 \cdot 10^{-5}$	1·255	1·667 ‡	0·746	$1 \cdot 873 \cdot 10^{-4}$	2·44
Ne ..	11·10	—	—	0·150	2·965	2·48
A ..	3·94	0·123	1·667	0·0745	2·105	2·51
Xe ..	1·21	—	—	0·0227	2·105	2·58
H₂ ..	36·3	3·407	1·399	2·406	0·852	1·76
N₂ ..	5·14	0·244	1·401	0·175	1·673	1·76
O₂ ..	5·35	0·218	1·401	0·1531	1·925	1·79
Air ..	5·22	0·239	1·402	0·1715	1·733	1·76
NO ..	4·93	0·231	1·397	—	1·737	1·73
CO ..	5·05	0·246	1·405	—	1·677	1·72
CO₂ ..	3·25	0·2015	1·300	0·160	1·428	1·45
N₂O ..	3·34	0·220	1·317	—	1·364	1·47
H₂S ..	2·81	0·2389	1·317	—	1·154	1·34
SO₂ ..	1·80	0·1527	1·258	0·1061	1·204	1·35

* Hercus and Laby, *Proc. Roy. Soc.*, A, Vol. 95, p. 190 (1919). For an interesting indirect determination of the thermal conductivity of krypton, see Brüche and Littwin, *Zeits. f. Physik*, Vol. 67, p. 362 (1931).
† W. G. Kannuluik and E. H. Carman, *Proc. Phys. Soc.*, B. Vol. 65, p. 701 (1952).
‡ Theoretical value.

The theory given by Jeans accounts for these values of f satisfactorily. This indicates that the individual numerical factors with which the expressions (10) and (14) are mutiplied by Jeans are themselves satisfactory: this is important on account of the use made of these equations to deduce the values of molecular diameters given in the next section.

10. The Molecular Diameter and the Mean Free Path.

It will be seen that equations (10) and (14) both give a means of determining λ, the mean free path, and therefore of obtaining the value of the molecular diameters of various gases. We give in Table II the values of the molecular diameter σ given by Kaye and Laby,* and also the mean free path of a molecule at standard atmospheric pressure at $0°$ C. It will be seen that the two sets of values for the molecular diameters are in satisfactory agreement.

TABLE II.—VALUES OF MOLECULAR DIAMETER σ, AND MEAN FREE PATH

Gas	Value of $\sigma . 10^8$ from		Mean free path at 1 atmosphere pressure and $0°$ C. (cm.)
	Viscosity	Cond. of heat	
Hydrogen	2·47	2·40	$18·3 . 10^{-6}$
Helium	2·18	—	28·5
Carbon monoxide ..	3·50	3·31	9·3
Ethylene	4·55	4·68	5·5
Nitrogen	3·50	3·31	9·4
Nitric oxide	3·40	3·40	9·1
Oxygen	3·39	3·11	10·0
Argon	3·36	—	10·0
Carbon dioxide ..	4·18	4·32	6·3
Nitrous oxide ..	4·27	4·20	6·1

Upper limits for the molecular diameter can be deduced from the volume occupied by one gram-molecule in the solid or the liquid state. The values so obtained agree well with those given in Table II.

The whole question has been considered in detail by Rankine,† who takes into account the fact that the molecules resemble ellipsoids more closely than spheres.

11. The Thermal Conductivity of Gases at Very Low Pressures.

The values given in Table II for the mean free paths of the molecules of various gases refer to atmospheric pressure (approximately

* These values are deduced from equations (10) and (14), corrected by multiplication by the factors referred to in the last section.

† Rankine, *Proc. Roy. Soc.*, A, Vol. 98, pp. 360, 369 (1921); Vol. 99, p. 331 (1921).

10^6 dynes per square centimetre) and $0°$ C. Since the mean free path is inversely proportional to the density, the numbers in the last column of the table without the multiplying factor 10^{-6} give the mean free paths in centimetres of the molecules of the various gases at $0°$ C. and at a pressure of 1 dyne per square centimetre, or of $0\cdot00076$ mm. of mercury.

It will be seen that even at pressures of the order of $\frac{1}{10}$ mm. or higher it is easily possible to obtain wires whose diameters are small compared with the mean free path.

Suppose that such a wire is maintained at a temperature slightly above that of the surrounding gas. A gas molecule after leaving the wire will on the average travel a distance of the order of the mean free path before it strikes another gas molecule, and the probability is very small that it will strike the wire again before it has made many collisions with other gas molecules. It can thus be assumed that the gas molecules striking the wire are at the temperature of the surrounding gas.*

Consider an element of the surface. If in the gas in the neighbourhood of the element there are dn_1 molecules per unit volume whose velocities lie between the limits c_1 and $c_1 + dc_1$ with the normal component of the velocity directed towards the surface, the number of such molecules which strike the element of surface per unit area per second is $\frac{1}{2}c_1 dn_1$ (see Chapter III). Each such molecule carries up translational energy $\frac{1}{2}mc_1^2$, so that the total amount of translational energy carried up to the element of surface per unit area per second by molecules of velocity c_1 is given by

$$dE_1 = \tfrac{1}{4}mc_1^3 dn_1.$$

Thus the total translational energy E_1 brought up to the element per unit area per second is

$$E_1 = \tfrac{1}{4}m \int_{c_1=0}^{c_1=\infty} c_1^3 dn_1.$$

If velocities are distributed according to Maxwell's law (see Chapter III),

$$dn_1 = \frac{4n_1}{\sqrt{\pi}} \frac{c_1^2}{\alpha_1^3} e^{-c_1^2/\alpha_1^2} dc_1,$$

where n_1 is the total number of molecules per unit volume in the immediate neighbourhood of the element for which the normal component of the velocity is directed towards the element, and α_1 is their most probable velocity. Thus

$$\int_{c_1=0}^{c_1=\infty} c_1^3 dn_1 = 4n_1 \frac{\alpha_1^3}{\sqrt{\pi}} = \tfrac{1}{2}\pi n_1(\bar{c}_1)^3,$$

since

$$\alpha_1 = \tfrac{1}{2}\bar{c}_1\sqrt{\pi},$$

where $\bar{c}_1$ is the mean velocity. Thus, substituting in the equation for E_1, we obtain

$$E_1 = \tfrac{1}{8}\pi mn_1(\bar{c}_1)^3.$$

---

* It is easy to show that, if the wire is stretched along the axis of a tube of reasonable size, the heat flow is not sufficiently great to produce a temperature difference in the gas itself which is in any way comparable with that between the wire and the gas molecules striking it.

Similarly the amount of translational energy carried away per unit area of the element per second is given by

$$E_2 = \tfrac{1}{8}\pi m n_2 (\bar{c}_2)^3,$$

where the suffix 2 refers to molecules in the immediate neighbourhood of the element for which the normal component of the velocity is directed away from the surface.

The net loss of energy per second per unit area of the element of surface in the form of translational energy is therefore given by

$$E_t = \tfrac{1}{8}\pi m \{ n_2 (\bar{c}_2)^3 - n_1 (\bar{c}_1)^3 \}.$$

Now we have (see Chapter III, equation (31a))

$$n_1 \bar{c}_1 = n_2 \bar{c}_2 = \tfrac{1}{2} n \bar{c}_1, \quad \ldots \ldots \ldots \quad (17)$$

where n is the *total* number of molecules per unit volume of the gas. Substituting in the previous equation, we have

$$E_t = \tfrac{1}{16}\pi m n \bar{c}_1 \{ (\bar{c}_2)^2 - (\bar{c}_1)^2 \}. \quad \ldots \ldots \quad (18)$$

If ρ_1 is the mean rotational and vibrational energy of the molecules striking the element of surface, the amount of rotational energy brought up per unit area per second is given by

$$E_1' = \rho_1 \int_{c_1=0}^{c_1=\infty} \tfrac{1}{2} c_1 \, dn_1 = \tfrac{1}{2}\rho_1 n_1 \bar{c}_1.$$

It is assumed that rotational and translational energy are independently distributed among the molecules. Similarly, the amount of rotational energy carried away from the element per unit area per second is given by

$$E_2' = \tfrac{1}{2}\rho_2 n_2 \bar{c}_2.$$

The net loss of energy by the element per unit area per second in the form of rotational energy is therefore given by

$$E_\rho = \tfrac{1}{4} n \bar{c}_1 (\rho_2 - \rho_1). \quad \ldots \ldots \ldots \quad (19)$$

Combining equations (18) and (19) and using the results given in Chapter III, equations (6), (8), (21), (24), and in Chapter VI, equation (4), we obtain for Q, the total heat loss from unit area of the wire per second,

$$Q = \frac{1}{4}\frac{\gamma+1}{\gamma-1}\sqrt{\frac{2R}{\pi M}}\, p \, \frac{(T_2 - T_1)}{\sqrt{T_1}} \text{ erg cm.}^{-2}\text{sec.}^{-1}, \quad \ldots \quad (20)$$

where γ is the ratio of the specific heats of the gas, R the gas constant measured in ergs per degree, M the molecular weight ($O_2 = 32$), and p the pressure in dynes per sq. cm. It is assumed that the gas molecules leaving the solid are at the temperature T_2 of the solid.

Experiments on the loss from electrically heated wires under these conditions were first carried out by Knudsen and by Soddy and Berry.[*] The experiments show that in general the heat loss from a heated wire is less than would be expected from equation (20).

---

[*] Knudsen, *Ann. d. Physik*, Vol. 34, p. 593 (1911); Soddy and Berry, *Proc. Roy. Soc.*, A, Vol. 83, p. 254 (1910); Vol. 84, p. 576 (1911). See also Smoluchowski, *Ann. d. Physik*, Vol. 35, p. 983 (1911).

This effect is explained when we consider that the average energy of the gas molecules leaving a surface will not necessarily correspond to the temperature of the surface, but will depend also on the temperature of the molecules before they strike the surface. Let the molecules leaving the surface whose temperature is T_2 have on the average energy corresponding to a temperature T_2' and let T_1 be their temperature before striking the surface. Knudsen, following Smoluchowski, assumed that, for small temperature differences, the change in the temperature of the gas molecules is proportional to the difference between the temperature of the surface and that of the oncoming molecules, that is, that

$$T_2' - T_1 = a(T_2 - T_1). \quad \ldots \ldots \quad (21)$$

The constant a is called the *accommodation coefficient*.

Substituting from equation (21) in (20), we obtain for the heat loss per unit area per second

$$Q = \frac{1}{4} \frac{\gamma + 1}{\gamma - 1} \sqrt{\frac{2R}{\pi M}} \, pa \, \frac{(T_2 - T_1)}{\sqrt{T_1}}. \quad \ldots \ldots \quad (22)$$

This equation is in accord with the experimental results, which show that for a given gas the loss is proportional to p and to $(T_2 - T_1)$. The fact that the loss is proportional to p is the basis of the Pirani gauge. All the quantities in equation (22) except a can be measured and thus a can be determined. In deducing equation (22) we have assumed that the accommodation coefficient is the same for rotational energy as for translational energy. In some cases this is at least approximately true,[*] but strictly speaking equation (22) can only be applied to monatomic gases, for which $\gamma = 5/3$. Eucken and Bertram [†] have shown that if a nickel wire with the surface roughened by oxidation is used, a is nearly unity and from the heat loss the specific heat of complex molecules can be found.

Ordinarily values of a ranging from about 0·3 for helium up to nearly unity for gases with heavy molecules are obtained. Roberts [‡] has carried out experiments with helium carefully freed from adsorbable impurities. He has shown that by flashing the wire so as to remove all adsorbed films from its surface very much lower values of the accommodation coefficient (0·057 for helium and a tungsten wire at room temperature and 0·025 at 79° K.) are obtained. Only on the basis of experiments carried out under such definite conditions can an accurate theory of the interaction between gas atoms and solid surfaces be developed.[§]

LIQUIDS

12. The thermal conductivities of liquids have been determined by various methods. As they do not differ in principle from those used for solids and gases, and as the results obtained have not as yet received any satisfactory theoretical interpretation, we shall not consider them in detail.

Lees ‖ has used a modification of his method for solid non-conductors (see Section 21) which gives accurate results. The liquid is contained in a closed vessel of ebonite, which replaces the solid non-conductor. Correction is made for the heat conducted through the walls of the containing vessel.

[*] Knudsen, *Ann. d. Physik*, Vol. 6, p. 129 (1930).

[†] Eucken and Bertram, *Zeits. f. phys. Chem.*, B, Vol. 31, p. 372 (1936).

[‡] Roberts, *Proc. Roy. Soc.*, A, Vol. 129, p. 146 (1930); Vol. 135, p. 192 (1932).

[§] See A. R. Miller, *The Adsorption of Gases on Solids* (Cambridge Monographs on Physics), Cambridge University Press (1949).

‖ Lees, *Phil. Trans.*, Vol. 191, p. 418 (1898); Kaye and Higgins, *Proc. Roy. Soc.*, A, Vol. 122, p. 633 (1929); Martin and Lang, *Proc. Phys. Soc.*, Vol. 45, p. 523 (1933).

Goldschmidt * has used a modification of the hot-wire method of Schleier-macher (see Section 6). The liquid is contained in a very narrow tube with the heated wire running down the centre.

Bridgman † has used a method in which the liquid is contained between two concentric cylinders. His work had the special object of determining the variation of the thermal conductivity with pressure.

Callendar ‡ has measured the heat carried away by a liquid flowing through an electrically heated metal tube.

The work of Nettleton § on the determination of the conductivity of mercury by a flow method is also of interest.

METALS

Direct Methods

13. In the case of metals, which are good conductors, a rod or bar of the substance is nearly always used. The earliest work is that of Forbes, whose method has been considerably modified by Callendar ‖ and others. In this method one end of the bar is heated and the other end cooled. The heating can be carried out electrically, and the cooling by passing a stream of water through a spiral tube. The heat flowing into the water can be determined from the rate of flow and the rise of temperature; the heat supplied to the other end can be determined electrically. The temperature distribution in the bar can be determined by means of thermocouples attached to various points, and thus the temperature gradient at any point can be obtained. The heat flowing across any section of the bar is equal to the heat flowing into the water *plus* a small correction for the heat lost from the surface of the bar between the section considered and the cool end; an independent check on the heat flow is obtained, since it is also equal to the electrical energy supplied *minus* the heat loss from the surface of the bar between the section considered and the hot end of the bar. By careful lagging of the bar the losses can be made small, so that the temperature gradient is practically uniform. The small corrections for heat loss can be deter-mined by heating the whole bar up to a uniform temperature and measuring the rate of cooling. The thermal capacity of the bar being known, the rate of loss of heat per unit area for a given temperature excess above the surroundings can then be deduced.

The range of temperature over which this method can be used is limited. On this account Lees ¶ modified the method in such a way

---

* Goldschmidt, *Phys. Zeits.*, Vol. 12, p. 417 (1911).

† Bridgman, *Proc. Am. Acad.*, Vol. 59, p. 141 (1923).

‡ Callendar, *Phil. Trans.*, Vol. 199, p. 110 (1902).

§ Nettleton, *Phil. Mag.*, Vol. 19, p. 587 (1910); *Proc. Phys. Soc. London*, Vol. 22 (1910); and Vol. 25 (1913).

‖ See " Conduction of Heat ", *Encycl. Brit.*, 11th Edition; see also Bidwell, *Phys. Rev.*, Vol. 28, p. 584 (1926).

¶ Lees, *Phil. Trans.*, A, Vol. 208, p. 381 (1908).

that small specimens could be used (7 or 8 cm. long and 0·585 cm. in diameter). He was thus able to enclose the whole apparatus in a Dewar flask and to use the method down to liquid-air temperatures.

His apparatus is illustrated in fig. 11.5. The metal rods R were accurately turned metal cylinders of the size mentioned above. They were placed vertically, the lower end fitting into a copper disc D, of 2·69 cm. diameter, 1·2 cm. thick in the centre, 1 cm. thick at the circumference, which in its turn fitted accurately into the lower end of a copper cylinder T, of 2·69 cm. internal, 3·32 cm. external, diameter, 9·5 cm. long, closed at the top.

On the rods three thin brass sleeves, A, B, and C, were placed, the fit being such that the sleeves could be slid along the rod without the application of more than a small force. The outer surface of each sleeve was covered with shellac varnish, thinly dusted with marble powder, and allowed to dry. Over this insulating layer wire was wound, in the case of C, a heating coil of No. 40 platinoid wire, and in the case of A and B thermometer coils of pure platinum wire. Copper leads were used and were supported on the wooden bobbins W and S so as to prevent strains in the thin wires wound on the sleeves.

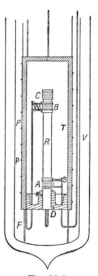

Around the outside of the copper tube T an insulated platinoid wire p was wound. This wire had the same resistance as the heater wound on the sleeve C. Whenever the heating current was switched off the heating coil C it was switched on to the heating coil p, so that the amount of heat supplied to the apparatus remained constant. In addition a further coil P was wound on the outside of the tube to allow the temperature of the tube, if necessary, to be rapidly raised.

The whole apparatus was supported on a wire frame F, inside a straight Dewar tube V.

The rod, sleeves, and edges of the copper disc forming the base of the tube were smeared with olive oil to improve the thermal contacts. None of these contacts came into the direct line of flow of heat within the region of measurement.

Fig. 11.5

After the temperature of the apparatus had become steady, the difference, if any, between the resistances of the two thermometer coils was measured with no heating current on either of the heating coils.

An electric current was then switched on to the heating coil on the rod and adjusted so that the difference between the resistances of the two thermometer coils was of the desired order of magnitude. The heating current was then switched from rod to tube, and allowed to flow until the difference between the resistances of the two thermometer coils became constant. This difference and the actual resistance of the lower coil was then measured, and also the rate of supply of heat to the heating coil.

The current was then switched from tube to rod and again allowed to flow until the difference between the resistances of the two thermometer coils became steady. This difference was then measured and also the actual resistance of the lower coil, and the rate of supply of heat to the heating coil; then the current was again switched from rod to tube and the measurements repeated.

The mean of the two differences found when the current flowed round the tube, subtracted from the difference found when the current flowed round the rod, gives, so long as the rate of rise of temperature of the apparatus is regular, the difference of resistance that would be produced if the heating current were supplied to the rod and the temperature of the tube were kept constant (for the proof of this, reference must be made to the original paper). It thus enables us to calculate the thermal conductivity of the rod.

For the measurements at low temperatures the Dewar tube was filled with liquid air, and when the apparatus had cooled down, the remaining liquid was poured out.

Grüneisen and Goens * have also used a modification of the direct method at low temperatures. The metal specimen, with a heating coil at one end and thermocouples for measuring the temperature gradient, is enclosed in a high vacuum. At low temperatures radiation losses are negligible, so that no effects due to heat losses arise.

The results obtained by these methods are of considerable importance, since they give an independent verification of the accuracy of those obtained using the less direct electrical method about to be described (see Section 19, Table III, and fig. 11.8).

Electrical Methods

14. Kohlrausch † pointed out that a simple way of determining the thermal conductivity of a metal is to measure the temperature distribution in the metal when it is heated by an electric current. The theory of the method depends on the fact that, when a steady state has been reached, the heat gained by any element by conduction *plus* the heat generated by the electric current in the element is zero. We shall consider the simplest case, but the one which is most important in practice, namely that of a cylinder.

In this case we may suppose that the current lines are parallel to the axis. We shall assume too that heat losses are negligible and that the flow of heat is

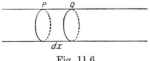

Fig. 11.6

also parallel to the axis, in other words, that the surfaces of equal temperature and the equipotential surfaces are the same. Let x be the position co-ordinate, measured along the axis, of the plane P (fig. 11.6); let v and T be the electric potential and temperature of the same plane; and let $(x + dx)$, $(v + dv)$, and $(T + dT)$ be the values of the same quantities for the plane Q. Let A be the cross-section of the bar, and let K be the thermal conductivity, and σ the electrical conductivity. Both K and σ are functions of the temperature, and therefore vary along the length of the bar.

The heat flowing in unit time into the element over the area P is equal to

$$-KA\frac{dT}{dx},$$

* Grüneisen and Goens, *Zeits. f. Physik*, Vol. 44, p. 615 (1927); see also Kannuluik and Laby, *Proc. Roy. Soc.*, A, Vol. 121, p. 640 (1928).

† Kohlrausch, *Ann. d. Phys.*, Vol. 1, p. 132 (1900).

and that flowing into it over the area Q in unit time is equal to

$$+KA\frac{dT}{dx} + \frac{d}{dx}\left(KA\frac{dT}{dx}\right)dx.$$

The net gain of heat by conduction in unit time is therefore

$$A\frac{d}{dx}\left(K\frac{dT}{dx}\right)dx,$$

since A is constant.

The electrical energy supplied to the element in unit time is equal to the square of the potential difference between P and Q multiplied by the electrical conductivity of the element, that is, to

$$A\sigma\left(\frac{dv}{dx}\right)^2 dx.$$

When a steady state has been reached, the total rate of gain of heat by the element must be zero; we have therefore *

$$A\frac{d}{dx}\left(K\frac{dT}{dx}\right)dx + A\sigma\left(\frac{dv}{dx}\right)^2 dx = 0,$$

that is,

$$\frac{dK}{dx}\frac{dT}{dx} + K\frac{d^2T}{dx^2} + \sigma\left(\frac{dv}{dx}\right)^2 = 0.† \quad \cdot \quad \cdot \quad \cdot \quad \cdot \quad (23)$$

We may write

$$\frac{dT}{dx} = \frac{dT}{dv}\frac{dv}{dx},$$

and

$$\frac{d^2T}{dx^2} = \frac{d^2T}{dv^2}\left(\frac{dv}{dx}\right)^2 + \frac{dT}{dv}\frac{d^2v}{dx^2}.$$

---

* If ordinary practical electrical units are used, heat energy must also be measured in watt-seconds.

† The simplest case is that in which we assume that K and σ are constant along the length of the bar. In this case equation (23) becomes

$$K\frac{d^2T}{dx^2} + \sigma\left(\frac{dv}{dx}\right)^2 = 0.$$

Substituting in this the value of $\dfrac{d^2T}{dx^2}$ from the equations following (23), we obtain

$$K\frac{d^2T}{dv^2}\left(\frac{dv}{dx}\right)^2 + K\frac{dT}{dv}\frac{d^2v}{dx^2} + \sigma\left(\frac{dv}{dx}\right)^2 = 0.$$

Now the current i at any point is $i = -A\sigma\dfrac{dv}{dx}$, and, since this must be constant and both A and σ are constant, we obtain $\dfrac{d^2v}{dx^2} = 0$. The above equation then becomes, since, if there is any current flowing, $\left(\dfrac{dv}{dx}\right)^2$ cannot equal zero,

$$K\frac{d^2T}{dv^2} + \sigma = 0,$$

the solution of which is $\dfrac{K}{\sigma}T + \tfrac{1}{2}v^2 + \alpha v + \beta = 0,$

where α and β are integration constants.

If also we put $K' = \dfrac{dK}{dT}$, we have

$$\frac{dK}{dx} = K' \frac{dT}{dv} \frac{dv}{dx}.$$

Using these relations, equation (23) becomes

$$K' \left(\frac{dT}{dv}\right)^2 \left(\frac{dv}{dx}\right)^2 + K \frac{d^2T}{dv^2} \left(\frac{dv}{dx}\right)^2 + K \frac{dT}{dv} \frac{d^2v}{dx^2} + \sigma \left(\frac{dv}{dx}\right)^2 = 0. \quad . \quad (24)$$

The current i at P is given by $i = -A\sigma \dfrac{dv}{dx}$. Since $\dfrac{di}{dx} = 0$, and A is constant, we obtain

$$\frac{d\sigma}{dx} \frac{dv}{dx} + \sigma \frac{d^2v}{dx^2} = 0,$$

and if in this we put $\dfrac{d\sigma}{dT} = \sigma'$, we obtain

$$\sigma' \frac{dT}{dv} \left(\frac{dv}{dx}\right)^2 + \sigma \frac{d^2v}{dx^2} = 0,$$

as the condition for constancy of current along the bar.

We now substitute the value of $\dfrac{d^2v}{dx^2}$ from this equation in equation (24), which becomes

$$\frac{\sigma}{K} + \left(\frac{K'}{K} - \frac{\sigma'}{\sigma}\right) \left(\frac{dT}{dv}\right)^2 + \frac{d^2T}{dv^2} = 0. \quad . \quad . \quad . \quad . \quad (25)$$

The solution of this equation is

$$\int_{T'}^{T} \frac{K}{\sigma} dT + \tfrac{1}{2}v^2 + \alpha v + \beta = 0, \quad . \quad . \quad . \quad . \quad (26)$$

where α and β are integration constants and T' is arbitrary.

15. Experiments of Jaeger and Diesselhorst.

Jaeger and Diesselhorst * have applied the method in a very accurate series of experiments on a large number of metals at 18° C. and 100° C. The values of the integration constants in equation (26) can be determined by measurements of the temperatures and potentials at two points of the bar; a measure of the same quantities at another point then suffices to determine the value of K/σ.

Let v_1, v_2, v_3, and T_1, T_2, T_3, be the potentials and temperatures respectively at three points of the bar. We shall for the moment suppose that there are no heat losses, so that Kohlrausch's equation can be applied. We use the extreme values v_1 and v_3, T_1 and T_3, to obtain the values of α and β.

* Jaeger and Diesselhorst, *Abhand. d. Reichsanstalt*, Vol. 3, p. 269 (1900); *Sitz. Ber. d. Berl. Akad.*, Vol. 38, p. 719 (1899); see also Duncan, *Applied Science Soc. M'Gill Univ., Toronto* (1899–1900), for a method worked out by Callendar; see also Kannuluik, *Proc. Roy. Soc.*, A, Vol. 131, p. 320 (1931); Vol. 141, p. 159 (1933).

We then have from equation (26)

$$\alpha = -\frac{1}{v_1 - v_3}\int_{T_3}^{T_1}\frac{K}{\sigma}\,dT - \tfrac{1}{2}(v_1 + v_3),$$

$$\beta = \frac{v_3}{v_1 - v_3}\int_{T'}^{T_1}\frac{K}{\sigma}\,dT - \frac{v_1}{v_1 - v_3}\int_{T'}^{T_3}\frac{K}{\sigma}\,dT + \tfrac{1}{2}v_1 v_2.$$

For the other point the relation between T_2 and v_2 is therefore

$$\int_{T'}^{T_2}\frac{K}{\sigma}\,dT + \tfrac{1}{2}v_2^2 - \tfrac{1}{2}v_2(v_1 + v_3) + \tfrac{1}{2}v_1 v_3 + \frac{v_3}{v_1 - v_3}\int_{T'}^{T_1}\frac{K}{\sigma}\,dT$$

$$-\frac{v_1}{v_1 - v_3}\int_{T'}^{T_3}\frac{K}{\sigma}\,dT - \frac{v_2}{v_1 - v_3}\int_{T_3}^{T_1}\frac{K}{\sigma}\,dT = 0. \quad \text{. . .} \quad (27)$$

In the actual experiment v_1 and v_3 were measured at the two ends of the bar and v_2 at the centre. The two ends were maintained at the same temperature. We have then

$$T_1 = T_3,$$

and on account of the symmetrical arrangement

$$v_2 = \frac{v_1 + v_3}{2}. \quad \text{. . . . .} \quad (28)$$

On account of the equality of T_1 and T_3 the last term on the left-hand side of equation (27) vanishes; and the two terms preceding the last may be combined to give $-\int_{T'}^{T_1}\frac{K}{\sigma}\,dT$. This in turn may be combined with the first term to form the definite integral $\int_{T_1}^{T_2}\frac{K}{\sigma}\,dT$. If further we substitute in equation (27) the value of v_2 given by equation (28), we obtain

$$\int_{T_1}^{T_2}\frac{K}{\sigma}\,dT = \tfrac{1}{8}(v_3 - v_1)^2. \quad \text{. . . . . .} \quad (29)$$

If $\left[\dfrac{K}{\sigma}\right]$ is the arithmetic mean value of $\dfrac{K}{\sigma}$ in the interval T_1 to T_2, equation (29) gives

$$\left[\frac{K}{\sigma}\right] = \frac{1}{8}\frac{(v_3 - v_1)^2}{(T_2 - T_1)}. \quad \text{. . . . . . .} \quad (30)$$

Thus $\left[\dfrac{K}{\sigma}\right]$ can be determined from a measurement of the potential difference between the two ends of the bar, and of the temperature difference between the ends and the middle.

Jaeger and Diesselhorst worked out the correction necessary for heat loss from the surface, and verified their formula by varying the conditions of experiment. They also showed that any effects due to variation of temperature in passing from the axis to the outside of the bar caused by heat loss from the surface were negligible.

Bars of the metals 1 or 2 cm. in diameter and 20 or 30 cm. long were used. They were heated by the passage of an electric current through them, and the ends were kept in constant-temperature baths.

In order that there should be a difference of temperature of 3 or 5 degrees between the middle and the ends of the bars, it was necessary in the case of good conductors to use a current of about 350 amp.

To make the heat loss definite, the bar of metal was surrounded by a cylindrical copper cover, with double walls through which water or steam was circulated.

16. Meissner's Experiments.

The method has been used by Meissner * to measure the thermal conductivity of copper down to temperatures as low as 20° absolute. His apparatus is illustrated in fig. 11.7

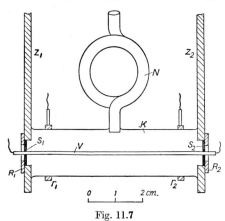

Fig. 11.7

V, the copper specimen, was 7 cm. long and 1 mm. in diameter; it had two copper discs S_1 and S_2 soldered to it, which passed through holes in the heavy copper blocks Z_1 and Z_2. These discs were soldered to rings R_1 and R_2, which in turn were soldered to Z_1 and Z_2. Concentric with V a constantan tube K was hard soldered to Z_1 and Z_2: the walls of this tube were 0·1 mm. thick. The space between V and K could be evacuated through the tube N, so that heat losses from the surface of V were negligible. A small correction was necessary for the current flowing through the tube K. This was determined by measuring the potential difference between r_1 and r_2 and dividing by the resistance of K, which was large compared with that of V, and was estimated from the temperature.

Meissner obtained the ratio of the thermal to the electrical conductivity by measuring the resistance of the specimen and the potential difference between its ends with two different currents flowing through it, the ends being at the same temperature throughout. (The modification of the theory to suit this case has been worked out by Diesselhorst—see Meissner's paper. What it amounts to is that the value of $(T_2 - T_1)$ in equation (30) is determined from the known law of distribution of temperature, the measured resistance, and the temperature coefficient of resistance.) Actually a small correction was

* Meissner, *Ber. deut. phys. Ges.*, Vol. 12, p. 262 (1914).

necessary for the fact that the ends did not remain at exactly the same temperature with different currents; this correction was determined by thermocouples soldered to S_1 and S_2 with their other ends in the bath in which the whole apparatus was immersed.

17. High Temperatures.

The electrical method has also been used for the determinations that have been carried out at high temperatures. The results obtained leave little room for generalization, as they are so divergent. Reference should be made for further information on this subject to: Angell, *Phys. Rev.*, Vol. 33, p. 421 (1911), who used a modification of Kohlrausch's method in which the radial temperature gradient was measured; Worthing, *Phys. Rev.*, Vol. 4, p. 535 (1914); Langmuir, *Phys. Rev.*, Vol. 7, p. 151 (1916). See also Konno, *Phil. Mag.*, Vol. 239, p. 542 (1920); Holm, *Zeits. f. techn. Physik*, Vol. 10, p. 621 (1929).

Theoretical

18. Most of the experimental work on the conductivity of metals has been concerned with the specific object of testing the truth of the Wiedemann-Franz law. This law states that the ratio of the thermal and electrical conductivities is the same for all metals at the same temperature. Lorenz * extended the law by adding that the value of the ratio of the two conductivities is proportional to the absolute temperature.

Jaeger and Diesselhorst (see Section 15) made measurements on the twelve metals, copper, silver, gold, zinc, cadmium, aluminium, tin, lead, palladium, platinum, nickel, and iron, and found that the mean value of K/σ at 18° C. was 7.9×10^{-11} e.s.u. We shall see below that the theoretical value of this ratio at this temperature is 7.89×10^{-11} e.s.u., which shows remarkable agreement. Furthermore, the results collected in Section 19, Table III, show that at ordinary temperatures the law is obeyed with considerable accuracy. The conclusion that must be drawn is that the same agents are responsible for the transfer of heat as of electricity, and, as modern theories of the metallic state assume that electrons are responsible for the latter, we must assume that they are responsible for the former also.

From the time of Drude,† the basic assumption that has been made in the theory of metals is that the distinctive character of a metal is due to some of the electrons being " free "; that is, some electrons, numbering one or two per atom, are not bound to any particular atom,

---

* Lorenz, *Pogg. Ann.*, Vol. 147, p. 429 (1872).

† Drude, *Ann. d. Physik*, Vol. 1, p. 566; Vol. 3, p. 369 (1900).

but are able to traverse the ionic lattice. The assumption of such free electrons is sufficient to explain the *fact* of thermal and electrical conductivity (although not the details of it). Using this assumption, Drude used the methods of the kinetic theory of gases, applying equation (9) to the free-electron gas. He was able to deduce the Wiedemann-Franz law giving the dependence of the ratio of the thermal to the electrical conductivity on the absolute temperature. A more rigorous deduction, using the Maxwell-Boltzmann distribution law, was given by Lorentz.* The quantum theory of metals gives

$$\frac{K}{\sigma} = \frac{\pi^2}{3J}\left(\frac{k}{e}\right)^2 T. \qquad \ldots \ldots \quad (31)$$

The quantum theory is considered very briefly below, and references are given to the development of this theory.

19. Experimental Results.

We may consider briefly the experimental results and their bearing on the theory. The results collected in Table III show that at ordinary temperatures the laws of Wiedemann and Franz and of Lorenz are obeyed with considerable accuracy for pure metals, but that at lower temperatures the value of $K/\sigma T$ falls off.

TABLE III

Values of $\left(\dfrac{K}{\sigma T}\right)$. K is measured in watts per centimetre-degree, σ in reciprocal ohms per centimetre cube. In these units $\dfrac{\pi^2}{3J}\left(\dfrac{k}{e}\right)^2 = 2\cdot42 \cdot 10^{-8}$.

Metal	Result of Lees' direct method					Jaeger and Diesselhorst	
	$-170°$ C.	$-100°$C.	$-50°$ C.	$0°$ C.	$18°$ C.	$18°$ C.	$100°$ C.
Aluminium ..	$1\cdot50 \cdot 10^{-8}$	$1\cdot81$	$1\cdot98$	$2\cdot09$	$2\cdot13$	$2\cdot19$	$2\cdot27$
Copper ..	$1\cdot85$	$2\cdot17$	$2\cdot26$	$2\cdot30$	$2\cdot32$	$2\cdot29$	$2\cdot32$
Silver	$2\cdot04$	$2\cdot29$	$2\cdot36$	$2\cdot33$	$2\cdot33$	$2\cdot36$	$2\cdot37$
Zinc	$2\cdot20$	$2\cdot39$	$2\cdot40$	$2\cdot45$	$2\cdot43$	$2\cdot31$	$2\cdot33$
Lead	$2\cdot55$	$2\cdot54$	$2\cdot52$	$2\cdot53$	$2\cdot51$	$2\cdot46$	$2\cdot51$
Iron	$3\cdot10$	$2\cdot98$	$2\cdot93$	$2\cdot97$	$2\cdot99$	$2\cdot76$	$2\cdot85$
Manganin ..	$5\cdot94$	$4\cdot16$	$3\cdot58$	$3\cdot41$	$3\cdot34$	$3\cdot14$	$2\cdot97$

This falling off is confirmed by the work of Meissner, whose results for copper are illustrated in fig. 11.8, and whose values at the higher

---

* Lorentz, *Proc. Amsterdam Acad.*, Vol. 7, pp. 438, 585 (1905); see A. H. Wilson, *The Theory of Metals*, Cambridge, 1936, Section 1.4.

temperatures agree with those of Lees, which are shown as crosses in the figure. It will be seen that at 20° K. its value is only one-seventh of what it is at 0° C. Further confirmation of this falling off is obtained from the work of Onnes and Holst * on the conductivity of mercury, which shows that when the mercury has reached the " supercon- ducting state " (where its resistance drops to zero) the thermal con- ductivity still remains finite.

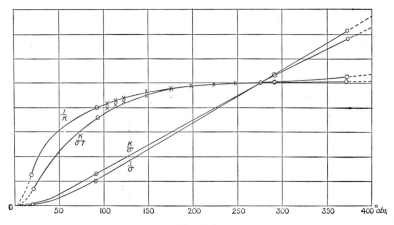

Fig. 11.8

We may summarize the results shown in fig. 11.8 as follows:

(1) At ordinary temperatures the law of Lorenz is true, but at low temperatures there is a marked falling off in the value of the ratio $K/\sigma T$, which appears to approach the value zero at the absolute zero.

(2) The value of the thermal conductivity increases as the tem- perature falls, but not so rapidly as does that of the electrical conduc- tivity; it appears to become infinite at the absolute zero.

Part of the variation of the ratio $K/\sigma T$ with temperature may be due to the fact first pointed out by Koenigsberger † that the thermal conductivity of a metal is not due entirely to the electrons, but in part to a process similar to that which takes place in electrical insulators (see Sections 21–3). De Haas and de Nobel ‡ have separated the two effects in bismuth by working with magnetic fields at low temperatures.

* Onnes and Holst, *Leiden Comm.*, No. 133c (1913).

† Koenigsberger, *Phys. Zeits.*, Vol. 8, p. 237 (1907).

‡ De Haas and de Nobel, *Physica*, Vol. 5, p. 449 (1938). See Eucken, *Zeits. f. phys. Chem.*, Vol. 134, p. 220 (1928); *Phys. Zeits.*, Vol. 29, p. 563 (1928), for a discussion of results obtained by Grüneisen and Goens, *Zeits. f. Physik*, Vol. 44, p. 615 (1927).

20. Difficulties of the Theory.

One of the fundamental difficulties of the classical theory is that it is assumed that the electrons have an amount of energy corresponding to the equipartition of energy between atoms and electrons, that is to say, their energy would play an important part in the specific heat of metals. The number of electrons necessary is not so small as to make their effect negligible. It is a perfectly definite experimental result, however, that at ordinary temperatures both solid conductors and solid non-conductors have the same value for the atomic heat, namely, that which they would have *if only the atoms and no free electrons were present.*

This difficulty has been removed in the theory of metals first developed by Sommerfeld.* In the older theory it is assumed that energy is distributed among the electrons in a metal according to the Maxwellian law. In Sommerfeld's theory, on the other hand, it is assumed that the electrons obey the Fermi-Dirac statistics,

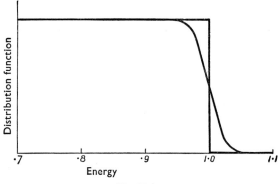

Fig. 11.9

which may be regarded as a plausible extension of the Pauli exclusion principle to the whole assembly of electrons in a metal. In this theory the contribution of the electrons to the specific heat is proportional to the absolute temperature and only of the order of one per cent at $1000°$ K.

The Fermi-Dirac distribution function is plotted in fig. 11.9. The sharp curve represents the distribution at $0°$ K. and the rounded curve that at $1500°$ K. In each case the flat part extends back parallel to the axis of abscissæ till it meets the axis of ordinates. The scale of abscissæ is inserted to show the position of the origin. It will be seen that only a small proportion of the total number of electrons is affected even when the temperature is raised to $1500°$ K. For an electron in a metal there is a series of possible stationary or eigen states. If the number of these, per unit volume of the metal, which have energies between the values E and $E + dE$ is $N(E)\,dE$, the number of electrons having energies between E and $E + dE$ is equal to the ordinate at E multiplied by $2N(E)\,dE.$

---

* Sommerfeld, *Zeits. f. Physik*, Vol. 47, pp. 1, 43 (1928). For a general introductory account, see Darrow, *Reviews of Modern Physics*, Vol. 1, p. 90 (1929). For a fuller discussion, see Fowler, *Statistical Mechanics*, 2nd edition, Cambridge (1936), p. 404; A. H. Wilson, *The Theory of Metals*, Cambridge (1936); Mott and H. Jones, *The Theory of the Properties of Metals and Alloys*, Clarendon Press, Oxford (1936).

The value of $K/\sigma T$ predicted by the Sommerfeld theory is $\pi^2(k/e)^2/3J$, which agrees closely with the experimental values at ordinary temperatures. Stoner † has given a valuable summary, with numerical calculations, of the theory of the contribution of electrons to the specific heat.

SOLID NON-METALS ‡

21. The determination of the thermal conductivity in the case of solid non-metals presents problems different from those arising in the case of metals. The conductivities are much lower in general, and, if a long rod or bar of the substance were used, the losses from the sides would be considerable compared with the flow of heat in the substance itself. For this reason a piece of the substance is used of which the transverse dimensions are at least as great as the thickness in the direction of the flow of heat. Accurate results can be obtained at ordinary temperatures by a method used by Kaye and Roberts § to determine the conductivity of bismuth crystals; ‖ the method is a slight modification of one devised by Ezer Griffiths. In this case the bismuth was about 1 cm. by 2 cm. in area, and 1 or 2 mm. thick. It was contained between two copper blocks, one of which had inside it a heating coil of platinum wire insulated from it by mica strips, and the other had a spiral of copper tubing soldered to it, through which a current of water flowed. Methods of this type have the advantage that the flow of heat through the specimen can be determined both from the electrical energy supplied and from the heat flowing into the water, which is measured from the rate of flow and the rise of temperature. After correction for the small losses from the blocks these two measures of the heat flow agreed closely. The thermal contact between the surfaces of the copper blocks and those of the specimen, all of which were optically flat, was improved by smearing them with glycerine. The temperatures of the copper blocks were determined by thermo-couples; a small correction was necessary for the temperature drop in the contacts.

This method, although accurate, can be used only over a limited range of temperatures. That used by Lees ¶ does not suffer from this

---

† Stoner, *Phil. Mag.*, Vol. 25, p. 899 (1938).

‡ Such substances include building and other materials of commercial importance, with which we need not deal here. A summary of the work on such materials will be found in the article by Schofield, "Heat, Conduction of ", *A Dictionary of Applied Physics*, Vol. I. For conduction through powders, see Aberdeen and Laby, *Proc. Roy. Soc.*, A, Vol. 113, p. 459 (1927); Pirani and v. Wangenheim, *Zeits. f. techn. Physik*, Vol. 10, p. 413 (1929); Kannuluik and Martin, *Proc. Roy. Soc.*, A, Vol. 141, p. 144 (1933).

§ Kaye and Roberts, *Proc. Roy. Soc.*, A, Vol. 104, p. 98 (1923); see also Kaye and Higgins, *Phil. Mag.*, Vol. 8, p. 1056 (1929).

‖ The thermal conductivity of bismuth is considerably lower than that of most metals.

¶ Lees, *Phil. Trans.*, Vol. 191, p. 399 (1898).

disadvantage, but in Lees' apparatus only one measurement of the heat flow is made. The method is illustrated in fig. 11.10.

The heating coil was contained between two copper discs C (about 1 mm. thick) and U (about 3 mm. thick). S was the substance to be measured and M another copper disc about 3 mm. thick. The thermal contact of S with U and M was improved by smearing them with glycerine. The temperatures of all the copper blocks were measured by thermocouples. After assembling the apparatus it was varnished all over so that it should have the same emissivity (see Chapter XX), and was placed in a constant-temperature enclosure.

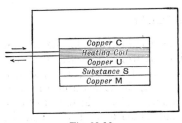

Fig. 11.10

The theory of the method is as follows.

Let H = the rate at which energy is supplied to the heating coil, after a steady state has been reached.

h = heat loss per second per square centimetre for one degree excess of temperature of the apparatus over that of the enclosure.

t = excess of temperature over that of enclosure.

x = thickness of disc.

r = radius of discs.

The heat received per second and given up to the air by the disc M is

$$\pi r^2 h \left(1 + \frac{2x_M}{r} \right) t_M.$$

The heat received per second by S and given up to the air from its exposed surface or passed on to M is

$$\pi r^2 h \left(1 + \frac{2x_M}{r} \right) t_M + \pi r^2 h \frac{2x_S}{r} \left(\frac{t_M + t_U}{2} \right).$$

If K is the thermal conductivity of the disc S, the heat flowing through it is

$$\pi r^2 K \left(\frac{t_U - t_M}{x_S} \right).$$

We may assume that the heat flowing through the disc is the mean of the heat flowing into it and the heat flowing out of it, that is, the heat flowing through S is the mean of the first two quantities above; we have, therefore,

$$K \left(\frac{t_U - t_M}{x_S} \right) = h \left[t_M + \frac{2}{r} \left\{ \left(x_M + \frac{x_S}{4} \right) t_M + \frac{x_S}{4} t_U \right\} \right].$$

This gives K in terms of h and the temperatures and thicknesses of the plates. We can obtain h in terms of H, the heat supplied to the heating coil, from the consideration that the total heat supplied to the apparatus must be equal to that given up from the various surfaces. We have, therefore,

$$H = \pi r^2 h \left\{ t_U + t_M + \frac{2}{r} \left(x_M t_M + x_S \frac{t_M + t_U}{2} + x_U t_U + x_C t_C \right) \right\}.$$

Thus K is expressed in terms of quantities which can be measured.

22. Thermal Conductivity of Crystals at Low Temperatures.

Eucken * has used a modification of Lees' method to determine the conductivities of certain simple crystals, such as rock salt, at low temperatures. His results are of considerable importance. The apparatus used is illustrated in fig. 11.11.

a was the source of heat, consisting of two copper plates with an insulated heating coil between them. The plates were soldered together, and one of them had a rim round it so that the heating coil was completely surrounded by copper. The surfaces of *a*, which were 3 cm. square, were made flat and polished. *a* rested on a block of pine *e*, which in turn rested on a copper plate *d*. *b* was the substance to be investigated. Its surfaces were made flat and on it rested a copper plate *c*, which also had flat surfaces. The plates *c* and *d* were held together by two screws not shown in the figure.

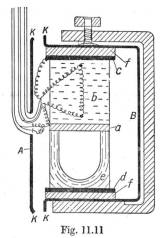

Fig. 11.11

Copper blocks *f* were soldered to the copper vessel B, which contained the apparatus, and the plates *c* and *d* fitted closely between these blocks so that they were as nearly as possible at the same temperature as *f*. The copper lid A was soldered to B at K.

The temperatures of the plates *a* and *c* were measured by thermocouples. The two junctions of another thermocouple were inserted as shown into two small holes bored in the substance to be investigated, so as to give the temperature gradient in the actual substance.

When working at low temperatures it is not possible to use a liquid to improve the contacts between the surfaces. Eucken therefore used a gas. It will be seen that the correction for the temperature drop in the contacts, and the correction for loss of heat by conduction from the sides of the specimen, both depend on the conductivity of the gas filling the apparatus. By using air, hydrogen, and carbon dioxide to fill the apparatus he was able to determine these corrections. The conductivities of these gases at the various temperatures used were determined by separate experiments using the heated-wire method.

Correction was also made for the heat conducted through the pine block supporting *a*, and for losses by radiation from the surface of the specimen.

The results of the experiments show that *the thermal conductivity of such bodies is inversely proportional to the absolute temperature.* This is shown by the following table given by Eucken, which gives the reciprocal of the thermal conductivities of various substances at various temperatures, and which indicates the relationship very clearly.

* Eucken, *Ann. d. Physik*, Vol. 34, p. 185 (1911); see also Eucken and Kuhn, *Zeits. f. phys. Chem.*, Vol. 134, p. 193 (1928). For ice, see Arzybyschew and Parfianowitsch, *Zeits. f. Physik*, Vol. 56, p. 441 (1929). See also de Haas and Biermasz, *Leiden Comm.*, No. 251*b* (1938); *Physica*, Vol. 5, p. 320 (1938).

Table IV

T	T/273	Reciprocal of thermal conductivity ($1/K$)				
		NaCl	KCl	SiO_2 *	SiO_2 †	$CaCO_3$ ‡
373	1·365	60 . 1·44	60 . 1·41	30·7 . 1·51	57·8 . 1·30	97·5 . 1·21
273	1·000	1·00	1·00	1·00	1·00	1·00
195	0·714	0·67	0·67	0·69	0·72	0·75
83	0·304	0·26	0·33	0·28	0·30	0·27

* Quartz parallel to the axis.   † Quartz perpendicular to the axis.   ‡ Calcspar perpendicular to the axis.

Theoretical

23. Debye * has worked out the kinetic theory of the transfer of heat in such bodies from the point of view of the propagation of elastic waves in a continuous medium. He showed that if the vibrations of the medium are truly harmonic the various wave trains move independently, so that any arbitrary distribution of energy among them is permanent and there is no mechanism by which a condition of thermal equilibrium can be set up.

He therefore included in the equation of motion non-linear terms in the displacement and attempted to show that these permitted interchange of energy between the different wave trains and establishment of thermal equilibrium. The whole set of waves gives rise to local variations of density, the laws of which were worked out by Smoluchowski.† Debye regarded any given train of waves as being scattered at a stationary system of density variations due to all the trains and worked out the loss of energy of a given train in a given distance. By this method he accounted for Eucken's result concerning the relation between conductivity and absolute temperature.

When, however, account is taken of the fact that the points at which the scattering takes place are moving with the same order of velocity as the waves themselves, it has been shown that Debye's result no longer holds.

Pauli ‡ showed that it is necessary to take into account the atomic nature of the solid lattice, as opposed to the continuum treated by Debye, and Peierls § has worked out the theory for a three-dimensional lattice and obtained satisfactory agreement with the experimental results.

According to the theory of Peierls the thermal conductivity of a crystal lattice will increase with decreasing temperature. For a crystal of finite size a temperature will ultimately be reached at which the free path of the elastic waves becomes comparable with the dimensions of the crystals and effects due to scattering of the

* Debye, *Wolfskehl-Vorträge zu Göttingen* (Leipzig, 1914).

† Smoluchowski, *Boltzmann-Festschrift*, p. 626 (1904); *Ann. d. Physik*, Vol. 25, p. 205 (1908). See also Einstein, *Ann. d. Physik*, Vol. 33, p. 1275 (1910), and Report of Solvay Conference (1911); Yositosi Endo, *Sci. Rep. of Univ. of Tohoku, I,* Ser. 11, p. 181 (1922).

‡ Pauli, *Verh. d. deuts. phys. Ges.*, Vol. 6, p. 10 (1925).

§ Peierls, *Ann. d. Physik*, Vol. 3, p. 1055 (1929).

waves at the boundaries will increase the resistance to the flow of heat. Casimir *
has pointed out the importance of this effect in connexion with some measurements by de Haas and Biermasz † of the effect of the size of the specimen used
on the apparent specific resistance for heat flow. He has discussed the theory of
the propagation of the elastic waves assuming that they are diffusely scattered
at the side of a cylindrical crystal, and has shown that, if the only resistance is
due to this scattering, the apparent specific conductivity K of a crystal of radius r
is given by $K = BrT^3$, where B is a constant which can be evaluated in terms
of the elastic constants of the material. At a given temperature the specific resistance to heat flow will, according to this law, be inversely proportional to r.

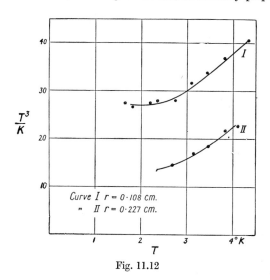

Fig. 11.12

Thus the flow under a given temperature gradient will be proportional to r^3,
which is, as it should be, the same law as for the flow of a gas when the only
resistance is due to diffuse scattering of the molecules at the walls of the tube
(see Chapter III, Section 19). It will be seen from the above equation that for the
temperature region in which the theory is applicable, T^3/K should be constant.
In fig. 11.12 the experimental values of T^3/K obtained by de Haas and Biermasz
are plotted against T for two specimens of silica. At the lowest temperatures
T^3/K appears to approach a constant value. In the constant region near 2° K.
the value of T^3/K is inversely proportional to r, as theory indicates. Casimir has
also shown in the case of a potassium chloride crystal that the absolute value of
B is of the order predicted by the theory. Imperfection of the crystals affects the
results and some evidence of this was found.

* Casimir, *Physica*, Vol. 5, p. 495 (1938).
† De Haas and Biermasz, *Physica*, Vol. 5, pp. 320, 619 (1938).

B. CONVECTION

24. Transfer of heat in a fluid is said to take place by convection when the fluid itself moves. We shall consider the heat loss from a solid body immersed in the fluid. There are two distinct cases: (1) When the motion of the fluid is due solely to the presence of the hot body in it. The fluid near the hot body is heated; its density is thus changed, and it moves under the influence of gravity. This is called *natural convection*. (2) When the relative motion of the fluid and the hot body is maintained by some external agency. This is called *forced convection*.

Convection, either natural or forced, can best be treated by dimensional methods.* In dealing with thermal problems by dimensional methods it is necessary to introduce another primary quantity in addition to the length, mass, and time. Temperature is the most convenient quantity to choose; we shall denote the dimensions of temperature by θ. Quantity of heat has the dimensions of energy, that is, ML^2T^{-2}.

Natural Convection

25. We consider h, the heat loss per unit area per unit time from geometrically similar bodies placed in a fluid. Since we consider only geometrically similar bodies, the size of any one is completely determined by its linear dimension in any one direction. h depends on the following quantities, the dimensions of which are given (the student should prove for himself that the dimensions are those given, and should carry out the details of all the calculations sketched below):

	Symbol	Dimensions
1. The temperature excess of the body	θ	θ
2. Thermal conductivity of fluid	K	$MLT^{-3}\theta^{-1}$
3. Thermal capacity per *unit volume* of fluid ..	c	$ML^{-1}T^{-2}\theta^{-1}$
4. Temperature coefficient of density change of fluid	a	θ^{-1}
5. Acceleration of gravity	g	LT^{-2}
6. Linear dimensions of body	l	L
7. Kinematical viscosity	ν	L^2T^{-1}

1, 2, and 6 must obviously be included. We may make the following comments on the other quantities.

---

* These methods were first applied to the problem of forced convection by Rayleigh (*Nature*, Vol. 95, p. 66 (1915)). The method has been extended to the case of natural convection by Davis (*Phil. Mag.*, Vol. 40, p. 692 (1920)). In later papers Davis has collected a large number of experimental results and has added experimental results of his own. These papers, which should be consulted for full details, are as follows: *Phil. Mag.*, Vol. 41, p. 899 (1921); Vol. 43, p. 329 (1922); Vol. 44, p. 926 (1922); Vol. 47, pp. 972, 1057 (1924). The subject is treated from the point of view of hydrodynamics in Vol. 44, pp. 920, 940 (1922), and in a correcting note, Vol. 49, p. 285 (1925).

3. Note that we use the thermal capacity per *unit volume*. In this case the density ρ of the fluid is not involved and is omitted from the above table; the reason is that, since we use the thermal capacity of unit volume, we are concerned with the volume of the fluid which moves past the solid, and not with its mass.

4 and 5. We shall assume that g and a occur only in the form of a product ga. This is equivalent to assuming that the only effect of density change is on the weight. In other words, we neglect in the dimensional treatment the effect of change of density on the other properties such as the viscosity; we take such changes into account in applying the final result obtained by the dimensional treatment to practical problems by using numerical values for quantities, such as the viscosity, which apply to a temperature which is the mean of that of the body and that of the mass of the fluid. The term ga is of the correct form to give the effect of change of weight, as the following considerations show. The force acting on a volume V whose density is $\rho + \Delta\rho$ immersed in a fluid of density ρ is $g\Delta\rho V$. The term $\Delta\rho$ depends on $d\rho/d\theta$; but the acceleration produced by this force is *inversely* proportional to the mass of fluid, and this mass is proportional to ρ. It is the acceleration which determines the velocity of the fluid, and the velocity determines the *volume* flowing. The occurrence of ρ in the denominator of the expression ga or $(g/\rho)d\rho/d\theta$ is therefore correct.

7. The kinematical viscosity ν is defined as η/ρ, where η is the ordinary coefficient of viscosity. η determines the force retarding the motion of the fluid, and therefore η/ρ or ν determines the retardation produced by the viscous forces. It is the retardation which affects the volume flowing.

Following the ordinary method of treating dimensional problems, we shall suppose that h is given by the relation

$$h = \theta^x K^y c^z (ga)^t l^u \nu^w.$$

Using the dimensions given in the above table, we obtain for the dimensions of h

$$M^{y+z} L^{y-z+t+u+2w} T^{-3y-2z-2t-w} \theta^{x-y-z-t}.$$

Actually h has the dimensions $\quad M T^{-3}$.

We have therefore
$$y + z = 1,$$
$$y - z + t + u + 2w = 0,$$
$$-3y - 2z - 2t - w = -3,$$
$$x - y - z - t = 0.$$

From these equations we may determine the values of any four of the quantities x, y, z, t, u, w in terms of the other two. We obtain

$$x = 1 + t,$$
$$y = 1 - 2t - w,$$
$$z = 2t + w,$$
$$u = 3t - 1.$$

Substituting these values in the expression for h, we obtain

$$h = \left(\frac{\theta K}{l}\right) \left(\frac{\theta ga^2 l c^3}{K^2}\right)^t \left(\frac{c\nu}{K}\right)^w,$$

or
$$\frac{hl}{\theta K} = \left(\frac{\theta ga c^2 l^3}{K^2}\right)^t \left(\frac{c\nu}{K}\right)^w.$$

Since the terms $(\theta g a c^2 l^3 / K^2)$ and $(c\nu/K)$ both have zero dimensions, we may have any number of terms or products of terms involving these quantities. We must therefore write the last equation in the form

$$\frac{hl}{\theta K} = F\left(\frac{\theta g a c^2 l^3}{K^2}\right) \cdot f\left(\frac{c\nu}{K}\right), \quad \ldots \ldots \quad (32)$$

where F and f are functions left undetermined by dimensional considerations.

We shall apply this equation to cylinders of which the length is great compared with the diameter. In this case h, the heat loss per unit area per second, does not depend on the length but only on the diameter d; we may therefore substitute d for l in equation (32). Further, if H is the *heat loss per unit length per second per degree temperature excess*, we have

$$H = \frac{\pi h d}{\theta}.$$

Thus for this case equation (32) becomes

$$\frac{H}{K} = F\left(\frac{\theta g a c^2 d^3}{K^2}\right) \cdot f\left(\frac{c\nu}{K}\right). \quad \ldots \ldots \quad (33)$$

26. Practical Applications of the Formula.

We shall now consider the use of this formula to express the results of experiments. It is convenient to consider two sets of results: (a) those of experiments on the cooling of cylinders in air and other diatomic gases only, (b) those of the whole of the experiments that have been carried out on both gases and liquids.

(a) *Diatomic Gases.*—For all diatomic gases the quantity $c\nu/K$ has very nearly the same value. For we have $c = \rho c_p$, and $\nu = \eta/\rho$, therefore

$$\frac{c\nu}{K} = \frac{\gamma c_v \eta}{K},$$

where γ is the ratio of the specific heats; γ has nearly the same value for all diatomic gases, and so has $c_v \eta / K$ (see equation (16) and Section 9, Table I). For all diatomic gases, then, the second function on the right of equation (33) is constant. Further, in the first function we may write $1/\nu^2$ for c^2/K^2. Also g is a constant, and for a constant temperature of the surroundings a is a constant for all gases. (The student should prove this last statement for himself, bearing in mind the meaning of a as outlined above.)

In this particular case, therefore, equation (33) becomes

$$\frac{H}{K} = F_1\left(\frac{\theta d^3}{\nu^2}\right). \quad \ldots \ldots \ldots \quad (34)$$

If then the experimental data on the natural convective cooling of long cylinders are plotted with values of H/K as ordinates and corresponding values of $\theta d^3/\nu^2$ as abscissæ, all the results should lie on a single curve. The values of K and ν which are to be used are those corresponding to the mean temperature of the wire and its surroundings. This is done in fig. 11.13, in which the logarithms are to the base 10, the calorie is the unit of heat, and the other units are c.g.s. The agreement between the results for steam pipes and for fine wires is very remarkable.

The following example illustrates the practical use that can be made of the results of convection experiments as given in fig. 11.13.

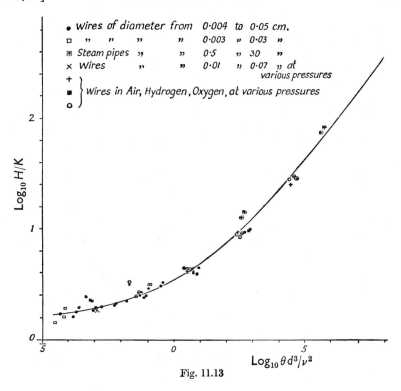

Fig. 11.13

EXAMPLE

Calculate from fig. 11.13 the heat loss per centimetre length of a steam pipe 5 cm. in diameter which is at a temperature of 115° C. and is in a room at a temperature of 15° C. Values of K and ν for air at various temperatures are given in the following table, from which the required values can be obtained by interpolation. (Answer, approx. 0·4 cals. per second.)

Temperature (°C.)	K	ν
0	$0\cdot55 \cdot 10^{-4}$	0·13
100	0·72	0·23
200	0·86	0·35
300	1·01	0·48
400	1·14	0·62

(b) *General.*—Davis has measured the heat loss from wires of diameters 0·0083 and 0·0155 cm. in toluene, carbon tetrachloride, aniline, olive oil, glycerine and air. For toluene $c\nu/K = 7\cdot24$ and for glycerine $c\nu/K = 7940$, so that liquids of a wide range of properties are included in the selection.

Referring to equation (33), Davis has pointed out that it is probable that g and ν always occur together in the form g/ν, since the steady velocity of the viscous streams is determined by a balance between the accelerating forces due to gravity and the retardation due to viscous forces. In this case equation (33) assumes the form

$$\frac{H}{K} = F_2\left(\frac{\theta g a c d^3}{K \nu}\right). \quad \cdots \cdots \cdots \quad (35)$$

That this is consistent with the experimental results is shown by fig. 11.14. The upper part of the curve is the representation on the present basis of the upper part of the curve for gases plotted in fig. 11.13. The various points fit on the present curve

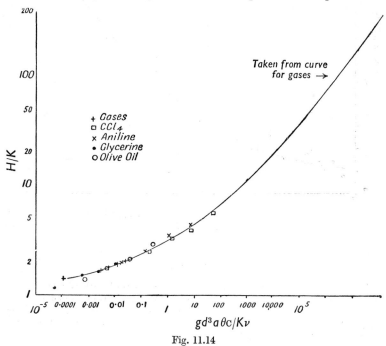

Fig. 11.14

just as well as they do on the curve in fig. 11.13, because for the particular case of diatomic gases the two equations (34) and (35) are the same. It will be realized that it is very remarkable that the results for the cooling of a wire in olive oil and the cooling of a large pipe in air should all fall on one continuous curve. This result is one of the most beautiful examples of the applicability of the principle of similitude to physical problems.

Forced Convection

27. In dealing with forced convection we assume that the gravity currents are negligible compared with the relative velocity of the immersed body and the fluid which is maintained by some external agent. In this case the variables on which the heat loss per unit area depends are:

	Symbol	Dimensions
1. The temperature excess of the body	θ	θ
2. Thermal conductivity of fluid	K	$MLT^{-3}\theta^{-1}$
3. Thermal capacity per *unit volume* of fluid ..	c	$ML^{-1}T^{-2}\theta^{-1}$
4. Relative velocity of fluid and immersed body	v	LT^{-1}
5. Linear dimensions of body	l	L
6. Kinematical viscosity	ν	L^2T^{-1}

As in Section 26, it may be shown that, if the heat loss h per unit area in 1 sec. is given by

$$h = \theta^x K^y c^z v^t l^u \nu^w,$$

then

$$x = 1,$$
$$y = 1 - t - w,$$
$$z = t + w,$$
$$u = t - 1.$$

We have therefore

$$h = \frac{\theta K}{l} F\left(\frac{cvl}{K}\right) \cdot f\left(\frac{cv}{K}\right), \quad \ldots \ldots \quad (36)$$

where F and f are functions left undetermined by dimensional considerations.

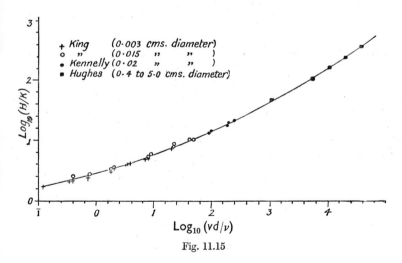

Fig. 11.15

As before, if H is the *heat loss per unit length per second per degree temperature excess* from a long cylinder of diameter d, we have

$$\frac{H}{K} = F\left(\frac{cvd}{K}\right) \cdot f\left(\frac{cv}{K}\right). \quad \ldots \quad \ldots \quad \ldots \quad (37)$$

Diatomic Gases.—The most important application of this formula is to diatomic gases. For these cv/K = constant, so that the last equation becomes

$$\frac{H}{K} = F\left(\frac{vd}{v}\right). \qquad \cdots \cdots \cdots \quad (38)$$

The experimental results in which $\log_{10} H/K$ is plotted against $\log_{10}(vd/v)$ are shown in fig. 11.15. The results fit closely to equation (38).

The above account illustrates the methods used in dealing with convection problems. For further details and other applications, reference should be made to the papers of Davis cited above. See also *Report on Heat Transmission by Convection and Radiation*, published by the Food Investigation Board (1921); G. I. Taylor, *Report Adv. Committee Aeronautics*, Vol. 9, p. 423 (1916–17); Stanton, *Rep. Adv. Comm. Aeron.*, p. 16 (1916–17); Gröber, *Zeits. d. Vereines deutsch. Ing.*, Vol. 70, p. 1125 (1926); Schmekel, *Zeits. f. techn. Physik*, Vol. 9, p. 49 (1928); Schiller and Burbach, *Phys. Zeits.*, Vol. 29, p. 340 (1928); Prandtl, *Phys. Zeits.*, Vol. 29, p. 487 (1928); Schiller, *Zeits. f. techn. Physik*, Vol. 9, p. 490 (1928); and for a general account, *Handbuch der Experimentalphysik*, Vol. 9, Part 1, p. 268.

28. The Propagation of Heat in a Conducting Medium.

We now show that the general equation for the propagation of heat in a conducting medium is

$$K\left(\frac{\partial^2 T}{\partial x^2} + \frac{\partial^2 T}{\partial y^2} + \frac{\partial^2 T}{\partial z^2}\right) = c\,\frac{\partial T}{\partial t}, \qquad \cdots \cdots \quad (39)$$

where K is the thermal conductivity, c is the specific heat per unit volume, x, y, z are rectangular co-ordinates, and t is the time.

Consider a small rectangular prism whose sides are parallel to the axes of co-ordinates and are of length δx, δy, δz. Let the centre of the prism be at the point x, y, z (all positive) where the temperature is T, and the component temperature gradients are $\partial T/\partial x$, $\partial T/\partial y$, $\partial T/\partial z$. Consider the flow of heat across the ends parallel to the y, z plane. The area of each end is $\delta y\,\delta z$. The temperature gradient at the end with the smaller x co-ordinate is $\left(\dfrac{\partial T}{\partial x} - \dfrac{\delta x}{2}\dfrac{\partial^2 T}{\partial x^2}\right)$, and the heat flowing out of the prism across this plane in a time dt is by equation (1)

$$K\,\delta y\,\delta z\left(\frac{\partial T}{\partial x} - \frac{\delta x}{2}\frac{\partial^2 T}{\partial x^2}\right)dt.$$

Similarly, the heat flowing into the prism across the plane with the larger x co-ordinate in time dt is

$$K\,\delta y\,\delta z\left(\frac{\partial T}{\partial x} + \frac{\delta x}{2}\frac{\partial^2 T}{\partial x^2}\right)dt.$$

The net gain of heat across these two faces in time dt is therefore

$$K \, \delta x \, \delta y \, \delta z \, \frac{\partial^2 T}{\partial x^2} \, dt.$$

Similar relations apply to the other two pairs of faces, so that the total gain of heat by the prism in time dt is

$$K \, \delta x \, \delta y \, \delta z \left(\frac{\partial^2 T}{\partial x^2} + \frac{\partial^2 T}{\partial y^2} + \frac{\partial^2 T}{\partial z^2} \right) dt.$$

Since this gain of heat is also given by

$$c \, \delta x \, \delta y \, \delta z \, \frac{\partial T}{\partial t} \, dt,$$

the required result follows immediately.

The solution of equation (39) often has to be carried out by numerical integration. This has been discussed by Hartree and his colleagues * and a practical method for the numerical evaluation of the solutions of the partial differential equation of heat conduction has been given by Crank and Nicolson.†

When the cross-section of the specimen varies with the distance x along its axis, and the temperature is uniform over any cross-section perpendicular to the axis, the equation of heat propagation reduces to

$$\frac{\partial^2 T}{\partial x^2} + X \frac{\partial T}{\partial x} = \frac{c}{K} \frac{\partial T}{\partial t}, \quad \ldots \ldots \quad (40)$$

where X is a function of x only. The deduction of this equation is left as an exercise to the student.

---

* Eyres, Hartree, Ingham, Jackson, Sarjant and Wagstaff, *Phil. Trans. Roy. Soc.,* A, Vol. 240, p. 1 (1946).

† Crank and Nicolson, *Proc. Cambridge Phil. Soc.,* Vol. 43, p. 50 (1947).

CHAPTER XII

The Second Law of Thermodynamics

1. We have already seen that the study of the conversion of work into heat has led to a result of fundamental importance and of wide application, namely, the first law of thermodynamics or the law of the conservation of energy. The study of the converse problem, the conversion of heat into work, leads to results of equal importance. This problem can be examined by considering the properties of heat engines.

We shall consider the ordinary piston and cylinder type of heat engine. Such an engine functions on account of the changes in the temperature, pressure, volume, or other parameters which specify the state of the substance contained in the cylinder. This substance is called the *working substance*.

For the sake of definiteness we shall suppose that the working substance is a gas because we are familiar with the fact that the volume of a gas can be made to undergo considerable changes easily. The general reasoning applies equally well whatever the working substance may be—liquid, vapour, mixture of liquid and vapour, solid.

2. Reversible Processes.

Suppose that we have a gas in a non-conducting cylinder with a movable piston. When the system is in equilibrium, the pressure exerted by the gas on the piston must be exactly balanced by the pressure of the piston on the gas. If now we wish to change the volume of the gas, we must have a difference between the pressure p exerted by the gas on the piston and the pressure p' exerted by the piston on the gas; if expansion is to take place, the former must be the greater. If the work done by the gas on its surroundings in this case is to be measured by the product of its pressure into its change of volume, it will be seen that p and p' must differ only by an infinitesimal amount. In this case the expansion will take place infinitely slowly and no kinetic energy will be developed either in the piston or in the form of eddies in the gas. Throughout the process the gas is in equilibrium with its surroundings. Such a change may be called a mechanically reversible change. It is obvious that the piston must be free from friction. The reason why such a change is called reversible is that, if the

316

process is carried out in the reverse direction, the whole system goes through exactly the same series of changes in the reverse direction; for example, the pressure corresponding to a given volume is always the same. From the way in which the process is carried out, namely, infinitely slowly, such changes are often referred to as quasi-static.

Similar considerations apply to the flow of heat into and out of the gas. For example, in a reversible isothermal change, as the gas expands, heat flows into it from the surroundings to maintain its temperature constant. For the process to be reversible requires that, in addition to the above mechanical conditions, the temperature of the body must differ from the surroundings by only an infinitesimal amount. Exactly the same amount of heat will then be received during a given stage in the expansion as will be given up during the corresponding stage of the compression, and the work done in compression will equal that gained in the corresponding expansion.

It should be noted that friction and eddy formation introduce irreversible thermal effects as well as irreversible mechanical effects. Their result is that mechanical energy is converted into heat, and in the reverse process not only does reconversion of this heat into mechanical energy not take place, but more mechanical energy is converted into heat by the friction or eddies. Thus irreversibility can arise both from the passage of heat across the boundary separating the system from the external world, and also from within the system itself.

3. The Carnot Cycle.

The way in which a heat engine works is illustrated by the following example. We suppose that the gas is contained in a cylinder with a moving piston, and that it is taken through what is called a *Carnot cycle*. We shall suppose that all the processes are carried out reversibly. Let us suppose further that the sides of the cylinder and the piston are perfectly non-conducting, and that the base of the cylinder is made of perfectly conducting material. In order that we may be able to isolate the gas completely from its surroundings, we shall suppose that we have a perfectly non-conducting cap which fits on the base.

We shall require a source of heat which we shall suppose maintained at temperature T_1, and a receiver of heat or a refrigerator maintained at a constant temperature T_2.

We shall represent the changes that take place in the gas on a diagram, in which pressures are plotted as ordinates and volumes as abscissæ (see fig. 12.1). Such a diagram is called an indicator diagram.

We shall suppose that the mass of gas in the cylinder is fixed, and that we start with it in the condition represented by the point A on the diagram, its temperature being T_1 and its volume V_1.

(i) The insulating cap is placed on the cylinder and the gas is allowed to expand by an adiabatic quasi-static process. Since no heat is supplied to it, its temperature falls. We continue the process until it reaches the value T_2, the temperature of the refrigerator. Its condition is now represented by the point B, and its volume is V_2.

(ii) We now place the body in contact with the refrigerator, and compress the gas. It follows the isotherm BC, corresponding to the temperature T_2, and gives up heat to the refrigerator. The volume is now V_3.

(iii) We now place the cap on the cylinder, and compress the gas. It follows the adiabatic line CD, and we stop when the point D, at which the temperature is T_1, is reached.

(iv) The cylinder is placed in contact with the source of heat and the gas is allowed to expand. It follows the isotherm DA corresponding to the temperature T_1. In doing so it absorbs heat from the source. The process is stopped at the point A.

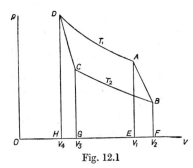

Fig. 12.1

We shall consider the work done by the gas on its surroundings, and by the surroundings on the gas, in carrying out the process. During the isothermal expansion DA the gas does work on the surroundings represented by the area DAEH; and during the adiabatic expansion AB it does work on the surroundings represented by the area ABFE. On the other hand, during the isothermal compression BC the surroundings do work on the gas represented by the area BCGF; and during the adiabatic compression CD the surroundings do work on the gas represented by the area CDHG. It will be seen that the net result is that the gas does external work, represented by the area ABCD, on the surroundings. Now at the end of the process the gas has returned to exactly its original state—this is what is meant by a cyclic process. Therefore this work cannot have been done at the expense of its internal energy. From the first law of thermodynamics we deduce that Q_1, the heat absorbed from the source during the expansion AB, must be greater than Q_2, the heat given up to the refrigerator during the process CD, and that the difference must be equal to the heat equivalent of the external work done.

It will be seen that the arrangement which we have described is a heat engine, because it can be used to convert heat into useful external work.

It is very important to notice that not all of the heat received from the source is converted into work, but that some of it is given up to the refrigerator. This is typical of all heat engines, and we call *the ratio of the amount of heat converted into useful external work to the amount of heat absorbed from the source of heat* the *efficiency* of the heat engine. The efficiency of an engine working in a Carnot cycle is

$$\frac{Q_1 - Q_2}{Q_1}$$

4. The Second Law of Thermodynamics.

The study of the efficiency of heat engines is all based on the second law of thermodynamics. The truth of this law is established by the correctness of the many deductions made from it which are capable of direct test. Amongst these are deductions from the Clausius-Clapeyron equation about the effect of pressure on boiling-point and freezing-point (Chapter XVI, Section 8); the consistency of the values of equilibrium constants determined by various methods (Chapter XVIII, Section 16); the agreement between the observed degree of dissociation of, for example, water vapour, and that calculated from equilibrium constants (Chapter XVIII, Section 18); the agreement between the observed and calculated values of the electromotive forces of cells (Chapter XVIII, Section 23); the agreement between the observed and calculated properties of steam (Appendix 3). No exception to it has ever been discovered and it and the first law of thermodynamics are regarded as the most fundamental principles of physics which have so far been discovered.

The principle on which it was based follows from a study of heat engines and has been stated in various ways. Clausius stated it in the form:

It is not possible for a self-acting machine working in a cyclical process, unaided by any external agency, to make heat pass from one body to another at a higher temperature.

That is to say, heat will not pass spontaneously from a cold body to a warmer one. In order to make it do so it is necessary to do external work of some sort, as in a refrigerating machine; this produces changes of some sort in another system.

Kelvin stated it in the form: *It is impossible, by means of inanimate material agency, to derive mechanical effect from any portion of matter by cooling it below the temperature of the coolest body of its surroundings.*

Planck stated it in the form: *It is impossible to construct an engine which will work in a complete cycle and produce no effect except the raising of a weight and the cooling of a heat reservoir.*

Considerable ingenuity has been displayed * to use the apparatus of formal logic to show that the statements of the principle by Clausius and by Planck are equivalent. The most thorough examination of the

---

* See, for example, C. N. Hamtil, *Amer. Journ. Physics*, Vol. 22, p. 93 (1954).

logical relationships between the three statements has been given by Ehrenfest-Afanassjewa * and the student who is interested in this particular by-way should refer to this paper.

The important point is that each of these statements can be used to show that there exist an absolute temperature (T) and a function of state called the entropy (S) and that these are related to the quantity of heat (dQ) supplied to the system by the relation

$$dQ \leqslant T \, dS.$$

In this relation the inequality applies to an irreversible (natural) change and the equality to a reversible (quasi-static) change. This is the content of the second law of thermodynamics. In the following sections we shall show how the Clausius statement can be used to derive this relation following the method of Carnot, Clausius, and Kelvin. In Section 12 we shall consider a more mathematical analysis of this question and shall see that in it the reciprocal of T appears as an integrating factor of the Pfaffian differential expression for dQ, leading to the complete differential dS.

5. The Efficiency of a Reversible Heat Engine.

The problem to be solved in connexion with the efficiency is: How are we to get the maximum external work from a given amount of heat? The answer to this question was first given by Carnot in 1824, in his *Réflexions sur la puissance motrice du feu et sur les machines propres à développer cette puissance*. Carnot showed that the maximum amount of work is to be obtained by an engine working in a strictly reversible manner in all its operations, all heat being taken in at the highest temperature, and any heat that is rejected being rejected at the lowest temperature. Carnot's engine is, of course, an ideal one. We have already described the series of reversible operations, namely: (i) Adiabatic expansion, during which the temperature of the working substance falls from T_1, the temperature of the source, to T_2, the temperature of the refrigerator; (ii) Isothermal compression, during which heat is given up reversibly to the refrigerator at temperature T_2; (iii) Adiabatic compression, by which the working substance is brought back to the temperature of the source; (iv) Isothermal expansion, during which heat is taken in reversibly from the source at temperature T_1 till it reaches its original volume.

More work is done by the working substance on its surroundings during processes (i) and (iv) than is done by the surroundings on the working substance during the other two operations. There is thus a net gain of work, which is obtained at the expense of heat taken from the source. Every operation involved is entirely reversible, and there-

---

* T. Ehrenfest-Afanassjewa, *Zeits. f. Physik*, Vol. 33, p. 933 (1925).

fore, if the working substance goes through the same series of operations in the reverse direction, the same amount of heat will be taken from the refrigerator as was given up to it in the direct cycle, and the same amount of heat will be given to the source as was taken from it in the former case. Also, on the whole, external work will be done on the working substance equal to the external work gained in the direct cycle. The net result of the process is that the hot body receives both heat transferred from the cold body and the heat equivalent of the work done. The engine working in the reverse direction is therefore a *refrigerating machine.*

We shall now use the principle stated by Clausius to prove what Carnot showed, that is, that *no engine can be more efficient than a perfectly reversible engine working between the same temperatures.*

Let us suppose that we have a heat engine A which is more efficient than a reversible engine B when working between the same temperatures. If the two engines do the same amount of external work W, this means that the quantity of heat Q' which A takes from the source is less than the quantity of heat Q which B takes from it. Now, since B is reversible, it will, if driven in the opposite direction, so that it absorbs external work W, give up a quantity of heat Q to the source of heat.

Let us then couple the two engines together so that A drives B backwards, and let them use the same source and refrigerator. Let A supply external work W, and let B absorb this amount of external work. The net result will be that the source gains heat Q from B, while A abstracts heat Q' from it. Since Q' is less than Q, the source on the whole gains heat; and, since no external work is performed on the system, this heat can only come from the cold body. In other words, the coupled engines form a self-acting machine, which can, unaided by any external agency, make heat pass continuously from a cold body to a warmer one. This contradicts Clausius' principle and is impossible, and the conclusion is that no engine can be more efficient than a perfectly reversible engine working between the same temperatures.

A direct corollary of this result is that all perfectly reversible engines working between the same temperatures are equally efficient. Among other things, therefore, *the efficiency of a perfectly reversible engine is independent of the working substance employed, and depends only on the temperatures of the source and the refrigerator.*

6. The Thermodynamic Scale of Temperature.

We have seen in Chapter I that any property which varies with the temperature can be used to define a temperature scale. Since the efficiency of a perfectly reversible engine depends only on the temperatures of the source and the refrigerator, we can define a temperature scale in terms of the efficiency of perfectly reversible engines. Such a scale will have the advantage over all others that it will be independent of the properties of any particular body, and will in fact be based on the fundamental principles of thermodynamics only.

When the working substance in a perfectly reversible engine goes through a Carnot cycle, the ratio of the quantity of heat Q_1, taken from the source of heat, to Q_2, that given up to the refrigerator, depends only on the temperatures of the source and the refrigerator. Let us then define a thermodynamic scale of temperature such that on this scale the temperatures T_1 and T_2 of these two bodies are proportional to the quantities of heat transferred to and from them in the Carnot cycle; that is, we define

$$\frac{T_1}{T_2} = \frac{Q_1}{Q_2}.$$

To fix the size of the degree on the thermodynamical scale of temperature, a numerical value is assigned * to the triple point of water. Let this value be T_{tr}; actually T_{tr} has been given the numerical value 273·16° K. Let the temperature of the source be the triple point of water and let the quantity of heat absorbed from it in the Carnot cycle be Q_{tr}. If the quantity of heat given up to the refrigerator is Q, then the temperature of the refrigerator on the thermodynamical scale, $T°$ K, is

$$T = \frac{Q}{Q_{tr}} T_{tr}. \quad \ldots \ldots \ldots \quad (2)$$

Alternatively, the temperature of the refrigerator could be the triple point of water. Then Q_{tr} would be the quantity of heat given up to it, and the temperature of the source, from which a quantity of heat Q is absorbed, would be given by equation (2).

The efficiency of a reversible engine working between the absolute temperatures T_1 and T_2 is

$$\frac{T_1 - T_2}{T_1}.$$

7. Comparison of Thermodynamic and Gas Scales of Temperature.

We now have to compare the thermodynamic scale of temperature with the gas scale that we have used previously. To do this we shall suppose that the working substance in a Carnot engine is a gas in the ideal condition of vanishingly small density. From the experimentally determined properties of this perfect gas we shall calculate the heat

---

* International Union of Pure and Applied Physics, document S.G. 48-6 (1948); see also references in Chapter I, Section 4.

exchanged with the source and the refrigerator. These properties are as follows:

(i) A perfect gas obeys Boyle's law; that is, we have

$$pV = A,$$

where A is constant at constant temperature.

(ii) The internal energy of a perfect gas at a fixed temperature is independent of its volume, that is, it obeys Joule's law (see Chapter III, Section 1).

(iii) The specific heat at constant volume of a perfect gas at a given temperature is independent of its volume. This follows from (ii).

It follows from (iii) above and from Chapter VI, equation (4), that the specific heat at constant pressure is also independent of the volume of the gas.

Since there is no change in the internal energy of a perfect gas with volume, the heat Q_1 taken in from the source during the isothermal expansion DA (measured in ergs) is equal to the work done. We have therefore

$$Q_1 = \int_{V_4}^{V_1} p\, dV.*$$

But for an isothermal change at temperature T_1, we have

$$p = \frac{(pV)_1}{V},$$

where $(pV)_1$ is constant at constant temperature, and therefore

$$Q_1 = (pV)_1 \int_{V_4}^{V_1} \frac{1}{V}\, dV$$

$$= (pV)_1 \log\left(\frac{V_1}{V_4}\right). \quad \cdot \quad \cdot \quad \cdot \quad \cdot \quad \cdot \quad (3)$$

Similarly, the heat Q_2 given up to the refrigerator is equal to the work done on the working substance during the isothermal compression BC, that is,

$$Q_2 = (pV)_2 \log\left(\frac{V_2}{V_3}\right). \quad \cdot \quad \cdot \quad \cdot \quad \cdot \quad \cdot \quad (4)$$

* We have seen in Chapter VI, Section 1, that, when a body expands against a uniform external pressure p, the external work done by the body is equal to p multiplied by the increase in volume. If the pressure varies, we consider an infinitesimal change of volume dV, during which the pressure p remains appreciably constant. The work done during this infinitesimal change is $p\, dV$, and the total work done by the body, when its volume changes from V_1 to V_2, is equal to $\int_{V_1}^{V_2} p\, dV$.

We must now prove that

$$\frac{V_1}{V_4} = \frac{V_2}{V_3}.$$

Since A and D both lie on the same isotherm, we have

$$p_1 V_1 = p_4 V_4,$$

and similarly

$$p_2 V_2 = p_3 V_3.$$

Also, since B and A lie on the same adiabatic, we have (see equation (21a), Chapter VI *)

$$p_2 V_2{}^\gamma = p_1 V_1{}^\gamma,$$

and similarly

$$p_3 V_3{}^\gamma = p_4 V_4{}^\gamma.$$

We are assuming that γ is constant for all values of the temperature and volume. From the last two equations we obtain

$$\frac{p_2 V_2{}^\gamma}{p_3 V_3{}^\gamma} = \frac{p_1 V_1{}^\gamma}{p_4 V_4{}^\gamma}.$$

Substituting in this the relation

$$\frac{p_2 V_2}{p_3 V_3} = \frac{p_1 V_1}{p_4 V_4} = 1,$$

which we obtain from the first two equations, we have

$$\left(\frac{V_2}{V_3}\right)^{\gamma-1} = \left(\frac{V_1}{V_4}\right)^{\gamma-1},$$

or

$$\frac{V_2}{V_3} = \frac{V_1}{V_4}. \quad \cdot \ \cdot \ \cdot \ \cdot \ \cdot \ \cdot \ \cdot \ \cdot \ \cdot \ \cdot \quad (5)$$

Substituting this result in equations (3) and (4), we obtain

$$\frac{Q_1}{Q_2} = \frac{(pV)_1}{(pV)_2}.$$

Thus, from equations (1) and (2) we have

$$\frac{T}{T_{tr}} = \frac{(pV)}{(pV)_{tr}}. \quad \cdot \ \cdot \ \cdot \ \cdot \ \cdot \ \cdot \ \cdot \quad (6)$$

---

* The use of these equations implies both that the gas is a perfect gas and that C_v, and hence C_p and γ, are independent of the temperature. We shall assume in this chapter, for the sake of simplicity, that we are using such a gas. The general argument is not affected by this assumption. If it is not made, the only difference is that the adiabatic changes must be infinitesimal. (Compare equations (21) and (21a) of Chapter VI).

where the subscript $_{tr}$ signifies the triple point of water, the symbol T refers to a temperature measured on the thermodynamic scale and the values of (pV) at the different temperatures all refer to the same mass of gas.

In other words, if any substance occurring in nature obeys Boyle's law and if in addition the internal energy of that substance is independent of the volume, a measurement of the values of pV at a given temperature and at the triple point of water for a given mass of the substance enables us to obtain the value T of the temperature on the thermodynamic scale by substituting the measured values of pV in equation (6). A perfect gas, that is, a gas in the ideal condition of vanishingly small density, has these properties, and therefore the values of pV for a perfect gas can be used in equation (6).

We have already seen that the value of (pV) for a perfect gas is the limiting value, as the pressure becomes vanishingly small, of the value of (pV) for an actual gas. Equation (6) is therefore equivalent to

$$\frac{T}{T_{tr}} = \frac{\underset{p\to 0}{\mathrm{Lim}}\,(pV)}{\underset{p\to 0}{\mathrm{Lim}}\,(pV)_{tr}}. \quad \cdots \cdots \quad (7)$$

It will now be realized that temperatures on the gas scale have a much more fundamental significance than was apparent from their definition. They are independent of the properties of any particular substance and are identical with temperatures on the thermodynamical scale.

A reversible engine with $T_2 = 0$ has an efficiency equal to unity. This gives a meaning to the absolute zero. Note that the energy of random motion need not be zero.

Entropy

8. If a substance which is undergoing a reversible or quasi-static change absorbs a quantity of heat dQ at temperature T, its *entropy* is said to increase by an amount dQ/T. Thus, if dS is the change in entropy in this reversible change, we *define*

$$dS = \frac{dQ}{T}. \quad \cdots \cdots \cdots \quad (8)$$

It must be stressed that the change which the substance undergoes must be *reversible*. Later we shall be able to attach a meaning to the change in entropy of a substance when it passes from a condition A to a condition B (see Section 10 below) by an irreversible process, but, for the moment, this is left undefined.

Entropy plays a most important part in the development of the theory of thermodynamics, because, as we shall show, the change in the entropy of a substance depends only on its initial and final conditions and not on the particular reversible process by which it passes from one to the other. In other words, the entropy of a substance is a definite function of its state, like its pressure or its volume. On the other hand, the quantity of heat absorbed by a substance in passing from one state to another by a reversible process depends on the actual process by which the passage takes place.

9. Change of Entropy in a Carnot Cycle.

Let us first consider the changes which take place in the entropy of the working substance when it goes through a Carnot cycle.

During both the adiabatic expansion and the adiabatic compression no heat is taken in or rejected by the working substance. Therefore, since both these changes are reversible ones, the change in entropy in both is zero. We have only to consider the isothermal changes. During the isothermal expansion the working substance takes in an amount of heat Q_1 and its temperature T_1 remains constant; its entropy therefore increases by Q_1/T_1. During the isothermal compression it gives out an amount of heat Q_2 at temperature T_2; its entropy therefore decreases by Q_2/T_2. The net change of entropy during the whole process is $\left(\dfrac{Q_1}{T_1} - \dfrac{Q_2}{T_2}\right)$. By the definition of absolute temperature this is equal to zero. We see that *when the working substance is taken through a complete Carnot cycle, its total change in entropy is zero.*

10. Change of Entropy in any Reversible Cycle.

We shall now consider the change in the entropy of the working substance when it is taken through any reversible cycle of changes; that is to say, when it goes through a series of changes, all of which are reversible, and such that finally it returns to its original condition. The changes are represented in fig. 12.2. We suppose that the substance passes round the cycle AB in the direction shown by the arrows.

Instead of following the smooth curve AB, let us consider the entropy changes when we take the working substance through the series of Carnot cycles, of which *abcd, efgh, ijkl, mnop, qrst* are typical. The portions of the cycles *bh, fl, jp, nt,* and so on are traversed once in one direction and once in the reverse direction, and their effects are thus cancelled out. The net effect of the whole process is that the working substance traverses the broken curves *abefijmnqr* and *stopklghcd.* When the distance between the successive adiabatic lines becomes infinitesimal, these broken curves coincide with the smooth curves. The whole of the cycle from A to B and back again to A can be traversed in this way. Further, from the result obtained in the preceding paragraph, the gain in entropy along *ab* is equal to the loss along *cd*, and so on for each infinitesimal cycle. The net change in the entropy of the working substance in passing round the complete reversible cycle is therefore zero.

It follows immediately that the change in the entropy of the working substance in passing from condition A to condition B by one reversible path is equal in magnitude but opposite in sign to the change in

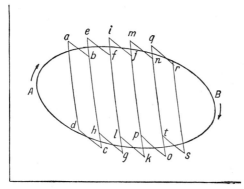

Fig. 12.2

entropy in passing from B to A by any other reversible path. In other words, the change in the entropy of the working substance in passing from condition A to condition B is the same by whatever reversible path the change takes place; *that is, the entropy of a substance is a definite function of its condition, just like its pressure, its volume, its temperature, or its internal energy.* Thus, by whatever path a substance passes from condition A to condition B, the change in its entropy has a unique value which depends only on the two states A and B. That the entropy is a function of state implies a definition of the change in entropy in an irreversible process, and this ensures the truth of the theorem proved in this section, whether the path traversed in going from state A to state B is reversible or irreversible.

The fact that the entropy is a function of state is a direct deduction from the second law of thermodynamics. It can be regarded as a statement of that law.

11. Analytical Statement.

We shall now consider how we can put this result in a convenient analytical form. If a substance absorbs an infinitesimal quantity of heat dQ at temperature T and if all the changes which it undergoes in doing so are perfectly reversible, its change in entropy dS is equal to dQ/T; that is,

$$dQ = T\,dS. \quad \ldots \ldots \quad (8')$$

Now we have already seen from the first law of thermodynamics that, if a substance absorbs heat dQ, and if the external forces during the process do work on it equal to dW,* the increase in the internal energy of the substance dU is given by

$$dU = dQ + dW. \quad \ldots \ldots \quad (9)$$

If, as is usually the case, the only external force is a uniform pressure p, we have

$$dW = -p\,dV, \quad \ldots \ldots \quad (10)$$

and the above equation becomes

$$dU = dQ - p\,dV. \quad \ldots \ldots \quad (11)$$

Therefore, in the reversible change, the result of which is expressed in equation (8), the change in the internal energy dU is given by

$$dU = T\,dS - p\,dV. \quad \ldots \ldots \quad (12)$$

All the quantities occurring in this equation are functions of the condition or state of the body only; in other words, *all the differentials are perfect differentials.*

This fact is of considerable importance. The consequence of all the thermodynamic parameters which occur in equation (12) being functions of state is that equation (12) holds for all changes whatever. By whatsoever kind of path a substance goes from one state A to another state B, equation (12) holds for the changes in the values of the thermodynamic variables which occur in it. It should be noted that this is so, even though equation (8), by which equation (12) was deduced from the first law of thermodynamics (equation (9)), is valid only for reversible or quasi-static changes. The point is that, since the differentials which occur in equation (12) are perfect differentials, it is valid for all changes *whatever their nature.* For a reversible or quasi-static change the two terms on the right-hand side of equation (12) can be identified respectively with the heat absorbed by the substance and the work done by the external forces. *It is only in the case of a reversible change that this identification can be made.* If the change is *irreversible,* the heat absorbed by the system is *less* than

---

* dW is to be reckoned positive if the changes in the volume of the body take place in the direction of the external forces, so that these forces do work; it is to be reckoned negative if the changes in volume take place in the opposite direction to that in which the forces act, so that work is done by the body against the forces. For example, if the volume of a body increases by dV against an external pressure p, $dW = -p\,dV$.

$T\,dS$, and the external work done on the system is *greater* than $-p\,dV$; but the sum of the heat absorbed by the system and work done on it by the external forces is still equal to the change in internal energy of the system. It should also be noticed that equation (12) implies that for any changes in the state of the system

$$\left(\frac{\partial U}{\partial S}\right)_V = T, \quad \ldots \ldots \quad (13)$$

and

$$\left(\frac{\partial U}{\partial V}\right)_S = -p. \quad \ldots \ldots \quad (14)$$

Equation (12) depends on the fact established in the preceding section. As we have said, this is a direct deduction from the second law of thermodynamics. Therefore we can regard as direct consequences of the second law all the deductions that we make on the assumption that all the differentials occurring in equation (12) are perfect differentials. On the other hand, dQ is not a perfect differential, but represents only an infinitesimal quantity of heat, and for a cycle $\int dQ$ is not zero, but is equal to the work done. dW is also not a perfect differential.

dS and dU are defined by equations (8) and (9). If we want to use S and U and not their derivatives, we must integrate (8) and (9) from a fixed but arbitrary lower limit, so that S and U both contain an arbitrary constant. In other words, only *changes* in S and U are significant.

It is important to note that the internal energy, the entropy, and the volume are all proportional to the mass of the substance under consideration, while the temperature and the pressure are independent of it. The above equations are written for a gram-molecule. In our notation, they apply to unit mass if we write u, s, v for U, S, V, and to an arbitrary mass if we write U, S, V.

The condition of a given mass of a body (say 1 gram-molecule) can be defined by U, T, S, p, V, or combinations of them, of which only two are independent. It is necessary to specify which are being taken as independent, and, in writing a differential coefficient, to mention which for the time being is considered as the other independent one and is kept constant in the differentiation.

12. Carathéodory's Principle.

We have already seen that the heat absorbed or given out in any process is not a function of the state of the system; it depends on the path by which the system goes from its initial to its final state. The introduction of the entropy arises from the search for a function, having some relation to the heat supplied, which is a function of state.

The work done on a fluid when its volume changes reversibly by an amount dV is $-p\,dV$. The first law then takes the form

$$dQ = dU + p\,dV. \qquad \ldots \ldots \quad (15)$$

For a system of bodies that are separated by either adiabatic or diathermal walls, both the energy function and the work performed are additive. We then have

$$dQ = \sum_i dQ_i = \sum_i dU_i + \sum_i p_i dV_i. \qquad \ldots \quad (16)$$

When a body undergoes a quasi-static, adiabatic change of state, it passes through a succession of equilibrium states. Thus, if the state of the body is plotted in a space which has the thermodynamic parameters which specify its state as axes, the adiabatic curve so obtained must satisfy equations of the forms (15) and (16). These equations which express the first law of thermodynamics are differential equations for the adiabatic curves. Expressing the internal energy as a function of the parameters of state, V and T, we get

$$dQ = \left(\frac{\partial U}{\partial V} + p\right)dV + \frac{\partial U}{\partial T}\,dT = 0. \quad \ldots \quad (17)$$

Equation (16) is of interest only in the case of bodies in thermal contact, so that they have a common temperature T. It then becomes

$$dQ = \sum_i \left(\frac{\partial U_i}{\partial V} + p_i\right)dV_i + \frac{\partial}{\partial T}\left(\sum U_i\right)dT = 0. \quad \ldots \quad (18)$$

The equations (17) and (18) are called Pfaff's differential equations. It can be shown that if dQ is a function of only two variables it always has an integrating factor; that is, for a thermodynamical system which can be specified completely by two parameters, in general, a system of *one* component, dQ always has an integrating factor. This is not so, however, for a Pfaff differential equation, such as equation (18), which refers to a system of *two or more components*. In fact, in this case, the existence of an integrating factor is an exception—a peculiarity. The content of the second law of thermodynamics is essentially that the Pfaff's differential equations which occur in thermodynamics have just the peculiarity required in order that dQ should always have an integrating factor. The mathematical condition that a Pfaff differential equation shall have an integrating factor is that as close as we please to any point in the space there should be other points which cannot be reached from the first point by passing along a solution curve of the differential equation. Carathéodory's principle states that *to any state of a substance there are other states, which are specified by values of the thermodynamical parameters as close as we please to the values which specify the first state, and which cannot be reached from the first state by an adiabatic process;* that is, there are neighbouring states which cannot be reached from the initial state by quasi-static, adiabatic processes; in other words, there are neighbouring states of the system which do not lie on an adiabatic curve through the initial state. It should be noted that Carathéodory's principle is an immediate deduction from the experiments of Joule described in Chapter II.

This is precisely the condition required in order that equation (18) may be integrable. It is immediately clear that for a system of *one component*, whose state is determined by two variables, the principle does not provide any new information; for a Pfaff differential expression in two variables always has an integrating factor. It does, however, provide new information for a system of *two or more components*; it assures us that, for such a system of two substances in thermal equilibrium, there is an integrating factor of dQ; that is, the function of state of the system called the entropy exists. In fact, if there is one integrating factor there are infinitely many. This implies that from the incomplete differential dQ for such a system we can always construct a perfect differential. It can be shown that this makes it possible to demonstrate the existence of a universal temperature function, independent of the properties of any particular substance. The simplest integrating factor is $1/T$, and the corresponding complete differential is

$$dS = \frac{dQ}{T}. \qquad \ldots \ldots \ldots \quad (8)$$

It should be noted that the need for a new principle to establish the second law of thermodynamics can only arise in systems of two or more components. This fact, which is clear in the presentation from Carathéodory's principle, is analogous to the use of *two* engines going through Carnot cycles between the same source and sink in reverse directions, in the historical development of thermodynamics (see Sections 4 and 5 above).

Carathéodory's principle forms the basis of the logical presentation of the second law of thermodynamics by analytical methods. This is not to denigrate the work of the founders of thermodynamics who developed its theory from a consideration of heat engines carrying out cyclical processes. This historical development provides an insight of its own on the subject of heat and thermodynamics.

For a full discussion of Carathéodory's principle, the student should consult the original papers.*

* Carathéodory, *Math. Ann.*, Vol. 67, p. 355 (1909); Born, *Phys. Zeit.*, Vol. 20, pp. 218, 249, 282 (1921); Ehrenfest-Afanassjewa, *Zeits. f. Physik*, Vol. 33, p. 933 (1925).

CHAPTER XIII

Thermodynamic Relations and their Use

1. We now proceed to develop equation (12) of Chapter XII analytically, remembering that all the differentials are perfect differentials. In this way we obtain the following important and useful results.

2. Maxwell's Four Thermodynamic Relations.

The state of a homogeneous body is completely specified if we know its mass and any two of the variables occurring in equation (12) of Chapter XII. We shall assume in what follows that we always deal with unit mass of the substance, or with one gram-molecule; if we are dealing with unit mass, we shall indicate all the quantities by small capital letters, and if we are dealing with a gram-molecule we shall use ordinary-sized capital letters to specify them. For the moment we shall take any two independent variables x and y, and later we shall substitute for x and y suitable pairs of the variables T, S, p, and V.

We have from equation (11), Chapter XII,

$$\frac{\partial U}{\partial x} = T \frac{\partial S}{\partial x} - p \frac{\partial V}{\partial x},$$

$$\frac{\partial U}{\partial y} = T \frac{\partial S}{\partial y} - p \frac{\partial V}{\partial y}.$$

Differentiating the first equation with respect to y, and the second with respect to x, we obtain

$$\frac{\partial}{\partial y} \frac{\partial U}{\partial x} = \frac{\partial T}{\partial y} \frac{\partial S}{\partial x} + T \frac{\partial}{\partial y} \frac{\partial S}{\partial x} - \frac{\partial p}{\partial y} \frac{\partial V}{\partial x} - p \frac{\partial}{\partial y} \frac{\partial V}{\partial x},$$

$$\frac{\partial}{\partial x} \frac{\partial U}{\partial y} = \frac{\partial T}{\partial x} \frac{\partial S}{\partial y} + T \frac{\partial}{\partial x} \frac{\partial S}{\partial y} - \frac{\partial p}{\partial x} \frac{\partial V}{\partial y} - p \frac{\partial}{\partial x} \frac{\partial V}{\partial y}.$$

Since dU, dS, and dV are all perfect differentials, we have

$$\frac{\partial}{\partial y} \frac{\partial U}{\partial x} = \frac{\partial}{\partial x} \frac{\partial U}{\partial y},$$

and similar relations for S and V. Using this fact, we obtain from the last pair of equations the following important relation,

$$\frac{\partial T}{\partial y} \frac{\partial S}{\partial x} - \frac{\partial p}{\partial y} \frac{\partial V}{\partial x} = \frac{\partial T}{\partial x} \frac{\partial S}{\partial y} - \frac{\partial p}{\partial x} \frac{\partial V}{\partial y}. \qquad \cdots \quad (1)$$

We now substitute for the independent variables x and y any pair of the quantities S, T, V, and p. The four most important relations are obtained by substituting S and V, S and p, T and p, T and V, as the respective pairs of independent variables.

Let us first put $x = S$ * and $y = V$. Remembering that x and y are independent variables, that is, that $\partial x/\partial y = 0$, or in this case that $\partial S/\partial V$ (or $\partial V/\partial S$) vanishes, equation (1) gives

$$\left(\frac{\partial T}{\partial V}\right)_S = -\left(\frac{\partial p}{\partial S}\right)_V . \quad \cdots \cdots \quad (2)$$

Similarly, putting $x = S$ and $y = p$, we obtain

$$\left(\frac{\partial T}{\partial p}\right)_S = \left(\frac{\partial V}{\partial S}\right)_p . \quad \cdots \cdots \quad (3)$$

With $x = T$ and $y = p$, we obtain

$$\left(\frac{\partial V}{\partial T}\right)_p = -\left(\frac{\partial S}{\partial p}\right)_T , \quad \cdots \cdots \quad (4)$$

and finally, with $x = T$ and $y = V$, we obtain

$$\left(\frac{\partial S}{\partial V}\right)_T = \left(\frac{\partial p}{\partial T}\right)_V . \quad \cdots \cdots \quad (5)$$

Equations (2) to (5) are known as *Maxwell's four thermodynamic relations*. Their meanings should be expressed in words by the student. Writing s, v for S, V, similar relations hold for unit mass. For an alternative derivation of Maxwell's relations, the reader is referred to Example 12 at the end of Chapter XVI.

3. Specific Heats.

Let us for the moment return to the expression of the first law of thermodynamics (equation (11), Chapter XII):

$$d\mathrm{u} = dq - p\,dv.$$

If the temperature of a body changes by an amount dT, its specific heat c is defined by the relation

$$\mathrm{c} = \frac{dq}{dT}.$$

Thus,
$$\mathrm{c}\,dT = d\mathrm{u} + p\,dv. \quad \cdots \cdots \quad (6)$$

* S constant strictly means an *isentropic* change. Considering reversible changes, the second law of thermodynamics then implies that there is no exchange of heat with the surroundings, that is, that S constant refers to a reversible *adiabatic* change.

If the heating is carried out at *constant volume* we have $dv = 0$ and $c = c_v$, and equation (6) becomes

$$c_v = \left(\frac{\partial u}{\partial T}\right)_v. \qquad \ldots \ldots (7)$$

If the heating is carried out at *constant pressure* we have $dp = 0$ and $c = c_p$, and equation (6) becomes

$$c_p = \left(\frac{\partial u}{\partial T}\right)_p + p\left(\frac{\partial v}{\partial T}\right)_p. \qquad \ldots \ldots (8)$$

Since u is a function of v and T, we may write

$$du = \left(\frac{\partial u}{\partial T}\right)_v dT + \left(\frac{\partial u}{\partial v}\right)_T dv,$$

or, at constant pressure,

$$\left(\frac{\partial u}{\partial T}\right)_p = \left(\frac{\partial u}{\partial T}\right)_v + \left(\frac{\partial u}{\partial v}\right)_T \left(\frac{\partial v}{\partial T}\right)_p. \qquad \ldots \ldots (9)$$

Substituting this value of $(\partial u/\partial T)_p$ in equation (8), we obtain

$$c_p = \left(\frac{\partial u}{\partial T}\right)_v + \left[p + \left(\frac{\partial u}{\partial v}\right)_T\right]\left(\frac{\partial v}{\partial T}\right)_p,$$

or, from (7), $$c_p = c_v + \left[p + \left(\frac{\partial u}{\partial v}\right)_T\right]\left(\frac{\partial v}{\partial T}\right)_p. \qquad \ldots \ldots (10)$$

This is as far as the first law of thermodynamics will take us. Using the second law as expressed in equation (11), Chapter XII, we have

$$\left(\frac{\partial u}{\partial v}\right)_T = T\left(\frac{\partial s}{\partial v}\right)_T - p;$$

and substituting in this the value of $(\partial s/\partial v)_T$ given by the fourth Maxwell thermodynamic relation (equation (5)) we obtain

$$\left(\frac{\partial u}{\partial v}\right)_T = T\left(\frac{\partial p}{\partial T}\right)_v - p.$$

Substituting this in equation (10), we have

$$c_p - c_v = T\left(\frac{\partial p}{\partial T}\right)_v \left(\frac{\partial v}{\partial T}\right)_p. \qquad \ldots \ldots (11)$$

This relation enables us to determine the difference in the specific heats at constant volume and at constant pressure from a knowledge only of the equation of state (see Example 6 at the end of this chapter).

As it stands the relation cannot be applied to solids, because we do not in this case know the value of $(\partial p/\partial T)_v$. Since, however, p is a function of v and T, we have

$$dp = \left(\frac{\partial p}{\partial T}\right)_v dT + \left(\frac{\partial p}{\partial v}\right)_T dv.$$

Putting $dp = 0$, we obtain

$$\left(\frac{\partial p}{\partial T}\right)_v = -\left(\frac{\partial p}{\partial v}\right)_T \left(\frac{\partial v}{\partial T}\right)_p, \qquad \cdots \cdots (12)$$

and substituting this value of $\left(\frac{\partial p}{\partial T}\right)_v$ in equation (11), we obtain

$$c_p - c_v = -T\left(\frac{\partial p}{\partial v}\right)_T \left(\frac{\partial v}{\partial T}\right)_p^2. \qquad \cdots \cdots (13)$$

Since $(\partial p/\partial v)_T$ is necessarily negative, this relation shows that c_p is always greater than c_v. Only in the limiting case, when the coefficient of expansion is equal to zero (e.g. for water at $4°$ C.), is $c_p = c_v$.

We use equation (13) to reduce measurements of the specific heats of solids at constant pressure to constant volume. For this purpose we put it in the following form. If κ is the isothermal compressibility, we have

$$\kappa = -\frac{1}{v}\left(\frac{\partial v}{\partial p}\right)_T,$$

and if α is the coefficient of *linear* expansion,

$$3\alpha = \frac{1}{v}\left(\frac{\partial v}{\partial T}\right)_p.$$

Substituting these values in equation (13), it becomes

$$c_p - c_v = \frac{9\alpha^2 v}{\kappa} T. \qquad \cdots \cdots (14)$$

Further important and useful relations concerning specific heats are given in the examples at the end of this chapter.

THE JOULE-KELVIN EFFECT

4. In Chapter V, Section 3, we have considered the general nature of the Joule-Kelvin effect which accompanies the streaming of a gas through a porous plug or through a valve.

The chief difficulty in making accurate measurements of the effect is the error due to loss or gain of heat. Owing to the narrowness of the channels in the plug, the increase in the kinetic energy of the gas in passing through them may cause the temperature of the gas there to be considerably below that of the gas on either side of the plug. There is thus a conduction of heat parallel to the direction of flow of the gas. This does not alter the temperature of the gas once a steady state is reached. The difficulty arises on account of the heat conducted *across* the direction of flow. This is best eliminated by the use of a guard-ring.

Eumorfopoulos and Rai* have carried out preliminary experiments using a flat plate of alundum for the plug and using a guard-ring. They have made a very careful study of the heat losses in this type of apparatus.

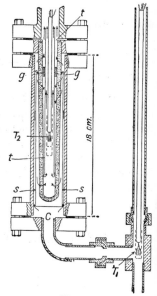

Fig. 13.1

An extensive series of experiments on air have been carried out by Hoxton.† He used the radial flow type of plug introduced by Regnault. A similar method has been used by Roebuck.‡ The apparatus used by Hoxton is shown in fig. 13.1.

The plug consists of a cylindrical tube of porous earthenware closed at one end (a Pasteur filter), and is shown dotted in the figure. The flow of gas through the plug is radial towards the axis. After passing through the plug the gas flows out parallel to the axis. The purpose of this construction is to afford thermal protection.

The whole of the apparatus shown in the figure is immersed in a constant-temperature bath, the surface of which is 44 cm. above the point T_1. Air after passing through about 8 m. of pipe immersed in the bath passes the platinum thermometer T_1. It enters the plug casing at C and travels upward between the wall of the casing and a bright tinned radiation shield *ss*. Its path is indicated by arrows. After passing over the top of the radiation shield it fills the space immediately outside the plug. It then flows through the plug in two streams divided by the guard-ring *gg*. Within the plug is a glass tube *tt* which causes the whole of the lower stream to pass the platinum thermometer T_2. The upper stream is prevented from passing the thermometer. The guard-ring prevents effects due to conduction of heat along the material of the plug. The plug is in general at a temperature which differs from that of the casing. The radiation shield prevents transfer of heat between the two by radiation.

The thermometers T_1 and T_2 are connected differentially.

For full details of the methods used to maintain steady pressures and a constant rate of flow, reference must be made to the original paper.

* Eumorfopoulos and Rai, *Phil. Mag.*, Vol. 2, p. 961 (1926).

† Hoxton, *Phys. Rev.*, Vol. 13, p. 438 (1919). This paper contains a summary of previous work.

‡ Roebuck, *Proc. Amer. Acad.*, Vol. 60, p. 537 (1925); Vol. 64, p. 287 (1929).

5. Theory of the Joule-Kelvin Effect.

We first apply the first law of thermodynamics as expressed in equation (9), Chapter XII, namely $\Delta u = \Delta q + \Delta w$. In contrast to the case in Section 3 of Chapter V no heat enters the gas, so that $\Delta q = 0$.‡ The net work done by the external forces on unit mass of the gas is $(p_1 v_1 - p_2 v_2)$, where the suffix 1 refers to the high- and the suffix 2 to the low-pressure side of the plug. That is,

$$\Delta w = p_1 v_1 - p_2 v_2.$$

If the internal energy of unit mass is u_1 before and u_2 after passing through the plug,

$$\Delta u = u_2 - u_1.$$

Using these three results, the first law of thermodynamics gives us

$$u_2 - u_1 = p_1 v_1 - p_2 v_2,$$

or

$$u_2 + p_2 v_2 = u_1 + p_1 v_1.$$

This we write in the form

$$\Delta(u + pv) = 0. \quad \cdots \cdots \quad (15)$$

We use the sign Δ to indicate the change in any quantity in passing through the plug.

If the pressure difference is small, we may write equation (15) in the form

$$\Delta u + p\Delta v + v\Delta p = 0. \quad \cdots \cdots \quad (16)$$

Using equation (12), Chapter XII, this becomes

$$T\Delta s + v\Delta p = 0. \quad \cdots \cdots \quad (17)$$

We have further

$$\Delta s = \left(\frac{\partial s}{\partial T}\right)_p \Delta T + \left(\frac{\partial s}{\partial p}\right)_T \Delta p.$$

Substituting from this equation in equation (17), we obtain

$$T\left(\frac{\partial s}{\partial T}\right)_p \Delta T + \left[T\left(\frac{\partial s}{\partial p}\right)_T + v\right]\Delta p = 0. \quad \cdots \quad (18)$$

We have (see Example 1 at end of this chapter)

$$T\left(\frac{\partial s}{\partial T}\right)_p = c_p,$$

‡ For the so-called isothermal Joule-Kelvin effect in which heat is supplied as in Chapter V, Section 3, see F. G. Keyes and S. C. Collins, *Proc. Nat. Acad. Sci.*, Vol. 18, p. 328 (1932); A. Eucken, K. Clusius and W. Berger, *Zeits. f. techn. Physik*, Vol. 13, p. 267 (1932); A. Eucken and W. Berger, *ibid.*, Vol. 15, p. 369 (1934).

and from equation (4) $\left(\dfrac{\partial s}{\partial p}\right)_T = -\left(\dfrac{\partial v}{\partial T}\right)_p.$

Substituting these values in equation (18), it becomes

$$c_p \Delta T + \left[v - T\left(\dfrac{\partial v}{\partial T}\right)_p\right]\Delta p = 0,$$

or $\Delta T = \dfrac{T\left(\dfrac{\partial v}{\partial T}\right)_p - v}{c_p}\,\Delta p.$ . . . . . (19)

This gives the Joule-Kelvin effect, ΔT, for a given change of pressure Δp, in terms of the specific heat of the gas at constant pressure and the equation of state of the gas.

6. The Enthalpy.

The quantity $(v + pv)$ is generally called the enthalpy (cf. footnote on Chapter VIII, Section 10) and is usually denoted by H. It is convenient to use this function in dealing with the Joule-Kelvin effect.

We have

$$\left(\dfrac{\partial H}{\partial p}\right)_T = \left(\dfrac{\partial v}{\partial p}\right)_T + p\left(\dfrac{\partial v}{\partial p}\right)_T + v.\quad . . . . . (20)$$

From equation (12), Chapter XII, we obtain

$$\left(\dfrac{\partial v}{\partial p}\right)_T = T\left(\dfrac{\partial s}{\partial p}\right)_T - p\left(\dfrac{\partial v}{\partial p}\right)_T.$$

Substituting in this equation the value of $(\partial s/\partial p)_T$ from equation (4), and using the result in equation (20), we have

$$\left(\dfrac{\partial H}{\partial p}\right)_T = v - T\left(\dfrac{\partial v}{\partial T}\right)_p.\quad . . . . . (21)$$

Comparing this with equation (19), we obtain for the Joule-Kelvin effect

$$c_p\left(\dfrac{\Delta T}{\Delta p}\right) = -\left(\dfrac{\partial H}{\partial p}\right)_T.\quad . . . . . (22)$$

This expression for the Joule-Kelvin effect enables us to analyse it into two parts; for we have

$$\left(\dfrac{\partial H}{\partial p}\right)_T = \left(\dfrac{\partial v}{\partial p}\right)_T + \left(\dfrac{\partial(pv)}{\partial p}\right)_T,$$

and therefore $c_p\left(\dfrac{\Delta T}{\Delta p}\right) = -\left(\dfrac{\partial v}{\partial p}\right)_T - \left(\dfrac{\partial(pv)}{\partial p}\right)_T.$ . . . (23)

The first term on the right-hand side represents the departure from Joule's law (internal energy of a gas at constant temperature is independent of the volume); the second term represents the departure from Boyle's law.

$(\partial v/\partial p)_T$ is always negative for a gas because the potential energy of the attractive forces between the molecules is diminished by decreasing the volume or by increasing the pressure. Thus, since Δp is necessarily negative, *the part of ΔT which arises from departure from Joule's law is always negative;* this corresponds to *a cooling effect.*

In Chapter IV, Section 5, fig. 4.5, it will be seen that $\{\partial(pv)/\partial p\}_T$ can be either positive or negative according to the conditions. Generally speaking, for low temperatures and pressures it is negative. In this case the effect due to departure from Boyle's law is also a cooling, which increases the cooling due to departure from Joule's law. If, on the other hand, $\{\partial(pv)/\partial p\}_T$ is positive, the effect due to departure from Boyle's law produces a heating which acts against the cooling due to departure from Joule's law. For a given mean pressure of the gas there is in general a certain temperature at which the two effects balance, so that the net effect is zero. This temperature is called the *inversion temperature* for the given mean pressure. At higher temperatures there is a heating effect and at lower temperatures a cooling effect.

7. Equation of State based on Measurement of the Joule-Kelvin Effect.

If we know the equation of state of a gas and also the variation of the specific heat with temperature and pressure, we can calculate the value of the Joule-Kelvin effect from equation (19). Similarly, if we know the variation of the Joule-Kelvin effect and of the specific heat with temperature and pressure, we can deduce the equation of state (see Planck, *Thermodynamik*, 7th edition, Section 159).

8. Determination of Absolute Thermodynamic Temperatures from Measurements made on an Empirical Temperature Scale.

The Joule-Kelvin effect is given by equation (19),

$$\frac{\Delta T}{\Delta p} = \frac{T\left(\dfrac{\partial v}{\partial T}\right)_p - v}{c_p}. \qquad \cdots \cdots \quad (19)$$

In this equation T is the absolute thermodynamic temperature defined, in Chapter XII, Section 6, in terms of the efficiency of an ideal heat engine. For the present purpose we must assume that we know nothing whatever about the measurement of T. That is to say, none of the quantities in equation (19) except v and Δp can be measured.

We can assume, however, that we have an empirical thermometer, say, for example, a platinum resistance thermometer or a pressure gauge to measure a vapour pressure, whose readings we shall denote by T'. This thermometer we can use to measure the various thermal properties of a gas, coefficient of expansion, specific heat, and Joule-Kelvin effect.

T, the absolute thermodynamic temperature, is a function of T', so that we can write

$$\frac{\partial v}{\partial T} = \frac{\partial v}{\partial T'}\frac{dT'}{dT},$$

$$\Delta T = \Delta T'\frac{dT}{dT'},$$

$$c_p = \left(\frac{d_Q}{dT}\right)_p = \left(\frac{d_Q}{dT'}\right)_p\frac{dT'}{dT} = c_p'\frac{dT'}{dT}.$$

Substituting these values in equation (19), we obtain for $\Delta T'$, the Joule-Kelvin effect measured on our empirical thermometer,

$$\frac{\Delta T'}{\Delta p} = \frac{T\left(\dfrac{\partial v}{\partial T'}\right)_p\dfrac{dT'}{dT} - v}{c_p'}.$$

For convenience we shall write

$$\frac{\Delta T'}{\Delta p} = \mu';$$

it must be emphasized that μ' is a quantity that can be directly measured. Substituting this in the last equation, we have

$$\frac{dT}{T} = \frac{\left(\dfrac{\partial v}{\partial T'}\right)_p}{v + c_p'\mu'}dT'.$$

Integrating, and writing T_{tr} for the temperature of the triple point of water on the absolute thermodynamic scale and T_{tr}' for this temperature on the empirical scale, this becomes

$$\log\frac{T}{T_{tr}} = \int_{T_{tr}'}^{T'}\frac{\left(\dfrac{\partial v}{\partial T'}\right)_p}{v + c_p'\mu'}dT'. \quad \cdot \quad \cdot \quad \cdot \quad (24)$$

All the quantities under the integral sign can be expressed as experimentally determined functions of the empirical temperature T', and the integral can be evaluated graphically or otherwise.

Thus, from measurements made in terms of an empirical temperature scale, it is possible to determine temperatures on the thermodynamic scale. In general, this involves the use of the second law which is introduced in the present analysis by the use of equation (19), which is a direct deduction from it.

9. The Numerical Value Assigned to the Triple Point of Water.

It has already been noted that Kelvin pointed out that the size of the degree can be specified by assigning a numerical value to a single fixed point and that the thermodynamical temperature scale is now specified in this way (Chapter I, Section 4). The fixed point chosen for this purpose is the triple point of water. It has been pointed out also that to maintain the immediate usefulness of existing thermometric measurements, it is desirable to choose the numerical value to be assigned to the triple point of water so that the ice and the steam points on the thermodynamical scale will differ by 100 degrees Kelvin. The analysis of the preceding section can be used for this purpose.

On the thermodynamical scale, the ice point is defined as $0.0100°$ K. below the triple point of water which we denote by T_{tr}. Let the numerical values determined on the empirical temperature scale for the ice and steam points be T_0' and T_s' respectively. Then, from equation (24), we have

$$\log \frac{(T_{tr} - 0.0100) + 100}{T_{tr} - 0.0100} = \int_{T_0'}^{T_s'} \frac{(\partial \text{v}/\partial T')_p}{\text{v} + \text{c}'_p/\mu'} \, dT'. \quad . \quad (25)$$

All the quantities under the integral sign can be determined as functions of the empirical temperature by experiments made in terms of it. The integral can therefore be evaluated and equation (25) then gives the value of T_{tr} which will define the degree on the thermodynamical scale so that it is the same as the centigrade degree hitherto used. It is on this basis that the value $273.16°$ K. exactly has been given to the triple point of water on the thermodynamical scale. Reference can be made to a recent analysis by Stille * of measurements made at Berlin, Leiden, Tokio, and Boston, for a discussion of the numerical value chosen.

EXAMPLES

1. Show that
$$\text{c}_p = T \left(\frac{\partial \text{s}}{\partial T} \right)_p, \quad \text{c}_v = T \left(\frac{\partial \text{s}}{\partial T} \right)_v;$$

and therefore that
$$\left(\frac{\partial \text{s}}{\partial T} \right)_p = \gamma \left(\frac{\partial \text{s}}{\partial T} \right)_v.$$

(Use the definition of specific heats in Section 3, namely, $\text{c} = d\text{Q}/dT$, and put $d\text{Q} = T \, d\text{s}$.)

As an exercise in the use of Maxwell's relations, the student should also show that

$$\left(\frac{\partial p}{\partial \text{v}} \right)_s = \gamma \left(\frac{\partial p}{\partial \text{v}} \right)_T,$$

$$\left(\frac{\partial \text{v}}{\partial T} \right)_s = \frac{1}{1 - \gamma} \left(\frac{\partial \text{v}}{\partial T} \right)_p,$$

and
$$\left(\frac{\partial p}{\partial T} \right)_s = \frac{\gamma}{\gamma - 1} \left(\frac{\partial p}{\partial T} \right)_v.$$

It should, however, be remembered that these relations can be derived using only the first law of thermodynamics (see Section 14 of Chapter VI).

* U. Stille. *Messen und Rechnen in der Physik*, Vieweg, Brunswick (1955), p. 322.

2. It is shown in books on sound that Υ, the velocity of sound in a medium, is given by

$$\Upsilon = \sqrt{\frac{K}{\rho}},$$

where ρ is the density of the medium, and K is the adiabatic bulk modulus defined by the relation

$$K = -v\left(\frac{\partial p}{\partial v}\right)_s.$$

Show, using the relation between the adiabatic and isothermal bulk moduli, that

$$\Upsilon^2 = \gamma\left(\frac{\partial p}{\partial \rho}\right)_T.$$

3. Show that
$$\left(\frac{\partial c_v}{\partial v}\right)_T = T\left(\frac{\partial^2 p}{\partial T^2}\right)_v.$$

(We have, from Example 1, $(\partial s/\partial T)_v = c_v/T$, and from equation (5), $(\partial s/\partial v)_T = (\partial p/\partial T)_v$. Differentiate the first equation with respect to v at constant temperature, and the second with respect to T at constant volume, and equate the results.)

4. Show that
$$\left(\frac{\partial c_p}{\partial p}\right)_T = -T\left(\frac{\partial^2 v}{\partial T^2}\right)_p.$$

(Use Example 1 and equation (4) and proceed as in Example 3.)

5. Using the simplified Van der Waals equation of state as given in equation (18), Chapter IV, show that the Joule-Kelvin effect given by equation (19) becomes

$$\frac{\Delta T}{\Delta p} = \frac{1}{C_p}\left(\frac{2a}{RT} - b\right).$$

6. Show from equation (11) that for a gas for which the equation of state is $pV = RT + Bp$ (compare equation (6), Chapter VI) the difference between the atomic heats at constant pressure and at constant volume is to a first approximation given by

$$C_p - C_v = R + 2\frac{\partial B}{\partial T}p$$

n agreement with equation (10), Chapter VI.

7. The behaviour of a gas is represented by a Van der Waals equation of state. Show that, for it,

$$C_p - C_v = R\,\frac{p + a/V^2}{p - a/V^2 + 2ab/V^3}\quad\text{exactly},$$

and
$$C_p - C_v = R\frac{(RT)^2 + ap}{(RT)^2 - ap}\quad\text{approximately}.$$

Show also that if higher powers of p have to be included, then

$$\Upsilon = \Upsilon_0 + (\Upsilon_0 - 1)\left[\frac{2ap}{(RT)^2} + \frac{6a}{(RT)^3}\left(\frac{a}{RT} - b\right)p^2 + \dots\right].$$

Clark and Katz * have found that a power series of this form fits their measurements of γ at various pressures. From this equation it should then be possible †
to determine the constant a of Van der Waals' equation. The values obtained
for simple molecules are in fair agreement with those found from critical data.
but the agreement for polar molecules is rather poor.

Other thermodynamic relations are given in the Appendix, and the student
who wishes to have further practice in the manipulation of partial differential
coefficients should verify these relations. This should not be attempted until
Chapter XVI, Section 12, has been read.

* Clark and Katz, *Can. Journ. Res.*, Vol. 18, A, p. 23 (1940); Vol. 19, A, p. 111
(1941); Vol. 21, A, p. 1 (1943).

† Rundle, *Journ. Amer. Chem. Soc.*, Vol. 66, p. 1797 (1944).

CHAPTER XIV

Power Cycles*

1. The development of thermodynamics has to some extent been connected with the study of actual heat engines. Carnot discovered the method by which the maximum amount of work could be obtained from a given amount of heat with the source of heat and the refrigerator at given temperatures. The essential points laid down by him were that, in order to obtain the maximum amount of work, (a) all the processes occurring in the heat engine must be reversible, (b) the heat received by the working substance must *all* be taken in at the temperature of the source, and the heat given up by the working substance must *all* be given up at the temperature of the refrigerator—the processes during which the temperature of the working substances changes from that of the source to that of the refrigerator and vice versa must therefore be adiabatic. Later, the discovery of the first law of thermodynamics made it posssible to show (see Chapter XII) that the actual maximum possible efficiency η of an engine with the source of heat at temperature T_1 and with the refrigerator at temperature T_2 is given by

$$\eta = \frac{T_1 - T_2}{T_1}. \qquad \cdots \cdots \cdots \quad (1)$$

The efficiency is defined as the ratio of the work obtained to the heat supplied.

In practice it is of course impossible to realize either of the conditions (a) or (b) laid down by Carnot, but the value of his work and of the consequent study of the highly idealized reversible engines postulated by him is that it gives us an ideal standard by which the performance of an actual heat engine may reasonably be judged. It shows for example that it is quite impossible to hope that the most perfectly designed engine will convert into useful work *all* the heat supplied to it.

2. The Working Substance.

The first problem that arises in connexion with an actual heat engine is the choice of the working substance. The substances most easily obtainable for the purpose are air and water.

---

* The student may omit this chapter if he desires, as none of the results obtained therein is used in subsequent chapters.

It must be realized that the amount of work from a heat engine depends on the amount of heat that the working substance can absorb from the source of heat. On account of the small volumetric specific heat of air the necessity for absorbing a large quantity of heat from the source of heat makes it essential, if air is the working substance, to have a very bulky engine or else to heat the air to a very high temperature. Bulk in an engine is a great disadvantage, and the latter is the only possible practicable alternative; it has been achieved in the internal-combustion engine, which is described in Sections 17 to 20. An entirely satisfactory alternative is to use water as the working substance. The large amount of heat required to vaporize a liquid makes it possible for a comparatively small quantity of water, in the process of vaporization, to absorb a large amount of heat from the source of heat. A further advantage of using water as the working substance is that water heated in a closed boiler to comparatively low temperatures develops comparatively high pressures; for example, the vapour pressure of water at 200° C. is about 16 atmospheres.

STEAM-ENGINES

The Reciprocating Steam-engine

3. The Carnot cycle for an engine employing saturated steam as the working substance is shown in fig. 14.1. We start at the point A at which the pressure in the cylinder is equal to the vapour pressure of water at the temperature T_1 of the source of heat. The effect of supplying heat is to cause more liquid to vaporize. The pressure remains constant but the piston is forced out and work is done. At the point B the source of heat is removed and the expansion is continued adiabatically. This cools the steam down, and the process is continued until the steam reaches the temperature T_2 of the refrigerator. The cylinder is now placed in contact with the refrigerator and the piston is forced in. The pressure remains constant at the vapour pressure corresponding to the temperature T_2, and vapour is condensed. The process is continued until the point D, which lies on the adiabatic through A, is reached. The refrigerator is now removed, and the steam is compressed adiabatically until the starting-point A is reached.

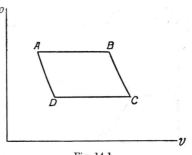

Fig. 14.1

It will be seen that carrying out in practice a Carnot cycle as described involves heating and cooling the cylinder containing the working substance as well as the working substance itself. This is obviously a waste of heat. In practice, therefore, we use a separate boiler and condenser (refrigerator). As we shall see, the separate boiler does not involve any essential change in the Carnot cycle; but the separate condenser does do so, and, further, it involves some sacrifice in the *theoretical* efficiency. The actual arrangement is shown in fig. 14.2. Steam from the boiler enters the cylinder through the pipe B, the valve in which is open. In doing so it forces the piston P forwards and thus imparts motion to the fly-wheel W. G is merely a guide. At a certain point, say F, in the stroke of the piston the valve in B is automatically closed by a mechanism attached to the piston itself. From this point onwards to the end of the forward stroke the expansion of the steam in the cylinder is adiabatic. The point F is so chosen that at the end of the stroke the vapour is at the temperature of the condenser. At the beginning of the backward stroke the valve in the tube C, which leads to the

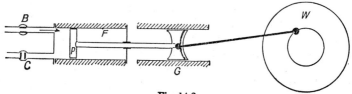

Fig. 14.2

condenser, is automatically opened and remains open until the end of the back-ward stroke. The whole of the steam in the cylinder is thus condensed in the condenser. In order to restore the system to its original condition it is necessary to pump the condensed water from the condenser back to the boiler. This is accomplished by a subsidiary feed pump attached to the driving mechanism. If p_1 is the pressure in the boiler and p_2 that in the condenser, and if v is the volume in the *liquid* state of the mass of steam which enters the cylinder at each stroke, the work done by the feed pump in each stroke is $(p_1 - p_2)v$; this work must be taken into account in reckoning the efficiency of the engine.

4. The Rankine Cycle.

If we assume that all the changes in the steam-engine described take place reversibly, the cycle of operations which the working substance passes through is that shown in fig. 14.3. This cycle is called the Rankine cycle. It is important to note that, since we assume reversibility of all operations, *the maximum possible efficiency of an engine of the type described is that deduced from the corresponding Rankine cycle; this must, therefore, be the standard by which we judge the performance of an actual steam-engine.*

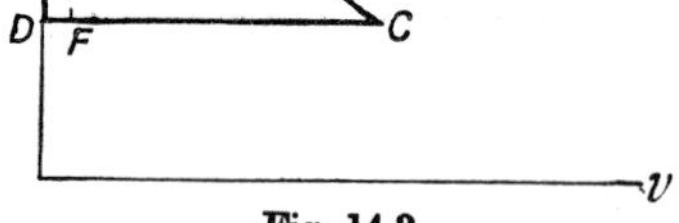

The mass of working substance is that filling the cylinder at the point of cut-off. At A it is in the state of water in the boiler (volume $= v_w$ *). AB represents its evaporation in the boiler and its passage into the cylinder, and corresponds exactly to the first stage of the Carnot cycle.

Fig. 14.3

BC represents the adiabatic expansion of the steam in the cylinder. The steam is cooled, and at the point C its temperature is that of the condenser. At this stage the steam is in general wet and contains drops of water. BC corresponds exactly to the second stage of the Carnot cycle.

* All volume changes in water due to changes of temperature or pressure are re-garded as negligible.

CD represents the backward stroke of the piston and the condensation of the steam in the condenser. The pressure remains constant throughout at the vapour pressure corresponding to the temperature of the condenser. It is in the last part of this stage and in the succeeding stage that the Rankine cycle differs from the Carnot cycle.

DA represents the transfer of the cold condensed water from the condenser to the boiler. *At* the point A the water is heated to the boiler temperature.

We have mentioned in the last section that, in transferring the condensed water from the condenser to the boiler, the feed pump does work. This work is represented by the area AEFD, where DF (or AE) is the volume of the condensed water. The actual work obtained from the process is, therefore, represented by the area EBCF, and not by the area ABCD. In actual calculations we determine the area ABCD and make a correction, which is always small, for the area AEFD. Note that E and F are not points on the cycle.

The Rankine cycle is less efficient than the Carnot cycle, if in both cases the boiler and condenser are at the same temperature. The reason for this is that in the Rankine cycle the heat which is taken in at the point A is not taken in with the liquid working substance at the highest temperature, i.e. the temperature of the boiler.

5. The Entropy-Temperature Diagram.

The changes which take place in a Rankine cycle can be conveniently represented on a diagram in which absolute temperatures are plotted as ordinates and entropies as abscissæ. Such a diagram is shown in fig. 14.4. The stages with similar lettering in figs. 14.3 and 14.4 correspond to each other. AB represents the evaporation of the water at constant temperature. BC represents the adiabatic expansion, CD′ the isothermal compression and condensation and, *at* D′, the transfer of the cold water to the boiler, D′A the heating to the boiler temperature.

The heat absorbed by the working substance is represented by the area D′AB*n*lD′, and that rejected by the area D′C*n*lD′.

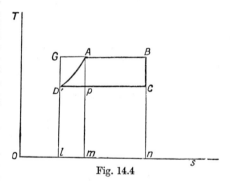

Fig. 14.4

The balance represented by the area ABCD′A is converted into useful work. The efficiency of the cycle is the ratio of the area ABCD′A to the area D′AB*n*lD′. The efficiency of the Carnot cycle with the boiler and condenser at the same temperatures is represented by the ratio of BC to B*n*, or by the ratio of the area D′GBCD′ to the area GB*n*lG. It will be seen that the Rankine cycle is less efficient than the corresponding Carnot cycle.

6. Rankine Cycle with Superheated Steam.

In the last paragraph we have assumed that the steam is delivered to the cylinder at the temperature at which it is evaporated from the liquid. In general this is not the case, and the steam is superheated after evaporation by passing through pipes on which the furnace gases play. The pressure remains constant at the vapour pressure corresponding to the temperature of the boiler, and, therefore, fig. 14.3 applies unaltered to this case. The entropy-temperature diagram must be altered as shown in fig. 14.5. A*a* represents the evaporation of the water at constant temperature, and *a*B the superheating of the steam at constant pressure. BC represents

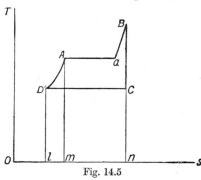

Fig. 14.5

the adiabatic expansion of the steam. During this process the steam is cooled and at C it is in general wet, consisting of a mixture of drops of condensed water and of water vapour. CD′ represents the compression and complete condensation and, *at* D′, the transfer of the cold water to the boiler. D′A represents the heating of this water from the temperature of the condenser to that of the boiler. The efficiency is the ratio of the area D′A*a*BCD′ to the area *l*D′A*a*BC*nl*.

7. The Calculation of the Efficiency of the Rankine Cycle.

We may calculate the efficiency of the Rankine cycle from the measured properties of steam. It is important to realize exactly what the result so obtained means. Let us consider the case of superheated steam considered in the last section and represented in fig. 14.5. It is necessary to know the condition of the steam when it enters the cylinder; this is completely determined if we know its pressure (the vapour pressure at the temperature of the *water* in the boiler) and its temperature. Further, we must know the temperature of the condenser. *The calculation of the efficiency of the Rankine cycle tells us the maximum amount of work that can be obtained from each unit mass of steam that enters the cylinder in a given condition, with the condenser at the given temperature.* It tells us nothing about the efficiency of production of the steam, that is to say, it tell us nothing about the furnace losses; this is a separate problem.

The actual numerical calculations are most simply carried out in terms of the total heat defined in Chapter XIII, Section 6. The total heat H in calories * of unit mass of a substance is defined by the relation

$$\text{H} = \text{U} + p\text{v}/J, \qquad \ldots \ldots \ldots \quad (2)$$

where U is the internal energy (measured in calories), p is the pressure, v is the volume, and J is the mechanical equivalent of heat. An important property of this function is that for a body heated at constant pressure the heat supplied is measured by the change in the total heat; for we have

$$\text{heat supplied} = \text{U}_2 - \text{U}_1 + p(\text{v}_2 - \text{v}_1)/J = \text{H}_2 - \text{H}_1. \quad \ldots \quad (3)$$

We shall now consider how (*a*) the work done, and (*b*) the heat supplied, can be expressed in terms of the total heat.

(*a*) *The Work Done.*—We shall carry out all our calculations in terms of unit mass of the working substance. If a mass m enters the cylinder at each stroke, we simply have to multiply the work done and also the heat supplied by m in order to obtain the work done and the heat supplied for each stroke of the piston.

* In this chapter only we shall, for the sake of convenience in using tables, assume that all quantities of heat are measured in calories.

If $_sv_1$ is the volume occupied by unit mass of the working substance in the condition in which it enters the cylinder, whether it be superheated or saturated steam, and p_1 is the pressure, the work done in calories per unit mass in forcing the piston out during the process AB (see fig. 14.3) is $p_1{_sv_1}/J$. Similarly, if $_sv_2$ is the volume of unit mass of the working substance in the condition in which it leaves the cylinder (that is, the volume of unit mass of the mixture of saturated vapour and of condensed water drops), and p_2 is the vapour pressure, the work done in calories *on* unit mass of the working substance in forcing it out of the cylinder in the process CD is $p_2{_sv_2}/J$. The net work done by unit mass of the working substance during the processes AB and CD is therefore

$$(p_1{_sv_1} - p_2{_sv_2})/J.$$

By the first law of thermodynamics, the work done by the working substance during an adiabatic expansion is equal to the *diminution* in the internal energy. If then $_su_1$ is the internal energy of unit mass in the condition represented by B on any of the diagrams (for example, fig. 14.5), and $_su_2$ is the internal energy of unit mass of the mixture of water vapour and drops of condensed liquid in the condition represented by the point C, the work done by the working substance in the adiabatic expansion is

$$_su_1 - {_su_2}.$$

The work done during the heating of the condensed water from the temperature of the condenser to that of the boiler, due to the thermal expansion of the water, is negligible.

The total work done by unit mass of the working substance in passing round the cycle, apart from the work spent in the feed pump, is therefore

$$({_su_1} + p_1{_sv_1}/J) - ({_su_2} + p_2{_sv_2}/J).$$

By the definition of the total heat, this is equal to

$$_sH_1 - {_sH_2}, \qquad \cdots \cdots \cdots \quad (4)$$

where $_sH_1$ is the total heat of unit mass of steam in the condition in which it enters the cylinder, and $_sH_2$ is the total heat of unit mass of steam after the adiabatic expansion.

We have already mentioned in Section 3 that we have to subtract from this the work done in the feed pump used to transfer the liquid from the condenser to the boiler. This work is equal to $(p_1 - p_2)v_w/J$ calories; we may assume that v_w, the volume of unit mass of liquid, is a constant.

The net external work done by unit mass of the working substance is therefore

$$_sH_1 - {_sH_2} - (p_1 - p_2)v_w/J. \qquad \cdots \cdots \cdots \quad (5)$$

(b) *The Heat Supplied.*—Let us consider the most general case, represented in fig. 14.5. We have already mentioned that, if a substance is heated at constant pressure, the heat supplied is equal to the increase in the total heat. We have to calculate the heat supplied in passing from the point D′ to the point B. At D′ we have water at the temperature of the condenser, but under the pressure p_1 of the boiler; at B we have superheated steam at the pressure of the boiler. The heating therefore takes place at constant pressure, and the heat supplied to unit mass is equal to the total heat of unit mass in the condition represented by the point B *minus* the total heat of unit mass in the condition represented by the point D′.

If $_w\text{H}_2$ is the total heat of unit mass of water at the temperature of the condenser and under the vapour pressure p_2 of water at this temperature (this is the quantity found in steam tables, see Section 9), the total heat of water at the temperature of the condenser and under the pressure p_1 of the *boiler* is equal to

$$_w\text{H}_2 + (p_1 - p_2)v_w/J.$$

This is the total heat of unit mass of water in the condition represented by the point D'. If we write $_s\text{H}_1$ for the total heat of unit mass of steam in the condition in which it enters the cylinder (i.e. in the condition represented by the point B), the heat supplied to unit mass of the working substance is

$$_s\text{H}_1 - _w\text{H}_2 - (p_1 - p_2)v_w/J. \qquad \ldots \ldots \quad (6)$$

From expressions (5) and (6) the efficiency of the cycle is

$$\frac{_s\text{H}_1 - _s\text{H}_2 - (p_1 - p_2)\text{v}_w/J}{_s\text{H}_1 - _w\text{H}_2 - (p_1 - p_2)\text{v}_w/J}. \qquad \ldots \ldots \quad (7)$$

8. The Use of Steam Tables.

The values of the total heat of steam, whether saturated or superheated, and of water are given in steam tables (see Section 9); the entropies of steam and water under various conditions are also given in these tables. Let us consider how we can use such tables to determine the values of the quantities $_s\text{H}_1$, $_s\text{H}_2$, and $_w\text{H}_2$, which occur in expressions (5), (6), and (7).

No difficulty arises in the case of $_s\text{H}_1$ and $_w\text{H}_2$. $_s\text{H}_1$ is the total heat of steam in the condition in which it enters the cylinder; this condition is determined by the temperature and pressure (provided the steam is not wet), and the total heat can be read directly from the tables. Similarly, $_w\text{H}_2$ is the total heat of water at the temperature of the condenser and under its own vapour pressure; this also can be read directly from the tables.

$_s\text{H}_2$ is the total heat of the wet steam at the temperature of the condenser. This depends on the proportions of water and saturated vapour in the mixture at the end of the adiabatic expansion. This quantity is calculated as follows. We find from the tables the value of $_s\text{S}_1$, the entropy of the steam when it enters the cylinder, that is, before the adiabatic expansion. Since the expansion is adiabatic we have, if $_s\text{S}_2$ is the entropy of the mixture of water and steam at the end of the expansion,

$$_s\text{S}_2 = _s\text{S}_1.$$

We may find from the tables the value of $(_s\text{S}_2)_{\text{sat.}}$, the entropy of dry saturated steam at the temperature of the condenser, and also of $(_s\text{H}_2)_{\text{sat.}}$, the total heat of dry saturated steam at the temperature of the condenser. Now, in passing from the dry saturated condition to the condition of wet steam, the heat *given out* is

$$T_2\{(_s\text{S}_2)_{\text{sat.}} - _s\text{S}_2\},$$

or

$$T_2\{(_s\text{S}_2)_{\text{sat.}} - _s\text{S}_1\},$$

where T_2 is the absolute temperature. The process takes place at constant pressure, and therefore this quantity is the *diminution* in total heat in passing from the dry saturated condition to the wet condition. We have therefore

$$_s\text{H}_2 = (_s\text{H}_2)_{\text{sat.}} - T_2\{(_s\text{S}_2)_{\text{sat.}} - _s\text{S}_1\}. \qquad \ldots \ldots \quad (8)$$

All the quantities occurring on the right-hand side can be obtained from the tables, and therefore $_sH_2$ can be calculated.

9. Numerical Calculations.

In carrying out the calculations given below, the numerical data set out in Tables I to III will be required. The *mean calorie* is the unit of heat, so that total heats are measured in mean calories per gram, and entropies in thermal units per gram. Absolute temperatures are obtained by adding 273·2 to the centigrade temperatures given in the tables.* The condition of water at 0° C. and under its own vapour pressure is taken as the zero condition for both total heat and entropy.

TABLE I

General Conversion Factors

Mechanical equivalent of heat, $J = 4·186 \cdot 10^7$ ergs per calorie.

1 lb. per square inch $= 6·90 \cdot 10^4$ dynes per square centimetre.

1 atmosphere $= 14·7$ lb. per square inch.

Volume of 1 gram of water $= 1$ c.c.

TABLE II

Properties of Saturated Steam and of Water under Saturation Pressure

Pressure (lb. per square inch)	Temperature (°C.)	Total heat, saturated steam	Entropy, saturated steam	Total heat, water under saturation pressure
300·0	214·32	673·96	1·5219	—
280·0	210·77	673·25	1·5274	—
240·0	203·09	671·64	1·5395	—
200·0	194·35	669·69	1·5538	—
180·0	189·48	668·53	1·5620	—
140·0	178·31	665·69	1·5818	—
100·0	164·28	661·82	1·6082	—
4·0	67·23	625·38	1·8600	67·11
3·0	60·83	622·53	1·8833	60·70
2·0	52·27	618·67	1·9159	52·15
1·5	46·49	616·02	1·9392	46·37
1·0	38·74	612·46	1·9724	38·63
0·5	26·41	606·73	2·0299	26·33

* These numerical values are taken from the tables in Callendar's *Properties of Steam*. A short account of the methods used in compiling these tables is given in the Appendix.

TABLE III

Properties of Superheated Steam

Pressure (lb. per square inch)	Temperature 300° C.		Temperature 250° C.		Temperature 200° C.	
	Total heat	Entropy	Total heat	Entropy	Total heat	Entropy
300	724·50	1·6176	695·85	1·5652	—	—
200	728·82	1·6682	701·77	1·6188	673·07	1·5611
100	733·15	1·7506	707·69	1·7041	681·41	1·6513

In Table IV we give the data for Rankine cycles with saturated steam at various initial pressures and with a condenser pressure of 1 lb. per square inch. All the results can be obtained from Tables I, II, and III above, and the student should carry out the necessary calculations in Tables, IV, V, and VI for himself. It will be seen from the table that, above 240 lb. per square inch (about 16 atmospheres), a considerable increase in the pressure of the saturated steam admitted to the cylinder has only a small effect on the efficiency.

TABLE IV

Efficiency of Rankine Cycle with Saturated Steam, and a Condenser Pressure of 1 lb. per square inch

Initial pressure (lb. per square inch)	Adiabatic heat drop to 1 lb. per square inch (calories per gram)	Work done per gram of steam allowing for work in feed pump (calories)	Heat supplied per gram (calories)	Efficiency of Rankine cycle	Efficiency of Carnot cycle with same temperature limits
300	202·0	201·5	634·8	0·317	0·360
280	199·6	199·1	634·1	0·314	0·356
240	194·2	193·8	632·6	0·306	0·345
200	187·7	187·4	630·7	0·297	0·333
180	184·1	183·8	629·6	0·291	0·326
140	175·0	174·8	626·8	0·279	0·309
100	163·0	162·8	623·0	0·261	0·287

In Table V we give the data for a few cases in which superheated steam is admitted to the cylinder. The first three cases illustrate the loss in efficiency which takes place when all the heat is not supplied at the highest temperature.

TABLE V

Efficiency of Rankine Cycle with Superheated Steam and a
Condenser Pressure of 1 lb. per square inch

Initial pressure and temperature		Adiabatic heat drop to 1 lb. per square inch (calories)	Work done per gram of steam allowing for work spent in feed pump (calories)	Heat supplied per gram of steam (calories)	Efficiency of Rankine cycle	Efficiency of Carnot cycle with same temperature limits
lb. per sq. in.	°C.					
300	300	222·7	222·2	685·4	0·324	0·456
200	300	211·2	210·9	689·9	0·306	0·456
100	300	189·9	189·7	694·3	0·273	0·456
100	200	169·1	168·9	642·6	0·263	0·341

Table VI shows the considerable increase in the theoretical efficiency caused by a small change in the temperature (and pressure) of the condenser, and therefore illustrates the importance of having the condenser at as low a temperature as possible.

TABLE VI

Efficiency of Rankine Cycle with Saturated Steam at an Initial Pressure of 180 lb. per square inch and Various Condenser Pressures

Final pressure (lb. per square inch)	Adiabatic heat drop from initial pressure of 180 lb. per square inch (calories)	Work done per gram of steam allowing for work spent in feed pump (calories)	Heat supplied per gram of steam (calories)	Efficiency of Rankine cycle
4	144·6	144·3	601·1	0·240
3	153·3	153·0	607·5	0·252
2	164·8	164·5	616·1	0·267
1·5	173·1	172·8	621·9	0·278
1·0	184·1	183·8	629·6	0·291
0·5	202·0	201·7	641·9	0·314

10. Mollier's Total Heat-Entropy Diagram.

Calculations similar to the above can be very simply carried out graphically by a method introduced by Mollier. The Mollier diagram is illustrated in fig. 14.6, which is not drawn to scale. Total heats of unit mass are plotted as ordinates and entropies as abscissæ.* Lines of constant temperature, or isothermals, are shown broken. The heavy line FKG is the critical isothermal. The heavy line HKM is the boundary curve which shuts off the heterogeneous region. The critical isothermal and the boundary curve touch at the point K, which is the critical point. Isobars or lines of constant pressure are shown as ordinary black lines; inside the heterogeneous region the isobars coincide with the isothermals. Further, inside the heterogeneous region the isobars and the isothermals are straight lines. The slope of these lines is equal to the absolute temperature.

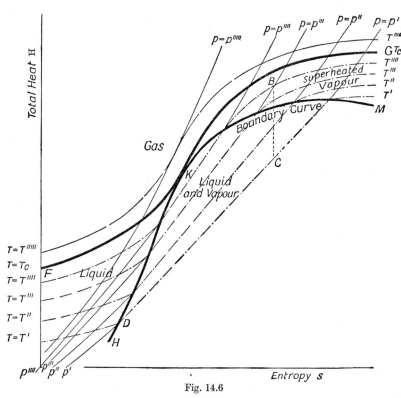

Fig. 14.6

The student should prove this for himself by showing that $(\partial \mathrm{H}/\partial \mathrm{s})_p = T$. Thus, if p constant means T constant, as it does in the heterogeneous region, the result follows.

The student should also prove that for a perfect gas the isothermals are straight lines parallel to the entropy axis. In the heterogeneous region it is usual to show also lines of constant dryness, but for the sake of clearness these have not been

---

* Callendar has shown that a convenient diagram is obtained if total heats are plotted as ordinates and logarithms of the pressure are plotted as abscissæ. On such a diagram the adiabatic lines are almost straight, and it has the advantage over the Mollier diagram that all the quantities usually required are measured on scales which do not vary appreciably from one part of the diagram to another. This diagram is used in the same way as the Mollier diagram.

drawn. Above the critical isothermal FKG the substance is in the gaseous state; in the region GKM it is in the state of a superheated vapour; along the line KM it is in the state of saturated vapour; in the region FKH it is in the state of a liquid; and in the region to the right of HKM it is in a heterogeneous condition and consists of a mixture of water and saturated vapour.

The Mollier diagram for steam can be drawn by using steam tables. We shall suppose that fig. 14.6 refers to steam. Let us suppose further that we wish to determine the maximum amount of work that can be obtained per unit mass of superheated steam which enters the cylinder at a pressure p''' and at a temperature T'''', the temperature of the condenser being T'. The condition of the steam when it enters the cylinder is represented by the point B at which the isobar $p = p'''$ and the isothermal $T = T''''$ cut. The total heat corresponding to the point B is therefore the term $_sH_1$ of expression (5). The adiabatic expansion is represented by the line BC drawn perpendicular to the entropy axis, and the condition of the wet steam at the end of this expansion is represented by the point C in which this line cuts the isothermal $T = T'$. The value of the total heat corresponding to this point is the term $_sH_2$ of expression (5). The calculation of the remaining term in expression (5) representing the small amount of work done by the feed pump presents no difficulty.

The term $_wH_2$ of expression (6) is the total heat corresponding to the point D.

It will be realized how the calculations are simplified by the use of a diagram of this sort.

11. The Measurement of the Performance of a Steam-engine.

The object of designers of steam-engines is to construct an engine that shall approach as closely as possible in its behaviour to that postulated in the Rankine cycle. The departure of a given engine from the conditions of the ideal cycle can be measured in two ways: (a) we can determine the actual cycle of changes through which the working substance passes and compare this with the ideal cycle, and (b) we can determine the actual amount of work produced by each unit mass of steam and compare it with the amount deduced from expression (5).

(a) *Watt's Indicator Diagram.*—To determine the actual cycle of changes through which the working substance passes, we attach to the end of the cylinder a small cylinder containing a piston which moves against a spring. The position of this piston is a measure of the pressure in the main cylinder. The linear motion of this piston is recorded on a piece of paper. At the same time the paper is displaced in a direction at right angles to the motion of the pressure-measuring piston by a distance proportional to the actual motion of the working piston of the engine. Thus we have recorded on axes at right angles to one another the volume occupied by the working substance and the corresponding pressures in the cylinder. This diagram is called a Watt's *indicator diagram.* The type of

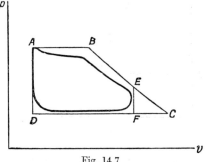

Fig. 14.7

diagram obtained with an actual engine and the corresponding Rankine cycle ABCD are shown in fig. 14.7. Actually in practice it is found to be inadvisable to attempt to expand the steam adiabatically right down to the pressure of the condenser, and the end of the stroke occurs at the point E on the ideal diagram. At this point the valve to the condenser is opened and the pressure falls suddenly to that in the condenser. The reason for this procedure is that in the region ECF the pressure is so low that the work obtained is not more than sufficient to counterbalance the loss due to the frictional forces which oppose the motion.

(b) *The Brake Efficiency.*—The area of the Watt's indicator diagram is a measure of the energy which the changes in the working substance make available for the performance of useful work. It is not, however, a real test of the performance of the engine, because some of this energy is used up in overcoming the unavoidable frictional forces between the moving parts of the engine itself. The most satisfactory test of the actual performance is to measure the actual work done in a dynamometer or brake attached to the shaft of the engine. At the same time it is necessary to measure also the temperature and pressure of the steam supplied to the cylinder and the amount of steam required to produce a given amount of work. This last quantity can be determined by measuring the rate at which the level of water in the boiler falls.

Neither of these tests measures the work produced by the consumption of a given amount of fuel, and neither, therefore, gives any information about losses of heat in the furnace itself, but the study of such losses and the problem of furnace design lie outside the range of thermodynamics.

12. Multiple-expansion Engines.

One of the most important losses in an actual engine is due to the fact that the steam entering the cylinder has to heat the cylinder itself. This loss is greater the greater the difference between the temperatures of the boiler and the condenser. On the other hand, thermodynamical considerations show that it is an advantage to have this difference of temperature as large as possible. The best

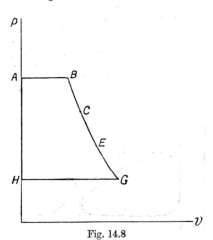

Fig. 14.8

way of getting over this difficulty is to carry out the expansion of the steam in stages. The steam from the boiler enters the first cylinder and is expanded adiabatically to the point C in fig. 14.8. The steam passes from the exhaust of the first cylinder not into a condenser but into the second cylinder. In this process its pressure and its volume remain unchanged, and no net work is done, since the work spent in expelling it from one cylinder is equal to the work gained when it enters the other. When all the steam has entered the second cylinder, the valve between the two cylinders is closed and the steam is expanded adiabatically to the point E. On the back stroke of the second cylinder the exhaust steam is transferred to a third cylinder in which it is expanded adiabatically along the line EG until it reaches the temperature of the condenser. The exhaust steam from this third cylinder passes to the condenser. Such an engine, in which the expansion takes place in three stages in three successive cylinders, is called a triple-expansion engine. If the expansion takes place in four stages it is called a quadruple-expansion engine. The use of a multiple-expansion engine increases losses due to friction effects in passing through valves, but these are less serious than the heat losses which such engines are designed to diminish.

The Steam-turbine

13. A different type of engine for converting the energy of steam into useful work is the steam-turbine, which resembles the well-known water-wheel. The action of one type of steam-turbine is shown diagrammatically in fig. 14.9 (a) and (b). WW' in each figure represents a portion of the outside of the turbine wheel with blades B_1, B_2, B_3, &c., attached to it. Steam coming from the nozzle N at a high velocity strikes against the blades and in passing between them its direction of motion is altered as shown by the arrows; this causes the wheel to rotate in the direction shown by the heavy arrows. The portions cc' and cd, ee' and ef, &c., of each blade fit with as small clearance as possible the case in which the wheel moves, so that the leakage of steam round the edges of the blades is reduced to a minimum. In general there are a number of nozzles arranged symmetrically around the turbine wheel.

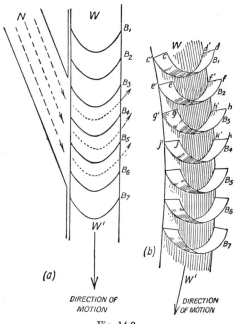

The turbine possesses the following advantages over the ordinary type of steam-engine.

(a) It is more efficient. There are two reasons for this: (i) there is no periodic change in the temperature of any part of the engine, so that the type of loss discussed in Section 12 is avoided; (ii) it is possible to expand the steam right down to the pressure of the condenser, so that the loss represented by the area EFC in fig. 14.7 is avoided.

(a) DIRECTION OF MOTION

(b) DIRECTION OF MOTION

Fig. 14.9

(b) It is more compact, so that less space is required by an engine of given power. This is of considerable importance in the case of marine engines.

(c) It produces a uniform non-periodic torque.

In the type of turbine illustrated in fig. 14.9 the channels between the blades do not converge and there is very little change in the pressure of the steam in passing along them. Such a turbine is called an *impulse turbine* to distinguish it from that described below in Section 14. If heat losses are negligible, the steam is in the same thermal condition when it leaves the blades as when it enters them, and in working out the ideal theory of any engine we assume that there are no heat losses. In this case the work done by the steam is equal to its loss in kinetic energy. The maximum efficiency is attained if the whole of the kinetic energy of the steam leaving the nozzle is converted into work, so that the velocity of the steam leaving the blades relative to the fixed casing containing the nozzle is zero. Assuming that the motion of the jet of steam leaving the nozzle is parallel to that of the wheel, and that the motion of the steam leaving the blades, if any, is also parallel to the motion of the wheel, the student should show that the condition for zero velocity of the steam leaving the blades is

$$2w' = w, \quad \ldots \ldots \ldots \ldots \quad (9)$$

where w' is the tangential velocity of the blades and w is the velocity of the steam leaving the nozzle.

Under ordinary boiler conditions the velocity of a jet of steam expanding through a single nozzle to the condenser pressure amounts to something of the order of 3000 or 4000 ft. per second, so that to attain maximum efficiency the tangential velocity of the turbine wheel would have to be of the order of 2000 ft. per second. Such velocities are not in general possible from the point of view of safety, and, further, the problems of gearing down to the velocities required to drive ordinary machinery are of considerable difficulty. It is usual, therefore, to lower the steam velocity by allowing the expansion of the steam from the boiler pressure to the condenser pressure to take place in stages through successive sets of nozzles. The steam expands through the first set of nozzles and, after passing the first set of blades as shown in fig. 14.9 (a) and (b), it expands through another set of nozzles and impinges on another set of blades, and so on. All the different sets of blades are attached to the same shaft, and the motion of the steam is parallel to the shaft. As the steam pressure progressively decreases, the volume increases. This increase is accommodated by increasing the height of the blades in successive stages. Likewise, an increase in the size of the successive sets of nozzles is necessary. Such a turbine is called a *compound impulse turbine*. Parsons was the first to suggest allowing the pressure drop to take place in stages.

14. The Reaction Turbine.

In the impulse turbine practically all the expansion takes place in the nozzles and practically none in the blades. The reaction turbine developed by Parsons differs from the impulse turbine in the shape of the channels between the blades. These channels are not parallel but are tapered like the nozzles, so that half of the expansion takes place in the nozzles and half in the blades themselves. As in the case of the impulse turbine, it is necessary to allow the expansion to take place in stages, and in this type the nozzles consist of fixed blades of exactly the same shape as the moving blades and attached to the case inside which the wheel rotates. The steam passes successively through fixed and moving blades. The increase in the volume of the steam in the successive stages is accommodated by increasing the blade height and also by increasing the diameters of the successive wheels on which the blades are set. The arrangement of a portion of one set of fixed and moving blades is shown diagrammatically in fig. 14.10. Ideally we may suppose that the steam is at rest when it enters the fixed blades, and that when it leaves them its motion is parallel to that of the moving blades. As it passes through the nozzle-shaped channels between the fixed blades as shown by the arrows, it is accelerated. If the blades are so designed that its velocity on leaving the fixed blades is the same as that of the moving blades themselves, it will be

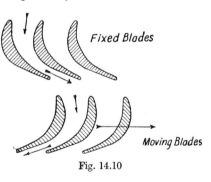

Fixed Blades

Moving Blades

Fig. 14.10

at rest relatively to the moving blades. It enters the moving blades, and in passing through them is accelerated in the opposite direction as shown by the arrows.
It leaves the moving blades with a backward velocity (relative to them) equal to
the forward velocity (relative to the fixed blades) of the moving blades themselves.
It is therefore at rest relative to the next set of fixed blades which it enters and
the process is repeated. The acceleration of the steam in passing through the
moving blades produces a reaction on the blades; hence the name reaction turbine.

Actually it is found that the maximum efficiency is obtained if

$$\frac{w'}{w} = 0.75 \text{ to } 0.95, \qquad \ldots \ldots \ldots \quad (10)$$

where w' is the velocity of the blades and w that of the steam.

It will be realized that the names impulse and reaction as applied to turbines
must not be taken too literally, but they are convenient to distinguish the two
types.

15. The Work Obtainable from a Turbine.

In calculating the maximum amount of work which can be obtained from
each unit mass of steam that passes through a turbine we shall assume that there
is no loss of heat by conduction. Further, we shall assume that all the kinetic
energy developed in the steam is converted into work. Our problem then is
to find the amount of kinetic energy developed in steam expanding through a
nozzle from one condition to another.

Let us imagine steam expanding through a nozzle from a point or cross-
section where the pressure is p_1 to another point where the pressure is p_2. Let
w_1 and w_2 be the velocities of the steam at the two points, and let v_1, u_1 and
v_2, u_2 be the volumes and internal energies of unit mass at the two points. In
passing from one cross-section to another, unit mass of the steam gains kinetic
energy equal to

$$\frac{w_2{}^2 - w_1{}^2}{2J} \text{ calories,}$$

where J is the mechanical equivalent of heat. Since we assume no loss of heat
to the surroundings, it follows from the first law of thermodynamics that the
gain of kinetic energy is equal to the loss of internal energy $(u_1 - u_2)$, plus the
work done on unit mass of the steam as it passes from one cross-section to the
other; this work (see Chapter V, Section 3) is equal to

$$(p_1v_1 - p_2v_2)/J \text{ calories.}$$

We therefore have

$$(w_2{}^2 - w_1{}^2)/2J = u_1 - u_2 + (p_1v_1 - p_2v_2)/J$$

$$= H_1 - H_2, \qquad \ldots \ldots \ldots \quad (11)$$

where $H_1 - H_2$ is the decrease in the total heat. If, as is usually the case, the
velocity of the steam in its initial condition (e.g. in the boiler) is zero, it follows
that the kinetic energy developed by the steam is equal to the drop in its total
heat. *The maximum amount of work obtainable from each unit mass of steam that
passes through a turbine is therefore equal to the difference between the total heat
of unit mass of steam in the condition in which it leaves the boiler and in the condition
in which it enters the condenser.*

In working out the above theory we have made no assumption as to whether the passage of the steam through the nozzle is frictionless and takes place without the formation of eddies or otherwise. If it is frictionless, the expansion through the nozzle is adiabatic and the maximum amount of work is equal to the adiabatic heat drop in passing from the condition of the steam leaving the boiler to that of steam at the temperature of the condenser. Under this ideal condition the maximum amount of work obtainable from unit mass of steam in passing through a turbine is therefore the same as that obtainable in an engine working on a Rankine cycle.

Actually, owing to the effects of friction, the expansion through a nozzle is something between adiabatic expansion, which is reversible, and the completely irreversible expansion through a porous plug which is described and considered in Chapter V, Section 3, and Chapter XIII, Sections 4–6. In the latter type of expansion there is no change in the total heat and no appreciable kinetic energy is generated, but there is an increase in the entropy (see Chapter XV). The effect of the actual expansion that takes place in a turbine can best be represented on a Mollier diagram as in fig. 14.11. In the first stage the pressure falls from p_1 to p_2, in the second from p_2 to p_3, and so on. The lines $p_1, p_2 \ldots$ are the constant-pressure lines on the Mollier diagram. a_1 represents the condition of the steam when it enters the turbine. If the expansion in the first stage were adiabatic, it would be represented by the line a_1b_1. If the friction were very large so that the expansion resembled that through a porous plug, it would be represented by the line a_1d_1. Actually it lies between the two, and is represented by the line a_1a_2, and the expansion in the second stage is represented by a_2a_3. The drop in total heat in the first stage is represented by the line a_1c_1, and this line therefore represents the maximum work obtainable from the steam in the first stage. The quantity η_s, which is defined by the relation

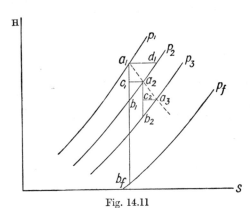

Fig. 14.11

$$\eta_s = \frac{a_1c_1}{a_1b_1},$$

is called the *stage efficiency*. It is the ratio of the actual maximum amount of work obtainable in the first stage to that which would be obtainable if the expansion were adiabatic. The maximum amount of work obtainable from the whole expansion of the steam is equal to

$$\Sigma \eta_s(a_1b_1).$$

If we assume that the stage efficiency is constant, the maximum amount of work obtainable becomes

$$\eta_s \Sigma a_1b_1.$$

We shall define the efficiency ratio of the turbine, η_t, as the ratio of the maximum work available to that which would be available if the expansion were adiabatic. If p_f is the condenser pressure, we have

$$\eta_t = \frac{\eta_s \sum a_1 b_1}{a_1 b_f}.$$

Now the quantity $\sum a_1 b_1 / (a_1 b_f)$ is called the *reheat factor*, which we shall denote by *r*. Since the constant-pressure lines on a Mollier diagram diverge as H and s increase, the reheat factor is always greater than unity. We have

$$\eta_t = \eta_s r,$$

so that the efficiency ratio is always greater than the stage efficiency, being equal to the stage efficiency multiplied by the reheat factor.

r is called the reheat factor because it depends on the friction in the nozzles, and the effect of this friction is to convert some of the kinetic energy of the steam into heat. Some, but by the second law not all, of this heat can be reconverted into kinetic energy in the next stage. For any given value of η_s the value of the reheat factor can be calculated from the thermodynamic properties of steam.

16. The Theory of Jets.

It will be seen that, in designing a turbine, it is important to be able to calculate the rate of flow of steam through a jet of given dimensions under given conditions. In carrying out such calculations we shall assume that the changes are adiabatic. Further, Callendar has pointed out that the changes take place so rapidly that there is no time for condensation to take place at any stage, so that the steam remains supersaturated. Under these conditions the adiabatic equation for the steam, whether superheated or supersaturated, may (see Appendix) be written as

$$p\mathbf{v}^\nu = \text{constant},$$

where ν is a constant.

We have seen in Section 15 that steam, starting from rest in a condition in which its total heat per unit mass is H_0 and expanding to a condition in which its total heat is H, acquires velocity w given by

$$\frac{w^2}{2J} = (H_0 - H),$$

where J is the mechanical equivalent of heat.

For an adiabatic change we have

$$J\left(\frac{\partial H}{\partial p}\right)_s = \mathbf{v},$$

and therefore

$$J(H_0 - H)_s = -\int_{p_0}^{p} (\mathbf{v}\,dp)_s = \frac{\mathbf{v}}{\nu - 1}\, p_0 \mathbf{v}_0 \left\{1 - \left(\frac{p}{p_0}\right)^{\frac{\nu-1}{\nu}}\right\}.$$

For adiabatic expansion through the nozzle we have, therefore,

$$w = \sqrt{\frac{2\nu}{\nu - 1}\, p_0 \mathbf{v}_0 \left\{1 - \left(\frac{p}{p_0}\right)^{\frac{\nu-1}{\nu}}\right\}}. \qquad \dots \dots \quad (12)$$

The specific volume, $\mathbf{v}$, at any stage is given by

$$\mathbf{v} p^{1/\nu} = \mathbf{v}_0 p_0^{1/\nu}. \qquad \dots \dots \dots \quad (13)$$

Now, if X is the cross-section at any point of the nozzle, the condition of steady flow requires

$$\frac{Xw}{\mathbf{v}} = \mu,$$

where μ is a constant, and is equal to the mass leaving the nozzle per second. Using equation (13) in this, we obtain

$$\frac{X}{\mathbf{v}_0} w \left(\frac{p}{p_0}\right)^{\frac{1}{\nu}} = \mu. \quad \dots \dots \quad (14)$$

For a given fall in pressure w is calculated from equation (12), and, for a given rate of flow through the nozzle, the cross-section X of the nozzle at the point at which the pressure is p can be calculated by substituting the value of w in equation (14). In this way we obtain

$$X = \mu \mathbf{v}_0 \left(\frac{p}{p_0}\right)^{-\frac{1}{\nu}} \left[\frac{2\nu}{\nu-1} p_0 \mathbf{v}_0 \left\{1 - \left(\frac{p}{p_0}\right)^{\frac{\nu-1}{\nu}}\right\}\right]^{-\frac{1}{2}}. \quad \dots \quad (15)$$

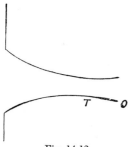

Fig. 14.12

If the values of X are calculated for values of (p/p_0) gradually diminishing from unity, it is found that X first diminishes, but that it reaches a minimum, after which it increases. This shows that the nozzle should be shaped as shown in fig. 14.12. The point of minimum cross-section T is called the throat. The opening is at O. The position of the throat is the position where X is a minimum, and this is found by differentiating X in equation (15) with respect to p, or more conveniently with respect to (p/p_0). In this way we obtain for p_t, the pressure at the throat,

$$\frac{p_t}{p_0} = \left(\frac{2}{\nu+1}\right)^{\frac{\nu}{\nu-1}}. \quad \dots \dots \quad (16)$$

The pressure ratio given by equation (16) is sometimes called the *critical pressure ratio*, for, if the pressure drop is less than the critical, the nozzle is convergent throughout, while, if the pressure drop is greater than the critical, the nozzle must have the convergent-divergent form.

The cross-section of the opening necessary for a given rate of flow with a given pressure drop is calculated in all cases from equation (15). If the pressure drop is greater than the critical, the cross-section which the throat must have is calculated by substituting the value $\left(\frac{2}{\nu+1}\right)^{\frac{\nu}{\nu-1}}$ for $\left(\frac{p}{p_0}\right)$ in equation (15).

The velocity at the throat, w_t, is obtained by substituting $\left(\frac{2}{\nu+1}\right)^{\frac{\nu}{\nu-1}}$ for (p/p_0) in equation (12), giving

$$w_t = \sqrt{\frac{2\nu}{\nu+1} p_0 \mathbf{v}_0}. \quad \dots \dots \quad (17)$$

The student should show that this is the velocity of sound in the vapour under the conditions prevailing at the throat * (see Example 5 at the end of Chapter XIII). Osborne Reynolds † pointed out that this explains the interesting fact that the rate of discharge depends only on the throat area, and is not increased by diminishing the back pressure and using a correspondingly longer nozzle. The reason is that no pressure or other changes can be propagated with a velocity greater than that of sound. The only effect of diminishing the back pressure is to increase the velocity of the issuing steam.

INTERNAL-COMBUSTION ENGINES

17. In the case of internal-combustion engines we may assume as a first approximation that air is the working substance. Actually the air is mixed with a small quantity of combustible gas or vapour, the combustion of which inside the cylinder heats the air to a high temperature. Air may be assumed to behave as a perfect gas, and the Carnot cycle for a perfect gas is shown in fig. 14.13. AB and CD are isothermal processes, while BC and DA are adiabatic processes.

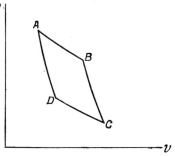

Fig. 14.13

We have seen in dealing with the steam-engine that practical considerations, which are concerned with the use of a separate condenser, make it impossible to attempt to follow the Carnot cycle in actual steam-engines. Similarly, entirely different practical considerations show that it is inadvisable to attempt to follow the Carnot cycle in an actual internal-combustion engine. These considerations are as follows. The cylinder of the engine must be designed to stand the difference between $p_{max.}$, the highest pressure developed, and $p_{atmos.}$, the atmospheric pressure. On the other hand, we may define a quantity, which we shall call the mean effective pressure, $p_{eff.}$, by the relation

$$p_{eff.} = \frac{\text{work obtained}}{\text{volume of piston stroke}} = \frac{\text{area ABCD}}{(v_c - v_a)}.$$

Unless the ratio of $(p_{max.} - p_{atmos.})$ to the mean effective pressure $p_{eff.}$ is comparatively small, it is necessary to have an engine which is extremely heavy and bulky and yet of comparatively small output. A numerical example will show that this condition is not fulfilled in the case of the Carnot cycle. Later we shall compare numerically various cycles in this and in other respects. In all cases we shall assume that the minimum pressure is 1 atmosphere or $1\cdot01 \cdot 10^6$ dynes per square centimetre, and that the maximum and minimum temperatures are the same, namely, 2000° absolute and 350° absolute respectively; in the case of the Carnot cycle the minimum pressure is p_c, the maximum temperature is T_a (or T_b), and the minimum temperature is T_c (or T_d). In each cycle it is necessary to make one other *arbitrary* assumption in order to fix the cycle definitely; in the case of the Carnot cycle we shall assume that the ratio of the isothermal compression along CD is known, in other words, that the ratio v_c/v_d is known.

---

* Callendar has shown that not only for a fluid which obeys the simple adiabatic law $pv^\gamma = $ constant, but for any fluid, the throat velocity under adiabatic conditions is equal to the velocity of sound; see *The Properties of Steam*, p. 235 (1920).

† Osborne Reynolds, *Phil. Mag.* (March, 1886).

In making the calculations it can be assumed that air behaves as a perfect gas, of which the specific heats at constant pressure and at constant volume are independent of the temperature, so that the equation for adiabatic changes of unit mass is

$$pv^\gamma = \text{constant.}$$

The equation for isothermal changes of unit mass is

$$pv = \frac{R}{M} T,$$

where R is the gas constant and M is the " molecular weight ". The following numerical values can be used:

$$c_p = 1\cdot05 \cdot 10^7 \text{ ergs per degree,}$$

$$c_v = 0\cdot76 \cdot 10^7 \quad \text{,,} \quad \text{,,}$$

$$\gamma = 1\cdot39,$$

1 atmosphere $= 1\cdot01 \cdot 10^6$ dynes per square centimetre,

Volume occupied by 1 gm. of air at 350° abs. and at 1 atmosphere pressure $\Big\} = 990$ c.c.,

$$R/M = 2\cdot86 \cdot 10^6 \text{ ergs per degree per gram.}$$

Assuming that $T_a = 2000°$ absolute, $T_c = 350°$ absolute, $p_c = 1$ atmosphere, $v_c/v_d = 2$, and that the cylinder contains unit mass of gas, the student should prove the following algebraical and numerical results:

Work obtained from each cycle $= \dfrac{R}{M} (T_a - T_c) \log_e \dfrac{v_c}{v_d}$

$$= 3\cdot27 \cdot 10^9 \text{ ergs;}$$

Volume of stroke $= (v_c - v_a) = v_c \left\{ 1 - \dfrac{v_d}{v_c} \left(\dfrac{T_c}{T_a}\right)^{\frac{1}{\gamma - 1}} \right\}$

$$= 990 (1 - 0\cdot0057)$$

$$= 985 \text{ c.c.;}$$

Maximum pressure $= p_a = p_c \dfrac{v_c}{v_d} \left(\dfrac{T_a}{T_c}\right)^{\frac{\gamma}{\gamma - 1}}$

$$= 1\cdot01 \cdot 10^9 \text{ dynes per square centimetre;}$$

Efficiency $= 1 - \left(\dfrac{v_a}{v_d}\right)^{\gamma - 1} = 1 - \dfrac{T_c}{T_a}$

$$= 0\cdot83;$$

Mean effective pressure $= \dfrac{\text{work obtained}}{\text{volume of stroke}}$

$$= 3\cdot32 \cdot 10^6 \text{ dynes per square centimetre.}$$

We obtain, therefore, for the ratio of $(p_{\text{max.}} - p_{\text{atmos.}})$ to the mean effective pressure the very high value

$$\frac{(p_{\text{max.}} - p_{\text{atmos.}})}{p_{\text{eff.}}} = 300.$$

Actual Cycles

We shall now consider the ideal cycles for actual engines, and shall see that, without a very great sacrifice in thermal efficiency, they satisfy practical requirements, which the Carnot cycle does not.

18. The Otto Cycle.

The ordinary gas- or petrol-engine usually works on a cycle first described by Beau de Rochas in 1862, which was used practically by Otto in 1876. The characteristic of this cycle is that the heating takes place at constant volume. The action of an ideal engine working on this cycle is shown in fig. 14.14. At the point C the cylinder is filled with air charged with the combustible gas or vapour and at the pressure of the atmosphere; the temperature is slightly above atmospheric temperature because the cylinder is always warm owing to the preceding action. The air is compressed adiabatically to the point D, which is the end of the first backward stroke. At D a spark is passed and combustion takes place, heating the air at constant volume to the point A. The forward stroke in which the heated air expands adiabatically is represented by AB. At B a valve is opened and the pressure drops to that of the atmosphere. During the next backward stroke CE, the valve to the atmosphere remains open and the exhaust gases are expelled from the cylinder. In the succeeding forward stroke represented by EC the cylinder is again charged with air at atmospheric pressure mixed with an appropriate amount of petrol, so that the system has returned to its initial condition. The work lost in expelling the exhaust gases is exactly balanced by the work gained in refilling the cylinder. Therefore, neglecting the slight change in the composition of the gas mixture caused by the explosion (that is, assuming, for example, that the working substance is pure air throughout), the net effect of the processes BC, CE, and EC is exactly the same as if the gas in the cylinder were cooled at constant volume from the condition represented by the point B to that represented by the point C.

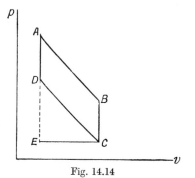

Fig. 14.14

We assume that T_c, the minimum temperature, or temperature of admission, is 350° absolute, that p_c is 1 atmosphere, that T_a, the maximum temperature, is 2000° absolute, and that 1 gm. of air is contained in the cylinder at the point C; these numbers all correspond to those used in making the calculations on the Carnot cycle. In order to fix the Otto cycle definitely, it is necessary to make one other arbitrary assumption. We shall assume that the temperature T_d corresponding to the point D is 650° absolute; this corresponds approximately to what is used in practice. We choose this particular arbitrary assumption because, in practice, it is necessary to adjust the adiabatic compression CD so that the temperature reached is not sufficiently high to cause the mixture to explode spontaneously, otherwise the explosion might take place before the end of the stroke CD. With these assumptions and using the numerical values given in Section 17, the student should prove the following algebraical and numerical results for the Otto cycle:

13

Work obtained from each cycle $= c_v(T_a - T_d)\left(1 - \dfrac{T_c}{T_d}\right)$

$$= 4{\cdot}74 \,.\, 10^9 \text{ ergs};$$

Volume of stroke $= (v_c - v_d) = v_c\left\{1 - \left(\dfrac{T_c}{T_d}\right)^{\frac{1}{\gamma-1}}\right\}$

$$= 787 \text{ c.c.};$$

Maximum pressure $= p_a = p_c\dfrac{T_a}{T_c}\left(\dfrac{T_d}{T_c}\right)^{\frac{1}{\gamma-1}}$

$$= 2{\cdot}82 \,.\, 10^7 \text{ dynes per square centimetre;}$$

Efficiency $= \left\{1 - \left(\dfrac{v_d}{v_c}\right)^{\gamma-1}\right\} = \left(1 - \dfrac{T_c}{T_d}\right)$

$$= 0{\cdot}46;$$

Mean effective pressure $= \dfrac{\text{work obtained}}{\text{volume of stroke}}$

$$= 6{\cdot}02 \,.\, 10^6 \text{ dynes per square centimetre.}$$

We obtain, therefore, for the ratio of $(p_{\max.} - p_{\text{atmos.}})$ to the mean effective pressure,

$$\frac{(p_{\max.} - p_{\text{atmos.}})}{p_{\text{eff.}}} = 4{\cdot}5.$$

This is an enormous improvement on the corresponding value for the Carnot cycle.

19. The Diesel Cycle.

A comparison of the results for the Carnot and the Otto cycles shows that in each case

Efficiency $= 1 -$ (ratio of temperatures at beginning and end of adiabatic compression).

The reason for the comparatively low efficiency of the Otto cycle is that it is impossible to raise the temperature very high by adiabatic compression, as the inflammable mixture would ignite spontaneously. This difficulty is overcome in the Diesel engine, with a considerable gain of efficiency, by introducing pure air into the cylinder at atmospheric pressure and compressing this pure air adiabatically to the maximum pressure allowable in the cylinder. A valve is then opened and a jet of inflammable liquid or vapour is forced into the cylinder at such a rate that, owing to spontaneous combustion of the vapour and the simultaneous increase of volume due to the motion of the piston, the pressure remains constant. The heating thus takes place at constant pressure.

In the Carnot cycle the heating and cooling both take place at constant temperature, while in the Otto cycle the heating and cooling both take place at constant volume. Before considering the actual Diesel cycle, we shall consider a cycle in which the heating and cooling both take place at constant pressure. Such a cycle is represented in fig. 14.15. CD and AF are adiabatic processes, while DA and FC represent heating and cooling respectively at constant pressure.

The student should show that for such a cycle the efficiency η is given by

$$\eta = 1 - \left(\frac{v_d}{v_c}\right)^{\gamma-1} = 1 - \frac{T_c}{T_d};$$

in other words, that, as in the case of the Carnot (or constant-temperature) and of the Otto (or constant-volume) cycles, we have

Efficiency $= 1 -$ (ratio of temperatures at beginning and end of adiabatic compression).

Considerations of mechanical simplicity make it impossible to carry the expansion AF right down to atmospheric pressure, and this stroke is stopped in an actual Diesel engine when the volume reaches the volume of admission, that is, the volume corresponding to the point C. At this point a valve to the outside air is opened. The actual Diesel cycle is shown in fig. 14.16. At the point C the

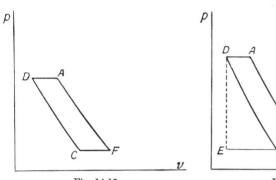

Fig. 14.15   Fig. 14.16

cylinder is full of air at atmospheric pressure. This is compressed adiabatically along CD until the point D, which is the end of the backward stroke, is reached. At D a valve is opened which allows a jet of liquid fuel to enter the cylinder. The temperature of the air in the cylinder is so high, on account of the adiabatic compression, that the fuel ignites immediately it enters the cylinder. The pressure in the fuel supply must be kept higher than that in the cylinder corresponding to the point D; this is accomplished by means of a subsidiary pump worked by the engine. The rate of supply of fuel is so adjusted that, as the piston moves out on its forward stroke, the pressure remains constant, so that this portion of the stroke is represented by DA. When the point A is reached the supply of fuel is automatically cut off, and for the rest of the stroke the expansion is adiabatic as shown by AB. At B a port to the air is opened so that the pressure immediately falls to that of the atmosphere represented by the point C. During the next stroke CE the cylinder is emptied, and on the backward stroke EC it is refilled with air and regains its initial condition C.

As in the case of the Carnot and Otto cycles, we shall assume that the minimum temperature T_c is 350° absolute, that p_c is 1 atmosphere, that T_a, the maximum temperature, is 2000° absolute, and that 1 gm. of air is contained in the cylinder at the point C. In order to fix the Diesel cycle definitely, it is necessary to make one other arbitrary assumption, and we shall assume that p_d, the maximum pressure, corresponding to the point D, is fixed and is equal to 34 atmospheres or $3 \cdot 43 \cdot 10^7$ dynes per square centimetre. The pressures used in practice

Similarly, it may be shown that:

All perfectly reversible refrigerating machines working between the same tempera-ture limits have the same coefficient of performance.

It follows from this last result that the coefficient of performance of any per-fectly reversible machine working between the temperature limits T_1 and T_2 ($T_1 > T_2$) is the same as that of a Carnot engine with a perfect gas as the work-ing substance, and is therefore equal to

$$\frac{T_2}{T_1 - T_2}. \qquad \cdot \quad \cdot \quad \cdot \quad \cdot \quad \cdot \quad \cdot \quad \cdot \quad \cdot \quad \bullet \quad (18)$$

22. The Working Substance.

The considerations brought forward in Section 2 apply to the choice of the working substance for a refrigerating machine. In general such a machine is required to maintain an enclosure of some sort at a temperature in the neigh-bourhood of $0°$ C. The heat abstracted from the enclosure, together with the heat equivalent of the work performed, is discharged into a stream of water at room temperature. It follows that the most convenient working substance is one which is a liquid with a reasonably high vapour pressure over the range of temperatures from just below $0°$ to $30°$ C.

Two substances, carbon dioxide and ammonia, are in common use.* If the Carnot cycle were followed exactly, the theoretical thermodynamic coefficient of performance, with the assumptions of no losses and of perfect reversibility of all processes, would not depend on the working substance, but only on the tem-perature limits. Actually, however, as we shall see below, we do not follow the Carnot cycle exactly in an actual machine. As will be readily understood from the calculations on the Rankine cycle given in Section 9, the theoretical coefficient of performance in such a case depends on the properties of the working sub-stance. It is found, in fact, that from the point of view of thermodynamic per-formance ammonia is more satisfactory than carbon dioxide. Ammonia has the further advantage over carbon dioxide that at ordinary temperatures the vapour pressure of carbon dioxide is very high. On the other hand, if ammonia escapes from the machine, it attacks brass or copper fittings. As a result of these con-siderations, when thermodynamic efficiency is the most important consideration, an ammonia machine is used, but on ships, where effective ventilation is difficult, it is more usual to employ the less harmful carbon dioxide.

23. The Cycle of an Actual Refrigerating Machine.

In the Carnot engine all the processes take place in a single cylinder. As explained in Section 3, this cannot be done in practice, and separate parts are used for the different processes. Assuming that there is no loss of heat, the work-ing substance can be taken through a Carnot cycle in the machine shown diagram-matically in fig. 14.17.† C may be supposed to be a tank containing brine which is to be kept cold, and A a condenser in which the heat given out by the condensing vapour is carried away by a current of circulating water. The condensed vapour passes from A into the expansion cylinder. It is here expanded adiabatically, and partially evaporated so that the temperature falls to that of C. It then passes into C and is further evaporated at constant temperature, taking up heat from the brine. On passing into the compression cylinder it is compressed adiaba-

---

* For domestic use a low-pressure plant with an air-cooled condenser is desirable. For these conditions sulphur dioxide is best. Methyl and ethyl chlorides are also used for small plants.

† Provided the vapour admitted to the compressor is wetter than the condition represented by the point C_2 in fig. 14.19.

The student should show that for such a cycle the efficiency η is given by

$$\eta = 1 - \left(\frac{v_d}{v_c}\right)^{\gamma-1} = 1 - \frac{T_c}{T_d};$$

in other words, that, as in the case of the Carnot (or constant-temperature) and of the Otto (or constant-volume) cycles, we have

Efficiency $= 1 -$ (ratio of temperatures at beginning and end of adiabatic compression).

Considerations of mechanical simplicity make it impossible to carry the expansion AF right down to atmospheric pressure, and this stroke is stopped in an actual Diesel engine when the volume reaches the volume of admission, that is, the volume corresponding to the point C. At this point a valve to the outside air is opened. The actual Diesel cycle is shown in fig. 14.16. At the point C the

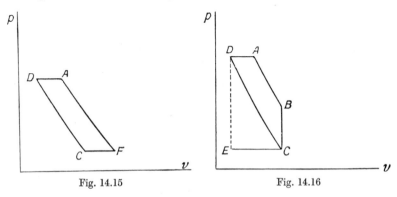

Fig. 14.15   Fig. 14.16

cylinder is full of air at atmospheric pressure. This is compressed adiabatically along CD until the point D, which is the end of the backward stroke, is reached. At D a valve is opened which allows a jet of liquid fuel to enter the cylinder. The temperature of the air in the cylinder is so high, on account of the adiabatic compression, that the fuel ignites immediately it enters the cylinder. The pressure in the fuel supply must be kept higher than that in the cylinder corresponding to the point D; this is accomplished by means of a subsidiary pump worked by the engine. The rate of supply of fuel is so adjusted that, as the piston moves out on its forward stroke, the pressure remains constant, so that this portion of the stroke is represented by DA. When the point A is reached the supply of fuel is automatically cut off, and for the rest of the stroke the expansion is adiabatic as shown by AB. At B a port to the air is opened so that the pressure immediately falls to that of the atmosphere represented by the point C. During the next stroke CE the cylinder is emptied, and on the backward stroke EC it is refilled with air and regains its initial condition C.

As in the case of the Carnot and Otto cycles, we shall assume that the minimum temperature T_c is 350° absolute, that p_c is 1 atmosphere, that T_a, the maximum temperature, is 2000° absolute, and that 1 gm. of air is contained in the cylinder at the point C. In order to fix the Diesel cycle definitely, it is necessary to make one other arbitrary assumption, and we shall assume that p_d, the maximum pressure, corresponding to the point D, is fixed and is equal to 34 atmospheres or $3\cdot43 \cdot 10^7$ dynes per square centimetre. The pressures used in practice are of this order. With these assumptions, and using the numerical values given in Section 17, the student should prove the following results:

$$\text{Work obtained from each cycle} = c_p\left\{T_a - T_c\left(\frac{p_d}{p_c}\right)^{\frac{\gamma-1}{\gamma}}\right\} - c_v\left\{T_a\left(\frac{p_c}{p_d}\frac{T_a}{T_c}\right)^{\gamma-1} - T_c\right\}$$

$$= 6 \cdot 2 \cdot 10^9 \text{ ergs;}$$

$$\text{Volume of stroke} = (v_c - v_d) = v_c\left\{1 - \left(\frac{p_c}{p_d}\right)^{\frac{1}{\gamma}}\right\}$$

$$= 912 \text{ c.c.;}$$

$$\text{Maximum pressure} = p_d$$

$$= 3 \cdot 43 \cdot 10^7 \text{ dynes per square centimetre:}$$

$$\text{Efficiency} = 1 - \frac{c_v\left\{T_a\left(\frac{p_c}{p_d}\frac{T_a}{T_c}\right)^{\gamma-1} - T_c\right\}}{c_p\left\{T_a - T_c\left(\frac{p_d}{p_c}\right)^{\frac{\gamma-1}{\gamma}}\right\}}$$

$$= 0 \cdot 56;$$

$$\text{Mean effective pressure} = \frac{\text{work obtained}}{\text{volume of stroke}}$$

$$= 6 \cdot 8 \cdot 10^6 \text{ dynes per square centimetre.}$$

We obtain, therefore, for the ratio of $(p_{\text{max.}} - p_{\text{atmos.}})$ to the mean effective pressure

$$\frac{(p_{\text{max.}} - p_{\text{atmos.}})}{p_{\text{eff.}}} = 4 \cdot 9.$$

This is only slightly higher than the value 4·5 for the Otto cycle.

The efficiency of the Diesel cycle, 0·56, is an improvement on that of the Otto cycle, 0·46, but of course falls short of the value 0·83 for the Carnot cycle with the same temperature limits. The efficiency of the Diesel cycle can be increased by diminishing the ratio of isobaric expansion v_a/v_d, but this seriously diminishes the output per cycle. The limiting value for the efficiency, when $v_a/v_d = 1$, is $(1 - T_c/T_a)$; and for the pressure limits specified above this is equal to 0·63. The student should prove this last statement by showing that the efficiency can be written in the form

$$1 - \frac{T_c}{T_d}\frac{\left(\frac{v_a}{v_d}\right)^\gamma - 1}{\gamma\left(\frac{v_a}{v_d} - 1\right)}.$$

Then, writing $v_a/v_d = 1 + \varepsilon$, it can be shown that, as ε approaches zero, the value of the factor by which T_c/T_d is multiplied approaches unity.

The use of a Diesel engine results in considerable fuel economy as compared with an engine working on a " constant-volume " cycle. It has the disadvantage that a high degree of mechanical perfection is required in the fit of the piston to stand the continued action of the high pressure during the working stroke, and this increases the friction losses. Further, a Diesel engine must be made heavy in order to stand the chance development of high pressures in the cylinder,

which occur if, at the beginning of the stroke, there is any leakage into the cylinder from the air in the high-pressure fuel supply. Such leakage may cause the initial pressure to be considerably higher than that of the atmosphere. The high-pressure fuel supply is itself sometimes a source of trouble.

20. Heat Losses.

In working out the above theory we have assumed that there are no heat losses and that all the heat developed by the combustion of the fuel is used in heating up the working substance. Further, we have assumed that air is the working substance. In making a more accurate quantitative study of the problem it is necessary to take into account the fact that the working substance is actually a mixture of gases, and that the mixture is different before and after the ignition of the fuel. Also, it is necessary to take into account the fact that the specific heats of all the gases involved vary with temperature. This last fact diminishes the calculated ideal efficiency to a considerable extent. We need not enter into the details of such calculations here, as they do not affect the principles which we have been considering. They are, however, of importance when we are comparing the actual and ideal performances of an engine. Owing to heat losses the actual efficiency is generally of the order 50 to 80 per cent of the theoretical efficiency.

REFRIGERATION

21. We shall now consider briefly the most common method of producing cold by mechanical means. According to the second law of thermodynamics heat cannot spontaneously pass from a cold body to a hotter one. To make it do so it is necessary to supply external work.

Let us first consider a Carnot engine with a perfect gas as the working substance, worked backwards between temperatures T_1 and T_2 $(T_1 > T_2)$. If q_2 is the heat abstracted from the cold body, and q_1 is the heat given up to the hot one, then, as in Chapter XII, Sections 6 and **7,**

$$\frac{q_1}{T_1} = \frac{q_2}{T_2}.$$

The useful refrigerating effect is measured by q_2, and the work performed to produce this effect is by the first law of thermodynamics equal to $(q_1 - q_2)$. The ratio

$$\frac{\text{refrigerating effect}}{\text{work spent}}$$

is called the *coefficient of performance* of the machine. For a Carnot engine we have

$$\text{coefficient of performance} = \frac{T_2}{T_1 - T_2},$$

which may be greater than 1.

The student should prove for himself that:

No refrigerating machine can have a higher coefficient of performance than a perfectly reversible machine working between the same temperature limits.

To prove this it is necessary to suppose the reversible machine run backwards so as to act as a heat engine and to drive the irreversible machine. By reasoning similar to that given in Chapter XII, Section 5, it may be shown that, if the irreversible machine has a higher coefficient of performance, the second law of thermodynamics is violated by the combined system.

Similarly, it may be shown that:

All perfectly reversible refrigerating machines working between the same tempera-ture limits have the same coefficient of performance.

It follows from this last result that the coefficient of performance of any per-fectly reversible machine working between the temperature limits T_1 and T_2 ($T_1 > T_2$) is the same as that of a Carnot engine with a perfect gas as the work-ing substance, and is therefore equal to

$$\frac{T_2}{T_1 - T_2}. \qquad \cdots \cdots \cdots (18)$$

22. The Working Substance.

The considerations brought forward in Section 2 apply to the choice of the working substance for a refrigerating machine. In general such a machine is required to maintain an enclosure of some sort at a temperature in the neigh-bourhood of 0° C. The heat abstracted from the enclosure, together with the heat equivalent of the work performed, is discharged into a stream of water at room temperature. It follows that the most convenient working substance is one which is a liquid with a reasonably high vapour pressure over the range of temperatures from just below 0° to 30° C.

Two substances, carbon dioxide and ammonia, are in common use.* If the Carnot cycle were followed exactly, the theoretical thermodynamic coefficient of performance, with the assumptions of no losses and of perfect reversibility of all processes, would not depend on the working substance, but only on the tem-perature limits. Actually, however, as we shall see below, we do not follow the Carnot cycle exactly in an actual machine. As will be readily understood from the calculations on the Rankine cycle given in Section 9, the theoretical coefficient of performance in such a case depends on the properties of the working sub-stance. It is found, in fact, that from the point of view of thermodynamic per-formance ammonia is more satisfactory than carbon dioxide. Ammonia has the further advantage over carbon dioxide that at ordinary temperatures the vapour pressure of carbon dioxide is very high. On the other hand, if ammonia escapes from the machine, it attacks brass or copper fittings. As a result of these con-siderations, when thermodynamic efficiency is the most important consideration, an ammonia machine is used, but on ships, where effective ventilation is difficult, it is more usual to employ the less harmful carbon dioxide.

23. The Cycle of an Actual Refrigerating Machine.

In the Carnot engine all the processes take place in a single cylinder. As explained in Section 3, this cannot be done in practice, and separate parts are used for the different processes. Assuming that there is no loss of heat, the work-ing substance can be taken through a Carnot cycle in the machine shown diagram-matically in fig. 14.17.† C may be supposed to be a tank containing brine which is to be kept cold, and A a condenser in which the heat given out by the condensing vapour is carried away by a current of circulating water. The condensed vapour passes from A into the expansion cylinder. It is here expanded adiabatically, and partially evaporated so that the temperature falls to that of C. It then passes into C and is further evaporated at constant temperature, taking up heat from the brine. On passing into the compression cylinder it is compressed adiaba-

---

* For domestic use a low-pressure plant with an air-cooled condenser is desirable. For these conditions sulphur dioxide is best. Methyl and ethyl chlorides are also used for small plants.

† Provided the vapour admitted to the compressor is wetter than the condition represented by the point C_2 in fig. 14.19.

tically and partially condensed until the temperature rises to that of A. It then
passes into A and the vapour is condensed at constant temperature, the heat
evolved being carried off by the stream of cooling water.

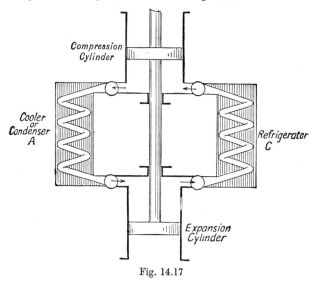

Fig. 14.17

For the sake of mechanical simplicity the expansion cylinder is omitted in
practice, and the liquid streams through a throttle valve from the condenser **A**
to the refrigerator C. The actual
arrangement is shown diagrammatically in fig. 14.18. In passing
through the throttle valve to the
lower pressure, part of the liquid is
evaporated until its temperature
falls to that of the refrigerator C.
Otherwise the processes are the same
as those described above.

The use of the throttle valve
and the corresponding deviation
from the Carnot cycle involves a
drop in the thermodynamical efficiency. Actual calculation shows,
however, that this drop is not very
great, while the gain in mechanical
simplicity is of great importance.

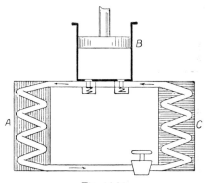

Fig. 14.18

24. The Use of the Mollier Diagram.

The processes occurring in a refrigerating machine can be most simply represented on a Mollier total heat-entropy diagram as in fig. 14.19. We assume that
there are no losses of heat. *ad* is the constant-pressure line corresponding to the
vapour pressure at the temperature of the condenser; *bc* is the constant-pressure
line at the pressure corresponding to the vapour pressure at the temperature
of the refrigerator.

The point d represents the condition of the vapour when it leaves the compressor and enters the condenser. This point is fixed if the temperature of the vapour as well as its pressure (the vapour pressure at the condenser temperature) is known. Since the compression is assumed adiabatic, the point c, representing the condition of the vapour when it enters the compressor, is obtained by drawing a line of constant entropy through d to meet the constant-pressure line bc, corresponding to the vapour pressure in the refrigerator. The position of c gives the wetness of the vapour entering the compressor. Alternatively, and this is what is usually done, we may assume that the wetness of the vapour entering the compressor is known. This fixes the point c. The point d, representing the condition of the vapour when it leaves the compressor, is obtained by drawing a line

Fig. 14.19

of constant entropy through c to meet the constant-pressure line corresponding to the vapour pressure in the condenser. The line cd represents the process of adiabatic compression.

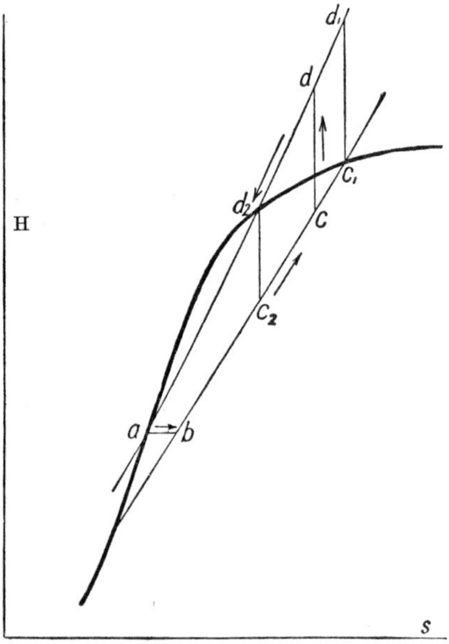

The line da represents the condensation in the condenser. At a the working substance is in the liquid condition at the condenser temperature.

The line of constant total heat ab drawn through the point a to meet the constant-pressure line bc, corresponding to the vapour pressure in the refrigerator, represents the passage through the throttle.

Finally, the line bc represents the evaporation in the refrigerator.

Three cases are shown in the figure for the same temperatures of refrigerator and condenser. The line c_1d_1 corresponds to the case when dry saturated vapour is admitted to the compressor. The line cd corresponds to the case when wet vapour is admitted to the condenser and is superheated by the adiabatic compression, and c_2d_2 to the case when the wet vapour admitted to the compressor is just turned into dry saturated vapour by the adiabatic compression.

Assuming no heat losses, the coefficient of performance may be calculated as follows. The value obtained gives a figure by which the performance of an actual engine working under the same conditions of pressure and temperature may be judged.

We have, since the processes in the condenser and the refrigerator both take place at constant pressure,

$$q_1 = \text{heat given up to condenser} = \text{H}_d - \text{H}_a,$$
$$q_2 = \text{heat abstracted from refrigerator} = \text{H}_c - \text{H}_b,$$
$$q_1 - q_2 = \text{work performed} = (\text{H}_d - \text{H}_a) - (\text{H}_c - \text{H}_b)$$
$$= \text{H}_d - \text{H}_c,$$

since $\text{H}_a = \text{H}_b$. Therefore,

$$\text{coefficient of performance} = \frac{(\text{H}_c - \text{H}_b)}{(\text{H}_d - \text{H}_c)}. \quad \ldots \quad (19)$$

25. Numerical Calculations.

A Mollier diagram for carbon dioxide has been published by the Institution of Mechanical Engineers. The values given in the following table were obtained from such a diagram. It is assumed that the temperature of the condenser is 25° C., and that the carbon dioxide is completely condensed and the liquid cooled to this temperature. The temperature of the refrigerator is −10° C. The table illustrates the loss in performance due to the substitution of the throttle valve for the expansion cylinder, and the effect on both the refrigeration effect and on the work performed. It also shows that, with the throttle, the vapour admitted to the compressor should be almost but not quite dry saturated.

Dryness of vapour admitted to compressor	With throttle			With expansion cylinder		
	Refrigeration effect	Work performed	Coefficient of performance	Refrigeration effect	Work performed	Coefficient of performance
1·0	39·1	8·6	4·5(5)	41·5	6·2	6·7
0·95	36·1	7·9	4·5(7)	38·5	5·5	7·0
0·9	32·9	7·2	4·5(7)	35·3	4·8	7·4
0·8	26·8	6·2	4·3(2)	29·2	3·8	7·7

If after the adiabatic compression the vapour is dry saturated at 25° C., the refrigeration temperature is −10° C., the vapour is completely condensed at 25° C., and there is an expansion cylinder, the working substance goes through a reversed Carnot cycle with temperature limits 25° and −10° C. The student should show that the coefficient of performance calculated from the diagram agrees with that deduced from expression (18) to within the limits of error of reading such a diagram.

26. The Electrolux Refrigerator.*

By an ingenious series of arrangements it is possible to construct a refrigerator which works continuously and which has no compression cylinder or valves and no moving parts. The system used is shown diagrammatically in fig. 14.20. The refrigerating effect is produced by the evaporation of liquid ammonia in the tubes T_3, down which it flows from the U-tube U as indicated by the droplets.

The boiler B, which is heated electrically or by a flame, contains an aqueous solution of ammonia, and the rest of the system is filled with hydrogen under pressure. The vapour, consisting of ammonia with some steam, passes through the rectifier T_1, which is air-cooled by fins to such an extent that the steam condenses, the resultant water running back into the boiler. The practically pure ammonia vapour passes on into the condenser tubes T_2, which are further cooled by means of fins, so that the ammonia condenses and collects in the U-tube U. Liquid overflows from U into the evaporator tube T_3.

* The author is indebted to Electrolux Ltd. for supplying the details on which this account is based.

Some of the liquid ammonia evaporates and the relatively heavy mixture of ammonia vapour and hydrogen falls down the tube T_7 into the absorber tube T_4. A stream of weak ammonia solution enters T_4 at the top and dissolves the ammonia vapour from the ammonia-hydrogen mixture, the resulting strong solution collecting in the vessel C. The hydrogen remaining after the ammonia has been absorbed is forced up the tube T_6 by the down-coming heavy mixture of gases in T_7 and again enters the evaporator T_3. A continuous circulation of hydrogen is thus maintained through the evaporator. This stream of gas, as it sweeps over the liquid ammonia, continually removes the vapour which the

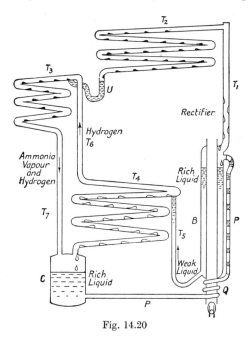

Fig. 14.20

liquid gives off in its tendency to establish the saturation vapour pressure. Hydrogen is used as the circulating gas because of the great difference in density between it and ammonia.

The flow of weak solution through the absorber T_4 is maintained as follows. From the vessel C a pipe P carries the rich solution to a coil Q at the base of the boiler. Partial vaporization of the liquid in the coil produces bubbles of vapour which carry the liquid up the vertical portion of P and deliver it into the boiler. The head of liquid maintained in the boiler in this way causes solution to flow along the tube T_5 and into the absorber T_1. A weak solution of ammonia is denser than a rich one and thus the solution passing through T_5 to the absorber is weak, since it comes from the bottom of the boiler.

REFERENCES

General:

J. A. Ewing, *Thermodynamics for Engineers*, Cambridge University Press, 1936.

G. F. C. Rogers and Y. R. Mayhew, *Engineering Thermodynamics, Work and Heat Transfer*, Longmans Green, 1957.

W. R. Wooton, *Steam Cycles for Nuclear Power Plant*, Temple Press, 1958.

Internal Combustion Engines:

D. R. Pye, *Internal Combustion Engines*, Oxford University Press, second edition, 1937.

H. R. Ricardo, *High-Speed Internal-Combustion Engines*, Blackie and Son, Ltd., fourth edition, 1953.

Turbines:

H. Cohen and G. F. C. Rogers, *Gas Turbine Theory*, Longmans Green, 1951.

W. J. Kearton, *Steam Turbine Theory and Practice*, Pitman, seventh edition, 1958.

H. Roxbee Cox (editor), *Gas Turbine Principles and Practice*, Newnes, 1955.

J. K. Salisbury, *Steam Turbines and Their Cycles*, Wiley, 1950.

Refrigeration:

S. J. Davies, *Heat Pumps and Thermal Compressors*, Constable, 1950.

B. F. Raber and F. W. Hutchinson, *Refrigeration and Air Conditioning Engineering*, Wiley, 1945.

N. R. Sparks and C. C. Dillio, *Mechanical Refrigeration*, McGraw-Hill, second edition, 1959.

Properties of Steam and Air:

J. H. Keenan and F. G. Keyes, *Thermodynamical Properties of Steam*, Wiley, 1951.

J. H. Keenan and J. Kaye, *Thermodynamical Properties of Air*, Wiley, 1945.

O. Lyle, *Efficient Use of Steam*, H.M.S.O., for the Ministry of Fuel and Power, 1940.

no heat exchange and the process has been carried out reversibly. The gases each occupy the same volume as the mixture did. We conclude that the entropy of a mixture of two gases, whose temperature is T and whose volume * is $\mathbf{V}$, is the same as the sum of the entropies of the two gases in the pure state, *each occupying the same volume $\mathbf{V}$ as the mixture*, and each being at the same temperature T.

We shall now put this result in a convenient form. The entropy of n gram-molecules of a perfect gas is, by equation (1),

$$ n\left\{ \int^{T} C_p \, d \log T - R \log p + \kappa \right\}. \qquad \dots \dots \quad (2) $$

For the entropy $\mathbf{S}$ of a mixture of perfect gases, in which the mixture occupies the same volume as each of the separate gases, we have

$$ \mathbf{S} = \sum n_i \left\{ \int^{T} (C_p)_i \, d \log T - R \log p_i + \kappa_i \right\}, \qquad \dots \quad (3) $$

where p_i is the partial pressure of the ith gas in the mixture, and n_i is the number of gram-molecules of it which are present. This is the mathematical expression of the result obtained in the preceding section.

The sum of all the partial pressures $p_1 + p_2 + p_3 + \dots$ is equal to the total pressure p of the mixture; the ratio of the partial pressures of the various gases is equal to the ratio of the numbers of gram-molecules of the various gases which are present in the mixture. We have, then,

$$ p_1 : p_2 : p_3 : \dots = n_1 : n_2 : n_3 : \dots . $$

Therefore,
$$ p_i = \frac{n_i}{n_1 + n_2 + n_3 + \dots} \, p \text{ (for all } i). $$

We now introduce the proportional concentrations (mole fractions) of the various molecules in the mixture:

$$ c_i = \frac{n_i}{n_1 + n_2 + n_3 + \dots} \text{ (for all } i). \qquad \dots \dots \quad (4) $$

We thus obtain
$$ p_i = c_i p \text{ (for all } i). $$

Using these relations in equation (3), we have

$$ \mathbf{S} = \sum n_i \left\{ \int^{T} (C_p)_i \, d \log T - R \log c_i p + \kappa_i \right\} $$

$$ = \sum n_i \left\{ \int^{T} (C_p)_i \, d \log T - R \log p + \kappa_i \right\} - R \sum n_i \log c_i. \quad \bullet \quad (5) $$

It should be noted that the first bracket of equation (5) does not depend on the partial pressures or volumes of the separate gases. It is the sum of the entropies of the individual gases, when the pressure of each is that of the mixture.

4. The Change of Entropy when Two Gases diffuse into one another.

Suppose we have two perfect gases at the same pressure p and the same temperature T, but occupying different volumes $\mathbf{V}_1$ and $\mathbf{V}_2$. If we allow them to

---

* In cases where confusion might otherwise arise we use $\mathbf{V}$ to denote the volume of a system or of an arbitrary mass to distinguish it from V, the volume of a gram-molecule. Similarly with the other symbols.

REFERENCES

General:

J. A. Ewing, *Thermodynamics for Engineers*, Cambridge University Press, 1936.

G. F. C. Rogers and Y. R. Mayhew, *Engineering Thermodynamics, Work and Heat Transfer*, Longmans Green, 1957.

W. R. Wooton, *Steam Cycles for Nuclear Power Plant*, Temple Press, 1958.

Internal Combustion Engines:

D. R. Pye, *Internal Combustion Engines*, Oxford University Press, second edition, 1937.

H. R. Ricardo, *High-Speed Internal-Combustion Engines*, Blackie and Son, Ltd., fourth edition, 1953.

Turbines:

H. Cohen and G. F. C. Rogers, *Gas Turbine Theory*, Longmans Green, 1951.

W. J. Kearton, *Steam Turbine Theory and Practice*, Pitman, seventh edition, 1958.

H. Roxbee Cox (editor), *Gas Turbine Principles and Practice*, Newnes, 1955.

J. K. Salisbury, *Steam Turbines and Their Cycles*, Wiley, 1950.

Refrigeration:

S. J. Davies, *Heat Pumps and Thermal Compressors*, Constable, 1950.

B. F. Raber and F. W. Hutchinson, *Refrigeration and Air Conditioning Engineering*, Wiley, 1945.

N. R. Sparks and C. C. Dillio, *Mechanical Refrigeration*, McGraw-Hill, second edition, 1959.

Properties of Steam and Air:

J. H. Keenan and F. G. Keyes, *Thermodynamical Properties of Steam*, Wiley, 1951.

J. H. Keenan and J. Kaye, *Thermodynamical Properties of Air*, Wiley, 1945.

O. Lyle, *Efficient Use of Steam*, H.M.S.O., for the Ministry of Fuel and Power, 1940.

CHAPTER XV

The Principle of the Increase of Entropy

1. As an introduction to the study of entropy changes in general we may consider the change of entropy in some simple cases in which it can be calculated directly.

2. The Entropy of a Perfect Gas.

Suppose we have a gram-molecule of a perfect gas, whose condition is represented by the point A in fig. 15.1, its pressure, volume, and temperature being respectively p_1, V_1, and T_1. We wish to calculate its change of entropy when it passes to another state represented by B, at which its pressure, volume, and temperature are respectively p_2, V_2, and T_2. To determine the change of entropy we have merely to take the gas from A to B by any *reversible* process and to calculate the entropy change from the heat changes involved.

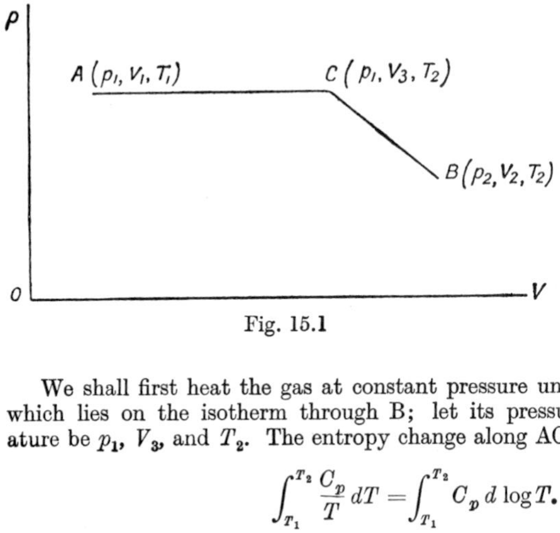

Fig. 15.1

We shall first heat the gas at constant pressure until it reaches the point C, which lies on the isotherm through B; let its pressure, volume, and temperature be p_1, V_3, and T_2. The entropy change along AC is equal to

$$\int_{T_1}^{T_2} \frac{C_p}{T} \, dT = \int_{T_1}^{T_2} C_p \, d\log T.$$

For a perfect gas C_p is a function of the temperature only * (see Chap. XII, Section 7).

We now allow the gas to expand isothermally from C to B. The work done by the gas is equal to

$$\int_{V_3}^{V_2} p \, dV = RT_2 \int_{V_3}^{V_2} \frac{dV}{V} = RT_2 \log \frac{V_2}{V_3},$$

and, since $p_1 V_3 = p_2 V_2$, this is equal to $RT_2 \log p_1/p_2$. The internal energy of a perfect gas is independent of its volume, so that the last expression gives the

* In what follows we do not make the simplifying assumption that the specific heat is independent of the temperature.

376

heat absorbed at the constant temperature T_2 during the reversible expansion. The change of entropy during the isothermal expansion is, therefore,

$$R \log \frac{p_1}{p_2}.$$

Adding the changes of entropy in passing from A to C and from C to B, we obtain for $(S_2 - S_1)$, the change in passing from A to B,

$$(S_2 - S_1) = \int_{T_1}^{T_2} C_p \, d \log T + R \log \frac{p_1}{p_2}.$$

We have already seen that we can measure only *changes* of entropy, just as we can measure only changes in internal energy. The expression for the value of the entropy in any given condition must always contain an arbitrary constant depending on the zero from which we measure. It will be seen from the above equation that we may write for the entropy S of a gram-molecule of a perfect gas at temperature T and pressure p,

$$S = \int^T C_p \, d \log T - R \log p + \kappa, \quad \ldots \ldots \text{(1)}$$

where κ is an arbitrary constant.

3. Entropy of a Mixture of Two Perfect Gases.

In order to calculate the entropy of a mixture of two perfect gases, it is necessary to find some reversible way of separating them. This can be done as follows. Suppose the gases are contained in a vessel of the kind illustrated in fig. 15.2. A and A′ are fixed walls, and B and B′ are coupled together and are movable. The distance between B and B′ is equal to that between A and A′. We shall suppose further that A is completely permeable to gas (1) and completely impermeable to gas (2), and that B′ is completely permeable to gas (2) and completely impermeable to gas (1).* We commence with B in contact with A, and therefore B′ in contact with A′, so that the gases are entirely mixed. We now move the system BB′ upwards. For simplicity we suppose that the whole is contained in a vacuum, so that no external work is done. The force on B is that due to the pressure of gas (1) in the space AB, and that on B′ is due to the pressure of gas (1) in the space AB′; these are equal and opposite.

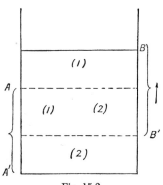

Fig. 15.2

Since B′ is completely permeable to gas (2), equal pressures are exerted on the two sides of B′ by this gas, and the net effect is zero. The net force acting on the coupled system BB′ is therefore zero, so that no external work is done in moving it. When B′ is in contact with A the gases are completely separated. If the vessel is completely insulated from its surroundings there is no gain or loss of heat, so that the total energy is unchanged, and the temperature of the gases is the same as was that of the mixture. The total change of entropy is zero, since there has been

* Substances with properties at least approximating to these are in certain cases known (see Chapter XVIII, Section 17, Number 6).

no heat exchange and the process has been carried out reversibly. The gases each occupy the same volume as the mixture did. We conclude that the entropy of a mixture of two gases, whose temperature is T and whose volume * is $\mathbf{V}$, is the same as the sum of the entropies of the two gases in the pure state, *each occupying the same volume* $\mathbf{V}$ *as the mixture*, and each being at the same temperature T.

We shall now put this result in a convenient form. The entropy of n gram-molecules of a perfect gas is, by equation (1),

$$n\left\{\int^{T} C_p\, d \log T - R \log p + \kappa\right\}. \quad \ldots \ldots \quad (2)$$

For the entropy $\mathbf{S}$ of a mixture of perfect gases, in which the mixture occupies the same volume as each of the separate gases, we have

$$\mathbf{S} = \sum n_i\left\{\int^{T} (C_p)_i\, d \log T - R \log p_i + \kappa_i\right\}, \quad \ldots \quad (3)$$

where p_i is the partial pressure of the ith gas in the mixture, and n_i is the number of gram-molecules of it which are present. This is the mathematical expression of the result obtained in the preceding section.

The sum of all the partial pressures $p_1 + p_2 + p_3 + \ldots$ is equal to the total pressure p of the mixture; the ratio of the partial pressures of the various gases is equal to the ratio of the numbers of gram-molecules of the various gases which are present in the mixture. We have, then,

$$p_1 : p_2 : p_3 : \ldots = n_1 : n_2 : n_3 : \ldots .$$

Therefore, $\qquad p_i = \dfrac{n_i}{n_1 + n_2 + n_3 + \ldots}\, p \ \text{(for all } i\text{)}.$

We now introduce the proportional concentrations (mole fractions) of the various molecules in the mixture:

$$c_i = \frac{n_i}{n_1 + n_2 + n_3 + \ldots} \quad \text{(for all } i\text{)}. \quad \ldots \ldots \quad (4)$$

We thus obtain $\qquad p_i = c_i p \ \text{(for all } i\text{)}.$

Using these relations in equation (3), we have

$$\mathbf{S} = \sum n_i\left\{\int^{T} (C_p)_i\, d \log T - R \log c_i p + \kappa_i\right\}$$

$$= \sum n_i\left\{\int^{T} (C_p)_i\, d \log T - R \log p + \kappa_i\right\} - R \sum n_i \log c_i. \quad (5)$$

It should be noted that the first bracket of equation (5) does not depend on the partial pressures or volumes of the separate gases. It is the sum of the entropies of the individual gases, when the pressure of each is that of the mixture.

4. The Change of Entropy when Two Gases diffuse into one another.

Suppose we have two perfect gases at the same pressure p and the same temperature T, but occupying different volumes $\mathbf{V}_1$ and $\mathbf{V}_2$. If we allow them to

---

* In cases where confusion might otherwise arise we use $\mathbf{V}$ to denote the volume of a system or of an arbitrary mass to distinguish it from V, the volume of a gram-molecule. Similarly with the other symbols.

diffuse into one another, the total pressure is p, the temperature T, and the final volume $(\mathbf{V}_1 + \mathbf{V}_2)$. The number of gram-molecules of each gas is given by the relations

$$n_1 = \frac{p\mathbf{V}_1}{RT}, \quad n_2 = \frac{p\mathbf{V}_2}{RT}.$$

From equation (2), $\mathbf{S}'$, the total entropy before diffusion, is given by the relation

$$\mathbf{S}' = n_1 \left\{ \int^T (C_p)_1 \, d\log T - R\log p + \kappa_1 \right\} + n_2 \left\{ \int^T (C_p)_2 \, d\log T - R\log p + \kappa_2 \right\}.$$

Using equation (5), $\mathbf{S}''$, the total entropy after diffusion, is given by

$$\mathbf{S}'' = \mathbf{S}' - R(n_1 \log c_1 + n_2 \log c_2).$$

The change in entropy is given by

$$\mathbf{S}'' - \mathbf{S}' = -R(n_1 \log c_1 + n_2 \log c_2). \quad \ldots \ldots \quad (6)$$

Since c_1 and c_2 are both necessarily less than one, this is necessarily positive. The difference $\mathbf{S}'' - \mathbf{S}'$ is called the entropy of mixing. It is a contribution which arises from the *distinguishability* of the molecules of *different species*. If two volumes of the same gas diffuse into one another, there is no entropy of mixing as all the molecules are indistinguishable. This is referred to as Gibbs' paradox.

5. The Principle of the Increase of Entropy.

The expansion of a gas into a vacuum and the diffusion of two gases into one another are both irreversible, as are all processes that occur in nature. Equations (1) and (6) show that both processes are accompanied by an increase in total entropy. This is found to be true of all processes that occur in nature for which we can carry out the direct calculation of the entropy change. We shall now prove that it is generally true and that every physical or chemical process occurring in nature involves an increase in the total entropy of the system or systems concerned.

It will first be necessary to consider some properties of the entropy of a system of bodies. We do this in (a), (b), (c), (d) below; then in (e) we deduce the required result.

(a) Let us suppose that we have two perfect gases side by side in two perfectly conducting vessels separated by a rigid, diathermic wall, so that they are always at the same temperature but in general at different pressures. Suppose that one or both of the gases undergoes a reversible change of volume, the temperature of the two remaining always the same by conduction, and no heat entering from outside. The change in the entropy of the first gas, $d\mathbf{S}_1$, is given by

$$d\mathbf{S}_1 = \frac{d\mathbf{Q}_1}{T_1},$$

and in the same time the change of entropy of the second gas is given by

$$d\mathbf{S}_2 = \frac{d\mathbf{Q}_2}{T_2}.$$

Since $T_1 = T_2$, and $d\mathbf{Q}_1 + d\mathbf{Q}_2 = 0$, we have

$$d\mathbf{S}_1 + d\mathbf{S}_2 = 0,$$

and for a finite change of condition

$$\mathbf{S}_1 + \mathbf{S}_2 = \text{constant.} \quad \ldots \ldots \ldots \quad (7)$$

That is to say, the sum of the entropies of the two gases remains constant.

(b) The process just described is reversible. Using the above result, we shall now prove that it is always possible to bring both gases from a completely arbitrary condition to any given condition by a reversible process without any change resulting in any other body, provided only that the sum of the entropies of the two gases is equal in the two conditions.*

We may suppose the initial condition of the two gases specified by their temperatures T_1 and T_2, and their specific volumes v_1 and v_2, and their final condition by their temperatures T_1' and T_2', and specific volumes v_1' and v_2'. We have

$$\mathbf{S}_1 + \mathbf{S}_2 = \mathbf{S}_1' + \mathbf{S}_2'. \quad \ldots \ldots \ldots \quad (8)$$

We compress or expand the first gas adiabatically until its temperature reaches T_2; we then place it in contact with the second gas, and compress it or expand it infinitely slowly. Heat flows from the first gas to the second or vice versa, and the entropy of the first gas is changed. We continue the process until its entropy becomes equal to $\mathbf{S}_1'$. By equation (7) the sum of the entropies of the two gases remains constant during this process, and at the end it is therefore equal to $\mathbf{S}_1 + \mathbf{S}_2$. The entropy of the second gas is therefore $(\mathbf{S}_1 + \mathbf{S}_2) - \mathbf{S}_1'$, and according to equation (8) this is equal to $\mathbf{S}_2'$.

We now separate the two gases and compress or expand them adiabatically until their temperatures are T_1' and T_2'. Since each has the required entropy, their specific volumes must be v_1' and v_2'.

During this process no change has occurred in any body, and in particular there has been no gain or loss of heat by the surroundings. We may suppose the necessary external work provided by the change in the position of a system of weights, and density changes in the surroundings may be avoided, since the process can be carried out in a vacuum.

(c) The same law must now be proved for any number of gases, viz. it is always possible to bring a system of n gases from any given condition to any other given condition by a reversible process without causing any change in any other body, provided only that the sum of the entropies of all the gases is the same in the two conditions, that is, that

$$\mathbf{S}_1 + \mathbf{S}_2 + \ldots + \mathbf{S}_n = \mathbf{S}_1' + \mathbf{S}_2' + \ldots + \mathbf{S}_n'. \quad \ldots \quad (9)$$

By successive combinations of the gases in pairs we can by the process described in the last section bring the entropy of the first gas to the required value, then that of the second gas, then that of the third, and so on up to the $(n-1)$th gas. In the whole process there is no change in the total entropy, since the increase in the entropy of one gas is always exactly equal to the decrease in the entropy of the gas with which it is in contact. So that, if the first $(n-1)$ gases have

* The total energy of the gases in the two conditions will not in general be the same. The necessary external work can be provided by the change of potential energy of a reversible mechanical system, which for the sake of definiteness we shall suppose to be a system of weights in a gravitational field. This, of course, involves no change in the internal condition of any body.

the required entropies, that is, S_1', S_2', ... $S'_{(n-1)}$, the entropy of the nth gas necessarily has the value

$$(S_1 + S_2 + \ldots + S_n) - S_1' - S_2' - \ldots - S'_{(n-1)},$$

which by equation (9) is the required value S_n'.

Each gas can now by reversible adiabatic compression or expansion be brought to the required temperature or volume, any external work required being supplied by movements in a system of weights.

(d) We have supposed up to the present that all of the n bodies with which we are dealing are perfect gases. The only reason for this supposition was that it can easily be seen that it is possible to change the temperature of a perfect gas to any desired extent merely by compressing or expanding it adiabatically, and that it is possible to change the entropy of a perfect gas to any desired extent by compressing it or expanding it in contact with another body with which it is in thermal equilibrium.

We shall now show that it is possible to bring a system of n bodies, *one of which is a perfect gas*, from any given equilibrium condition to any other desired equilibrium condition by a reversible process without causing any change in any other body (except in the position of a set of weights) provided only that the sum of the entropies of all the bodies is the same in the two conditions, that is, that equation (9) is true.

We shall suppose that the nth body is the perfect gas. We first compress or expand the gas until it has the same temperature as body 1. We then place it in contact with body 1, and by further compressing or expanding it we can use it as a source or sink of heat, and thus use it to change the entropy of body 1 to any desired extent. Provided that any changes that occur in body 1 take place in a strictly reversible manner, the gain of entropy of body 1 is exactly equal to the loss of entropy of the gas as in (a) above.*

Having changed the entropy of body 1 until it has the required value S_1', we proceed in exactly the same way with body 2, and so on. As in (c), at the end of the process the body n (in this case the perfect gas) must by equation (9) have the required entropy S_n'.

We can now by adiabatic processes, involving only the movement of pistons, bring each of the bodies to its desired final condition; this is specified by the value of the temperature or of one of the other variables.

(e) We shall now use this result to prove that *it is impossible to diminish the entropy of a system of bodies without causing a change in some body outside the system other than a change in the positions of a system of weights.*

Let us suppose that the entropies of the bodies are initially S_1, S_2, ... S_n, and that the body n is a perfect gas whose temperature is T_n and volume V_n. We shall now suppose that some process takes place which causes a diminution in the total entropy of the group of bodies without causing any change in any body outside the system (except in the position of a system of weights).

We now carry out the process described in (d) and bring each of the first $(n-1)$ bodies back to its original condition; this can be done as described with-

---

* We make no restrictions as to the nature of the changes that may occur in body 1, but we do assume that they can be carried out reversibly. It is not possible or necessary to consider in detail the mechanism required to carry out any particular change reversibly. We may mention, however, that any chemical reaction, since it never proceeds completely in one direction, but always proceeds to a condition in which all the re-acting substances are in equilibrium, can, at least ideally, be carried out reversibly. The mechanism is in general complicated, and consists of semi-permeable membranes attached to pistons. By moving these pistons the reaction can be made to proceed in either direction, and the work done during the movement can be obtained merely by alterations in the positions of a system of weights.

out any change in the total entropy. At the end of this process, therefore, the entropy of the nth body, the perfect gas, must be less than it was originally; we expand or compress it adiabatically until its temperature is restored to its original value T_n, its volume being now $\mathbf{V}_n'$. From equation (1) we see that $\mathbf{V}_n'$ must necessarily be less than $\mathbf{V}_n$.

We can now allow the perfect gas to expand into a vacuum as in Joule's experiment, so that its volume becomes $\mathbf{V}_n$. Its temperature does not change during this process, so that the whole system is now exactly in its original condition.

Since the whole system is in its original condition, and since, further, no change has taken place in any body outside the system, in particular, no heat has been abstracted from any such body, the net external work done during the whole process must be zero.* And since, during the last step of the process, that is, the irreversible expansion of the perfect gas from the volume $\mathbf{V}_n'$ to the volume $\mathbf{V}_n$, the external work is zero, it follows that the external work in passing from the original condition to the last stage but one is zero. That is, in passing from the original condition to one in which no change has taken place in any body except that the volume of the perfect gas has been reduced from $\mathbf{V}_n$ to $\mathbf{V}_n'$, its temperature being the same, the net external work is zero. In other words, without producing any change in any other body and without doing any net external work, the volume of the perfect gas has been reduced, its temperature remaining constant.

We can now show that this is a violation of the second law of thermodynamics. For let us suppose that the expansion from volume $\mathbf{V}_n'$ to volume $\mathbf{V}_n$ takes place not irreversibly, as we have supposed above, but reversibly and isothermally, the expanding gas being in contact with a heat reservoir at temperature T_n. Useful external work is done during this process. The process is cyclical and can be continued indefinitely, and the net result is that we can obtain an indefinite amount of external work merely by abstracting heat from a heat reservoir. This is in contradiction to the second law of thermodynamics,† and, therefore, the whole process which we have imagined is impossible. In other words, the assumption that it is possible by any physical or chemical process to diminish the entropy of a system of bodies, without producing any change in any body outside the system other than in the positions of a system of weights, leads to a violation of the second law of thermodynamics. It is, therefore, incorrect, and the proposition stated at the beginning of this section is proved.

If then a system of bodies passes by any physical or chemical process from one condition to another without causing any change in any body outside the system (except in the position of a set of weights), the entropy of the system is always greater in the final than in the original condition (or in the limiting case of a reversible change the entropies in the two conditions are equal). In other words, *every physical and chemical process which takes place in nature proceeds in such a way that the total entropy of all the bodies taking any part in the process is increased.* In the limiting case of a reversible process the total entropy remains constant. This is the principle of the increase of entropy.‡

* That is, the net change of potential energy of the system of weights in the whole cycle of changes is zero.

† If it were possible to obtain work in this way, we could use the work to drive a refrigerating machine which transferred heat from the same reservoir to a hotter one. The total result would be a self-acting machine which effected the cooling of a cold body and the transfer of heat from it to a hotter one. This is a violation of the second law.

‡ For a general discussion of the second law and the principle of increase of entropy, see Hausen, *Phys. Zeits.*, Vol. 35, p. 517 (1934).

CHAPTER XVI

The Conditions of Equilibrium of a Physical or Chemical System

General Laws governing Changes in a Physical or Chemical System

1. We shall now apply the principle of the increase of entropy, to-gether with the first law of thermodynamics, to determine general laws which govern the physical or chemical changes taking place in a system of bodies which we shall suppose at a common temperature T. We shall thus be able to determine the general conditions of equilibrium of such a system of bodies, which may be homogeneous or heterogeneous.

The expression of the first law for an infinitesimal change in the system is

$$dU = dQ + dW, \qquad \ldots \ldots \quad (1)$$

where U is the total or internal energy of the system, dQ is the heat flowing into the system while the infinitesimal change is taking place, and dW is the work done on the system by the external forces.

The expression of the principle of increase of entropy is

$$dS + dS_0 \geqslant 0, \qquad \ldots \ldots \quad (2)$$

where S is the entropy of the system and S_0 that of the surrounding medium. The equality sign refers to reversible or quasi-static changes, which are an ideal limiting case and do not occur in practice. The inequality sign refers to natural changes.

We may suppose that any changes in the surrounding medium take place reversibly,* so that

---

* The advantage of making this assumption is that it enables us to assert that the gain of entropy of the system we are considering is greater than the heat gained divided by the temperature. If we did not make this assumption, equation (3) would become

$$dS - \frac{dU - dW}{T} + \epsilon > 0,$$

where ϵ is an essentially positive quantity, representing what we may for convenience call the degree of irreversibility of the changes taking place in the surrounding medium. This relation can be established by considering the case in which the transfer of heat is the same as before, but supposing that all changes taking place in the system are reversible, while those in the surrounding medium are irreversible. It is obviously more valuable to be able to say that dS is greater than $(dU - dW)/T$, than to say that dS *plus* an essentially positive quantity is greater than $(dU - dW)/T$, since the former statement contains the latter, while the latter does not contain the former.

$$dS_0 = -\frac{dQ}{T},$$

and equation (2) becomes

$$dS - dQ/T \geqslant 0.$$

Substituting from (1), we have

$$dS - \frac{dU - dW}{T} \geqslant 0, \quad \ldots \ldots \quad (3)$$

or
$$dU - T\,dS \leqslant dW. \quad \ldots \ldots \quad (4)$$

The left-hand side of this relation cannot in general be integrated, but in the cases which are important in practice the use of another relation, expressing the conditions under which the change takes place, together with (4), enables us to integrate the latter, and thus to obtain a law applicable to finite changes. We now consider these cases.

2. Adiabatic Changes.

For a system which is thermally isolated from its surroundings so that there cannot be any exchange of heat with them, we have $dQ = 0$. Thus, in an infinitesimal adiabatic change we have, from equation (1),

$$dU = dW,$$

and then, from equation (4),

$$dS \geqslant 0.$$

The equality sign holds for a reversible process, and the inequality sign for a natural process. There are two cases to be considered: the infinitesimal change can take place with either the volume or the pressure of the system kept constant. If the change takes place at constant volume, the work done on the system is zero, and we have

$$dU = 0, \quad dV = 0, \quad dS \geqslant 0, \quad \ldots \ldots \quad (5)$$

for the two cases of natural and reversible processes. If the system is kept at constant pressure during the adiabatic change, the work done on the system is given by

$$dW = dU = -p\,dV = -d(pV),$$

so that
$$d(U + pV) = 0.$$

Thus, if we define the heat content or total heat by *

$$H = U + pV,$$

* Compare Section 12 of Chapter IV.

we have, for an infinitesimal change at constant pressure, that

$$d\mathbf{H} = 0, \quad dp = 0, \quad d\mathbf{S} \geqslant 0, \quad . \quad . \quad . \quad . \quad (6)$$

where the equality sign holds for a reversible change and the inequality sign for a natural process.

3. Isothermal Changes.

If the temperature is held constant, equation (4) becomes

$$d(\mathbf{U} - T\mathbf{S}) \leqslant d\mathbf{W}; \quad . \quad . \quad . \quad . \quad . \quad (7)$$

that is, the increase of the quantity $(\mathbf{U} - T\mathbf{S})$ is less than, or in the limiting case equal to, the work done on the system from outside.

Let us write * $$\mathbf{U} - T\mathbf{S} = \mathbf{F}. \quad . \quad . \quad . \quad . \quad . \quad (8)$$

We have for an isothermal *reversible* change

$$d\mathbf{F} = d\mathbf{W},$$

or, integrating, $$\mathbf{F}_2 - \mathbf{F}_1 = \int_1^2 d\mathbf{W}; \quad . \quad . \quad . \quad . \quad (9)$$

that is, in an isothermal reversible change the increase in the value of the quantity $\mathbf{F}$ is equal to the work done on the system from outside, or in an isothermal reversible change the decrease in the value of the quantity $\mathbf{F}$ is equal to the work obtainable from the system. For this reason Helmholtz named the quantity $\mathbf{F}$ the *free energy* of the system; $\mathbf{U}$ is the *total or internal energy*; the difference $\mathbf{U} - \mathbf{F} = T\mathbf{S}$ we may call the *bound energy*. We shall refer to $\mathbf{F}$ as the *Helmholtz free energy*.

For an irreversible isothermal change we have

$$d\mathbf{F} < d\mathbf{W},$$

or, integrating, $$\mathbf{F}_2 - \mathbf{F}_1 < \int_1^2 d\mathbf{W}; \quad . \quad . \quad . \quad . \quad (10)$$

---

* It is most important to realize the exact meaning of this equation and of the quantities occurring in it. We have already noticed that we have no way of knowing the absolute value of the internal energy of a body, and that all we can measure is the change in internal energy in passing from one state to another. The quantity $\mathbf{U}$ is the change in the internal energy of the body in passing from some arbitrarily fixed zero condition (which may be expressed in terms of the temperature and the specific volume) to that condition to which the value of $\mathbf{U}$ refers. In this case $\mathbf{U}$ has a perfectly definite meaning.

In a similar way we have seen that we can attach no meaning to the absolute entropy of a body, and that we can only measure changes of entropy. The entropy $\mathbf{S}$ in a given condition is the change in the entropy of the body in passing from a fixed arbitrary zero condition to the given condition. This zero condition is taken as the same as the zero from which measurements of $\mathbf{U}$ are made.

In the zero condition we have therefore $\mathbf{U} = 0$ and $\mathbf{S} = 0$; it follows from equation (7) that in this condition the value of $\mathbf{F}$ for the body is also equal to zero. Provided the zero condition is definitely specified, the quantities $\mathbf{U}$, $\mathbf{S}$, and $\mathbf{F}$ all have perfectly definite values.

It follows that $d\mathbf{F}$ is a perfect differential.

that is, in an isothermal irreversible process the increase in the free energy is less than the work done on the system. In other words, the work gained from an isothermal change is always numerically less than, or in the limiting case equal to, the decrease in the free energy of the system. The diminution in the free energy therefore represents the maximum work that can be obtained from the system.

Up to the present we have considered the change in the free energy in isothermal changes only. For a change in which the temperature is not constant, we have, from equation (8),

$$d\mathbf{F} = d\mathbf{U} - T\,d\mathbf{S} - \mathbf{S}\,dT, \quad \ldots \ldots \quad (11)$$

and, substituting in this from (4), we have

$$d\mathbf{F} \leqslant d\mathbf{W} - \mathbf{S}\,dT.$$

This relation is not, however, of great practical use.

4. As in considering a thermally isolated system, the infinitesimal changes which we are considering can be carried out with the system kept either at constant volume or at constant pressure. For an infinitesimal change at constant volume, the work done on the system is zero, and we have

$$dT = 0, \quad d\mathbf{V} = 0, \quad d\mathbf{F} \leqslant 0, \quad \ldots \ldots \quad (12)$$

corresponding to natural and reversible changes respectively. Thus, for changes at constant temperature and constant volume, the Helmholtz free energy falls or remains constant. If, on the other hand, we suppose not the volume but the pressure to be kept constant during the infinitesimal change, the work done on the system is given by

$$d\mathbf{W} = -p\,d\mathbf{V}.$$

In this case, equation (4) becomes

$$d\mathbf{U} - T\,d\mathbf{S} + p\,d\mathbf{V} \leqslant 0.$$

Thus, for a change at constant temperature and constant pressure,

$$d(\mathbf{U} - T\mathbf{S} + p\mathbf{V}) = 0. \quad \ldots \ldots \quad (13)$$

If we define a function $\mathbf{G}$ by

$$\mathbf{G} = \mathbf{U} - T\mathbf{S} + p\mathbf{V}, \quad \ldots \ldots \quad (14)$$

in this case, the conditions become

$$dT = 0, \quad dp = 0, \quad d\mathbf{G} \leqslant 0, \quad \ldots \ldots \quad (15)$$

where the equality sign refers to a reversible process, and the inequality sign refers to a natural process. The quantity $\mathbf{G}$ is called the *thermo·*

dynamic potential at constant pressure, or the *Gibbs function,* or the *Gibbs free energy.* Thus, for changes at constant pressure and constant temperature, in which all the work is mechanical, the Gibbs function falls or (in the limiting case) remains constant.

Conditions of Equilibrium

5. Up to the present we have dealt with the changes taking place in a system. We now consider the general conditions of equilibrium. For any natural change we have, from equation (3),

$$d\mathbf{S} - \frac{d\mathbf{U} - d\mathbf{W}}{T} > 0.$$

We now consider a *virtual* change in the system, that is, a conceivable change which is considered for the purpose of calculation. We shall use the sign δ to denote the change in a function during a virtual change, and reserve d to be used for that in an actual change. Any infinitesimal virtual change in a system is necessarily reversible, for a naturally occurring change represents an approach towards equilibrium. If the system is already in equilibrium, the virtual change cannot be a natural one; nor can a virtual infinitesimal change be an *unnatural* change, that is, a change for which the opposite inequality signs to those in equations (5), (6), (12), and (15), for a natural process, hold—for any infinitesimal virtual change can be effected also in the opposite sense. If this were done with respect to an unnatural change, it would lead to a natural change; and this would again contradict the assumption that the system is in complete equilibrium. Thus, for a system in equilibrium, every infinitesimal virtual change must be reversible. For such a change, we have

$$\delta\mathbf{S} - (\delta\mathbf{U} - \delta\mathbf{W})/T = 0. \quad \ldots \ldots \quad (16)$$

If this equation is satisfied, the system is in absolutely stable equilibrium. On the other hand, even if, for a given change,

$$\delta\mathbf{S} - (\delta\mathbf{U} - \delta\mathbf{W})/T > 0,$$

the change will not necessarily take place. In this case the equilibrium is unstable or metastable: for example, a supercooled liquid.

It must be noted that the virtual changes considered must be consistent with the prescribed external conditions. For instance, for an isolated system they must be such that there is no loss or gain of heat, and so on. We shall now consider some special cases of this kind.

In this case, therefore, the system is in equilibrium if the Helmholtz free energy is a minimum. That equation (19) refers to a minimum, and not to a maximum, value of the Helmholtz free energy follows because in any *natural* process the Helmholtz free energy can only fall, or alternatively, it can be seen directly from equation (12).

If the infinitesimal virtual change is carried out at constant pressure, the work done on the system is given by

$$\delta W = -p\,\delta V = -\delta(pV);$$

equation (16) then becomes

$$\delta S - \delta U/T + \delta(pV)/T = -\delta(U - TS + pV)/T = 0,$$

or

$$\delta G = 0.$$

Thus, for an isothermal equilibrium at constant pressure, the conditions of equilibrium are given by

$$\delta T = 0, \quad \delta p = 0, \quad \delta G = 0. \quad . \quad . \quad . \quad (20)$$

In this case, therefore, the system is in equilibrium if the Gibbs function is a minimum. That equation (20) refers to a minimum, and not to a maximum, value of the Gibbs function follows from the fact that in any *natural* process the Gibbs function can only fall. Alternatively, it can be seen directly from equation (15).

Any one of the four sets of equilibrium conditions given by equations (17), (18), (19), and (20) is sufficient by itself, and has an equal claim with any of the others to be regarded as fundamental.

THE EQUILIBRIUM BETWEEN TWO STATES OF THE SAME SUBSTANCE

8. Clausius-Clapeyron Equation.

We shall now apply the above results to determine the conditions under which two given states of the same substance are in equilibrium. For the sake of definiteness we may consider the equilibrium between a liquid and its vapour, but exactly the same considerations apply to the equilibrium between solid and liquid or between vapour and solid.

We may imagine the substance enclosed in a cylinder with a moving piston, the external pressure on which is equal to the vapour pressure at the temperature under consideration. The condition for equilibrium is that given in Section 7, namely, that for a change consistent with the external conditions the change in the total Gibbs function of the system shall be zero. Such a change is to allow a small mass of the liquid dm to vaporize, the pressure and temperature remaining constant. The Gibbs function of the liquid falls by an amount $G_1\,dm$ and that of the vapour increases by an amount $G_2 dm$, where G_1 and G_2 are the Gibbs functions per unit mass of the liquid and vapour respectively at the temperature and pressure considered. The total change, dG, in the Gibbs function of the system is given by

$$dG = (G_2 - G_1)dm,$$

and the condition that this vanishes is that

$$G_1 = G_2; \quad \cdots \cdots \cdots \quad (21)$$

that is, that the Gibbs functions per unit mass of the liquid and the vapour are equal.

Writing the values for G_1 and G_2 in full, we obtain

$$U_1 - Ts_1 + pv_1 = U_2 - Ts_2 + pv_2,$$

or

$$T(s_2 - s_1) = (U_2 - U_1) + p(v_2 - v_1). \quad \cdots \quad (22)$$

The quantity on the left-hand side of this equation, the difference between the entropy of unit mass of the vapour and that of unit mass

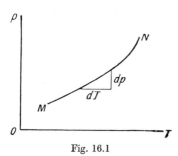

Fig. 16.1

of the liquid in the states in which they are in equilibrium multiplied by the absolute temperature, is the latent heat of vaporization. The importance of the equation is that it shows that the latent heat is divided into two parts: $(U_2 - U_1)$ represents the difference between the internal energies of vapour and liquid—called the internal latent heat—while $p(v_2 - v_1)$ represents the work done against the external pressure during vaporization — called the external latent heat.

We shall now determine the variation of p with temperature. If MN in fig. 16.1 is the vapour-pressure curve, and dp and dT are corresponding changes in p and T along the curve, the changes in G_1 and G_2 are

$$dG_1 = \left(\frac{\partial G_1}{\partial p}\right)_T dp + \left(\frac{\partial G_1}{\partial T}\right)_p dT; \quad dG_2 = \left(\frac{\partial G_2}{\partial p}\right)_T dp + \left(\frac{\partial G_2}{\partial T}\right)_p dT.$$

In order that equation (21) may be satisfied at all points on the curve we must have

$$dG_1 = dG_2,$$

or

$$\left(\frac{\partial G_1}{\partial p}\right)_T dp + \left(\frac{\partial G_1}{\partial T}\right)_p dT = \left(\frac{\partial G_2}{\partial p}\right)_T dp + \left(\frac{\partial G_2}{\partial T}\right)_p dT.$$

6. Equilibrium in a Thermally Isolated System. Adiabatic Equilibrium.

In this case, there is no exchange of heat with the surroundings and $d\mathbf{Q} = 0$. Thus, from equation (1),

$$d\mathbf{U} = d\mathbf{W}.$$

We have to consider two cases according as the infinitesimal change is carried out with the system kept at constant volume or at constant pressure. For a constant-volume change, no work is done on the system and equation (16) leads to the equilibrium conditions

$$\delta\mathbf{S} = 0, \quad \delta\mathbf{V} = 0, \quad \delta\mathbf{U} = 0. \quad . \quad . \quad . \quad (17)$$

For a constant-pressure change, an amount of work $-p\,\delta\mathbf{V}$ is done on the system, so that

$$\delta\mathbf{H} = \delta(\mathbf{U} + p\mathbf{V}) = \delta\mathbf{U} + p\,\delta\mathbf{V}$$

is zero. The equilibrium conditions are given by

$$\delta\mathbf{S} = 0, \quad \delta p = 0, \quad \delta\mathbf{H} = 0. \quad . \quad . \quad . \quad (18)$$

Thus, for a system which cannot exchange heat with its surroundings, the entropy has a maximum value when it is in equilibrium. That equations (17) and (18) correspond to a maximum, and not to a minimum, value of the entropy follows because in any *natural* process the entropy increases. Alternatively, it can be seen directly from equations (5) and (6).

7. Isothermal Equilibrium.

For a system which is maintained at constant temperature, equation (16) becomes

$$\delta(\mathbf{S} - \mathbf{U}/T) + \delta\mathbf{W}/T = 0,$$

or, using equation (8), $\quad \delta\mathbf{F} = \delta\mathbf{W},$

that is, for a system in equilibrium maintained at constant temperature, the free energy can fall only if the system does an equivalent amount of external work.

To derive the general conditions of isothermal equilibrium, we have again to consider the two cases in which, while the infinitesimal change is taking place, the system is kept at constant volume or at constant pressure. If the volume is kept constant, no external work is done by the system; it follows that the Helmholtz free energy must remain unaltered in an infinitesimal virtual change. Thus, the conditions of equilibrium are given by

$$\delta T = 0, \quad \delta\mathbf{V} = 0, \quad \delta\mathbf{F} = 0. \quad . \quad . \quad . \quad (19)$$

But from equations (39) and (40) below we have $\left(\dfrac{\partial G}{\partial p}\right)_T = v$, $\left(\dfrac{\partial G}{\partial T}\right)_p = -s$, and using these the above equation becomes

$$\frac{dp}{dT} = \frac{s_2 - s_1}{v_2 - v_1}.$$

But $(s_2 - s_1)$ is equal to λ/T, where λ is the latent heat of vaporization, so that

$$\frac{dp}{dT} = \frac{\lambda}{T(v_2 - v_1)}. \qquad \ldots \ldots (23)$$

This is the famous Clausius-Clapeyron equation giving the change of vapour pressure (or equilibrium pressure) with temperature. It should be noted that the derivative which occurs here is the rate of change *along the equilibrium curve*. We have already applied this equation in expressing the results of vapour-pressure measurements in Chapter VIII. If we write Δv for the difference in the specific volumes of the two states, and Δs for the difference in their entropies, the Clausius-Clapeyron equation can be written

$$\frac{dp}{dT} = \frac{\Delta s}{\Delta v}. \qquad \ldots \ldots (23')$$

The equation is a direct consequence of the second law of thermodynamics. All the quantities occuring in equation (23) can be measured directly, so that the truth of the equation and, therefore, of the second law of thermodynamics can be tested experimentally. We consider the following figures for the vaporization of water at 100° C. under a pressure of 1 atmosphere.

$T = 273 \cdot 15 + 100 = 373 \cdot 15$.

$v_2 = 1674$ c.c. according to Knoblauch, Linde, and Klebe (this is the volume of 1 gm. of saturated water vapour at 100° C.).

$v_1 = 1$ c.c.

$\dfrac{dp}{dT} = 27 \cdot 12$ mm. of mercury per degree at 100° C., according to the measurements of Holborn and Henning. This must be reduced to absolute units. Using the result that 1 atmosphere or 760 mm. of mercury is equal to $1 \cdot 013 \times 10^6$ dynes per square centimetre, we obtain

$$\frac{dp}{dT} = \frac{27 \cdot 12}{760} \times 1 \cdot 013 \times 10^6 \text{ dynes per square centimetre.}$$

These results enable us to calculate the value of the latent heat of vaporization as

$$\lambda = \frac{373 \cdot 15 \times 1673 \times 27 \cdot 12 \times 1 \cdot 013 \times 10^6}{760}$$

$$= 2256 \text{ joules},$$

which agrees with Henning's direct measurement of the latent heat at 100° C.

Similarly, equation (23) can be applied to the melting of solids. In this case λ is the latent heat of fusion and the subscript 1 refers to the solid and 2 to the liquid. We have

$$\frac{dT}{dp} = \frac{T(v_2 - v_1)}{\lambda}.$$

In general the liquid is less dense than the solid, so that v_2 is greater than v_1, and increasing the pressure raises the freezing-point. On the other hand, in the case of water the solid is less dense than the liquid, so that dT/dp is negative, and increasing the pressure lowers the freezing-point.

The actual lowering of the freezing-point of water can be calculated as follows using Osborne's value (see Chapter IX, Section 4) for the latent heat of fusion.

$$\lambda = 333 \cdot 5 \text{ int. joules per gram},$$
$$T = 273 \cdot 15,$$
$$v_2 = 1 \cdot 000 \text{ c.c. (volume of 1 gm. of water at 0° C.)},$$
$$v_1 = 1 \cdot 091 \text{ c.c. (volume of 1 gm. of ice at 0° C.)}.$$

We have, therefore,

$$\frac{dT}{dp} = - \frac{273 \cdot 15 \times 0 \cdot 091}{333 \cdot 5 \times 10^7} \text{ degrees per unit of pressure}$$

$$= - \frac{273 \cdot 15 \times 0 \cdot 091 \times 1 \cdot 013 \times 10^6}{333 \cdot 5 \times 10^7} \text{ degrees per atmosphere}$$

$$= - 0 \cdot 0075 \text{ degree per atmosphere.}$$

Moser * found by direct experiment the value

$$-0 \cdot 00748 \text{ degree per atmosphere},$$

which is in good agreement with the calculated value.

* H. Moser, *Ann. d. Physik*, Vol. 1, p. 341 (1929); see also Dewar, *Proc. Roy. Soc.*, A, Vol. 30, p. 533 (1880), who obtained the experimental value −0·0072 degree per atmosphere.

It will be recalled that on the thermodynamic temperature scale, the triple point of water is defined as 273·16° K. and the ice point is defined as 0·0100° K. less than this. The difference between this figure and the depression of the freezing-point calculated above is due to the effect of dissolved air.

The depression of the freezing-point of water by increase of pressure, or the melting of ice under pressure, has been adduced to explain a great many well-known phenomena. For example, if snow near the melting-point is squeezed between the hands, melting occurs at the points of greatest pressure, and the resulting liquid solidifies as soon as the pressure is removed. Thus a snowball is made. If the temperature is too much below the freezing-point, the pressure of the hand is not sufficient to melt the snow, and the ball will not make.

If a bar of ice is supported at its two ends, and a wire with a heavy weight attached to it is looped round the middle, the weight causes the wire to press against the ice so that it is melted under the wire. The liquid so formed flows out from underneath and solidifies behind the wire. In this way the wire gradually cuts its way completely through the bar, but the bar is not cut in two. It should be noted that this experiment is usually conducted at ordinary room temperature and also that the wire will be a comparatively good conductor of heat. It appears that an important factor in the experiment is the ready supply of heat along the wire from that part of it at room temperature to the ice.

Experience shows that skis slide readily on snow at temperatures as low as —20° C. and that this is effected by the formation of a film of water under the ski. An order of magnitude calculation shows * that this cannot be due to pressure melting. Consider a heavy man weighing 100 Kgm. on skis of area 5000 sq. cm. If the area of contact of ski and snow is as little as one ten-thousandth of the actual area of the ski, the depression of the melting-point due to the pressure would be about 1° C. With a powder such as snow, which can pack down to accommodate the surface of the ski, the area of contact is probably much greater than has been assumed in this calculation. Thus, the depression of the freezing-point under pressure cannot provide an explanation of ski-ing at low temperatures.

The energy generated by friction between a ski and the snow when the ski is moved forward 1 cm. is approximately 0·25 joule. Even if the ski were making rubbing contact over its whole area this would be sufficient to raise the temperature of the snow from —20° C. to 0° C. and to melt the snow in a layer several molecules thick. The important point to notice is that appreciable quantities of energy are generated by friction as the ski moves over the snow. This will be sufficient to cause local melting at the points of contact between the surface of

* F. P. Bowden and D. Tabor, *The Friction and Lubrication of Solids*, Clarendon Press, Oxford (1950), Chapter III.

the ski and the snow, and it is probably this that makes ski-ing possible at low temperatures.

We shall conclude this study of the equilibrium between two states of the same substance by obtaining a relation involving the specific heats of liquid and vapour and the latent heat of vaporization.

We have
$$\frac{\lambda}{T} = s_2 - s_1,$$

where as before the subscript 2 refers to the vapour and the subscript 1 to the liquid. Differentiating with respect to T, we obtain

$$\frac{1}{T}\frac{d\lambda}{dT} - \frac{\lambda}{T^2} = \left(\frac{\partial s_2}{\partial T}\right)_p + \left(\frac{\partial s_2}{\partial p}\right)_T \frac{dp}{dT} - \left(\frac{\partial s_1}{\partial T}\right)_p - \left(\frac{\partial s_1}{\partial p}\right)_T \frac{dp}{dT}.$$

Using equation (4), Chapter XIII, and Example 1, p. 341, this becomes

$$\frac{1}{T}\frac{d\lambda}{dT} - \frac{\lambda}{T^2} = \frac{(c_p)_2}{T} - \left(\frac{\partial v_2}{\partial T}\right)_p \frac{dp}{dT} - \frac{(c_p)_1}{T} + \left(\frac{\partial v_1}{\partial T}\right)_p \frac{dp}{dT}.$$

$\dfrac{dp}{dT}$ is given by equation (23),

$$\frac{dp}{dT} = \frac{\lambda}{T(v_2 - v_1)}.$$

Using this, we obtain

$$(c_p)_2 - (c_p)_1 = \frac{d\lambda}{dT} - \frac{\lambda}{T} + \frac{\lambda}{v_2 - v_1}\left\{\left(\frac{\partial v_2}{\partial T}\right)_p - \left(\frac{\partial v_1}{\partial T}\right)_p\right\}. \quad (24)$$

This equation has been applied in Chapter VIII, Section 24.

9. The Specific Heat of a Saturated Vapour.

Just as we defined the specific heats at constant pressure and at constant volume, so we can define other specific heats. If c is the specific heat under any conditions, the first law of thermodynamics gives the relation

$$c = \frac{du}{dT} + p\frac{dv}{dT}.$$

It is of interest to consider the case in which a vapour is heated and at the same time its volume is changed in such a way that it always remains in the saturated condition. We shall indicate the specific heat of the vapour under these conditions by $(c_s)_2$, the *specific heat of the saturated vapour*. We have

$$(c_s)_2 = \frac{d\mathrm{u}_2}{dT} + p_2 \frac{d\mathrm{v}_2}{dT}, \quad \ldots \ldots \ldots \quad (25)$$

where p_2 is the pressure of the saturated vapour at temperature T, and where the differential coefficients refer to changes along the saturation curve.

We cannot say from first principles whether $(c_s)_2$ will be positive or negative. While the vapour is heated, it must, if it is to remain saturated, be compressed at the same time, because the specific volume of a saturated vapour diminishes with increasing temperature. Heat is generated by the compression, and it is possible that this heat may be sufficient to superheat the vapour. On this account there are two possible cases. (1) The heat of compression is so great that the saturated vapour is superheated by adiabatic compression. In this case, in order that the vapour may remain saturated, it is necessary to extract heat from it, and $(c_s)_2$ is negative. (2) The heat of compression is not enough to keep the vapour saturated when it is compressed adiabatically. In this case heat must be supplied, and $(c_s)_2$ is positive. The limiting case in which $(c_s)_2 = 0$ is also possible. In this case the curve of saturated vapour pressure coincides with the curve of adiabatic compression.

We now determine the value of $(c_s)_2$ from equation (23). We first write the equation for the liquid corresponding to (25) for the vapour:

$$(c_s)_1 = \frac{d\mathrm{u}_1}{dT} + p_1 \frac{d\mathrm{v}_1}{dT}. \quad \ldots \ldots \ldots \quad (26)$$

This specific heat corresponds to heating in which the pressure is always maintained equal to the vapour pressure. If the outer pressure is not too large it has very little influence on the specific heat, and the second term on the right of equation (26) is small compared with the first, so that we can put

$$(c_s)_1 = (c_p)_1. \quad \ldots \ldots \ldots \quad (27)$$

Taking the difference between (25) and (26), we obtain

$$(c_s)_2 - (c_s)_1 = \frac{d(\mathrm{u}_2 - \mathrm{u}_1)}{dT} + p_2 \frac{d(\mathrm{v}_2 - \mathrm{v}_1)}{dT},$$

since p_1 is equal to p_2.

Since $\lambda = T(\mathrm{s}_2 - \mathrm{s}_1)$, we have, by differentiating equation (22),

$$\frac{d\lambda}{dT} = \frac{d(\mathrm{u}_2 - \mathrm{u}_1)}{dT} + p_2 \frac{d(\mathrm{v}_2 - \mathrm{v}_1)}{dT} + (\mathrm{v}_2 - \mathrm{v}_1)\frac{dp_2}{dT},$$

so that

$$(c_s)_2 - (c_s)_1 = \frac{d\lambda}{dT} - (\mathrm{v}_2 - \mathrm{v}_1)\frac{dp_2}{dT},$$

or, from (27) and (23),

$$(c_s)_2 = (c_p)_1 + \frac{d\lambda}{dT} - \frac{\lambda}{T}. \quad \ldots \ldots \ldots \quad (28)$$

For water vapour at $100°$ C. we have from experiment

$$(c_p)_1 = 1\cdot01 \text{ (the specific heat of liquid water at } 100° \text{ C.),}$$

$$\frac{d\lambda}{dT} = -0\cdot64,$$

$$\lambda = 539,$$

$$T = 373,$$

so that $$(c_s)_2 = 1\cdot01 - 0\cdot64 - 1\cdot44 = -1\cdot07,$$

a negative quantity.

We see, therefore, that water comes under class (1), and that adiabatic compression of saturated water vapour superheats it. In the same way it follows that adiabatic expansion of saturated water vapour causes it to become supersaturated, so that, if nuclei are present, it condenses and forms a fog.

HETEROGENEOUS SYSTEMS

10. Definition of Phase, Component.

The equilibrium conditions which we have developed so far in this chapter are applicable to pure species or to systems of fixed composition. That is, we have been concerned with the equilibrium between different states of aggregation of the same substance. We shall now consider the equilibrium between mixtures of various substances. The following definitions are important.

Each different, physically homogeneous part of a system is called a *phase*. For example, if a mass of water exists partly in the solid, partly in the liquid, and partly in the vapour state of aggregation, the system contains three phases.

The number of *components* of a system is defined as the number of substances the masses of which in each phase determine completely the physical condition of the phase, provided the pressure p and the temperature T are known. The components selected to describe the system must be independent and sufficient in number to define the composition completely. For complicated systems, analytical criteria can be developed to determine the appropriate components to select.*

The simplest way of arriving at the total number of components of a system is the following. Take the total number of chemical elements present in the system; these can be divided into two groups, such that the mass of all the elements in the first group is known if the mass of each element in the second group is known. The number of elements in the second group is the number of components of the system. Let us take some examples.

Consider an aqueous solution of sulphuric acid. The elements present are H, S, and O. If we know the masses of H and S, the mass of O can be deduced. This is therefore a system of two components. It is important to note that the actual molecular species present do not concern us here. For example, in this particular case we have present H_2SO_4 molecules and also hydrated H_2SO_4 molecules, H^+ ions and SO_4^- ions, H_2O molecules, and complex $(H_2O)_n$ molecules.

Now suppose we have an aqueous solution of NaCl, NaBr, KCl, and KBr. If we know the masses of H, Na, K, and Br, the masses of O and of Cl can be deduced; for the mass of H fixes the mass of O, and the number of equivalents

* Brinkley, *Journ. Chem. Phys.*, Vol. 14, p. 563 (1946).

of Cl must necessarily be equal to the sum of the numbers of equivalents of Na and K less the number of equivalents of Br. This is therefore a system of four components.

11. Complete Description of a Phase.

The volume and the chemical composition of a phase are not sufficient to give a complete description of it, for the phase might be able to absorb or to lose heat without either its volume or its chemical composition changing. For a complete description of a phase, one more variable must be specified. To do this, we could choose the temperature, pressure, internal energy, or entropy. The phase is then completely specified by its composition and a pair of other variables. In the preceding sections, we have considered a phase of fixed composition, that is, one in which the components have fixed masses, and we have been able to specify it by one pair of variables. If, for example, the system is in an electromagnetic field, other pairs of variables are required to complete the description of it. We have already examined such a case in considering the process of adiabatic demagnetization (Section 16 of Chapter V). There we introduced the " magnetic Gibbs function " which depended also on the pair of variables, magnetic field strength and magnetization.

12. Relations Between the Thermodynamical Functions.

We now consider a general heterogeneous system. To start with, it is convenient to describe a given phase by its chemical composition, which is specified by the number of moles n_i of each species i, its volume $\mathbf{V}$ and its entropy $\mathbf{S}$. Then, any of the properties of the phase can be regarded as a function of the independent variables $\mathbf{V}$, $\mathbf{S}$ and the n_i. For example, if we consider the internal energy, the change it undergoes, corresponding to any variation in either the state or the composition of the phase, is given by

$$d\mathbf{U} = \left(\frac{\partial \mathbf{U}}{\partial \mathbf{S}}\right)_{\mathbf{V}, n_i} d\mathbf{S} + \left(\frac{\partial \mathbf{U}}{\partial \mathbf{V}}\right)_{\mathbf{S}, n_i} d\mathbf{V} + \sum_i \left(\frac{\partial \mathbf{U}}{\partial n_i}\right)_{\mathbf{S}, \mathbf{V}, n_j} dn_i, \quad (29)$$

where the suffix n_j refers to all the molar quantities of the type n_i except n_i itself; that is, this differentiation is carried out keeping the mole fractions of all the components, except the species i, constant. The partial derivatives which occur in this expression are functions of the state of the given phase, and neither of its surroundings nor of the way in which it reached its actual state. If we introduce quantities μ_i defined by

$$\mu_i = \left(\frac{\partial \mathbf{U}}{\partial n_i}\right)_{\mathbf{S}, \mathbf{V}, n_j}, \quad \ldots \ldots \quad (30)$$

then, using equations (13) and (14) of Chapter XII, we obtain

$$d\mathbf{U} = T d\mathbf{S} - p d\mathbf{V} + \sum_i \mu_i dn_i, \quad . \quad . \quad (31)$$

where T and p are the temperature and the pressure of the given phase. The quantity μ_i is called the *partial potential of the component i in the given phase.* The use of partial potentials, first introduced by Willard Gibbs,* simplifies the discussion of chemical equilibria, and of equilibria which involve changes in the composition of one or more phases, very greatly. Equation (31) is equivalent to the relations

$$T = \left(\frac{\partial \mathbf{U}}{\partial \mathbf{S}}\right)_{\mathbf{V}, n_i}, \quad \cdots \cdots \cdots \quad (32)$$

$$p = -\left(\frac{\partial \mathbf{U}}{\partial \mathbf{V}}\right)_{\mathbf{S}, n_i}, \quad \cdots \cdots \cdots \quad (33)$$

and

$$\mu_i = \left(\frac{\partial \mathbf{U}}{\partial n_i}\right)_{\mathbf{S}, \mathbf{V}, n_j}. \quad \cdots \cdots \cdots \quad (34)$$

The various thermodynamical functions can be expressed in terms of $\mathbf{U}$ and its partial derivatives with respect to the independent variables $\mathbf{S}$ and $\mathbf{V}$. We have

$$\mathbf{F} = \mathbf{U} - T\mathbf{S} = \mathbf{U} - \mathbf{S}\left(\frac{\partial \mathbf{U}}{\partial \mathbf{S}}\right)_{\mathbf{V}, n_i} = \left[\frac{\partial (\mathbf{U}/\mathbf{S})}{\partial (1/\mathbf{S})}\right]_{\mathbf{V}, n_i}, \quad \cdot \quad (35)$$

$$\mathbf{G} = \mathbf{U} - T\mathbf{S} + p\mathbf{V} = \mathbf{U} - \mathbf{S}\left(\frac{\partial \mathbf{U}}{\partial \mathbf{S}}\right)_{\mathbf{V}, n_i} - \mathbf{V}\left(\frac{\partial \mathbf{U}}{\partial \mathbf{V}}\right)_{\mathbf{S}, n_i}, \quad (36)$$

and

$$\mathbf{H} = \mathbf{U} + p\mathbf{V} = \mathbf{U} - \mathbf{V}\left(\frac{\partial \mathbf{U}}{\partial \mathbf{V}}\right)_{\mathbf{S}, n_i} = \left[\frac{\partial (\mathbf{U}/\mathbf{V})}{\partial (1/\mathbf{V})}\right]_{\mathbf{S}, n_i}. \quad \cdot \quad (37)$$

We have seen that the Gibbs function is defined by the relation

$$\mathbf{G} = \mathbf{U} - T\mathbf{S} + p\mathbf{V}.$$

Differentiation of this relation, and use of equation (31), yields the relation

$$d\mathbf{G} = -\mathbf{S}\,dT + \mathbf{V}\,dp + \sum_i \mu_i dn_i. \quad \cdots \cdots \quad (38)$$

In this case, T, p and the n_i have been chosen as the independent variables. This differential expression is equivalent to the set of relations

$$\mathbf{S} = -\left(\frac{\partial \mathbf{G}}{\partial T}\right)_{p, n_i}, \quad \cdots \cdots \cdots \quad (39)$$

$$\mathbf{V} = \left(\frac{\partial \mathbf{G}}{\partial p}\right)_{T, n_i}, \quad \cdots \cdots \cdots \quad (40)$$

and

$$\mu_i = \left(\frac{\partial \mathbf{G}}{\partial n_i}\right)_{T, p, n_j}. \quad \cdots \cdots \cdots \quad (41)$$

* Willard Gibbs, *Trans. Connecticut Acad.*, Vol. 3, p. 108 (1875); p. 343 (1877).

The other thermodynamical functions can be expressed in terms of G and its partial derivatives with respect to the independent variables T and p. We get

$$U = G - T\left(\frac{\partial G}{\partial T}\right)_{p,\, n_i} - p\left(\frac{\partial G}{\partial p}\right)_{T,\, n_i}, \qquad \cdots \quad (42)$$

$$H = G - T\left(\frac{\partial G}{\partial T}\right)_{p,\, n_i} = \left[\frac{\partial\,(G/T)}{\partial\,(1/T)}\right]_{p,\, n_i}, \qquad \cdots \quad (43)$$

and

$$F = G - p\left(\frac{\partial G}{\partial p}\right)_{T,\, n_i} = \left[\frac{\partial\,(G/p)}{\partial\,(1/p)}\right]_{T,\, n_i}. \qquad \cdots \quad (44)$$

With respect to the choice of T, p and the n_i as independent variables, G, regarded as a function of these variables, is called the *characteristic function*. All the other thermodynamical functions can be expressed in terms of G and its differential coefficients with respect to T, p and the n_i. This choice of independent variables and characteristic function is probably the most useful in the study of physical and chemical equilibria. But other choices are possible. As we have seen at the beginning of this section, U is the characteristic function corresponding to S, V and the n_i as independent variables; H is that corresponding to the choice of S, p, and the n_i as independent variables; and F is that corresponding to the choice of T, V and the n_i as independent variables. For each of these possible choices, the student should determine the other thermodynamical functions in terms of the appropriate characteristic function and its differential coefficients with respect to the particular independent variables.

13. Chemical Equilibrium Between Phases.

We shall now consider the thermodynamic equilibrium of a system of C components and of P phases. We shall suppose that the pressure p and the temperature T are the same throughout the system, and that both remain constant. For simplicity we may suppose that the system is contained in a cylinder with a movable piston, and that the pressure on the piston is kept constant while the whole is contained in a constant-temperature bath. The components of the system will be denoted by subscript italic letters and the phases by superscript Greek letters. Thus $n_i{}^\alpha$ is the number of moles of species i in the phase α, while G^α is the Gibbs function of the phase α. The Gibbs function of the whole system is

$$G = \sum_\alpha G^\alpha. \qquad \cdots \cdots \quad (45)$$

For a system at constant temperature and constant pressure, the condition of equilibrium is that

$$dG = \sum_\alpha dG^\alpha = 0. \qquad \ldots \ldots \quad (46)$$

First consider a system of two phases α and β. For the transfer of dn_i moles from phase α to phase β, condition (46) becomes

$$dG^\alpha + dG^\beta = -dn_i \, \mu_i{}^\alpha + dn_i \, \mu_i{}^\beta = 0,$$

or

$$\mu_i{}^\alpha = \mu_i{}^\beta. \qquad \ldots \ldots \ldots \quad (47)$$

Thus, the condition that the two phases should be in equilibrium with regard to species i is that its partial potential should have the same value in each of the phases.

For the general case of any number of components in any number of phases, using equation (38) in condition (46), we get at constant temperature and pressure

$$\sum_i \sum_\alpha \mu_i{}^\alpha dn_i{}^\alpha = 0. \qquad \ldots \ldots \quad (48)$$

In this equation, the $dn_i{}^\alpha$ are not all arbitrary. The conservation of matter requires that

$$\sum_\alpha dn_i{}^\alpha = 0 \quad \text{(for all } i\text{)}. \qquad \ldots \ldots \quad (49)$$

The necessary and sufficient condition for the satisfaction of (48) subject to the constraint (49) is that

$$\mu_i{}^\alpha = \mu_i{}^\beta = \mu_i{}^\gamma = \ldots \quad \text{(for all } i\text{)}. \qquad \ldots \quad (50)$$

Thus, the condition of equilibrium of the system is that for each component, with regard to which the system is in equilibrium, its partial potential has a common value in all the phases of the system.

It should be noted that as long as all the phases of a system are at the same temperature, the conditions (50) of chemical equilibrium for the different species are independent of one another. They are also independent of the conditions of pressure (that is, mechanical) equilibrium. If two phases α and β are separated by a fixed wall which is permeable to some components i, but impermeable to other components k, the condition that the two phases are in equilibrium with regard to the species i is that

$$\mu_i{}^\alpha = \mu_i{}^\beta. \qquad \ldots \ldots \ldots \quad (51)$$

But now, when this condition is satisfied, in general we will also have

$$p_\alpha \neq p_\beta \quad \text{and} \quad \mu_k{}^\alpha \neq \mu_k{}^\beta. \qquad \ldots \ldots \quad (52)$$

A partial equilibrium of this kind is called a *membrane equilibrium*. The possibility of realizing such an equilibrium provides the warrant for considering such semi-permeable membranes in the description of physical problems. The difference in pressure in the two phases is the *osmotic pressure* across the membrane.

14. The Phase Rule.

The set of equations (50) give $P - 1$ equations to be satisfied for each component. Thus, for the system to be in equilibrium,

$$C(P - 1)$$

equations must be satisfied in all. Now consider the number of independent variables on which the quantities which occur in equation (50) depend. The number of moles of each component in a phase fixes both its composition and its total mass. Thus, the composition of any one phase is determined if we know the number of moles of $C - 1$ of the components in a given mass of the phase. The composition of the P phases therefore involves $P(C - 1)$ parameters. In addition, the quantities which occur in the equations (50) also depend on the pressure and the temperature of the system. There are therefore

$$P(C - 1) + 2$$

parameters in all to describe the system. The equations which express the conditions of equilibrium determine the values of $C(P - 1)$ of these parameters. The remaining parameters can be varied arbitrarily. The number of parameters of the system which can be varied arbitrarily, consistent with the maintenance of equilibrium, or the number of independent variables, is defined as the *number of degrees of freedom* of the system. Denoting this number by F, we then have

$$F = C - P + 2. \qquad \cdots \qquad (53)$$

This is the phase rule discovered by Willard Gibbs. We now consider some applications of it.

Applications of the phase rule to systems of various numbers of components form important branches of physical chemistry and of metallurgy. We may consider the following application to a system of one component, say water. We have $C = 1$.

(a) Supposing there is only one phase present, say the liquid, we have $P = 1$, and therefore

$$F = 2.$$

That is, there are two degrees of freedom. The pressure and temperature may therefore both be arbitrarily varied (within certain limits) without any change taking place in the nature of the phase present.

It is necessary to appeal to experiment to determine the range of these limits; they cannot be determined by thermodynamics alone.

(b) If there are two phases present, we have P = 2, and therefore

$$F = 1.$$

That is, there is only one degree of freedom. Suppose we consider the equilibrium between liquid and vapour. This means that at an arbitrarily fixed temperature the pressure at which liquid and vapour are in equilibrium is determined by the thermodynamic conditions of equilibrium, and that, if we vary the pressure arbitrarily, one or other of the phases will disappear. The equilibrium between two phases is represented by a line on the pressure-temperature diagram.

(c) If there are three phases present, we have P = 3, and therefore

$$F = 0.$$

There are no degrees of freedom, which means that the pressure and temperature at which three phases of one substance are in equilibrium are *both* determined by the thermodynamic equations of equilibrium. If we attempt to vary either the pressure or the temperature, one of the three phases will disappear. The point at which three phases are in equilibrium is called the *triple point*. At the triple point the lines representing the equilibrium between liquid-solid, liquid-vapour, and solid-vapour all intersect. For water the triple point occurs at a temperature of $+0.0100°$ C. under a pressure of 4.579 mm. of mercury.*

15. Gibbs-Duhem Relation.

Of the various quantities which have been introduced, the temperature, the pressure, and the partial potential have values which are constant throughout a phase, and which for a phase of a given kind and state are independent of the amount of each component present. These parameters are called *intensity factors*. Others of the quantities, such as the entropy, the volume and the number of moles, depend directly on the amount of material and have values for the whole system which are the sums of their values for the separate phases. These parameters are called *capacity factors* or *extensive properties*. In the various thermodynamical relations which have been developed, these parameters occur in pairs: temperature and entropy; pressure and volume; partial

* We may mention that the researches of Tammann (*Ann. d. Physik*, Vol. 2, p. 1424 (1900)) and of Bridgman (*Proc. Amer. Acad.*, Vol. 47, p. 441 (1912)) have shown that under high pressures the nature of the solid phase of water changes, and altogether five different kinds of ice have been discovered. These are called Ice 1 (ordinary ice), Ice 2, Ice 3, Ice 5, Ice 6. The name Ice 4 is omitted because Tammann found some, but not conclusive, evidence for the existence of this form. The existence of these different forms of ice gives rise to other triple points in the case of water. These points are given in the table.

Phases	Temp., °C.	Pressure
Ice 1, liquid, vapour.	$+0.0075$	4.579 mm. mercury.
Ice 1, liquid, Ice 3.	-22	2115 Kgm. cm.^{2}
Ice 3, liquid, Ice 5.	-17	3530 ,, ,,
Ice 5, liquid, Ice 6.	$+0.16$	6380 ,, ,,
Ice 1, Ice 2, Ice 3.	-34.7	2170 ,, ,,
Ice 2, Ice 3, Ice 5.	-24.3	3510 ,, ,,

potential and number of moles; magnetic field and magnetization. One factor in each pair is an intensity factor and the other is a capacity factor; the product of each pair has the dimensions of energy. The relationship between them is shown clearly by equations (32), (33), and (34), which define the intensity factors temperature, pressure, and partial potential as the differential coefficients of the internal energy with respect to the capacity factors entropy, volume, and number of moles.

The relation (38) for $d\mathbf{G}$ can be integrated for constant values of the intensity factors. Physically, this means increasing the amount of the system without altering its nature. Integration leads to the result

$$\mathbf{G} = \sum_i \mu_i n_i. \qquad \cdots \cdots \cdots \quad (54)$$

Differentiating the expression

$$\mathbf{G} = \mathbf{U} - T\mathbf{S} + p\mathbf{V},$$

and using equation (31) for $d\mathbf{U}$, we get

$$-\mathbf{S}\,dT + \mathbf{V}\,dp - \sum n_i\,d\mu_i = 0. \quad \cdots \cdots \quad (55)$$

The most important case of this general relation occurs under the conditions of constant pressure and constant temperature. It then reduces to

$$dT = 0, \quad dp = 0, \quad \sum_i n_i\,d\mu_i = 0, \quad \cdots \cdots \quad (56)$$

which gives a relation between the variations of the partial potentials of the components of a system when its composition is varied at constant pressure and constant temperature. Equation (56) is known as the Gibbs-Duhem formula.

Integration of the expressions $d\mathbf{U}$, $d\mathbf{H}$, and $d\mathbf{F}$ for constant values of the intensity factors leads in each case to equation (54). This implies that under *all possible given external constraints*, the condition of equilibrium of a system of several phases with regard to any component is that the partial potential of that component shall be the same in all the phases of the system. This can be seen independently by using equation (31) with the definitions of $\mathbf{U}$, $\mathbf{H}$, and $\mathbf{F}$ to determine the conditions of equilibrium when the composition of the system is varied.

It should also be noted that equation (21), which was obtained by elementary means for a *system of one component*, is identical with the general condition expressed by equation (50). For in this case

$$\mathbf{G}_i = \frac{\mathbf{G}_i}{n_i} = \left(\frac{\partial \mathbf{G}_i}{\partial n_i}\right)_{T,p} = \mu_i.$$

The student should also refer to Examples 13, 14, 15, and 16 at the end of this chapter.

EXAMPLES

1. If we have in a closed vessel some liquid and its vapour and also an indifferent gas, and if π is the partial pressure of the vapour and p the total pressure, show that

$$\frac{d\pi}{dp} = \frac{v_1}{v_2},$$

where v_1 is the volume of unit mass of the liquid and v_2 that of unit mass of the vapour.

(Let G_1 and G_2 be the thermodynamic potentials of 1 gm. of liquid and vapour respectively. At equilibrium $G_1 = G_2$. Applying the result expressed in equation (40) to this particular case, we have that at constant temperature $dG_1 = v_1 dp$ and $dG_2 = v_2 d\pi$ for any increase in the total pressure p on the liquid and the corresponding increase in π, the pressure on the vapour. If the system is still to be in equilibrium, $G_1 + dG_1$ must equal $G_2 + dG_2$, or $dG_1 = dG_2$. This leads directly to the required result, which gives the effect of pressure on the vapour pressure.)

2. If we assume that the liquid is incompressible and that the vapour obeys the laws of a perfect gas, show that

$$\log \frac{\pi}{\pi_0} = \frac{M v_1}{RT} (p - \pi_0),$$

where π_0 is the vapour pressure when no indifferent gas is present and M is the molecular weight of the vapour.

(We have in this case $v_1 = \text{constant}$ and $v_2 = RT/M\pi$, so that the equation of Example 1 becomes

$$\frac{d\pi}{\pi} = \frac{M v_1}{RT} dp.$$

Integrating at constant temperature and remembering that when $p = \pi_0$, π is also equal to π_0, we obtain the required result.)

3. Since for not too large changes of pressure $(\pi - \pi_0)$ is very small, show that we may write

$$\Delta\pi = \frac{v_1}{v_2} \Delta p.$$

(In the result of Example 2, use the fact that when x is small, $\log(1 + x) \simeq x$.)

4. At $0°$ C. the vapour pressure of water is 4.579 mm. of mercury when no indifferent gas is present. Show that under a total pressure of 764.58 mm. (that is, $(p - \pi_0) = 1$ atmosphere) the vapour pressure is increased by 0.0037 mm. Take $M = 18.02$, $R = 8.313 \cdot 10^7$ absolute units, 1 atmosphere $= 1.0132 \cdot 10^6$ dynes per square centimetre, $v_1 = 1$.

5. Show that the increase in the free energy of a liquid when its surface is increased isothermally by an amount $d\mathbf{A}$ is given by

$$d\mathbf{F}_s = \gamma d\mathbf{A},$$

where γ is the surface tension.

(We may assume that the density of the liquid is unaltered by increasing its surface, so that $p d\mathbf{V} = 0$. The increase in the free energy (see equation (8)) is the work done on a system during an isothermal reversible process, and this is $\gamma d\mathbf{A}$.)

6. Show that the increase in the total energy of a liquid when its surface is increased by an amount $d\mathbf{A}$ is given by

$$d\mathbf{U}_s = \gamma\,d\mathbf{A} + q\,d\mathbf{A},$$

or if the increase in the total energy when the surface is increased by unit amount is Γ, that

$$\Gamma\,d\mathbf{A} = \gamma\,d\mathbf{A} + q\,d\mathbf{A},$$

or
$$\Gamma = \gamma + q,$$

where q is the heat absorbed when the surface is increased isothermally by unit area. Note the difference between γ and Γ; γ is the *free energy* of the surface per unit area; Γ is the *energy* of the surface per unit area.

7. Show that if π is the vapour pressure of a drop of liquid of radius r, and if π_0 is that of a large mass of the liquid,

$$\log\frac{\pi}{\pi_0} = \frac{2\gamma}{r\rho}\frac{M}{RT},$$

assuming that the vapour obeys the laws of a perfect gas; γ is the surface tension of the liquid, ρ its density, and M the molecular weight of the vapour.

(Imagine a mass dm of the liquid transferred from the drop to the main liquid. We have

$$dm = 4\pi r^2 \rho\,dr,$$

$$\mathbf{A} = 4\pi r^2,$$

$$d\mathbf{A} = 8\pi r\,dr = \frac{2}{r\rho}\,dm,$$

where $\mathbf{A}$ is the area of the drop. The main liquid may be looked on as a sphere of infinite radius, so that adding the mass dm to it will not increase its area appreciably. The decrease in the area of the liquid surface is, therefore, equal to $d\mathbf{A}$, and the decrease in the free energy is

$$\gamma\,d\mathbf{A} = \frac{2\gamma}{r\rho}\,dm.$$

We may obtain another expression for the decrease in the free energy by imagining the transfer of the mass dm carried out reversibly and isothermally and calculating the external work done by the system in the process. Assuming the vapour to be an ideal gas, the work gained in evaporating 1 gm.-molecule of liquid from the small drop at the pressure π, expanding the vapour to the smaller pressure π_0, and condensing the vapour at the pressure π_0 is $RT\log\pi/\pi_0$. If M is the molecular weight of the vapour, the work gained in transferring a mass dm is

$$dm\,\frac{RT}{M}\log\frac{\pi}{\pi_0},$$

and this is the decrease in the free energy due to the transfer. Equating the two expressions for the decrease in the free energy, we obtain the required result.)

8. If π is very nearly equal to π_0, show that the result of the last example can be written

$$\pi = \pi_0\left(1 + \frac{2\gamma M}{r\rho \bar{R}\bar{T}}\right).$$

9. Using the relevant data given in Example 4 and taking $\gamma = 72$ dynes per centimetre for water at 18° C., find the relation between π and π_0.

10. Show that if the pressure and the entropy are taken as independent variables, then

$$T = \left(\frac{\partial \mathbf{H}}{\partial \mathbf{S}}\right)_{p,\, n_i} \qquad \cdots \cdots \cdots \cdots \quad (57)$$

$$\mathbf{V} = \left(\frac{\partial \mathbf{H}}{\partial p}\right)_{\mathbf{S},\, n_i} \qquad \cdots \cdots \cdots \cdots \quad (58)$$

$$\mu_i = \left(\frac{\partial \mathbf{H}}{\partial n_i}\right)_{\mathbf{S},\, p,\, n_j} \qquad \cdots \cdots \cdots \quad (59)$$

and find expressions for $\mathbf{U}$, $\mathbf{F}$, and $\mathbf{G}$ in terms of $\mathbf{H}$ and its differential coefficients.

11. Show that if the volume and the temperature are taken as independent variables, then

$$\mathbf{S} = -\left(\frac{\partial \mathbf{F}}{\partial T}\right)_{\mathbf{V},\, u_i} \qquad \cdots \cdots \cdots \quad (60)$$

$$p = -\left(\frac{\partial \mathbf{F}}{\partial \mathbf{V}}\right)_{T,\, n_i} \qquad \cdots \cdots \cdots \quad (61)$$

$$\mu_i = \left(\frac{\partial \mathbf{F}}{\partial n_i}\right)_{T,\, \mathbf{V},\, n_j} \qquad \cdots \cdots \cdots \quad (62)$$

and find expressions for $\mathbf{U}$, $\mathbf{G}$, and $\mathbf{H}$ in terms of $\mathbf{F}$ and its differential coefficients.

12. Show how equations (32) and (33), and (39) and (40) and the results given in Examples 10 and 11 can be used to derive the Maxwell relations.

13. Show that for a system of several phases, kept at constant temperature and volume, the condition of equilibrium is that all the phases be at the same pressure (mechanical equilibrium). If, under these conditions, the equilibrium between two phases is disturbed, show that the phase in which the pressure is greater will increase in volume at the expense of the phase in which the pressure is smaller.

14. A liquid and its vapour at constant pressure are thermally isolated from the external world. Find the condition of equilibrium.

15. Show that if two phases of a heterogeneous system are not in equilibrium, any species tends to pass from the phase in which it has the higher partial potential to the phase in which it has the lower partial potential.

16. Show that integration of the expressions for $d\mathbf{U}$, $d\mathbf{F}$, and $d\mathbf{H}$ for constant values of the *intensity* factors leads in each case to the equation

$$\mathbf{G} = \sum_i \mu_i n_i$$

What is the significance of this in connexion with the equilibrium of *two states of the same substance* under various conditions?

17. Show that the position of the straight line, in the p-V diagram of a Van der Waals gas, which determines the states of thermodynamical equilibrium in which vapour and liquid co-exist, can be determined by considering the Helmholtz free energy.

18. Determine the shape of the temperature-entropy curve for a Van der Waals gas. Determine the position of the line which corresponds to liquid and vapour existing together in thermodynamical equilibrium.

CHAPTER XVII

Transformations of Higher Order

1. Thermodynamical Functions.

In an ordinary phase transition, corresponding to a change of state, there is a jump in entropy, associated with the latent heat, and a jump in the specific volume, while the Gibbs free energy, although it is continuous, suffers a discontinuous change in gradient. This is illustrated by the diagrams in fig. 17.1. For ordinary transitions of the first order in a pure species, the Gibbs free energy per unit mass is the same for the two phases. At the temperature at which the change of phase takes place, there is a discontinuity in the slope of the Gibbs free energy, a step in the entropy curve, a break in the specific heat curve, the specific heat going to infinity on the low-temperature side, and a step in the specific volume curve. If in a p, T diagram, AB is

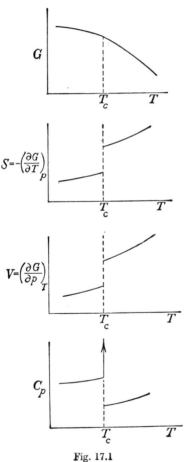

Fig. 17.1

Fig. 17.2

a line along which a phase transformation takes place (fig. 17.2), the phase change corresponds to passage from one side of the line to the other. For such a change for a

408

first-order transition we have

$$G_2 - G_1 = 0, \quad \ldots \ldots \ldots \quad (1)$$

$$\left(\frac{\partial G_1}{\partial T}\right)_p - \left(\frac{\partial G_2}{\partial T}\right)_p = s_2 - s_1 = \frac{Q}{T}, \quad \ldots \ldots \quad (2,$$

$$\left(\frac{\partial G_2}{\partial p}\right)_T - \left(\frac{\partial G_1}{\partial p}\right)_T = v_2 - v_1, \quad \ldots \ldots \quad (3)$$

where Q is the heat of transformation (latent heat), and v is the specific volume.

Detailed investigation of the transformation from liquid helium I to liquid helium II, which has been described qualitatively in Chapter V, Section 14, has shown that this phase transition is quite different.

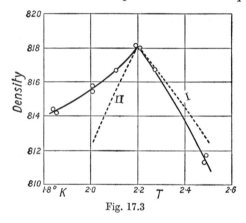

Fig. 17.3

The nature of the phase transition in liquid helium is indicated in figs. 17.3 and 17.4. In fig. 17.3 the density, measured by Onnes and Boks,[*] is plotted as a function of the absolute temperature. There is no step in the curve, but a discontinuity in the slope at the transition point. In fact, the expansion coefficient of helium II is negative, whereas that of helium I is positive. Likewise, the thermal measurements show no latent heat, but a sharp discontinuity in the specific heat. Fig. 17.4 is plotted from the measurements of Keesom and his colleagues.[†] This transformation in liquid helium is usually called a *lambda transformation*. Its discovery led Ehrenfest [‡] to examine the nature of these phase transitions of order higher than the first. By examining the behaviour of the Gibbs function and its differential

* Onnes and Boks, *Leiden Comm.*, No. 170b (1924).

† W. H. Keesom and Clusius, *Leiden Comm.*, No. 219e (1932); W. H. Keesom and A. P. Keesom, *ibid.*, No. 221d (1932).

‡ Ehrenfest, *Leiden Comm.*, No. 75b (1933); see also W. H. Keesom, *Helium*, Elsevier, Amsterdam (1942), Sections 5.2 and 5.3.

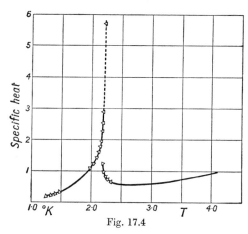

Fig. 17.4

coefficients in a second-order transition, we obtain an equation for it analogous to the Clausius-Clapeyron equation for a first-order transition.

For a transformation of the second order we have

$$G_2 - G_1 = 0, \qquad \ldots \ldots \ldots \quad (4)$$

$$\left(\frac{\partial G_1}{\partial T}\right)_p - \left(\frac{\partial G_2}{\partial T}\right)_p = 0, \text{ or } s_2 - s_1 = 0, \quad \ldots \ldots \quad (5)$$

$$\left(\frac{\partial G_2}{\partial p}\right)_T - \left(\frac{\partial G_1}{\partial p}\right)_T = 0, \text{ or } v_2 - v_1 = 0, \quad \ldots \ldots \quad (6)$$

$$\left(\frac{\partial^2 G_1}{\partial T^2}\right)_p - \left(\frac{\partial^2 G_2}{\partial T^2}\right)_p = \frac{c_{p_2}}{T} - \frac{c_{p_1}}{T}, \qquad \ldots \ldots \ldots \quad (7)$$

$$\left(\frac{\partial^2 G_2}{\partial p^2}\right)_T - \left(\frac{\partial^2 G_1}{\partial p^2}\right)_T = \left(\frac{\partial v_2}{\partial p}\right)_T - \left(\frac{\partial v_1}{\partial p}\right)_T = v(\kappa_1 - \kappa_2), \quad (8)$$

$$\left(\frac{\partial^2 G_2}{\partial T \partial p}\right) - \left(\frac{\partial^2 G_1}{\partial T \partial p}\right) = \left(\frac{\partial v_2}{\partial T}\right)_p - \left(\frac{\partial v_1}{\partial T}\right)_p = v(\alpha_2 - \alpha_1), \quad (9)$$

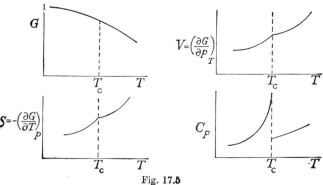

Fig. 17.5

where κ is the isothermal compressibility and α is the volume coefficient of expansion. These relations are illustrated in fig. 17.5.

To cover this case we need a generalization of the treatment given in Section 8 of Chapter XVI. Let x be a quantity which does not change in passing from one side to the other of the curve AB in fig. 17.2, and let Δp and ΔT be corresponding changes in p and T in passing along this curve. We have then

$$\frac{\Delta p}{\Delta T} = \frac{\left(\dfrac{\partial x_2}{\partial T}\right)_p - \left(\dfrac{\partial x_1}{\partial T}\right)_p}{\left(\dfrac{\partial x_1}{\partial p}\right)_T - \left(\dfrac{\partial x_2}{\partial p}\right)_T}. \qquad \ldots \ldots (10)$$

For a transformation of the first order we put $x = \mathrm{G}$ and obtain the Clausius-Clapeyron equation.

For a transformation of the second order we first put $x = \mathrm{s}$ and then $x = \mathrm{v}$ and obtain respectively

$$\frac{\Delta p}{\Delta T} = \frac{\left(\dfrac{\partial s_2}{\partial T}\right)_p - \left(\dfrac{\partial s_1}{\partial T}\right)_p}{\left(\dfrac{\partial s_1}{\partial p}\right)_T - \left(\dfrac{\partial s_2}{\partial p}\right)_T} = \frac{c_{p_2} - c_{p_1}}{T\left\{\left(\dfrac{\partial v_2}{\partial T}\right)_p - \left(\dfrac{\partial v_1}{\partial T}\right)_p\right\}} \qquad . \ (11)$$

and

$$\frac{\Delta p}{\Delta T} = \frac{\left(\dfrac{\partial v_2}{\partial T}\right)_p - \left(\dfrac{\partial v_1}{\partial T}\right)_p}{\left(\dfrac{\partial v_1}{\partial p}\right)_T - \left(\dfrac{\partial v_2}{\partial p}\right)_T}. \qquad \ldots \ldots (12)$$

From (11) and (12),

$$c_{p_2} - c_{p_1} = \frac{T\left\{\left(\dfrac{\partial v_2}{\partial T}\right)_p - \left(\dfrac{\partial v_1}{\partial T}\right)_p\right\}^2}{\left(\dfrac{\partial v_1}{\partial p}\right)_T - \left(\dfrac{\partial v_2}{\partial p}\right)_T}. \qquad \ldots (13)$$

Equation (11) is the analogue of the Clausius-Clapeyron equation; it can be written

$$\frac{\Delta p}{\Delta T} = \frac{c_{p_2} - c_{p_1}}{Tv(\alpha_2 - \alpha_1)}.$$

The theory has been extended by Rutgers and Wouthuysen [*] to cover the case when there is not a sudden jump in the specific heat curve but an anomaly like that shown in fig. 22.4 (p. 549).

* Rutgers and Wouthuysen, *Physica*, Vol. 4, pp. 235, 515 (1937). See also Landau, *Phys. Zeits. d. Sowjetunion*, Vol. 11, pp. 26, 545 (1937). For a general discussion of the λ-transformation in helium, see Keesom, *Leiden Comm.*, Suppt. 80*b*. Clusius and Perlick (*Zeits. f. phys. Chem.*, B, Vol. 24, p. 313 (1934)) have found a similar specific heat anomaly in methane at 20·4° K.

which have been carried out by Daunt and Mendelssohn.* Their experiments have done much to elucidate the transfer of liquid helium II over surfaces in the form of highly mobile films. The simplest type of experiment consists of immersing an empty vessel in a helium bath. It is then observed that the helium collects in the vessel until its level is the same as the outside bath, and it has been verified that this is accomplished, not by evaporation and condensation, but by a flow of liquid along the surface. It is found that the flow is always

such that the helium II collects at the lowest possible level, and that the volume of liquid which is transported in this way depends on the perimeter of the surface. It is therefore possible to define a rate of flow in cubic centimetres per second per centimetre perimeter over which the flow takes place. The rate of flow varies with the temperature (but appears to be almost constant below $1.5°$ K.), and is independent of level difference or of the material on which the film is formed. The reason for this is probably that the film flow takes place over an adsorbed layer of helium atoms. The helium film is of the order of several hundred atoms thick, and the average velocity through a helium II film, below $1.5°$ K., is about 20 cm. per sec. When liquid helium II is allowed to flow through fine capillaries, it apparently has a negligible viscosity. This is illustrated by the rates of flow which are plotted in fig. 17.8. This diagram is drawn from the results recently obtained by D. W. Osborne † and his colleagues in Chicago, using a method first employed by Giauque.‡ It should be mentioned that experiments in which the viscous properties are measured by the damping of the oscillations of a body immersed in it give different results from those for the flow through very fine capillaries. In these experiments the measured viscosity falls by a factor of about ten on passing through the lambda point. The thermal conductivity of the helium II is very high. The heat transported per unit temperature gradient is several hundred times as great as that in copper at room temperature. These results are probably to be explained in terms of the thermo-mechanical effect. A small temperature gradient sets up a

Fig. 17.7

    * Daunt and Mendelssohn, *Proc. Roy. Soc.*, A, Vol. 170, p. 423 (1939); Mendelssohn, *Report of the Physical Society Conference at Cambridge*, 1946, Vol. 2, p. 35 (1947); Bowers and Mendelssohn, *Nature*, Vol. 163, p. 870 (1949).

    † D. W. Osborne, Weinstock and Abraham, *Phys. Rev.*, Vol. 75, p. 988 (1949).

    ‡ Giauque, Stout and Barieau, *Journ. Amer. Chem. Soc.*, Vol. 61, p. 654 (1939).

where κ is the isothermal compressibility and α is the volume coefficient of expansion. These relations are illustrated in fig. 17.5.

To cover this case we need a generalization of the treatment given in Section 8 of Chapter XVI. Let x be a quantity which does not change in passing from one side to the other of the curve AB in fig. 17.2, and let Δp and ΔT be corresponding changes in p and T in passing along this curve. We have then

$$\frac{\Delta p}{\Delta T} = \frac{\left(\frac{\partial x_2}{\partial T}\right)_p - \left(\frac{\partial x_1}{\partial T}\right)_p}{\left(\frac{\partial x_1}{\partial p}\right)_T - \left(\frac{\partial x_2}{\partial p}\right)_T} . \quad \ldots \ldots \quad (10)$$

For a transformation of the first order we put $x = \mathrm{G}$ and obtain the Clausius-Clapeyron equation.

For a transformation of the second order we first put $x = \mathrm{s}$ and then $x = \mathrm{v}$ and obtain respectively

$$\frac{\Delta p}{\Delta T} = \frac{\left(\frac{\partial s_2}{\partial T}\right)_p - \left(\frac{\partial s_1}{\partial T}\right)_p}{\left(\frac{\partial s_1}{\partial p}\right)_T - \left(\frac{\partial s_2}{\partial p}\right)_T} = \frac{c_{p_2} - c_{p_1}}{T\left\{\left(\frac{\partial v_2}{\partial T}\right)_p - \left(\frac{\partial v_1}{\partial T}\right)_p\right\}} \quad . \quad (11)$$

and

$$\frac{\Delta p}{\Delta T} = \frac{\left(\frac{\partial v_2}{\partial T}\right)_p - \left(\frac{\partial v_1}{\partial T}\right)_p}{\left(\frac{\partial v_1}{\partial p}\right)_T - \left(\frac{\partial v_2}{\partial p}\right)_T} . \quad \ldots \ldots \quad (12)$$

From (11) and (12),

$$c_{p_2} - c_{p_1} = \frac{T\left\{\left(\frac{\partial v_2}{\partial T}\right)_p - \left(\frac{\partial v_1}{\partial T}\right)_p\right\}^2}{\left(\frac{\partial v_1}{\partial p}\right)_T - \left(\frac{\partial v_2}{\partial p}\right)_T} . \quad \ldots \quad (13)$$

Equation (11) is the analogue of the Clausius-Clapeyron equation; it can be written

$$\frac{\Delta p}{\Delta T} = \frac{c_{p_2} - c_{p_1}}{Tv(\alpha_2 - \alpha_1)}.$$

The theory has been extended by Rutgers and Wouthuysen[*] to cover the case when there is not a sudden jump in the specific heat curve but an anomaly like that shown in fig. 22.4 (p. 549).

[*] Rutgers and Wouthuysen, *Physica*, Vol. 4, pp. 235, 515 (1937). See also Landau, *Phys. Zeits. d. Sowjetunion*, Vol. 11, pp. 26, 545 (1937). For a general discussion of the λ-transformation in helium, see Keesom, *Leiden Comm.*, Suppt. 80*b*. Clusius and Perlick (*Zeits. f. phys. Chem.*, B, Vol. 24, p. 313 (1934)) have found a similar specific heat anomaly in methane at 20·4° K.

A discussion of higher-order transitions has been attempted * by expanding the Gibbs free energy of each phase as a Taylor's series, in terms of derivatives with respect to p and T. Such an analysis could, however, apply only to a transition which occurred at one point only, and not to a transition which takes place along an equilibrium curve.† All the higher-order transitions which have been observed experimentally are of this latter class. An expansion in a Taylor's series about a given point cannot give a description of the higher-order transitions which have been observed so far.

LIQUID HELIUM

2. Properties of Liquid Helium.

These equations can be applied to the transition in liquid helium. At 2·19° K. all the quantities in this equation are known from experiment except $(\alpha_2 - \alpha_1)$, the value of which can therefore be calculated. We have

$$\left(\frac{\Delta p}{\Delta T}\right)_\lambda = -81\cdot9 \times 10^6 \text{ dynes cm.}^{-2} \text{ deg.}^{-1},$$

and ‡
$$c_{p_2} - c_{p_1} = 7\cdot37 \times 10^7 \text{ erg gm.}^{-1} \text{ deg.}^{-1},$$

also
$$\frac{1}{v} = 0\cdot1462 \text{ cm.}^{-3}.$$

We thus obtain $\alpha_2 - \alpha_1 = -0\cdot0601 \text{ deg.}^{-1}$.

To obtain α_1 we draw a tangent to the curve for helium I at the transition point as shown by the dotted line (I) in fig. 17.3. We can then deduce the value of α_2 using the above value of $\alpha_2 - \alpha_1$. This is shown by the dotted line marked (II), and is seen to correspond reasonably with the experimental results for helium II.

This agreement, together with the discontinuity observed in the specific heat (fig. 17.4), establishes the phase change in liquid helium as a second-order transition. We have already seen that the application of an external pressure shifts the transition to a lower temperature (1·8° K. under its equilibrium melting pressure) as shown by the lambda line in figs. 5.8 and 5.10 (pp. 149, 151). It is evident that the phase transition in liquid helium is intimately related to the rapid change in the gradient of the melting-pressure curve. When we consider the connexion of the Nernst heat theorem with typical low-temperature phenomena (Chapter XIX), we shall see that this change

---

* Lyppe, *Phys. Rev.*, Vol. 69, p. 652 (1946).

† Bridgman, *Phys. Rev.*, Vol. 70, p. 425 (1946); Oldenburger, *ibid.*, p. 433.

‡ This is the difference between the specific heat of liquid helium II at 2·188° and that of liquid helium I at 2·194°. α_2 and α_1 must be taken to refer respectively to these two temperatures. For a discussion of this point, see Keesom, *Leiden Comm.*, Suppt. 80*b*, p. 19.

of gradient is related to the requirements of this law. Liquid and
solid helium can exist together in equilibrium down to the absolute
zero. The third law requires that the entropy difference between the
spatially ordered solid and the spatially disordered liquid shall vanish
in the neighbourhood of the absolute zero.* This can be achieved by
the liquid undergoing a transition to an ordered state, and it is generally
considered that at the lambda point liquid helium passes over into a
liquid phase which is *ordered in momentum space*. The observed discontinuities in the density, dielectric constant, surface tension, and
specific heat (Chapter V, Section 14) are
a consequence of this phase transition.

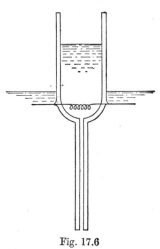

   The ordered state of liquid helium
manifests itself in unusual transport
properties. There are four main transport
effects: the thermomechanical effect, the
transfer of liquid helium over surfaces,
its flow through fine channels with vanishing viscosity, the very high thermal
conductivity. The thermomechanical
effect can be shown † very simply by
using the apparatus shown in fig. 17.6.
A tube with a capillary attached to its
end is immersed in liquid helium. An
electric heater is in the main part of the
tube, so that a steady flow of heat is
maintained down the capillary. Under
these conditions, the helium rises in the   Fig. 17.6
capillary until the level in the tube is
above that outside. This indicates that there is a pressure gradient in
the reverse direction to the heat flow. The effect was first observed
when radiant energy was incident on emery powder packed into the
bend of a U-tube.‡ In this case the fountain shown in fig. 17.7 is
observed. Since the discovery of the helium film § (the Rollin film)
which is formed on all surfaces in contact with liquid helium II, many
investigations have been carried out on its formation and its flow
properties. These are shown very clearly in a series of experiments

* For a discussion of the significance of the Nernst heat theorem in relation to the
existence of the liquid state down to the absolute zero, see F. E. Simon, *Nature*, Vol.
133, p. 529 (1934); A. R. Miller, *Nature*, Vol. 164, p. 325 (1949); F. E. Simon and
C. A. Swenson, *Nature*, Vol. 165, p. 829 (1950).

   † J. F. Allen and Reekie, *Proc. Cambridge Phil. Soc.*, Vol. 35, p. 114 (1939).

   ‡ J. F. Allen and H. Jones, *Nature*, Vol. 141, p. 243 (1938).

   § Rollin, *Actes du 7e Congrès intern. du Froid*, Vol. 1, p. 187 (1936); Kürti, Rollin
and Simon, *Physica*, Vol. 3, p. 266 (1936); Rollin and Simon, *ibid.*, Vol. 6, p. 219
(1939).

which have been carried out by Daunt and Mendelssohn.* Their experiments have done much to elucidate the transfer of liquid helium II over surfaces in the form of highly mobile films. The simplest type of experiment consists of immersing an empty vessel in a helium bath. It is then observed that the helium collects in the vessel until its level is the same as the outside bath, and it has been verified that this is accomplished, not by evaporation and condensation, but by a flow of liquid along the surface. It is found that the flow is always

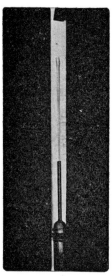

Fig. 17.7

such that the helium II collects at the lowest possible level, and that the volume of liquid which is transported in this way depends on the perimeter of the surface. It is therefore possible to define a rate of flow in cubic centimetres per second per centimetre perimeter over which the flow takes place. The rate of flow varies with the temperature (but appears to be almost constant below 1·5° K.), and is independent of level difference or of the material on which the film is formed. The reason for this is probably that the film flow takes place over an adsorbed layer of helium atoms. The helium film is of the order of several hundred atoms thick, and the average velocity through a helium II film, below 1·5° K., is about 20 cm. per sec. When liquid helium II is allowed to flow through fine capillaries, it apparently has a negligible viscosity. This is illustrated by the rates of flow which are plotted in fig. 17.8. This diagram is drawn from the results recently obtained by D. W. Osborne † and his colleagues in Chicago, using a method first employed by Giauque.‡ It should be mentioned that experiments in which the viscous properties are measured by the damping of the oscillations of a body immersed in it give different results from those for the flow through very fine capillaries. In these experiments the measured viscosity falls by a factor of about ten on passing through the lambda point. The thermal conductivity of the helium II is very high. The heat transported per unit temperature gradient is several hundred times as great as that in copper at room temperature. These results are probably to be explained in terms of the thermo-mechanical effect. A small temperature gradient sets up a

* Daunt and Mendelssohn, *Proc. Roy. Soc.*, A, Vol. 170, p. 423 (1939); Mendelssohn, *Report of the Physical Society Conference at Cambridge*, 1946, Vol. 2, p. 35 (1947); Bowers and Mendelssohn, *Nature*, Vol. 163, p. 870 (1949).

† D. W. Osborne, Weinstock and Abraham, *Phys. Rev.*, Vol. 75, p. 988 (1949).

‡ Giauque, Stout and Barieau, *Journ. Amer. Chem. Soc.*, Vol. 61, p. 654 (1939).

circulation of liquid, the normal helium atoms flowing towards the hotter part, and the transfer of heat is a result of this bodily transport of liquid.

The theory of a quantum liquid proposed by Landau * gives rise to two wave equations, corresponding to the propagation of waves with different velocities, instead of the usual sound equation and an equation for rapidly damped thermal waves. The wave equation

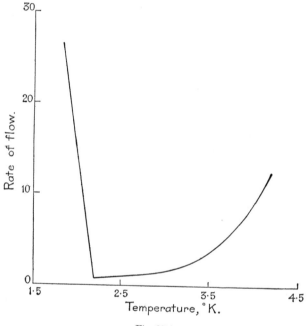

Fig. 17.8

corresponding to the higher velocity is that of the propagation of a pressure wave, that is, ordinary sound. The other wave equation corresponds to a wave with a velocity which rises at 1° K. to about one-tenth the velocity of sound from zero at the lambda point. This latter wave is associated with the propagation of temperature fluctuations in liquid helium II, and was measured first by Peshkov † in Moscow. It has been measured also at the Royal Society Mond Laboratory

* Landau, *Journ. Phys. U.S.S.R.*, Vol. 5, p. 71 (1941); *ibid.*, Vol. 8, p. 1 (1944); see also Tisza, *Nature*, Vol. 141, p. 643 (1938).

† Peshkov, *Journ. Phys. U.S.S.R.*, Vol. 8, p. 381 (1944); *Report of the Physical Society Conference at Cambridge*, 1946, Vol. 2, p. 19 (1947).

by D. V. Osborne,* who has made use of a pulse method. He has continued the measurements below 1° K., using the process of adiabatic demagnetization with a bomb of paramagnetic salt to reach these temperatures. In the neighbourhood of 1° K. there is little variation in the velocity of second sound, but at about 0·7° K. it begins to increase again, and at 0·1° K. has reached a value of about 150 m. sec.$^{-1}$.

It has been suggested that the unusual properties of liquid helium II are to be explained in terms of the condensation of a Bose-Einstein gas.† However, the properties of an assembly of particles obeying Bose-Einstein statistics, *allowing for the interactions between the particles*, have not yet been worked out exactly, and when the interactions are neglected, the condensation comes out to be of the third order, having a discontinuity in the *gradient* of the specific heat and not in the specific heat itself. Actually, particularly when the implications of the third law of thermodynamics are considered, it appears to be more likely that the *existence* of a low-temperature phase transition ‡ in the liquid state is a general quantal property of an assembly of interacting particles, whereas the particular form assumed by the " ordered state " below the transition temperature, that is, the *properties* of the low-temperature phase, depend upon the particular kind of quantum statistics appropriate to the particles of the assembly.

The suggestion that the phase transition in the helium isotope of mass 4 corresponds to the condensation of an ideal gas of Bose-Einstein particles led Tisza § to formulate the two-fluid hypothesis of liquid helium. This concept has provided a useful physical picture of many of the phenomena that have been observed in liquid helium. It has also proved fruitful in suggesting experiments. It has not, however, proved possible to correlate the macroscopic parameters which occur in the two-fluid theory with the quantities which occur in the analysis of the condensation of a gas of interacting Bose-Einstein particles. While this may not be decisive, it is a difficulty in the way of equating the transition in liquid helium to the condensation of an ideal Bose-Einstein gas.

A different approach was adopted by Landau ‖ who set up a quantum hydrodynamics in which the particle statistics play an apparently minor role but, for the energy spectrum in his theory, each elementary excitation must have an *integral* angular momentum and so obey Bose-Einstein statistics. He postulated that the excitations in

* D. V. Osborne, *Nature*, Vol. 162, p. 213 (1948), and private communication.

† F. London, *Nature*, Vol. 141, p. 643 (1938); *Phys. Rev.*, Vol. 54, p. 947 (1938); *J. Phys. Chem.*, Vol. 43, p. 49 (1939).

‡ See, for example, J. de Boer, *Progress in Low Temperature Physics*, Vol. 2, p. 13 (1957).

§ L. Tisza, *Phys. Rev.*, Vol. 72, p. 838 (1947); *ibid.*, Vol. 75, p. 885 (1949).

‖ L. Landau, *Journ. Physics (U.S.S.R.)*, Vol. 5, p. 71 (1941); *ibid.*, Vol. 8, p. 1 (1944); *ibid.*, Vol. 11, p. 91 (1947); *Phys. Rev.*, Vol. 75, p. 884 (1949).

liquid helium are of two kinds. The excitations of lowest energy are *phonons* or quantized sound waves; they have an energy pc where p is the momentum and c is the speed of sound in the liquid. Separated from these by a finite energy gap, Δ, are the *rotons* of energy

$$\Delta + \frac{(p - p_0)^2}{2\mu}$$

where p_0 is a constant and μ is an effective mass. The variation with temperature of the speed of second sound, its attenuation, and the viscosity of liquid helium have been explained on this basis.* This theory has also provided an account † of the thermodynamical properties of liquid helium.

The two-fluid theory can be interpreted in terms of Landau's theory of elementary excitations. His quantum hydrodynamics provides a mathematical description of a system of thermal excitations moving in an ideally ordered system of helium atoms in the ground state as background. The thermal excitations play the role of the " normal fluid " and the atoms in the ground state that of the " superfluid " of the two-fluid theory.

In a series of papers, Feynman ‡ has examined the characteristics of the wave function which satisfies the Schrödinger wave equation for all the atoms in the liquid. He has shown that excited states of compression exist but that states which involve internal motions without changing the density can be excited only by the expenditure of an appreciable excitation energy. These correspond to the phonons and rotons of Landau's theory. Feynman has also shown that there are no other excitations possible. It is this scarcity of low-energy excited states which is essential for an explanation of the properties of liquid helium.

Feynman has also suggested § that the energy spectrum for excitations in liquid helium could be determined by examining the inelastic scattering of thermal neutrons which have been passed through a polycrystalline filter. The energy-momentum relation which has been determined ‖ from such experimental studies confirms the validity of

* L. Landau and I. Khalatnikov, *J. Exp. Theor. Phys. (U.S.S.R.)*, Vol. 19, pp. 637, 709 (1949).

† D. de Klerk, R. P. Hudson, and J. R. Pelham, *Phys. Rev.*, Vol. 93, p. 28 (1954).

‡ R. P. Feynman, *Phys. Rev.*, Vol. 91, pp. 1291, 1307 (1953); *ibid.*, Vol. 94, p. 262, (1954).

§ R. P. Feynman and M. Cohen, *Phys. Rev.*, Vol. 102, p. 1189 (1956).

‖ J. L. Yarnell, G. P. Arnold, P. J. Bendt, and E. C. Kerr, *Phys. Rev.*, Vol. 113, p. 1379 (1959); *Phys. Rev. Letters*, Vol. 1 p. 9 (1958); D. G. Henshaw, *ibid.*, Vol. 1, p. 127 (1958).

the energy spectrum postulated by Landau in his theory. For a detailed account of the present state of the theory of liquid helium, the student can consult several recent critical reviews.*

3. Energy Relations for Helium.

Since the entropy difference between liquid and solid helium vanishes as the absolute zero is approached, it follows *a fortiori* that the heat of melting also vanishes. This implies that

$$(U_l - U_s) + p(V_l - V_s)$$

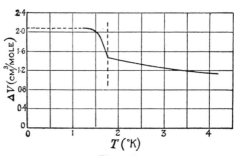

Fig. 17.9

vanishes as the absolute zero is approached. This could happen if the differences in both the energy and the specific volume were to vanish, but this would imply that the two phases became identical, and there is no evidence whatsoever in favour of this. The other alternative is that, as the temperature falls, $(U_l - U_s)$ approaches the value $-p(V_l - V_s)$.

It has been shown by Simon and Swenson † that the difference of volume between the liquid and the solid persists down to absolute zero. Their results are shown in fig. 17.9. Since the melting pressure remains positive, this necessitates that the energy term becomes minus the work term. This implies that at the lowest temperatures the energy of the solid must be greater than that of the liquid. No heat is developed at the absolute zero, so that the free energy given to the system in compressing the liquid to the solid state can result only in increasing the energy of the solid above that of the liquid. This is shown in fig. 17.10, which is reproduced from the paper by Simon and Swenson. This unique behaviour is possible on account of the volume

---

* R. B. Dingle, *Advances in Physics*, Vol. 1, p. 112 (1952); R. P. Feynman, *Progress in Low Temperature Physics*, Vol. 1, p. 17 (1955); J. de Boer, *ibid.*, Vol. 2, p. 13 (1957).

† F. E. Simon and C. A. Swenson. *Nature*, Vol. 165, p. 829 (1950).

dependence of the zero-point energy. Although the zero-point energy in liquid helium takes over to a great extent the role of the repulsive energy in an ordinary liquid, its volume dependence is quite different.*

Although the two phases of solid and liquid helium show many of the characteristics of their normal counterparts, the process of isothermal melting is quite different from that in a normal substance. Solid

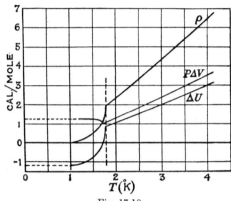

Fig. 17.10

helium cannot be melted by heating it—since there is no heat of melting at the lowest temperatures. It is a purely mechanical process, similar to the lifting of a weight or the compression of a spring. The thermodynamical expressions for this process do not contain any entropy terms.

4. Model of a Second-order Transition.

An interesting model of a second-order transition has been given by Gorter. A closed vessel contains only a liquid and its vapour. The vessel is of such a volume that, when all the material is in the vapour state, the density is less than the critical density. While there is both liquid and vapour in the container, the pressure is simply the equilibrium vapour pressure, and increases with the temperature. If the vapour behaves as a perfect gas, the vapour pressure follows a Kirchhoff relation; non-ideality of the vapour will make the vapour-pressure curve appear more convex, viewed from the origin. Also, in this temperature region, the thermal capacity of the whole system is simply the sum of the specific heats of the liquid and vapour (weighted according to the amount of each present) and of the latent heat of vaporization.

---

* F. E. Simon, *Nature*, Vol. 165, p. 529 (1934); H. D. Megaw and F. E. Simon, *Nature*, Vol. 138, p. 244 (1936); H. D. Megaw, *Phil. Mag.*, Vol. 28, p. 129 (1939).

Above the temperature at which the last drop of liquid vaporizes, the pressure inside the container is the gas pressure. If the vapour behaves as a perfect gas, this increases linearly with the temperature. Furthermore, in this high-temperature region the thermal capacity of the system consists only of the specific heat of the vapour. Thus, when the last drop of liquid vaporizes, there is a sudden drop in the thermal capacity, the fall in it depending upon the latent heat and the rate of

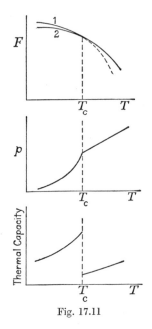

Fig. 17.11

vaporization at this temperature. For a pure liquid and its vapour in equilibrium, the Gibbs functions per unit mass are equal. Thus, throughout the transition the Gibbs function of the system " liquid plus vapour " is continuous. Above the temperature at which all the material becomes vapour, only the Gibbs function of the pure gas phase corresponds to a realizable state. Below this temperature the Gibbs functions both for vapour and for the vapour and liquid in equilibrium can be drawn, the latter being the smaller. The behaviour of the Gibbs function and the thermal capacity of the system, and of the pressure in the container for this model, are shown in fig. 17.11.

5. Other Examples of Second-order Transitions.

Many other systems apart from liquid helium show higher-order phase transitions: a ferromagnetic at its Curie temperature, a metal which becomes superconducting at its transition temperature in the absence of a magnetic field, some alloys at the temperature at which superlattice formation sets in. With some alloys, for example, copper-zinc in equal molar proportions, additional lines appear in their X-ray diffraction pattern below a certain temperature.* These superlattice lines correspond to the atoms *of the different kinds* taking up an ordered arrangement of sites with respect to each other. This transition to an ordered state is accompanied by discontinuities in the gradients of the elastic constants and of the resistance of the alloy, and a discontinuous change in its specific heat. Such changes can be explained in terms of the concept of the degree of order. We consider the phase change in a superconductor below, but for details of the theoretical treatments of these other transitions, the student should consult the original papers.†

6. Co-operative Assemblies.

In the simplest assemblies of statistical mechanics, the interactions between the systems composing the assembly can be neglected. This means simply that these interactions are irrelevant to our description of the particular properties of the assembly which are of interest. Perfect gases and ideal solutions are in this category. In other assemblies, the interactions are far from negligible in that they cause appreciable departures from the behaviour of non-interacting systems. The effect of the interactions is, however, still essentially a perturbation, even though in some cases it may be a strong perturbation. Slightly imperfect gases, slightly non-ideal solutions, and electrolytes are examples of assemblies of this character.

There are other assemblies of interest in statistical mechanics in which the interactions or coupling between the systems play a predominant role. These are assemblies in which the state of any particular system is governed by the states of the systems which are neighbours to it. The physical systems which have been mentioned in the previous section belong to this category. The arrangement of atoms in an alloy, of adsorbed particles on a surface, or of spins in a ferromagnetic material, are examples of this dependence. The spin direction, or the occupation of a site on a crystalline lattice, is determined by that of its neighbours. Again, the configuration of molecules in a solution is determined by the interactions between them;

---

* Johannson and Linde, *Ann. d. Physik*, Vol. 78, p. 439 (1925); Vol. 82, p. 449 (1927). The possibility was first discussed by Tammann, *Z. anorg. Chem.*, Vol. 107, p. 1 (1919). For later work, see Bradley and Jay, *Proc. Roy. Soc.*, A, Vol. 136, p. 200 (1932).

† Reviews have been given by Nix and Shockley, *Rev. Mod. Phys.*, Vol. 10, p. 1 (1938), and by Wannier, *ibid.*, Vol. 17, p. 50 (1945). See also Onsager and Kaufman, *Report of the Physical Society Conference at Cambridge*, Vol. 2, p. 137 (1947). A very instructive discussion of the physical processes taking place in the alloy is given by Bragg and Williams, *Proc. Roy. Soc.*, A, Vol. 145, p. 699 (1934); Vol. 151, p. 540 (1935); Williams, *ibid.*, Vol. 152, p. 231 (1935).

furthermore, in the case of a solution containing high-polymer molecules, the interconnexions between the segments of a polymer molecule imply constraints on the assembly which have to be described in the same statistical terms as those implied by strong molecular interactions. In all these cases, the physical behaviour of the assembly is largely determined by the interactions or coupling between the systems of which the assembly is built up. Fowler has called such assemblies *co-operative assemblies*.

Many approximate methods have been devised for taking account of the coupling between the systems of an assembly. These approximate methods give a qualitative account of the properties including critical conditions such as occur at transition points. It is becoming increasingly clear, however, that to give a precise description of critical phenomena in a co-operative assembly, exact mathematical methods must be devised to locate both the position and the type of singularity exactly. Some progress has been made recently in the solution of the mathematical problems which are involved.* The approximate methods are still of value, however, to provide a means of taking account of the coupling between the systems of the assembly when these, while dominating its behaviour, do not lead to critical conditions.†

SUPERCONDUCTIVITY

7. Properties of a Metal in the Superconducting State.

Another phase change of considerable interest is that which takes place when a metal becomes superconducting at very low temperatures. The phenomenon was observed first by Onnes,‡ who found that at about $4 \cdot 2°$ K. the potential difference across the ends of a capillary thread of mercury vanished. Thus there is no electric field within the metal, and an electric current can flow in it without being dissipated, that is, without any Joule heating. However, the magnetic behaviour of a superconductor indicates that this is not merely a phenomenon of perfect conductivity. The magnetic induction inside a supercon-

---

* Wannier, *Rev. Mod. Phys.*, Vol. 17, p. 50 (1945); Onsager, *Phys. Rev.*, Vol. 65, p. 117 (1944); *Report on Conference of Physical Society at Cambridge*, 1946, Vol. 2, p. 137 (1947); Domb, *Proc. Roy. Soc.*, A, Vol. 196, p. 36 (1949); *Nature*, Vol. 163, p. 775 (1949).

† Accounts of the use of these methods will be found in the research monographs by J. K. Roberts and by A. R. Miller on adsorbed monolayers cited in the closing section of Chapter VIII, in the articles on alloys cited in Section 20 above, and in A. R. Miller, *The Theory of Solutions of High Polymers*, Clarendon Press, Oxford (1948); also E. A. Guggenheim, *Mixtures: The Theory of Equilibrium Properties of Some Simple Classes of Mixtures, Solutions and Alloys*, Oxford (1952). An account of the nature of a statistical assembly, and of the way in which interactions are taken into account, can be found in the relevant chapters of R. H. Fowler, *Statistical Mechanics*, 2nd edition, Cambridge University Press (1936), and a brief explanation of the differences between ideal, slightly non-ideal, and co-operative assembles in A. R. Miller, *Endeavour*, Vol. 8, p. 140 (1949).

‡ Onnes, *Leiden Comm.*, No. 122b (1911).

ductor always vanishes.* This is referred to as the *Meissner effect*. The magnetic field does not, of course, vanish abruptly at the surface; it penetrates the superconductor to a small extent. A *penetration depth* λ can be defined by

$$\lambda = \frac{1}{HA} \int_v B \, dV,$$

where B is the magnetic induction at any point of the material, the integration is carried out over the whole volume, H is the external magnetic field, and A is the total surface area of the specimen. This definition is independent of any assumed law of variation of the magnetic induction with the distance from the surface. Throughout this section, we use this term to refer to the penetration depth of a *static* magnetic field. Corresponding to the skin depth of a normal metal to an applied high-frequency field, there is a corresponding penetration of a superconductor by a high-frequency field. There is no *a priori* theoretical reason why this latter quantity should be identical with the penetration depth of a static magnetic field. The penetration depth varies with the temperature, and the experimental results fit a law of variation given by †

$$\left(\frac{\lambda_0}{\lambda}\right)^2 = 1 - \left(\frac{T}{T_c}\right)^4, \quad \cdots \cdots \quad (14)$$

where λ_0 is the penetration depth at the absolute zero. It is also found that the electrical resistance can be restored by applying a sufficiently large magnetic field, depending on the temperature. The temperature dependence of the critical magnetic field is very nearly parabolic; some typical threshold curves are shown in fig. 17.12. Thus, at any temperature, a magnetic field less than a certain critical field H_c is excluded from a superconductor, whereas fields greater than H_c penetrate it, and it is restored to the normal state. The critical field-temperature curves divide the (HT) plane into two regions. For states represented by points bounded by the axes through the origin and the threshold field curve, the metal is superconducting; for states represented by points outside this region, the metal is in the normal state (fig. 17.13). From the experimentally determined curves, it can be seen that the gradient of the critical field curve is always negative; that it has a non-zero value at the ordinary transition temperature; and that as the temperature approaches the absolute zero, the gradient vanishes (see Chapter XIX, Section 8). The latter fact can only be deduced by

---

* Meissner and Ochsenfeld, *Naturwiss*, Vol. 21, p. 787 (1933); Meissner, *Proc. Roy. Soc.*, A, Vol. 149, p. 71 (1935).

† J. G. Daunt, A. R. Miller, A. B. Pippard and D. Shoenberg, *Phus Rev.*, Vol. 74, p. 842 (1948).

extrapolating the results, and is subject to any uncertainty which that entails.

In whatever way a metal reaches a given temperature less than its critical temperature, in the presence of an applied magnetic field, its state is always the same. This implies that the transition to the super-

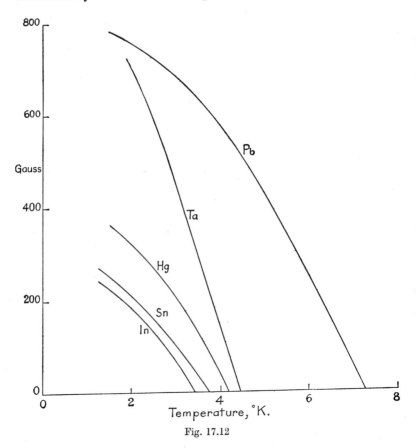

Fig. 17.12

conducting state is *reversible*. Thus, thermodynamical argument can be used to describe the transition in a magnetic field,* and, in fact, had been so used before its validity had been demonstrated by the discovery of the Meissner effect.† Before examining this thermo-

---

* Gorter and Casimir, *Physica*, Vol. 1, p. 306 (1934); Rutgers, *ibid.*, p. 1055 (1934); Vol. 3, p. 999 (1936).

† Keesom, *4e Congrès Phys. Solvay*, p. 288 (1924); Rutgers, see Nachtrag to Ehrenfest, *Leiden Comm.*, *Suppt.*, No. 75b (1933); Gorter, *Arch. Mus. Teyler*, Vol. 7, p. 378 (1933).

dynamical argument, it will be well first to indicate the other thermal properties shown by superconductors. In the transition from the superconducting to the normal state in the presence of a magnetic field, latent heat is evolved. This transition is a first-order phase change. In the transition at the ordinary transition temperature (in zero external field), there is no evolution of latent heat, but there is a specific-heat discontinuity. The electronic specific heat falls to about one-third of its value as the metal warms up through the transition temperature. This is a second-order transition. In the superconducting state, the electronic specific heat follows a cubic law in the

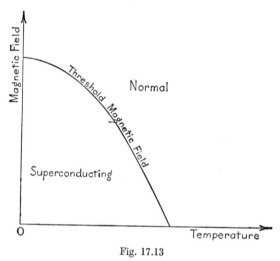

Fig. 17.13

temperature; for tin, this law is followed with a fidelity of about ±3 per cent, which is slightly greater than the claimed experimental accuracy.

From what has been said about the effect of a magnetic field, it follows that at temperatures below the ordinary transition temperature, the metal can be examined in both the normal and the superconducting states. When the thermal conductivity is measured, it is found that, as the temperature approaches the absolute zero, the thermal conductivity in the superconducting state tends to zero much more rapidly than does the thermal conductivity of the metal in the normal state. In fact, the ratio of the two also approaches zero as the temperature is reduced. Below 1° K., the ratio of the thermal conductivity in the superconducting state to that in the normal state falls approximately as the square of the temperature. It has been suggested that a superconducting metal could be used to make and break thermal contact at very low temperatures by applying and removing a small magnetic field.* It might provide a thermal switch for use in a double demagnetization or in a nuclear demagnetization (Sections 19 and 20 of Chapter V), or to set up a reciprocating heat pump.

The thermoelectric effects vanish in a superconductor. Thus, for a pair of metals, both of which are superconducting, there is no Peltier effect, nor any thermoelectric force at temperatures less than the transition temperature of the metal which has the lower transition temperature. For a single metal, the Thomson heat vanishes at temperatures below its superconducting transition temperature.

It has also been found that the transition temperature to the superconducting state can be lowered by applying very high hydrostatic pressures. This effect is negligible at the pressures at which experiments are ordinarily carried out, but it implies that the threshold curve in the (HT) plane, as in fig. 17.13, should be strictly replaced by a threshold surface in the three-dimensional (HTp) space. The student should examine the construction of this surface, and the relations between these quantities. The threshold curve shown in fig. 17.13 is the section of this surface by the plane $p = 0$.

Finally, the metals which are at present known to be superconducting are all to be found within certain groups in the periodic table of the elements. This indicates that in this phenomenon we are concerned with a property of the conduction electrons.

8. Thermodynamics of the Transition in a Magnetic Field.

At the transition in a magnetic field the Gibbs functions of the two phases are equal and they can exist together in equilibrium. For fields lower than the critical field, the superconducting state has the lower free energy, so that the metal goes into this state, whereas for fields greater than the critical field only the normal state can exist. If G_s is the Gibbs free energy per unit volume in the superconducting state in the absence of a field, and G_n is the Gibbs free energy per unit volume of the normal metal, the condition of equilibrium between the two phases is

$$G_n = G_s + H_c^2/8\pi. \quad . \quad . \quad . \quad . \quad (15)$$

For specimens which have a non-zero demagnetizing coefficient, that is, other than long rods, the transition of the whole body is spread over a range of external fields. Actually the body is divided up into a number of normal and superconducting regions (the intermediate state), and the field at the boundary of the regions is *always exactly* H_c *throughout the transition*. It can be shown that the condition (15)

* Daunt and Heer, *Phys. Rev.*, Vol. 76, pp. 854, 985 (1949).

for phase equilibrium applies also to a spread-out transition of this kind. Denoting the difference of the thermodynamic functions for the normal and the superconducting states by Δ, we can write

$$\Delta G = G_n - G_s = H_c^2/8\pi. \quad \ldots \ldots \quad (16)$$

Then

$$\Delta S = S_n - S_s = -\frac{\partial}{\partial T}(\Delta G) = -\frac{H_c}{4\pi}\frac{dH_c}{dT}. \quad \ldots \quad (17)$$

We have seen that the gradient of the critical-field curve is always negative. It follows from equation (17) that the entropy of the metal

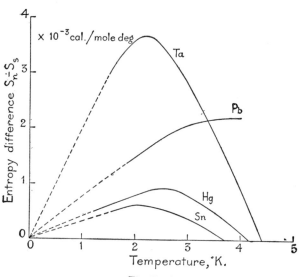

Fig. 17.14

in the superconducting state is less than that of the normal metal. The entropy difference vanishes at the ordinary transition temperature, since there H_c is zero. It also vanishes as the absolute zero is approached, since dH_c/dT tends to zero. The entropy differences for a number of superconductors are shown as a function of temperature, in fig. 17.14. It will be seen that the maximum entropy difference between the two states is of the order of 10^{-3} cal. per mole degree.

Differentiating equation (17), we obtain for the difference in specific heats

$$\Delta C = C_n - C_s = T\frac{d(\Delta S)}{dT} = -\frac{TH_c}{4\pi}\frac{d^2H_c}{dT^2} - \frac{T}{4\pi}\left(\frac{dH_c}{dT}\right)^2. \quad (18)$$

In the absence of a magnetic field, the increase in specific heat on cooling through the transition temperature is

$$\frac{T_c}{4\pi}\left(\frac{dH_c}{dT}\right)^2_{T_c}. \qquad \cdots \cdots \cdots \quad (19)$$

Thus, on cooling the metal in the absence of a magnetic field, there is a sudden jump in the specific heat on passing through the transition temperature, in agreement with the experimental observations.

In an *isothermal* transition from the superconducting to the normal state, in the presence of a magnetic field, it follows from equation (17) that heat will be absorbed. The amount of this latent heat, per unit volume of material, is given by

$$L = T\Delta S = -\frac{TH_c}{4\pi}\frac{dH_c}{dT}. \qquad \cdots \cdots \quad (20)$$

This latent heat vanishes at the ordinary transition temperature in the absence of a magnetic field, since the gradient of the threshold curve remains finite there. The result expressed by equation (20) is analogous to the Clausius-Clapeyron equation, with magnetic field and magnetization taking the place of pressure and volume as the thermodynamical variables. Equation (20) can also be obtained, in the way in which the Clausius-Clapeyron equation was obtained in Chapter XVI, Section 8, by considering the magnetic Gibbs function

$$\mathbf{G'} = \mathbf{U} - T\mathbf{S} - H\mathbf{M}. \qquad \cdots \cdots \quad (21)$$

The specific heat of a normal metal contains terms linear and cubic in the temperature. Using the experimental result that, in the superconducting state, the specific heat varies as the third power of the temperature, it can be shown that the threshold curve is necessarily parabolic. To demonstrate this it is necessary to assume that the entropy difference between the two states vanishes at the absolute zero and at the ordinary transition temperature. It should be noted, however, that the cubic specific-heat law for a superconductor cannot be deduced from the parabolic threshold curve.

9. Thermodynamic Functions of the Superconducting State.

It has been seen that superconductivity is a property of the conduction electrons. It has always appeared to be reasonable to assume that, in a superconductor, the electrons can occupy a group of " low-temperature " states in addition to the normal Fermi states.* For

---

* It should be noted, however, that too often this idea has been put in an objectionable form which appears to postulate the existence of " normal electrons " and " superconducting electrons ". Such a concept is contrary to the indistinguishability of the non-localized particles with which quantum statistics deals. The use of these terms leads, all too often, to statements about the electrons which are untenable, because of the crudely classical categories which they assume implicitly.

such an assembly of systems obeying quantum statistics, the free energy consists of the sum of contributions from the systems which occupy the two groups of states. By using the fact that, at the transition temperature, the energy and the entropy must go over to those for the electrons in a normal metal, thermodynamical functions for a metal in the superconducting state can be written down. The analysis which follows is adapted from that originally given by Casimir and Gorter.*

We introduce a parameter ω, which depends on the temperature, and is defined as the ratio of the occupation number of the low-temperature state at a temperature T to its occupation number at the absolute zero. Thus, the value of ω falls from unity at absolute zero to zero at the critical temperature, and it remains zero for all greater temperatures. When a metal becomes superconducting it changes to a state of lower entropy (fig. 17.14) and thus of greater order. The parameter ω can be interpreted as a measure of the degree of order, without making any postulate about how this ordered state is set up. Now consider the following thermodynamical term scheme for a superconductor in the absence of a magnetic field:

$$U_f = \tfrac{1}{2}\gamma T^2 (1 - \omega)^{\frac{1}{2}}, \qquad S_f = \gamma T (1 - \omega)^{\frac{1}{2}}; \quad . \quad . \quad (22)$$
$$U_l = -\beta\omega, \qquad S_l = 0. \quad . \quad . \quad . \quad . \quad (23)$$

Then, *in zero external field*, we have, for the Gibbs function and the Helmholtz free energy,

$$G = F = F_f + F_l = -\beta\omega - \tfrac{1}{2}\gamma T^2(1 - \omega)^{\frac{1}{2}}. \quad . \quad (24)$$

In these equations, γ is the Sommerfeld electronic specific heat, and β is a constant. As the critical temperature is approached, so that $\omega \to 0$, equations (22) go over into the Sommerfeld form for a normal metal.

It is assumed that the assembly is in statistical equilibrium, and that the occupation of the Fermi and of the low-temperature states is determined by this requirement. The condition for statistical equilibrium in the occupation of the two groups of states is the equality of the partial potentials of the systems in them. This condition is that $(\partial G/\partial\omega)_T$ shall vanish. We obtain

$$0 = \left(\frac{\partial G}{\partial\omega}\right)_T = -\beta + \tfrac{1}{4}\gamma T^2(1 - \omega)^{-\frac{1}{2}},$$

whence
$$\omega = 1 - (T/T_c)^4 = 1 - t^4, \quad . \quad . \quad . \quad (25)$$

* Casimir and Gorter, *Phys. Zeit.*, Vol. 35, p. 963 (1934); Gorter, *Physica*, Vol. 15, p. 55 (1949); see also A. R. Miller, *Australian Journ. Sci.*, Vol. 10, p. 172 (1948).

in which t is the reduced temperature, defined by T/T_c, and where the critical temperature T_c is defined in terms β and γ by

$$4\beta = \gamma T_c{}^2. \qquad \ldots \ldots \ldots \quad (26)$$

In the London electrodynamical equations for a superconductor, the square of the penetration depth of a static magnetic field is inversely proportional to the parameter ω which we have introduced. Thus, if we introduce λ_0 as the penetration depth at the absolute zero, equation (25) leads to

$$\left(\frac{\lambda_0}{\lambda}\right)^2 = 1 - \left(\frac{T}{T_c}\right)^4, \qquad \ldots \ldots \quad (27)$$

in agreement with the experimental data on the temperature variation of the penetration depth of a static magnetic field.

Further, the specific heat is given by

$$C_v = -T\frac{\partial^2 G}{\partial T^2} = -\frac{12\beta T^3}{T_c{}^4} + \frac{6\gamma T^3}{T_c{}^2} = +\frac{3\gamma}{T_c{}^2}T^3, \qquad . \quad (28)$$

using equation (26). As the specimen warms to the transition temperature, its specific heat approaches $3\gamma T_c$. Immediately on passing through the critical temperature, the metal becomes normal and the specific heat falls to γT_c. Thus, the term scheme which has been postulated gives a specific heat for a superconductor which depends on the cube of the temperature, and a discontinuity in specific heat of the right order on passing through the transition temperature. Finally, the fact that U_l does not depend explicitly on T accords with the rapid fall in the thermal conductivity of a superconductor, and with the fact that the thermo-electric effects vanish.

Recent experimental work, in which the specific heats of various superconductors have been measured over a relatively greater temperature range, indicates that the cubic law is only an approximation to the variation of the specific heat with temperature * which is better represented by an exponential law. This accords with deductions from the theory of superconductivity introduced by Bardeen, Cooper, and Schrieffer.†

It would be out of place in a textbook of thermodynamics to attempt to give an account of the electrodynamical properties of

---

* The experimental evidence is summarized in a review by M. A. Biondi, A. T. Forrester, M. P. Garfunkel, and C. B. Satterthwaite, *Rev. Mod. Phys.*, Vol. 30, p. 1109 (1958).

† L. N. Cooper, *Phys. Rev.*, Vol. 104, p. 1189 (1956); J. Bardeen, L. N. Cooper, and J. R. Schrieffer, *ibid.*, Vol. 106, p. 162 (1957); Vol. 108, p. 1175 (1957). For reviews of the theory reference can be made to articles by C. G. Cuper, *Adv. in Physics*, Vol. 8, p. 1 (1959) and I. M. Khalatnikov and A. A. Abrikosov, *ibid.*, Vol. 8, p. 45 (1959).

superconductors. In the preceding sections, these properties have been referred to only in so far as they are essential to the thermodynamical discussion and can be simply related to it. For a detailed discussion of the electrodynamical equations for superconductors, first developed by F. and H. London, the student should refer to Professor London's monograph.*

EXAMPLES

1. Using the magnetic Gibbs function

$$G' = U - TS - HM,$$

obtain an expression for the latent heat of the transition from the superconducting to the normal state in the presence of a magnetic field.

2. The specific heat of tin in the superconducting state follows a cubic law of variation with temperature to about ± 3 per cent. Show that the dependence of the threshold curve on temperature varies according to a parabolic law.

3. The states which can be occupied by an assembly of Fermi particles are divided into two groups A and B, so that the occupation numbers of these groups are n_a and n_b. Denoting the free energy of the particles by F, show that the condition for equilibrium in the occupation of the two groups of states is

$$\left(\frac{\partial F}{\partial x}\right)_T = 0,$$

where x has been written for $n_a/(n_a + n_b)$.

4. Show that the Clausius-Clapeyron equation applied to a solid-liquid transition leads to the relation

$$\frac{dp}{dT} - \frac{p}{T} = \frac{U_l - U_s}{T(V_l - V_s)}.$$

Hence show that if a tangent can be drawn to the melting-pressure curve from the point $p = 0$, $T = 0$, the energy difference between the liquid and solid must change sign at the point of contact. [This establishes one of the results of Section 3 of this chapter by a different method.]

5. Liquid helium (isotope 4) and its vapour of total mass 1 gram are enclosed in a sealed container which is kept at constant volume. The saturated vapour densities of helium at different temperatures are given in the following table.

Temperature (°K.)	2·5	3·0	3·5	4·0	4·5	5·0
Density (10^{-3} gm. cm.$^{-3}$)	1·67	3·89	7·22	12·8	21·7	41

By use of this table and the vapour-pressure curves given in Chapter V, determine the discontinuity in the thermal capacity of the system at the temperature at which the last drop of liquid vaporizes, for different volumes of the container. (See Section 4 of this chapter.)

* London, F., *Superfluids*, Vol. I., *Macroscopic Theory of Superconductivity* (John Wiley and Sons, Inc., New York, 1950).

CHAPTER XVIII

Chemical Equilibria

1. In Chapter XV, Section 3, we have obtained an expression for the entropy **S** of a mixture of perfect gases, namely,

$$\mathbf{S} = \Sigma\, n_j \left\{ \int^T (C_p)_j d \log T = R \log pc_j + \kappa_j \right\}, \quad \cdot \ \cdot \quad (1)$$

where n_j is the number of gram-molecules of the species j in the mixture, p is the *total* pressure of the mixture, c_j is the molecular concentration of the species j, that is,

$$c_j = \frac{n_j}{n_1 + n_2 + n_3 + \ldots}, \quad \cdot \ \ \cdot \ \ \cdot \ \ \cdot \quad (2)$$

and κ_j is a constant for a gram-molecule of the species j, depending on the state of the gas from which the entropy is measured.

We also require expressions for the total volume **V**, and for the total internal energy **U** of a mixture of perfect gases.

For the total volume **V** we have

$$\mathbf{V} = \frac{RT}{p}\, (n_1 + n_2 + \ldots) = \frac{RT}{p}\, \Sigma n_j. \quad \cdot \ \ \cdot \ \ \cdot \quad (3)$$

The internal energy of a single perfect gas depends only on its temperature and not on its volume. We may, therefore, write

$$\mathbf{U}_j = n_j \left\{ \int^T (C_v)_j dT + b_j \right\},$$

where b_j is a constant depending only on the arbitrarily fixed state of the gas from which changes of internal energy are measured—this zero conditon is taken to be the same for the given gas as that from which entropy changes are measured (see footnote on Chapter XVI, Section 3). For the total internal energy **U** of a mixture of gases we have

$$\mathbf{U} = \Sigma n_j \left\{ \int^T (C_v)_j dT + b_j \right\}. \quad \cdot \ \ \cdot \ \ \cdot \quad (4)$$

From these relations we may obtain an expression for the Gibbs free energy **G** of a mixture of perfect gases. Since

$$\mathbf{G} = \mathbf{U} - T\mathbf{S} + p\mathbf{V},$$

we have

$$\mathbf{G} = \Sigma n_j \left\{ \int^T (C_v)_j dT + b_j - T\int^T (C_p)_j d\log T + RT \log p c_j - \kappa_j T + RT \right\}.$$

Further, since $(C_p)_j = (C_v)_j + R,$

this becomes

$$\mathbf{G} = \Sigma n_j \left\{ \int^T (C_p)_j dT - T\int^T (C_p)_j d\log T + RT \log p + b_j - \kappa_j T \right\}$$
$$+ \Sigma n_j RT \log c_j. \quad \ldots \ldots \ldots \ldots \quad (5)$$

Apart from n_j outside the bracket, the first term on the right-hand side of this equation depends only on T and p; it is important to remember that p is the *total* pressure of the mixture. The concentrations c_j enter into the second term only.

Actually the term in the bracket on the right-hand side of equation (4) is the Gibbs free energy of a gram-molecule of the pure species j in the gas phase at temperature T and pressure p (the total pressure of the mixture of gases); we shall call this G_j, so that equation (4) becomes

$$\mathbf{G} = \Sigma n_j G_j + \Sigma n_j RT \log c_j.$$

Further, the Gibbs free energy of one gram-molecule of a pure species is equal to its partial potential, so that

$$G_j = \mu_{j,\,0},$$

and

$$\mathbf{G} = \Sigma n_j(\mu_{j,\,0} + RT \log c_j), \quad \ldots \ldots \quad (6)$$

where the partial potential of the pure species j at a pressure p and temperature T is given by

$$\mu_{j,\,0} = \int^T (C_p)_j dT - T\int^T (C_p)_j d\log T + RT \log p + b_j - \kappa_j T. \quad (7)$$

If the partial potential of the *species j in the mixture* is denoted by μ_j, then

$$\mu_j = \left(\frac{\partial \mathbf{G}}{\partial n_j}\right)_{T,\,p} = \mu_{j,\,0} + RT \log c_j. \quad \ldots \ldots \quad (8)$$

Equilibrium in a Gaseous System at Constant Pressure
and Temperature

2. This expression for the Gibbs free energy enables us to calculate the conditions for equilibrium in a mixture of gases which react chemically with one another. We shall suppose the reacting gases contained in a vessel and maintained at constant temperature and at constant pressure. If the gases are in equilibrium, then for any virtual change for which $\delta T = 0$ and $\delta p = 0$ we must have, by equation (20), Chapter XVI,

$$\delta \mathbf{G} = 0.$$

Such a possible virtual change is one in which an infinitesimal chemical change occurs, so that the numbers n_1, n_2, . . . of gram-molecules of the various molecular species present change by amounts δn_1, δn_2, ... The corresponding change in the value of $\mathbf{G}$ is obtained from equation (5) and must vanish, so that we have

$$\delta \mathbf{G} = \Sigma (G_j + RT \log c_j)\delta n_j + \Sigma n_j \delta(G_j + RT \log c_j) = 0$$

as the condition for equilibrium.

The second sum vanishes. For we have $\delta G_1 = \delta G_2 = \ldots = 0$, since G_1, G_2, . . . are functions of the pressure and temperature only, and these do not change; further, we have

$$\Sigma n_j \delta \log c_j = \frac{n_1}{c_1}\delta c_1 + \frac{n_2}{c_2}\delta c_2 + \ldots,$$

and substituting for n_1/c_1, n_2/c_2, . . . from equation (2) we obtain

$$\Sigma n_j \delta \log c_j = (n_1 + n_2 + n_3 + \ldots)\,(\delta c_1 + \delta c_2 + \ldots) = 0,$$

since $c_1 + c_2 + c_3 + \ldots = 1,$

and therefore $\delta c_1 + \delta c_2 + \ldots = 0.$

The condition for equilibrium therefore becomes

$$\Sigma (G_j + RT \log c_j)\delta n_j = 0. \quad \cdots \quad (9)$$

The equation for the chemical reaction may be written as follows:

$$\nu_1 A_1 + \nu_2 A_2 + \nu_3 A_3 + \ldots = 0, \quad \cdots \quad (10)$$

where A_1, A_2, . . . are the molecular formulæ of the various gases, and ν_1, ν_2, . . . are the numbers of molecules of each of them taking part in the reaction. Any particular ν is positive if the substance to which it refers is formed during the reaction, and negative if it disappears. Thus, in the equation representing the formation of water from oxygen and hydrogen,

$$2H_2 + O_2 \rightarrow 2H_2O,$$

the values of ν for the three components are -2, -1 and $+2$.
For such a reaction we must have

$$\frac{\delta n_1}{\nu_1} = \frac{\delta n_2}{\nu_2} = \frac{\delta n_3}{\nu_3} = \cdots,$$

so that the equilibrium equation (9) becomes

$$\sum \nu_j(G_j + RT \log c_j) = 0, \quad \cdots \quad (11)$$

or $\quad \nu_1 \log c_1 + \nu_2 \log c_2 + \cdots = -\dfrac{\nu_1 G_1 + \nu_2 G_2 + \cdots}{RT}.$

Since the expression on the right of this equation is constant at constant temperature and constant total pressure, we may write for the condition of equilibrium under these conditions

$$\sum \nu_j \log c_j = \log K_c, \quad \cdots \cdots \quad (12)$$

where for a given reaction K_c depends only on the temperature and pressure and not on the concentrations, and is given by

$$\log K_c = -\frac{\sum \nu_j G_j}{RT}. \quad \cdots \cdots \quad (13)$$

The equilibrium condition can be written in the equivalent form

$$c_1{}^{\nu_1} c_2{}^{\nu_2} c_3{}^{\nu_3} \cdots = K_c. \quad \cdots \cdots \quad (14)$$

This is the important *law of mass action*. Equation (14) means that the value of K_c can be determined once and for all for a given reaction at a given temperature and pressure by measuring the molecular concentrations of all the reacting substances when equilibrium has been attained. This value of K_c can then be used to calculate the final molecular concentrations of all the reacting substances if they are mixed in any known proportions and allowed to come to equilibrium under the same conditions of temperature and pressure.*

---

* In general, each G occurring in equation (9) contains an arbitrary constant depending on the zero for the particular gas from which thermodynamic quantities are measured. The actual value of K_c cannot, therefore, be deduced from equation (9). (For a further discussion of this, see Chapter XIX.) On the other hand, when K_c has been determined experimentally, equation (9) shows that, when we are considering the equilibrium of gases which react chemically, if there are x gases, only $x - 1$ of the arbitrary constants are independent. A similar remark applies to the thermodynamic potentials in Sections 22, 23, and 24.

3. The Heat of Reaction.

When a change takes place in a system, the heat $\delta\mathbf{Q}$ that must be supplied from outside is given by

$$\delta\mathbf{Q} = \delta\mathbf{U} + p\,\delta\mathbf{V},$$

where $\delta\mathbf{U}$ is the increase in the internal energy and $\delta\mathbf{V}$ the increase in the volume. From equations (3) and (4) we have, for the change considered in the preceding section, at constant temperature and constant total pressure,

$$\delta\mathbf{Q} = \Sigma\left\{\int^T(C_v)_j dT + b_j + RT\right\}\delta n_j$$

$$= \Sigma\left\{\int^T(C_p)_j dT + b_j\right\}\delta n_j.$$

The *heat of reaction* at constant pressure, H_p, is equal to $-\delta\mathbf{Q}$, when we substitute in the last expression $\delta n_1 = \nu_1$, $\delta n_2 = \nu_2$, and so on. We have, therefore,

$$H_p = -\Sigma\nu_j\left\{\int^T(C_p)_j dT + b_j\right\}. \qquad \ldots \quad (15)$$

It will be seen that the heat of reaction is *positive* if heat is *evolved* when the reaction proceeds in the direction indicated by equation (10).

The effect of change of temperature on the heat of reaction can easily be obtained from equation (15). If $_1H_p$ is the heat of reaction at temperature T_1, and $_2H_p$ is the heat of reaction at temperature T_2, the total pressure being the same in the two cases, we have

$$_2H_p - {_1H_p} = -\Sigma\nu_j\int_{T_1}^{T_2}(C_p)_j dT. \qquad \ldots \ldots \quad (16)$$

This difference can be determined if we know the specific heats of all the reacting gases as functions of the temperature.

4. The Effect of Change of Temperature on the Reaction Constant.

We obtain the effect of change of temperature on the reaction constant by differentiating equation (13) with respect to the temperature at constant pressure, obtaining

$$\left(\frac{\partial \log K_c}{\partial T}\right)_p = \frac{1}{RT^2}(\nu_1 G_1 + \nu_2 G_2 + \ldots) - \frac{1}{RT}\left(\nu_1\frac{\partial G_1}{\partial T} + \nu_2\frac{\partial G_2}{\partial T} + \ldots\right)_p.$$

Substituting from equation (7), this becomes

$$\left(\frac{\partial \log K_c}{\partial T}\right)_p = \frac{1}{RT^2}\Sigma\nu_j\left\{\int^T(C_p)_j dT + b_j\right\},$$

or, using equation (15),

$$\left(\frac{\partial \log K_c}{\partial T}\right)_p = -\frac{H_p}{RT^2}. \quad \ldots \ldots \quad (17)$$

This is the famous equation of Van't Hoff, and is usually called the *equation of the isochore of reaction.*

Referring to equation (14), it will be seen that equation (17) means that, if the reaction proceeds in the direction indicated by equation (10) with absorption of heat so that H_p is negative, increasing the temperature causes the reaction to proceed forwards, and vice versa. In other words, *an increase in the temperature causes the equilibrium to be displaced in the direction corresponding to absorption of heat from outside.*

Equation (17) can be used to determine heats of reaction from concentration measurements (see Section 13).

5. The Effect of Change of Pressure on the Reaction Constant.

In a similar way by differentiating equation (13) with respect to the pressure at constant temperature, we obtain

$$\left(\frac{\partial \log K_c}{\partial p}\right)_T = -\frac{1}{RT} \Sigma \nu_j \left(\frac{\partial G_j}{\partial p}\right)_T.$$

Using (7), this gives

$$\left(\frac{\partial \log K_c}{\partial p}\right)_T = -\frac{1}{RT} \Delta \mathbf{V}, \quad \ldots \ldots \quad (18)$$

where $\Delta \mathbf{V}$ is the increase in volume when the reaction takes place in the direction indicated by equation (10), and where ν_1 gram-molecules of the first substance, ν_2 gram-molecules of the second, and so on are the amounts transformed.

Qualitatively, equation (18) means that *increasing the pressure causes the equilibrium to be displaced in the direction in which the reaction proceeds with diminution of volume.*

6. The Principle of Le Chatelier.

The qualitative results expressed in equations (17) and (18) are summed up in the very important and useful principle of Le Chatelier:

A change of one of the factors of an equilibrium causes a rearrangement of the system in such a direction that the factor in question tends to experience a change in the opposite sense from the original change.

7. Equilibrium in Terms of Partial Pressures.

In many cases it is more convenient to express the equilibrium conditions in terms of partial pressures than in terms of molecular concentrations. If p_1 is the partial pressure of the first gas, p_2 that of the second gas, and so on, and if p is the total pressure, we have

$$c_1 = p_1/p, \quad c_2 = p_2/p, \quad \ldots.$$

Substituting these values in equation (10), we obtain for the equilibrium condition

$$p_1^{\nu_1} p_2^{\nu_2} p_3^{\nu_3} \ldots = p^{(\nu_1 + \nu_2 + \nu_3 + \cdots)} K_c = K_p, \quad . \quad . \quad (19)$$

where K_p is a constant if the temperature and pressure are constant. The value of K_p can be determined from measurements of the partial pressures of the reacting gases after equilibrium has been attained. The value of K_p so deduced can then be used to calculate the final partial pressures of all the reacting substances, if they are mixed in any given proportions, the temperature and total pressure being the same as before.

The relation between K_p and K_c is of course

$$K_p = p^{(\nu_1 + \nu_2 + \cdots)} K_c, \quad . \quad . \quad . \quad . \quad (20)$$

and, if the value of either of them is measured, that of the other can be deduced immediately.

K_p, like K_c, is a function only of the temperature and the total pressure.

We have $\quad \log K_p = (\nu_1 + \nu_2 + \ldots) \log p + \log K_c$.

Thus we obtain $\quad \left(\dfrac{\partial \log K_p}{\partial T} \right)_p = \left(\dfrac{\partial \log K_c}{\partial T} \right)_p = - \dfrac{H_p}{RT^2} \quad . \quad . \quad (21)$

from equation (17). This alternative form of the equation of the isochore of reaction shows that we may use the way in which either K_c or K_p varies with the temperature to determine the heat of reaction. We shall apply this result in Section 13.

8. Separation of Isotopes.

The thermodynamical properties of a substance depend on the vibrational frequencies of its molecules; these are affected by the masses of the atoms. Thus, it can be seen from equation (13) that the equilibrium constant for a reaction will depend on the isotopes which are involved. Attention was first directed to this question after the separation of deuterium. The marked differences in the properties of hydrogen and deuterium suggested that there might be small differences in the properties of isotopes of other light elements. Calculations of the equilibrium constants for isotopic exchange reactions involving isotopes of lithium, boron, carbon, oxygen, and nitrogen showed that these equilibrium constants differed from unity.* This indicated that the isotopes of these light elements differed in their thermodynamical properties. Thus, as a result of naturally occurring equilibrium processes, it could be expected that the isotopic constitution of different samples would vary, as a result of fractionation in these natural processes. By an exchange reaction is meant one between two molecular species which have an atom in common; the reaction consists of an exchange between the two species of the light and heavy isotopes of the common atom. An example of such a reaction is

$$\tfrac{1}{2}\,[CO_2{}^{16}]_{gas} + [H_2O^{18}]_{liquid} \rightleftharpoons \tfrac{1}{2}\,[CO_2{}^{18}]_{gas} + [H_2O^{16}]_{liquid}.$$

The calculated value of the equilibrium constant for the reaction proceeding to the right is 1·044. This shows that the oxygen isotope 18 is favoured in the carbon dioxide. The observed value of the equilibrium constant is 1·046 at the ice point. A comprehensive study of reactions of this type has been made by Urey,† and the equilibrium constants have been calculated. The departure of the equilibrium constants from unity are sufficient to indicate that in natural sources there will be a difference of a few per cent in relative isotopic abundance. Actually, the variations in isotopic abundance are more widespread than is generally supposed, and extend to quite heavy elements in the periodic table. Careful measurements have shown, for instance, that the ratio varies by up to five per cent.‡ Very large variations in the relative abundances of the helium isotopes of mass 3 and 4 have been found in helium from different natural sources,§ although the variation in some cases may be partly due to nuclear reactions in which only one of the isotopes is produced. It should also be noted that the variations in isotopic abundance are sufficient to affect the chemical atomic weights.

Use has been made of the small differences in the thermodynamical properties of isotopes to separate them in the laboratory. By using suitable exchange reactions, Urey and his colleagues ‖ have separated

---

* Urey and Greiff, *Journ. Amer. Chem. Soc.*, Vol. 57, p. 321 (1935).

† Urey, *Journ. Chem. Soc.*, p. 562 (1947).

‡ Thode, Macnamara, Lossing and Collins, *Journ. Amer. Chem. Soc.*, Vol. 70, p. 3008 (1948); Thode, Macnamara and Collins, *Canadian Journ. Res.*, Vol. 27, p. 361 (1949).

§ Aldrich and Nier, *Phys. Rev.*, Vol. 74, p. 1590 (1948).

‖ Thode and Urey, *Journ. Chem. Phys.*, Vol. 7, p. 34 (1939); Hutchison, Stewart and Urey, *ibid.*, Vol. 8, p. 532 (1940); Stewart and Cohen, *ibid.*, p. 904 (1940); Stevenson, Wagner, Beeck and Otvos, *ibid.*, Vol. 16, p. 993 (1948); Thode, *Research*, Vol. 2, p. 154 (1949).

the isotopes of nitrogen, carbon, sulphur, hydrogen, boron, and oxygen. The method has been used on a commercial scale to prepare heavy water.* In the catalytic exchange of hydrogen atoms between hydrogen gas and water, the latter contains between three and four times the concentration of deuterium as the gas in equilibrium with it. In this method a continuous countercurrent-flow arrangement in apparatus of the distillation-column type is used.

Reactions at Constant Temperature and Pressure in which Solids or Liquids take part

9. When an equilibrium is set up between various reacting gases and solids, the gases and the vapours of the solids (or liquids) must be in equilibrium. The vapour pressures of the solids remain constant throughout the reaction. For convenience we shall represent the partial pressures (vapour pressures) of those substances which are present in the solid or liquid state by the letter π, and, as before, the partial pressures of those which are present in the gaseous state only by the letter p, with suitable subscripts in each case.

10. Equilibrium Condition.

The equilibrium condition given by equation (19) may be written

$$p_1^{\nu_1} p_2^{\nu_2} p_3^{\nu_3} \ldots \pi_x^{\nu_x} \pi_y^{\nu_y} \ldots = K_p. \qquad (22)$$

Since all the π are constant at constant temperature, this gives

$$p_1^{\nu_1} p_2^{\nu_2} p_3^{\nu_3} \ldots = K_p', \qquad (23)$$

that is, the expression on the left-hand side is constant at constant temperature. This indicates that in applying the law of mass action we need consider only the partial pressures of those substances which are not present in the condensed state.

To illustrate this we may consider the simple case of the dissociation of solid ammonium hydrosulphide into ammonia and hydrogen sulphide according to the equation

$$NH_4HS \rightleftharpoons NH_3 + H_2S.$$

From equation (22) we have in the equilibrium condition

$$K_p = \frac{p_1 p_2}{\pi}, \qquad (24)$$

or
$$p_1 p_2 = K_p \pi = K_p'. \qquad (25)$$

The vapour density shows that the vapour is almost completely dissociated, so that the total pressure p is without sensible error equal to $(p_1 + p_2)$. At 25·1° C.

* Smyth, Rev. Mod. Phys., Vol. 17, p. 351 (1945), Sections 9–24.

the dissociation pressure amounts to 501 mm. of mercury—in this case the partial pressures of the two products are equal to one another, each being 250·5 mm. According as one or other of the gases preponderates in the mixture the partial pressures at the same temperature are as given in Table I.* It will be seen that, as is required by the theory, $p_1 p_2$ is sensibly constant.

TABLE I

NH$_3$ (p_1)	H$_2$S (p_2)	$p_1 p_2$
138	458	63,200
208	292	60,700
250·5	250·5	62,700
417	146	60,900
453	143	64,800

In these measurements the value of $(p_1 + p_2)$, the total pressure, does not remain constant, but this does not affect the constancy of $p_1 p_2$, since we can show that $\partial K_p'/\partial p = 0$. We have

$$\frac{\partial K_p'}{\partial p} = \pi \frac{\partial K_p}{\partial p},$$

so that we have to show that $\partial K_p/\partial p = 0$. We have, further, since $K_p = p K_c$,

$$\frac{\partial K_p}{\partial p} = K_c + p \frac{\partial K_c}{\partial p}.$$

We have

$$\frac{\partial K_c}{\partial p} = K_c \frac{\partial \log K_c}{\partial p} = -K_c \frac{1}{RT} \Delta \mathbf{V}$$

from equation (18). In this case $\Delta \mathbf{V} = +RT/p$, since $\Delta \mathbf{V}$ is the change in volume for the reaction between the *vapour* and the gases, so that

$$\frac{\partial K_c}{\partial p} = -\frac{K_c}{p},$$

and using this result in the expression for $\partial K_p/\partial p$, we obtain

$$\frac{\partial K_p}{\partial p} = 0,$$

as required.

11. Heat of Reaction.

In determining the relation between the heat of reaction and the equilibrium constant, we shall first consider the simple special case dealt with at the end of the last section. The value of K_p is given by equation (24). Applying equation (21), we obtain

$$\left(\frac{\partial \log K_p}{\partial T} \right)_p = -\frac{H_p'}{RT^2}, \quad \cdots \cdots \quad (26)$$

* See Nernst, *Theoretical Chemistry* (English translation), 5th edition, p. 559 (1923).

where H_p' is the heat given out when one gram-molecule of the *vapour* of ammonium hydrosulphide dissociates into ammonia and hydrogen sulphide. The heat evolved when one gram-molecule of *solid* ammonium hydrosulphide dissociates into ammonia and hydrogen sulphide is equal to $(H_p' - \Lambda)$, where Λ is the molecular latent heat of vaporization * of ammonium hydrosulphide at the temperature T. This is the actual heat of reaction, which we denote by H_p. We have then

$$\frac{H_p}{RT^2} = \frac{H_p'}{RT^2} - \frac{\Lambda}{RT^2}$$

$$= -\left(\frac{\partial \log K_p}{\partial T}\right)_p - \frac{\Lambda}{RT^2}$$

$$= -\left(\frac{\partial \log p_1 p_2}{\partial T}\right)_p + \frac{\partial \log \pi}{\partial T} - \frac{\Lambda}{RT^2}.$$

Referring to the Clausius-Clapeyron equation (3), Chapter VIII, we see that, if the vapour is assumed to obey the perfect gas laws and if the volume of the solid is neglected,

$$\frac{\partial \log \pi}{\partial T} = \frac{\Lambda}{RT^2},$$

so that the expression for H_p becomes

$$\left(\frac{\partial \log K_p'}{\partial T}\right)_p = -\frac{H_p}{RT^2},$$

in obtaining which we have used (25).

We have proved this relation only for the particular case. The proof of the general case, which is left to the reader, follows along exactly similar lines, using equations (21), (22), (23), and the Clausius-Clapeyron equation, and gives the same relation, namely,

$$\left(\frac{\partial \log K_p'}{\partial T}\right)_p = -\frac{H_p}{RT^2}, \qquad \ldots \quad \ldots \quad (27)$$

where $\qquad K_p' = p_1^{\nu_1} \cdot p_2^{\nu_2} \cdot p_3^{\nu_3} \ldots$

p_1, p_2, ... are the partial pressures of the reacting gases when a state of equilibrium has been reached, and ν_1, ν_2, ... are the number of molecules of each of the gases taking part in the reaction defined by equation (10). *Only the partial pressures of substances which are present in the gaseous state alone are included in the expression for* K_p', *that is,*

---

* Latent heat of evaporation is always heat absorbed from outside. Λ is regarded as a positive quantity (see equation (23), Chapter XVI), and therefore we must use the negative sign before it in the present case, in which heat absorbed is reckoned negative.

the vapour pressures of substances which are present in the liquid or solid states are omitted. Equation (27) under these conditions gives the actual heat evolved when the reaction occurs between the gaseous and condensed substances under a constant pressure and at constant temperature.

12. Effect of Temperature on the Heat of Reaction.

We may obtain the effect of change of temperature on the heat of reaction for a reaction in which solids take part from equation (16), which gives the effect of temperature on the heat of reaction between the vapours and gases, namely, on $_1H_p{}'$. We have

$$_2H_p{}' - {}_1H_p{}' = -\Sigma \nu_j \int_{T_1}^{T_2} (C_p{}^g)_j \, dT,$$

where $(C_p{}^g)_j$ is the specific heat at constant pressure of gas (or vapour) of the species j.

The measured heat of reaction at temperature T_1, which we shall denote by $_1H_p$, is given by

$$_1H_p = {}_1H_p{}' + \Sigma_s \nu_x({}_1\Lambda_x),$$

where $_1\Lambda_x$ is the molecular latent heat of vaporization of solid number x at temperature T_1, and the subscript s under the Σ sign indicates that the sum is to be taken only over those substances which are present as solids. A similar equation gives the measured heat of reaction at temperature T_2. Combining these results with the expression for the variation of the latent heat of vaporization with temperature (equation (4), Chapter VIII), we obtain for the difference between the measured heats of reaction at temperatures T_1 and T_2

$$_2H_p - {}_1H_p = -\Sigma_g \nu_j \int_{T_1}^{T_2} (C_p{}^g)_j \, dT - \Sigma_s \nu_x \int_{T_1}^{T_2} (C_p{}^s)_x \, dT, \quad . \quad (28)$$

where the subscript g under the Σ sign indicates that the summation is to be taken only over those substances which are not present in the solid state, and the subscript s is used as above.

Numerical Calculations

13. We shall now see how the foregoing relations may be used to calculate heats of reaction in special cases in which the equilibrium condition can be directly measured.

First let us consider the dissociation of nitrogen tetroxide,

$$N_2O_4 \rightleftharpoons 2NO_2.$$

The value of K_p (equation (19)) is in this case given by

$$K_p = \frac{p_2{}^2}{p_1},$$

where p_2 is the partial pressure of nitric oxide and p_1 is that of nitrogen peroxide. If α is the fraction of the total number of N_2O_4 molecules which are dissociated,

V is the volume occupied by a mass equal to one gram-molecule of N_2O_4, and p the total pressure, we have

$$p V = (1 + \alpha)RT,$$

$$p_1 V = (1 - \alpha)RT,$$

$$p_2 V = 2\alpha RT,$$

so that
$$K_p = \frac{p_2^2}{p_1} = \frac{4\alpha^2 RT}{(1 - \alpha)V} = \frac{4\alpha^2 p}{1 - \alpha^2}. \quad \ldots \ldots \quad (29)$$

The value of α may be calculated from measurements of the density of the equilibrium mixture. If d_0 is the density which the gas would have if no dissociation had taken place, and if d is the observed density, we have *

$$\frac{d_0}{d} = \frac{1 + \alpha}{1} \quad \text{or} \quad \alpha = \frac{d_0 - d}{d}.$$

Using this result in equation (21), we obtain

$$K_p = \frac{\left(\frac{d_0 - d}{d}\right)^2 p}{1 - \left(\frac{d_0 - d}{d}\right)^2} = \frac{4(d_0 - d)^2 p}{d_0(2d - d_0)}.$$

It makes no difference to the calculations, and it is more convenient, to use instead of the actual densities the specific gravities referred to air as standard. The value of d_0 is then equal to the molecular weight of undissociated N_2O_4 molecules divided by the average molecular weight of air, that is,

$$d_0 = \frac{92 \cdot 02}{28 \cdot 95} = 3 \cdot 179.$$

The following are the observed specific gravities at temperatures of $26 \cdot 7°$ C. and $111 \cdot 3°$ C. and at atmospheric pressure.

Temperature	Specific Gravity
$26 \cdot 7°$ C.	$2 \cdot 65$
$111 \cdot 3°$ C.	$1 \cdot 65$

If we assume that the heat of dissociation remains appreciably constant over the range of temperatures considered, these figures enable us to form an estimate of its magnitude, since they enable us to determine $\left(\dfrac{\partial \log K_p}{\partial T}\right)_p$; we obtain

$$\left(\frac{\partial \log K_p}{\partial T}\right)_p = \frac{4 \cdot 99}{84 \cdot 6}.$$

From equation (21), the heat of reaction is given by

$$H_p = -RT^2 \left(\frac{\partial \log K_p}{\partial T}\right)_p,$$

* In the general case in which one molecule dissociates into n molecules,
$$\frac{d_0}{d} = 1 + (n - 1)\alpha \quad \text{or} \quad \alpha = \frac{d_0 - d}{(n - 1)d}.$$

and using $R = 8\cdot314 \cdot 10^7$ ergs, and putting T (the mean temperature) $= 342°$ (absolute), we obtain

$$H_p = -57,400 \text{ joules,}$$

so that the dissociation of 92 gm. of N_2O_4 at constant pressure requires the supply of a considerable quantity of heat. The observed value,* deduced from specific-heat measurements on the dissociating gas, is about

$$-55,200 \text{ joules.}$$

We shall next consider the dissociation of ammonium hydrosulphide (solid) dealt with in Sections 10 and 11. In this case, to obtain the heat of dissociation of the solid we have to use the constant $K_p{}'$, which involves only the partial pressures of those substances (NH_3 and H_2S) which occur in the gaseous state alone. We have, according to equation (18a),

$$K_p{}' = p_1 p_2,$$

and, as we have shown at the end of Section 10, the value of $K_p{}'$ is independent of the total pressure ($p_1 + p_2$).

In this case we measure the dissociation pressure of the solid, so that the gases are present in the proportions in which they are produced by the reaction, that is, equimolecular proportions. We have, therefore, $p_1 = p_2 = p/2$, where p is the measured dissociation pressure, and thus we obtain

$$K_p{}' = \frac{p^2}{4}.$$

The measured dissociation pressures are as follows:

Temperature	*Dissociation Pressure*
9·5° C.	175 mm. of mercury.
25·1° C.	501 ,, ,,

From these results we obtain †

$$\frac{\partial \log K_p{}'}{\partial T} = + \frac{2\cdot10}{15\cdot6},$$

and for the heat of dissociation H_p we have

$$H_p = -RT^2 \frac{2\cdot10}{15\cdot6}$$

$$= -94,500 \text{ joules,}$$

for $T = 290\cdot5$. The measured value is

$$-95,000 \text{ joules.}$$

---

* See Nernst, *Theoretical Chemistry* (1923), p. 753; the result there given refers to a reaction at constant volume, to which it is necessary to add in this case $-RT$ to give the heat of reaction at constant pressure.

† The units in which p is measured are immaterial.

The Activity

14. The theory given above applies exactly to perfect gases and very closely to actual gases provided the densities or pressures are not too high. For high densities it is convenient to use the concept of activity introduced by Lewis.*

If a gram-molecule of a perfect gas at constant temperature changes from condition (1), in which the pressure is p_1, to condition (2), in which the pressure is p_2, the change in its partial potential is given by equation (7) as

$$\mu_2 - \mu_1 = RT \log \frac{p_2}{p_1},$$

or
$$d\mu = RT \, d \log p.$$

For a gas which is not perfect we shall *define* a quantity A, which we shall call the *activity*, by the relation

$$\mu_2 - \mu_1 = RT \log \frac{\mathsf{A}_2}{\mathsf{A}_1},$$

or
$$d\mu = RT \, d \log \mathsf{A}, \quad \ldots \ldots \ldots \quad (30)$$

or in the integrated form
$$\mu = RT \log \mathsf{A} + B, \quad \ldots \ldots \ldots \quad (31)$$

where B is a constant depending only on the temperature. The value of the constant B is determined, and the definition of the activity is completed, by laying down that at very low pressures

$$\underset{p \to 0}{\mathrm{Lim}} \, \mathsf{A} = p; \quad \ldots \ldots \ldots \ldots \quad (32)$$

this requirement uses the condition that in the limit of vanishing pressure, the behaviour of an actual gas approaches that of the ideal gas. For the partial potential of the species in the perfect gas state, we must therefore have, from equation (31),

$$\mu_0 = RT \log p + B,$$

whence the constant of integration in equation (31) is determined. Thus, in terms of the activity, the partial potential of an actual gas at pressure p is given by

$$\mu = \mu_0 + RT \log \mathsf{A}/p. \quad \ldots \ldots \ldots \quad (33)$$

15. Change of Activity with Pressure.

From the definition of G, and the first and second laws, an expression can be obtained for dG. From it, we have already deduced (Chapter XVI, equation (40)) that

$$\left(\frac{\partial G}{\partial p} \right)_T = V.$$

Thus, for a pure species we have, by equation (30),

$$\left(\frac{\partial \log \mathsf{A}}{\partial p} \right)_T = \frac{V}{RT}. \quad \ldots \ldots \ldots \quad (34)$$

* Lewis, *Proc. Amer. Acad.*, Vol. 43, p. 259 (1907).

If the equation of state is known, this equation can be integrated. The constant of integration is determined by equation (32), so that at a given temperature the activity can be determined as a function of the pressure.

16. Application to Equilibrium Problems.

The Gibbs function G of a mixture of gases containing n_1 gram-molecules of the first gas, n_2 gram-molecules of the second, and so on, is given by

$$G = \sum n_j(RT \log A_j + B_j).$$

As in Section 2, we consider a change at constant temperature and at constant total pressure, in which n_1 changes by δn_1, and so on. The change in G is given by

$$\delta G = \sum \delta n_j(RT \log A_j + B_j) + \sum n_j RT \, \delta \log A_j, \quad \cdots \quad (35)$$

since at constant temperature the quantities B_j do not change.

We shall now show that the second term vanishes. If p_j is the partial pressure of the first gas, we may write

$$\delta \log A_j = \frac{\partial \log A_j}{\partial p_j} \, \delta p_j.$$

Assuming that equation (34) is applicable to each gas in the mixture of gases, just as if the other gases were not present, the second term on the right of equation (35) becomes

$$\sum n_j V \, \delta p_j = V \sum \delta p_j = 0,$$

since $\sum \delta p_j$, the total change of pressure, is zero. V is the total volume.

Equation (35) may therefore be written

$$\delta G = \sum \delta n_j(RT \log A_j + B_j).$$

For equilibrium this must be equal to zero. We therefore have for the condition of equilibrium

$$\sum \nu_j(RT \log A_j + B_j) = 0,$$

where, as in equation (11), we have substituted ν_j for δn_j. This may be written

$$A_1^{\nu_1} A_2^{\nu_2} A_3^{\nu_3} \ldots = K_a, \quad \cdots \quad \cdots \quad (36)$$

where K_a is a constant if the temperature and total pressure remain constant. This equation must be used instead of equation (19), the ordinary law of mass action, at high densities. As we have mentioned in Section 15, the activities can be calculated if the equations of state of the reacting gases are known.

Lewis * has applied the method to experiments on the dissociation pressure of silver oxide. A similar method with a slightly different definition of the activity is widely applied to solutions.

In the detonation wave set up by an explosion, pressures of the order of 10^5 atmospheres are reached, and the interactions between the molecules of the product gases become of great importance in determining the behaviour of the wave. The interactions can be allowed for by using the higher-order terms in a series

---

* Lewis, *Journ. Amer. Chem. Soc.*, Vol. 28, pp. 139, 158 (1906); see also Lewis and Randall, *Thermodynamics and the Free Energy of Chemical Substances*, p. 480 (1923).

expansion of the equation of state and introducing an empirical activity.† The interaction energy can be expressed in terms of the coefficients of the expansion in powers of p as

$$E_i = -\tfrac{1}{2}Cp^2 - \tfrac{2}{3}Dp^3,$$

where the expansion has been taken as far as the term in p^3. H. Jones and A. R. Miller introduced a parameter p^*, the activity, defined by

$$\mu = \mu_0 + RT \log p^*/p,$$

where μ is the partial potential of the actual gas and μ_0 is that of a perfect gas at the same temperature and pressure. Then

$$RT \log p^*/p = Bp + \tfrac{1}{2}Cp^2 + \tfrac{1}{3}Dp^3.$$

The equilibrium constants for the chemical reactions taking place in the detonation wave-front could then be evaluated in terms of p^*. From these values the conditions in the wave-front, and the change in the composition of the product gases during their adiabatic expansion, were determined, assuming chemical and thermal equilibrium to be maintained during the expansion.

THE MEASUREMENT OF EQUILIBRIUM CONSTANTS

17. The measurement of equilibrium constants in gaseous systems is of such great importance in the development of modern thermodynamics that we must consider briefly the various methods by which the measurement can be carried out.

In this connexion it is important to understand what we mean when we say that a system is in thermodynamic equilibrium. If for a given change in the system $\delta G = 0$, the system is in equilibrium as regards that particular change. If, on the other hand, for a given change δG is positive, the change cannot take place spontaneously. If for the given change δG is negative, the change *can* take place spontaneously. Whether in the last case the change will or will not take place is a different question. There is a close analogy between this case and that of a body resting on a rough inclined plane. The body cannot spontaneously move up the plane and increase its gravitational potential energy, but it can spontaneously move down it; whether it will do so depends on the frictional force between the body and the plane. If the plane is horizontal, the body resting on it is in equilibrium. Incidentally this analogy indicates why G is sometimes called the thermodynamic potential.

Any question concerning the forces which oppose chemical reactions is outside the range of thermodynamics, just as the question of frictional forces in mechanics is outside the range of gravitational potential theory. The analogy is sufficient to show that this fact does not affect the importance of the thermodynamical criterion of equilibrium.

† H. Jones and A. R. Miller, *Proc. Roy. Soc.*, A, Vol. 194, p. 480 (1948).

To take an example: If water vapour is formed isothermally at constant pressure from hydrogen and oxygen gases at ordinary temperatures and under ordinary pressures, there is a large diminution in the thermodynamic potential of the system. But we know that these two gases can be kept together indefinitely without any appreciable change taking place. We conclude, therefore, that there is a strong force of some sort opposing the reaction. Thermodynamics tells us that the action can take place spontaneously; it does in fact readily do so in the presence of spongy platinum, which acts as a catalyst. The state of true thermodynamic equilibrium is reached only when free oxygen and hydrogen are present in very minute proportions; in other words, in the state of true thermodynamic equilibrium the degree of dissociation of water vapour is very small.

It is a general rule, however, that the velocity with which a chemical reaction proceeds increases rapidly as the temperature is raised. Thus many reactions, which at ordinary temperatures proceed at an infinitesimal rate, rapidly reach thermodynamic equilibrium at higher temperatures. The reaction just considered is a typical example. Some of the methods of studying chemical equilibria depend on this fact combined with the fact that at lower temperatures the velocity of reaction is negligible.

Many of the experimental methods have been developed by Nernst and his associates.* The most important are the following.

(1) *Manometric Methods.*—Reactions which are accompanied by a change of volume can be studied manometrically. Bodenstein † and others have applied this method at high temperatures. Under this head may be included also methods depending on the determination of gaseous densities. These direct methods are illustrated by the examples given in Sections 10 and 13.

(2) *The Streaming Method.*—Consider the scheme shown in fig. 18.1. The gas mixture is allowed to flow through a long tube. Between the points a and b the tube is kept at the temperature t at which the equilibrium is to be studied; from b to c the temperature is made to fall as quickly as possible, so that at the point c the temperature t' is so low that the velocity of reaction is vanishingly small. After leaving the tube the gas is collected and analysed. In order that the gas leaving the tube shall have a

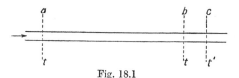

Fig. 18.1

composition corresponding to the equilibrium at temperature t, the two following conditions must be fulfilled: (1) the distance ab must be long enough to allow the gas to reach equilibrium; (2) the time of cooling in the part bc must be short enough to prevent any disturbance of this equilibrium. The first condition may

* See Nernst, *Theoretical Chemistry* (Eng. Trans.), 5th edition, p. 777 (1923).

† Bodenstein, *Zeits. f. Elektrochemie*, Vol. 16, p. 961 (1910); Vol. 22, p. 338 (1916); *Zeits. f. phys. Chem.*, Vol. 100, p. 68 (1922); see also Trautz and Stäckel, *Zeits. f. anorg. Chem.*, Vol. 122, p. 81 (1922); v. Wartenberg and Henglein, *Ber. d. deuts. chem. Ges.*, Vol. 55, p. 1003 (1922).

always be theoretically fulfilled by making *ab* long enough; practically it is best realized by widening the tube between *a* and *b* so that the velocity of flow is decreased. Another plan * is to fill the space between *a* and *b* with a catalyst. The second condition can best be fulfilled by making *bc* a narrow capillary tube.

The question as to whether the length of the tube *ab* is sufficiently great at the temperature *t* can always be determined by passing through the tube mixtures the compositions of which lie first on one side and then on the other of the equilibrium composition. The composition of the mixture leaving the tube should not be affected.

At low temperatures the chief source of error is due to the fact that equilibrium is not attained in *ab*. At high temperatures equilibrium is attained in *ab* but the disturbance in *bc* becomes more serious. In the latter case the gases leaving the tube have the same composition whatever the composition of the original mixture, but this composition is not necessarily the composition corresponding to equilibrium at temperature *t*. The curve in fig. 18.2 illustrates this. We may

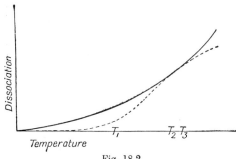

Fig. 18.2

suppose that the unbroken curve is the true curve representing, for example, the dissociation of water vapour. The dotted curve represents experimental values. From what we have said, the curve obtained at the lower temperatures depends on the composition of the mixture entering the apparatus; we consider this in a moment. Provided *ab* is sufficiently large compared with *bc* there is always a range of temperatures over which the experimental curve coincides with the true curve; that is, there is always a range of temperatures for which equilibrium is completely established in *ab* and for which the disturbance in *bc* is negligible. This is the range T_2T_3 in the figure. It will be noted that T_2 is the lowest temperature for which the composition of the mixture leaving the tube is independent of that entering it. This helps us to find the range T_2T_3. If the heat of reaction is known, an important check that the right region has been found is obtained from the fact that in this region the slope of the observed curve should agree with the slope calculated from equation (21).

At lower temperatures, where the velocity of reaction is measurable but too small for equilibrium to be attained (for example, somewhere in the region T_1), we can calculate the equilibrium by determining by graphical interpolation or otherwise the composition of the mixture which is not changed in passing through the apparatus.†

(3) *Explosion Method.*—In an explosion a gaseous mixture is really under the same conditions as in the streaming method; it is brought to a high temperature and then quickly cooled. But it is only at the high temperature for a very short time, so that the method is only applicable when the velocity of reaction is very

---

* See Knietsch, *Ber. d. deuts. chem. Ges.*, Vol. 34, p. 4069 (1901).

† See Sand, *Zeits. f. phys. Chem.*, Vol. 50, p. 465 (1904); Nernst and v. Wartenberg, *Zeits. f. phys. Chem.*, Vol. 56, p. 513 (1906). For the application of the streaming method to the ammonia equilibrium, see Haber, *Zeits. f. Elektrochemie*, Vol. 21, p. 89 (1915); Larson and Dodge, *J. Amer. Chem. Soc.*, Vol. 45, p. 2918 (1923), have also studied the ammonia equilibrium.

high. As a matter of fact equilibrium is nearly always disturbed during the cooling, and in general the method can only be regarded as an approximate one.

(4) *The Maximum Temperature of Explosions.*—In Chapter VI, Section 6, we have seen how the specific heats of gases at high temperatures can be measured by mixing various indifferent gases with an explosive mixture of, say, hydrogen and oxygen in a sealed bomb and measuring the maximum temperature attained when the explosion takes place. The temperature is actually measured by measuring the maximum pressure with the apparatus there described. The heat of the reaction between the explosive gases is known.

If at the maximum temperature attained water vapour is appreciably dissociated, all the hydrogen and oxygen present will not combine and the heat generated will be consequently diminished. Let us consider two cases: (1) when the inert gas is nitrogen, (2) when the explosive mixture is mixed with excess of hydrogen, so that the inert gas is hydrogen. In the former case the effect of the dissociation of water vapour will be felt, while in the latter the dissociation will be suppressed owing to the large excess of hydrogen (law of mass action). The consequence of this is that, supposing the molecular heats of hydrogen and nitrogen are equal, if m_1 is the number of gram-molecules of hydrogen that a given amount of explosive mixture can raise to a given temperature, and m_2 is the number of gram-molecules of nitrogen that an equal amount of explosive mixture can raise to the same temperature, m_1 is greater than m_2. From the measured values of m_1 and m_2 the degree of dissociation of water vapour can be calculated. Actually the molecular heats of nitrogen and hydrogen are not exactly equal, but by suitable variation of the experimental conditions the specific heats and the degree of dissociation can both be determined. For full details reference must be made to the papers of Bjerrum [*] and of Siegel,[†] who have developed the method.

(5) *Method of the Heated Catalyst.*—At temperatures at which the velocity of the reaction is still small in the body of the gas but large on the surface of a catalyst, all that is necessary is to heat the catalyst to a high temperature. This method has been used by Langmuir.[‡] It is very simple when the catalyst—e.g. a platinum wire—is electrically heated. In water vapour a short time is sufficient to establish the concentration of oxy-hydrogen gas which corresponds to the temperature of the wire. The temperature can be calculated from the electrical resistance.

(6) *Method of the Semipermeable Membrane.*—A very accurate method is to use a membrane which is permeable only to one component of an equilibrium

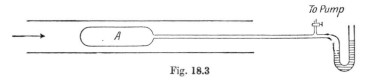

Fig. 18.3

mixture. At present we only possess such membranes for hydrogen, which diffuses through palladium, platinum, or iridium. The type of apparatus which can be used for determining the dissociation of water vapour, hydrogen sulphide, hydrogen bromide, &c., is illustrated in fig. 18.3. A is a vessel made of palladium, plati-

---

* Bjerrum, *Zeits. f. phys. Chem.*, Vol. 79, p. 513 (1912); *Zeits. f. Elektrochemie*, Vol. 18, p. 101 (1912).

† Siegel, *Zeits. f. phys. Chem.*, Vol. 87, p. 641 (1914). For a brief account see Partington and Shilling, *The Specific Heats of Gases*, pp. 128 and 176. See also Wohl, *Zeits. f. Elektrochemie*, Vol. 30, pp. 36, 49 (1924).

‡ Langmuir, *Journ. Amer. Chem. Soc.*, Vol. 28, p. 1357 (1906).

num, or iridium according to the temperature of the experiment, and is placed in an electric furnace. A capillary tube connects the vessel with a mercury pump and a manometer. After it has been evacuated, water vapour is passed over it, and after a short time the pressure of the hydrogen in the vessel corresponds to that of the hydrogen in dissociated water vapour at the temperature of the furnace.*

(7) *Measurement of Electromotive Force.*—This method is dealt with in Sections 19–25.

(8) *Calculation of a New Equilibrium from Measurements of Other Equilibria.*— This method is very widely used. Its application is illustrated by the following example.

The dissociation of hydrochloric acid gas according to the equation

$$2HCl \rightleftharpoons H_2 + Cl_2$$

has been studied and the equilibrium constant is known. We shall call this equilibrium constant $(K_c)_1$. We have by equation (13)

$$RT \log (K_c)_1 = 2G_{HCl\,(gas)} - G_{H_2} - G_{Cl_2}, \quad \ldots \ldots \quad (37)$$

where the G are the thermodynamic potentials of the various gases at the temperature T and at the total pressure p at which the equilibrium is measured.

Similarly the equilibrium constant of the Deacon process

$$4HCl + O_2 \rightleftharpoons 2Cl_2 + 2H_2O$$

is known. If the equilibrium constant in this case, measured under the same total pressure p and at the same temperature T as in the case of the dissociation of HCl, is $(K_c)_2$, we have

$$RT \log (K_c)_2 = 4G_{HCl\,(gas)} + G_{O_2} - 2G_{Cl_2} - 2G_{H_2O\,(gas)}, \quad \ldots \quad (38)$$

where the G are the thermodynamic potentials of the various gases at the temperature T and at the pressure p.

We shall now show that the equilibrium constant $(K_c)_3$ of the reaction

$$2H_2O \rightleftharpoons 2H_2 + O_2$$

(at the temperature T and the same total pressure p as in the two previous reactions) can be deduced from the measured equilibrium constants of the previous reactions. We have

$$RT \log (K_c)_3 = 2G_{H_2O\,(gas)} - 2G_{H_2} - G_{O_2}, \quad \ldots \ldots \quad (39)$$

where the G refer to the same temperature T and the same pressure p as in the previous reactions.

Subtracting equation (38) from *twice* equation (37), we obtain

$$RT \{2 \log (K_c)_1 - \log (K_c)_2\} = 2G_{H_2O\,(gas)} - 2G_{H_2} - G_{O_2}. \quad \bullet \quad (40)$$

Comparing equations (39) and (40), we see that

$$\log (K_c)_3 = 2 \log (K_c)_1 - \log (K_c)_2,$$

or

$$(K_c)_3 = \frac{(K_c)_1{}^2}{(K_c)_2}. \quad \ldots \ldots \ldots \quad (41)$$

Therefore, if $(K_c)_1$ and $(K_c)_2$ are known, $(K_c)_3$ can be immediately deduced. The relation between the K_p follows from equation (19).

* See v. Wartenberg, *Verh. d. deuts. phys. Ges.*, Vol. 8, p. 97 (1906); Preuner and Schupp, *Zeits. f. phys. Chem.*, Vol. 68, p. 157 (1909); Falkenstein, *ibid.*, p. 270.

18. Comparison of Values obtained using the Various Methods.

In order to compare the values for the equilibrium constant for a given reaction obtained from the various methods described above, it is necessary to consider how the equilibrium constant at a given temperature and pressure can be determined from measurements at another temperature and pressure.

We have, from equation (15),

$$\left(\frac{\partial \log K_p}{\partial T}\right)_p = -\frac{H_p}{RT^2},$$

where H_p is the heat of reaction at constant pressure. If H_p is measured at any given temperature, say T_1, and if the specific heats of all the reacting substances are known over a range of temperatures including T_1, then, by equation (16), H_p is known as a perfectly definite function of T for the range of temperatures for which the specific heats are known. Substituting this function of the temperature for H_p in the above equation, it may be integrated, giving

$$\left[\log K_p\right]_{T_0}^{T} = -\int_{T_0}^{T} \frac{H_p}{RT^2}\,dT. \quad \ldots \quad (42)$$

We thus obtain K_p as a function of T for a given total pressure, provided that we have an experimental determination of K_p with this total pressure at *one* temperature denoted by T_0.

The result is that we can calculate the value of K_p at any temperature in the range for which the specific heats are known. The effect of a variation in the total pressure may be taken into account, using equation (18).

Using the measured heat of reaction, and the measured values of the specific heats of the reacting gases, and determining the value of the quantity K_p at $T = T_0$ in equation (42) solely from the measurements of v. Wartenberg on the equilibrium constant, Nernst * has obtained an expression giving the equilibrium constant of the dissociation of water vapour as a function of the temperature. From this expression the degree of dissociation of water vapour at any temperature can be calculated. The calculated and observed values of α, the degree of dissociation, are given in Table II, together with a number referring to the method by which the observed result is obtained.

These results show that the values for the degree of dissociation obtained using the various different methods are consistent with one another. When we consider the wide range of temperatures involved and the enormous variation in the degree of dissociation from $4 \cdot 7 \cdot 10^{-28}$

---

* Nernst, *Theoretical Chemistry* (Eng. trans.), 5th edition, p. 782 (1923).

TABLE II

Temp., °Abs.	100a (observed)	100a (calculated)	Method	Observer
290	$4\cdot6\text{--}4\cdot8$. 10^{-26}	$4\cdot66$. 10^{-26}	7	Lewis, Brønsted.
700	$7\cdot6$. 10^{-9}	$5\cdot4$. 10^{-9}	8	
1300	$2\cdot7$. 10^{-3}	$2\cdot9$. 10^{-3}	5	Langmuir.
1397	$7\cdot8$. 10^{-3}	$8\cdot5$. 10^{-3}	2 ⎱	Nernst and v. Wartenberg.
1480	$1\cdot89$. 10^{-2}	$1\cdot86$. 10^{-2}	2 ⎰	
1500	$1\cdot97$. 10^{-2}	$2\cdot21$. 10^{-2}	5	Langmuir.
1561	$3\cdot4$. 10^{-2}	$3\cdot69$. 10^{-2}	2	Nernst and v. Wartenberg.
1705	$1\cdot02$. 10^{-1}	$1\cdot07$. 10^{-1}	6	Lowenstein.
2155	$1\cdot18$	$1\cdot18$	6	v. Wartenberg.
2257	$1\cdot77$	$1\cdot76$	6	v. Wartenberg.
2337	$3\cdot8$	$2\cdot7$	4	Bjerrum, Siegel.
2507	$4\cdot5$	$4\cdot1$	4	Bjerrum, Siegel.
2684	$6\cdot2$	$6\cdot6$	4	Bjerrum, Siegel.
2731	$8\cdot2$	$7\cdot4$	4	Bjerrum, Siegel.
3092	$13\cdot0$	$15\cdot4$	4	Bjerrum, Siegel.

to 0·13, the agreement between calculated and observed values is very remarkable and affords a striking proof of the second law of thermodynamics. It shows that, provided we know the specific heats of the reacting gases and the heat of reaction at any one temperature, one accurate determination of the degree of dissociation at equilibrium is sufficient to determine the equilibrium conditions over the whole range of temperature from ordinary temperatures up to nearly 3000° C.

Electromotive Force and Equilibrium Measurements

19. One of the most accurate methods of measuring an equilibrium constant is the determination of the electromotive force of a galvanic cell in which the reaction under consideration takes place. We shall therefore consider how this method is applied.

The method depends on the fact that in a galvanic cell a chemical reaction can in many cases be made to take place under effectively reversible conditions. We shall return later to a detailed consideration of this from the practical point of view. Meanwhile we shall assume reversibility and work out the theory.

According to equation (10), Chapter XVI, the total external work done by a system during an isothermal *reversible* change is a measure of the decrease of the free energy of the system; that is, it is a measure of the decrease in the value of $\mathbf{F}$ or $(\mathbf{U} - T\mathbf{S})$ for the system. In other words,

$$(\mathbf{F}_1 - \mathbf{F}_2) = \text{total work done by the system.}$$

In the present case the total work may appear in two forms, electrical energy and mechanical work due to changes of volume. We shall suppose that the total pressure p on the system remains constant. In this case, if V_1 is the initial and V_2 the final volume, we have

$$(F_1 - F_2) = \text{electrical energy obtained} + p(V_2 - V_1).$$

This equation gives immediately, since $G = F + pV$,

$$(G_1 - G_2) = \text{electrical energy obtained.} \qquad . \quad . \quad (43)$$

In other words, the electrical energy obtained is a direct measure of the diminution in the thermodynamic potential of the system, provided that the conditions already laid down are satisfied—all changes must take place reversibly, with temperature and total pressure on the system constant.

Referring to equation (13), in which the equilibrium constant for a gaseous reaction is expressed in terms of the thermodynamic potentials of the reacting gases, it will be realized that any method which enables us to measure changes in the Gibbs function will in all probability be useful in determining equilibrium constants. We shall consider details of the application later.

20. Reversible and Irreversible Cells.

Let us for the moment return to the question of the reversibility of cells.

To fix our ideas, let us consider the Daniell cell. This consists of an electrode of zinc in a solution of zinc sulphate and an electrode of copper in a solution of copper sulphate. The two solutions are separated by a division of porous material. The system can be represented as follows:

$$\text{Zn, ZnSO}_4(\text{Aq.}), \text{CuSO}_4(\text{Aq.}), \text{Cu.}$$

If the copper and zinc electrodes are connected together by a wire outside the cell, an electric current flows through the wire from the copper to the zinc. At the same time zinc goes into solution, so that the concentration of the zinc sulphate solution is increased, and copper is deposited on the copper electrode, so that the concentration of the copper sulphate solution is decreased. If the external circuit contains a source of electromotive force and a current is sent through the cell in the opposite direction from that described above, the changes in the cell are exactly reversed. Copper goes into solution and the concentration of the copper sulphate solution is increased, while zinc is deposited on the zinc electrode and the concentration of the zinc sulphate solution is diminished. Further, if equal quantities of electricity pass through the cell in the two cases, the cell is restored to exactly its original condition. (Any effects due to the slow diffusion of the solutions through the porous wall may be neglected.) Such a cell is called a reversible cell.

On the other hand, let us consider Volta's cell, which consists of an electrode of copper and an electrode of zinc dipping into a dilute solution of sulphuric acid, that is,

$$\text{Zn. H}_2\text{SO}_4(\text{Aq.}), \text{Cu.}$$

If the copper and zinc are connected by a wire, positive current flows through the wire from the copper to the zinc. At the same time zinc goes into solution and hydrogen gas is evolved from the copper. If a current is sent through the cell in the opposite direction, copper goes into solution and hydrogen is evolved from the zinc. It will be seen that in this case it is impossible to restore the cell to its original condition by passing the current through it in the opposite direction. Such a cell is called an irreversible cell.

In order that a cell may be reversible, it is necessary that the changes which take place at both electrodes be reversible. The following are the three most important types of reversible electrode.

(1) *Electrodes consisting of a metal in contact with a solution of one of its salts.* When positive current flows from the electrode to the solution, metal passes from the electrode into the solution; and, when current flows from the solution to the electrode, metal is deposited on the electrode. No other changes take place. Both of the electrodes in the Daniell cell are of this type.

(2) *An electrode such as a piece of silver covered with a deposit of silver chloride dipping in a solution of potassium chloride; in fact, a metal covered with a deposit of any insoluble salt of the metal dipping into a solution of some salt which has the same negative radical as the insoluble deposit.* In such a case, when positive electricity passes from the solution to the electrode the amount of insoluble deposit (silver chloride) is diminished and the amount of metal (silver) in the electrode is increased. When the current passes in the opposite direction, i.e. from the electrode to the solution, the reverse process takes place and the amount of insoluble deposit is increased, while the amount of metal in the electrode is diminished.

(3) *A few gas electrodes—hydrogen, chlorine, bromine, and iodine.* The hydrogen electrode consists of an inert metal, such as platinized platinum, saturated with hydrogen and dipping into a solution of an acid. The hydrogen with which the electrode is saturated is in equilibrium with free hydrogen gas at a definite pressure. The platinum dips into the solution and projects into the free gas. If positive electricity passes from the solution to the electrode, the amount of hydrogen gas is increased. If positive electricity passes from the electrode to the solution, hydrogen passes into solution and the amount of free gas is diminished. With chlorine, bromine, or iodine an electrode of platinum-iridium is used, dipping into a solution of a chloride, a bromide, or an iodide respectively. With these electrodes the passage of positive electricity from the solution to the electrode is accompanied by a diminution in the amount of gas.

21. The Reversible Electromotive Force.

We shall consider only cells in which both electrodes are reversible, so that by reversing the direction of the current flowing through the cell the chemical reaction that takes place in it can be exactly reversed.

Further, we must ensure that the chemical reaction takes place reversibly in the thermodynamic sense. For this it is necessary to have in the external circuit an electromotive force which opposes that due to the cell and which can be adjusted very accurately, for example, the cell may be connected to a potentiometer. The external electromotive force is adjusted so that a very small change in one direction or the other is sufficient to cause the cell to discharge or to be charged, i.e.

is sufficient to cause the reaction in the cell to proceed in one direction or the other. Under such conditions the reaction in the cell may be said to take place reversibly.

The minimum electromotive force which must be applied to the cell to charge it and the maximum electromotive force obtainable from the cell while it is discharging are equal, and each is equal to the reversible electromotive force of the cell. In order to produce a definite amount of chemical change in the cell, it is necessary to pass a definite amount of electricity through it; in order to restore the cell to its original condition it is necessary to pass an equal amount of electricity through it in the opposite direction. It follows then that the maximum amount of electrical work obtainable from discharging the cell from one state to another (that is, quantity of electricity passing multiplied by electromotive force) is equal to the minimum amount of electrical work required to charge the cell from the second state to the first, and each of these amounts of electrical work is numerically a measure of the change in the value of the thermodynamic potential of the cell in passing from one state to the other.

In measuring the electromotive force of a cell it is necessary to make sure that the value obtained does not depend on the direction in which the current flows through the cell, in other words, that effects due to polarization are negligible. Polarization can occur even with reversible electrodes. For example, consider two electrodes of copper in a solution of copper sulphate. When current is passed, the concentration of the solution is increased round the anode and diminished round the cathode. The concentration cell thus formed gives an electromotive force which opposes the one that is applied. With a sensitive galvanometer which will detect a current of 10^{-8} or 10^{-9} amperes in either direction errors due to polarization can be reduced to a minimum.

22. Quantity of Electricity.

The quantity of electricity which must pass through a given cell in order to produce a given amount of chemical change is given by Faraday's law. If F is the amount of electricity carried by 1 gram-molecule of a univalent ion in solution, the amount of electricity which must pass through the cell to cause n equivalents of any one of the reacting substances to appear or disappear is equal to

$$nF.$$

The numerical value of F is obtained as follows. The electrochemical equivalent of silver (the number of grams of silver deposited when one coulomb of electricity passes through a solution of a silver salt) is equal to 0.00111807. Silver forms a monovalent ion and its atomic weight is 107.88. The charge associated with 1 gram-equivalent of silver is, therefore, equal to 96,494 coulombs. This is the value of F.

If E is the reversible electromotive force of the cell, the change in the thermodynamic potential of the cell when n equivalents of any one of the reacting substances are transformed is numerically equal to

$$nFE.$$

If E is measured in absolute volts, we obtain for the change in the thermodynamical potential when n equivalents are transformed

$$\left. \begin{array}{l} 96{,}524 \; nE \text{ absolute joules (in physical units)} \\ \text{or} \qquad 96{,}497 \; nE \text{ absolute joules (in chemical units) *} \end{array} \right\} \quad \cdot \; \cdot \; (44)$$

The value of n is known in any particular case from the nature of the reaction and the valency of the reacting substances (see the examples given in Sections 23 and 24).

23. Sign Convention.

We write for the Daniell cell

Zn, $ZnSO_4$(Aq. conc. $= c_1$), $CuSO_4$(Aq. conc. $= c_2$), Cu, $+ x$ volts.

We mean that the electromotive force of the combination is x volts. The sign convention is that x is positive if positive electricity tends to flow from left to right *inside* the cell. If the copper and zinc are connected by a wire, the current *outside* the cell flows from the copper to the zinc, so that the copper is the positive pole. In specifying the electromotive force it is necessary to specify the concentrations of solutions and the pressures of gases.

Since zinc and copper are the positive ions in the two solutions, a current flowing from left to right in the cell means that zinc goes into solution and that copper is deposited; in other words, the chemical reaction taking place in the cell is

Zn $+ CuSO_4$(Aq. conc. c_2) $\rightarrow$ Cu $+ ZnSO_4$(Aq. conc. c_1), $+ x$ volts.

Writing x volts after the equation indicates that, when the reaction proceeds in the direction indicated by the equation, the cell in which the reaction takes place is capable of *yielding* electrical energy, and that the electromotive force of the cell under reversible conditions is x volts.

It follows that, when the reaction proceeds in the direction indicated by the equation, the Gibbs function of the system falls. In the case under consideration, if 1 gram-molecule of each of copper sulphate and zinc are transformed into 1 gram-molecule of each of zinc sulphate and copper, the *drop* in the thermodynamic potential is given by putting $E = x$ and $n = 2$ in expression (44); n is equal to 2 because

---

* U. Stille, *Messen und Rechnen in der Physik* (1955); J. A. Bearden and J. S. Thomsen, *Nuovo Cimento*, Supplemento al Vol. 5 (1957).

for the divalent ions zinc and copper 1 gram-molecule is equal to 2 equivalents. We have then

$$G_{\text{Cu}} + [G]_{\text{ZnSO}_4 \text{ (Aq. conc. } c_1)} - G_{\text{Zn}} - [G]_{\text{CuSO}_4 \text{ (Aq. conc. } c_2)} = -96{,}487 \times 2x \text{ joules.}$$

In this equation we have used the symbol $[G]_{\text{ZnSO}_4 \text{ (Aq. conc. } c_1)}$ to stand for

$$\frac{\partial G_{\text{Aq. solution of ZnSO}_4 \text{ of conc. } c_1}}{\partial \text{ (mass of ZnSO}_4 \text{ in solution)}} \times M_{\text{ZnSO}_4},$$

where M_{ZnSO_4} is the molecular weight in grams of ZnSO_4, a notation which we shall use throughout the rest of this chapter.

We have shown in Chapter XVI, Section 12, that the differential coefficient occurring in the above expression depends only on the concentration of the solution and not on its total mass. Reference should be made to the footnote on Section 2.

We are primarily concerned with gaseous reactions, and, therefore, with the thermodynamic potentials of various substances in the gaseous state. The example just given indicates, however, that as a result of electromotive force measurements we often obtain an expression involving the thermodynamic potentials of aqueous solutions. We need not on this account consider in detail the thermodynamic potentials of solutions, because when such thermodynamic potentials occur we always eliminate them by a method similar to that described in method 8 of Section 17 (see Section 25). We may mention in passing that such thermodynamic potentials are very important in chemistry, where so many of the reactions studied take place in aqueous solution.

24. Concentration Gas Cells.

As a simple application of the principles, let us consider the cell

$$\text{H}_2 \text{ (gas, press. } p_1), \ \text{H}_2\text{SO}_4 \text{ (Aq.)}, \ \text{H}_2 \text{ (gas, press. } p_2).$$

We shall suppose that p_1 is greater than p_2. All that happens when this cell functions is that hydrogen at pressure p_1 is changed into hydrogen at pressure p_2. The solution is not changed in amount or concentration. The cell reaction is therefore

$$\text{H}_2 \text{ (gas, press. } p_1) = \text{H}_2 \text{ (gas, press. } p_2), + E \text{ volts.}$$

The electromotive force should be independent of the concentration of the acid solution. One gram-molecule of hydrogen gas is equal to 2 equivalents, so that n in expression (44) is equal to 2. We have then

$$G_{\text{H}_2 \text{ (pressure } p_2)} - G_{\text{H}_2 \text{ (pressure } p_1)} = -2 \times 23{,}074 \times E.$$

At ordinary pressures hydrogen may be treated as a perfect gas, and, substituting on the left-hand side of this equation for the thermodynamic potential of the hydrogen from equation (7), we obtain

$$RT \log p_2 - RT \log p_1 = -2 \times 96{,}487 \times E.$$

R must be measured in joules.

In this case we see that the electromotive force may be calculated by measuring the pressures.*

Consider now the cell

$$\text{H}_2 \text{ (gas, press. } p\text{)}, \text{ HCl (Aq. conc. } c\text{)}, \text{ HgCl (solid), Hg (liq.).}$$

The reaction that takes place in this cell is

$$\text{H}_2 \text{ (gas, press. } p\text{)} + 2\text{HgCl} = 2\text{HCl (Aq. conc. } c\text{)} + 2\text{Hg}, + E \text{ volts.}$$

If 1 gram-molecule of hydrogen is transformed, n in expression (44) is equal to 2. We have then

$$2[G]_{\text{HCl (Aq. conc. } c\text{)}} + 2G_{\text{Hg (liq.)}} - 2G_{\text{HgCl (solid)}} - G_{\text{H}_2 \text{ (gas, press. } p\text{)}} = -2 \times 96{,}487 \times E.$$

Let us now keep the concentration of the acid and the temperature constant, and let us determine the change in the electromotive force of the cell with the pressure of the hydrogen. The first three terms on the left of the above equation remain constant, and substituting as above for the thermodynamic potential of 1 gram-molecule of hydrogen we obtain

$$E = \text{constant} + \frac{RT}{2 \times 96{,}487} \log p.$$

The value of the constant may be determined by a measurement at any one pressure. This equation for the above cell has been tested directly by Lewis † with the following results. The constant was determined with $p = p_0$.

$p - p_0$ (cm. of water)	E (observed) (volts)	E (calculated) (volts)
0	0·40089	(0·40089)
37	0·40134	0·40134
63	0·40163	0·40165
84	0·40190	0·40189

The agreement is very satisfactory. It gives a good confirmation of the theory and also indicates that the hydrogen electrode gives satisfactory results.

Before a gas electrode can be used with confidence it must be subjected to a test similar to the above.

25. Applications of the Method.

We may now consider some typical applications of the method to determine equilibrium constants.

Let us first take the dissociation of gaseous hydrogen chloride into hydrogen and chlorine. The direct way of studying this reaction would be to use the cell

$$\text{H}_2 \text{ (gas), HCl (Aq.), Cl}_2 \text{ (gas).}$$

* p_1 and p_2 are the partial pressures of the hydrogen, that is, measured pressure less the vapour pressure of solution.

† See Lewis and Randall, *Journ. Amer. Chem. Soc.*, Vol. 36, p. 1969 (1914); or Lewis and Randall, *Thermodynamics and the Free Energy of Chemical Substances*, p. 394.

It is found, however, that the variation of the electromotive force of such a cell with the pressure of the chlorine is not what would be expected theoretically (cf. Section 24).* The discrepancies are due to reactions between the chlorine and the electrolyte; the extent to which such reactions proceed depends on the pressure of the chlorine. We therefore proceed in the following manner.

(a) Lewis and Rupert † found that it was possible to make the effect of side reactions between the chlorine and the electrolyte negligible by using a small partial pressure of chlorine at the electrode. They employed the cell

Hg (liq.), HgCl (solid), HCl (Aq., conc. 0·1 M), Cl$_2$ (gas, press. p_1), E_1 volts.‡

The chlorine gas was diluted with air; the total pressure was about 1 atmosphere and the partial pressure of the chlorine varied from 0·003 to 0·05 atmosphere. (It is not possible to use hydrogen gas at the second electrode on account of reactions between the hydrogen and the gas with which the chlorine is diluted.)
The reaction that takes place in such a cell is

$$2Hg \text{ (liq.)} + Cl_2 \text{ (press. } p_1) = 2HgCl \text{ (solid)}, \ E_1 \text{ volts.}$$

The electromotive force is therefore independent of the concentration of the acid solution.
The equation for the thermodynamic potentials is

$$2G_{Hg \text{ (liq.)}} + G_{Cl_2 \text{ (press. } p_1)} - 2G_{HgCl \text{ (solid)}} = 2 \times 96,487 \times E_1 \text{ joules.} \quad (45)$$

(b) Now let us take the cell described in Section 24:

H$_2$ (gas, press. p_2), HCl (Aq., conc. 0·1 M), HgCl (solid), Hg (liq.), E_2 volts.

The cell reaction is

$$H_2 \text{ (pres. } p_2) + 2HgCl = 2HCl \text{ (Aq., conc. 0·1 M)} + 2Hg, \ E_2 \text{ volts,}$$

and the equation for the thermodynamic potentials is

$$G_{H_2 \text{ (press. } p_2)} + 2G_{HgCl \text{ (solid)}} - 2[G]_{HCl \text{ (Aq., conc. 1·0 M)}} - 2G_{Hg \text{ (liq.)}}$$
$$= 2 \times 96,487 \times E_2 \text{ joules.} \quad . \quad . \quad . \quad (46)$$

Adding equations (45) and (46), we obtain

$$G_{H_2 \text{ (press. } p_2)} + G_{Cl_2 \text{ (press. } p_1)} - 2[G]_{HCl \text{ (Aq., conc. 0·1 M)}}$$
$$= 2 \times 96,487 \times (E_1 + E_2). \quad . \quad . \quad . \quad (47)$$

We assume that all the determinations are made at the same temperature T, and that the thermodynamic potentials refer to this temperature.
(c) In order to be able to determine the equilibrium constant in the dissociation of *gaseous* hydrogen chloride, all that we need to determine now is the pressure of hydrogen chloride gas which is in equilibrium with a hydrogen chloride solution whose concentration is 0·1 M. Such a determination has been made by Bates and Kirschman.§ If p_3 is the partial pressure of gaseous hydrogen

---

* See Müller, *Zeits. f. phys. Chem.*, Vol. 40, p. 158 (1902).
† Lewis and Rupert, *Journ. Amer. Chem. Soc.*, Vol. 33, p. 299 (1911).
‡ By 0·1 M we mean 0·1 gram-molecules of HCl in 1000 gm. of water.
§ Bates and Kirschman, *Journ. Amer. Chem. Soc.*, Vol. 41, p. 1991 (1919).

chloride which is in equilibrium with an aqueous solution of concentration 0·1 M, we have *

$$G_{\text{HCl (press. } p_3)} = [G]_{\text{HCl (Aq., conc. 0·1 M)}}. \quad \cdots \cdots \quad (48)$$

Substituting from this equation in equation (47), we have

$$G_{\text{H}_2 \text{ (press. } p_2)} + G_{\text{Cl}_2 \text{ (press. } p_1)} - 2G_{\text{HCl (press. } p_3)}$$
$$= 2 \times 96{,}487 \times (E_1 + E_2) \text{ joules.} \quad . \quad (49)$$

p_1, p_2, p_3, and $(E_1 + E_2)$ are all known.

(d) It is now possible to determine the equilibrium constant for the reaction

$$\text{H}_2 + \text{Cl}_2 = 2\text{HCl},$$

at temperature T and under a total pressure p; this is what we set out to do. If K_c is the equilibrium constant for this reaction, we have from equation (13)

$$RT \log K_c = G_{\text{H}_2 \text{ (press. } p)} + G_{\text{Cl}_2 \text{ (press. } p)} - 2G_{\text{HCl (press. } p)}. \quad . \quad . \quad (50)$$

We shall suppose that p, p_1, p_2, and p_3 are all sufficiently small for the gases to be regarded as perfect. Using equation (7), we have

$$G_{\text{H}_2 \text{ (press. } p)} = G_{\text{H}_2 \text{ (press. } p_2)} + RT \log \frac{p}{p_2},$$

---

* The equilibrium condition in this case is given by equation (50), Chapter XVI. It is

$$\frac{\partial \mathbf{G}_{\text{mixture of HCl and H}_2\text{O vapours}}}{\partial \text{ mass of HCl vapour}} = \frac{\partial \mathbf{G}_{\text{Aq. solution of HCl, conc. 0·1 M}}}{\partial \text{ mass of HCl in solution}}.$$

Assuming that the vapours behave as perfect gases, we have by equations (6) and (2)

$$\mathbf{G}_{\text{mixture of HCl and H}_2\text{O vapours}}$$
$$= n_1 G_{1(T,p)} + n_2 G_{2(T,p)} + n_1 RT \log \frac{n_1}{n_1 + n_2} + n_2 RT \log \frac{n_2}{n_1 + n_2},$$

where n_1 and n_2 are the numbers of gram-molecules of HCl and H$_2$O in the vapour phase, and where $G_{1(T,p)}$ and $G_{2(T,p)}$ are the thermodynamic potentials of a gram-molecule of HCl and H$_2$O vapour respectively at the temperature T and at the pressure p; p is the total pressure of the mixture.

Now we have

$$\frac{\partial \mathbf{G}_{\text{vapour mixture}}}{\partial \text{ mass of HCl}} = \frac{\partial \mathbf{G}_{\text{vapour mixture}}}{\partial n_1} \frac{\partial n_1}{\partial \text{ mass of HCl}}.$$

Differentiating the above expression for $\mathbf{G}_{\text{vapour mixture}}$ with respect to n_1, we have

$$\frac{\partial \mathbf{G}_{\text{vapour mixture}}}{\partial n_1} = G_{1(T,p)} + RT \log \frac{n_1}{n_1 + n_2} = G_{1(T, p_3)},$$

where p_3 is the partial pressure of HCl in the mixture. Further, we have $\frac{\partial n_1}{\partial \text{ mass of HCl}} = \frac{1}{M_{\text{HCl}}}$, where M_{HCl} is the molecular weight of HCl in grams.

Thus we have

$$\frac{\partial \mathbf{G}_{\text{vapour mixture}}}{\partial \text{ mass of HCl}} = \frac{1}{M_{\text{HCl}}} G_{\text{HCl } (T, p_3)}.$$

And using this in equation (50), Chapter XVI, as written above, we obtain

$$G_{\text{HCl (press. } p_3)} = \frac{\partial \mathbf{G}_{\text{Aq. solution of HCl, conc. 0·1 M}}}{\partial \text{ mass of HCl in solution}} \times M_{\text{HCl}} = [G]_{\text{HCl (Aq., conc. 0·1 M)}}.$$

This is the required result.

and similar relations for Cl_2 and HCl. Substituting these values in equation (50), and using the result of the electromotive force measurements expressed in equation (49), we obtain

$$RT \log K_c = 2 \times 96{,}487(E_1 + E_2) + RT \log \left(\frac{p_3^2}{p_1 p_2}\right). \quad . \quad . \quad (51)$$

R must be expressed in joules. This equation gives us the equilibrium constant in terms of quantities all of which are directly measured. We may note that in this particular case the equilibrium constant is independent of the total pressure p.

We have already seen in Section 18 how the determination of the equilibrium constant at any one temperature enables us to deduce its value at other temperatures.

Let us now consider the application of this method to the determination of the dissociation of water vapour.

The direct method would be to use the cell

$$H_2 \text{ (gas)},\ H_2SO_4 \text{ (dilute solution)},\ O_2 \text{ (gas)},$$

in which the reaction is $2H_2 + O_2 \rightleftharpoons 2H_2O,$

the H_2O being formed as liquid water in the dilute solution. It is found in practice that the oxygen electrode does not give satisfactory results, owing probably to the formation of an oxide of platinum.

The following indirect method has been used by Brønsted.*

(a) Measure the electromotive force of the cell

$$H_2 \text{ (gas, press. } p\text{), KOH (Aq., conc. } c \text{), HgO (solid), Hg (liq.)},$$

in which the reaction is

$$H_2 \text{ (gas) + HgO (solid)} = H_2O \text{ (solut. KOH) + Hg (liq.)}.$$

(b) Measure the dissociation pressure of solid HgO.
(c) Measure the vapour pressure of liquid mercury.
(d) Measure the pressure of aqueous vapour over a solution of KOH of concentration c.

The combination of these to give the required result is left to the reader.

THE MEASUREMENT OF HEATS OF REACTION

26. The experimental methods adopted for determining heats of reaction vary with the nature of the reaction which is being studied. The following are the most important.

(1) *Reactions involving Solutions.*—For reactions between solutions the method of Thomson may be used. The apparatus is illustrated diagrammatically in fig. 18.4. One solution is contained in the vessel A and the other in the vessel B. They are brought to the same temperature, and the tap is then opened so that the solutions are mixed and the reaction takes place. The rise of temperature is

---

* Brønsted, *Zeits. f. phys. Chem.*, Vol. 65, pp. 84, 744 (1909).

measured. The thermal capacity of the apparatus is determined by the method of electrical heating.

The apparatus can be used to measure heats of dilution and heats of solution. It can also be used for reactions between solids and solutions. In the last case the solid is contained in B and the solution in A.

For reactions between gases and solutions, the solution is contained in B, and the gas is led in through a tube. Care must be taken that the gas is at the same temperature as the solution, or else a correction must be made for the heat carried along by the gas. If a gas is evolved during the reaction, the reaction must take

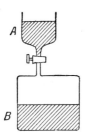

Fig. 18.4

place in a vessel immersed in the calorimeter. To this vessel is attached a long spiral tube which is immersed in the calorimeter. The gas passes through this tube, and when it leaves the apparatus it is at the same temperature as the calorimeter.

(2) *Heats of Combustion of Gases.*—Under this heading we may include not only combustion in oxygen, but in other gases such as chlorine.

If the reaction is to be carried out at constant volume, a known amount of the gas is mixed with the excess of oxygen in a closed steel vessel which is immersed in a calorimeter. The mixture is fired by the passage of an electric spark, and the heat evolved is measured from the rise of temperature of the calorimeter.[*] If necessary the gas remaining in the bomb can be analysed after the explosion.

For reactions at constant pressure, the gas is burned at a jet inside a vessel which is completely immersed in a calorimeter, and to which oxygen is supplied. The products of the reaction pass off through a long spiral immersed in the calorimeter, so that when they leave they are at the temperature of the calorimeter. Alternatively, a constant-flow calorimeter can be used.

(3) *Heats of Combustion of Solids.*—The solid is contained in a small crucible in a closed bomb, which is filled with compressed oxygen. A fine wire is in contact with the solid, which is fired by passing a current through this wire. The whole bomb is immersed in a calorimeter.[†]

A similar method may be used to determine the heat of combustion of liquids.[‡]

The thermal capacity of the calorimeter can, if desired, be determined by burning in it some solid whose heat of combustion is accurately known.[§]

(4) *The Contact Method.*—If a reaction between gases takes place to an appreciable extent only at the surface of a solid catalyst, the following method can be employed. The catalyst is heated electrically to a given temperature in the absence of the reacting gases, and the supply of electrical energy is measured. It is then heated to the same temperature in the presence of the reacting gases, and the supply of electrical energy is again measured. The difference between the electrical energy supplied in the two cases gives the heat of the reaction. The amount of reaction which takes place is determined by analysis of the gas. The method has been applied by Haber ‖ to determine the heat of formation of ammonia.

---

[*] See Berthelot, *Ann. Chim. et Phys.*, Vol. 23, p. 160 (1881); "Scholes Bomb Calorimeter", *Engineering*, Vol. 123, p. 499 (1927).

[†] See Parr, *Journ. Amer. Chem. Soc.*, Vol. 37, p. 2515 (1915); Roth, *Zeits. f. Elektrochemie*, Vol. 30, p. 417 (1924).

[‡] See, for example, Richards and Jesse, *Journ. Amer. Chem. Soc.*, Vol. 34, p. 1337 (1912).

[§] See Henning, *Zeits. f. phys. Chem.*, Vol. 97, p. 467 (1921).

‖ Haber, *Zeits. f. Elektrochemie*, Vol. 20, p. 603 (1914); Vol. 21, pp. 191, 206 (1915).

(5) *Equilibrium Measurements.*—The heat of reaction can be determined from equilibrium measurements, using the equation of Van't Hoff, (17) or (21). This method has been illustrated in Section 13.

(6) *Combination of Results.*—By a method analogous to number 8 in Section 16 results of measurements on reactions can be combined to give the heats of reactions that could not otherwise be studied. This method is widely used.

27. Heats of Reaction at Constant Pressure and Constant Volume.

If H_p is the heat of reaction at constant pressure and H_v is that at constant volume

$$H_p = H_v + RT \sum v_j,$$

where the v_j are the numbers of molecules of the components which take part in the reaction. They are taken as positive if the substances to which they refer are formed in the reaction, and negative if the substances to which they refer are consumed in the reaction. Thus if the heat of reaction at constant volume is measured, that at constant pressure can be deduced, and vice versa.

EXAMPLE

The pressure-volume relation of a mixture of gases is represented by a series expansion as far as the term in p^3. If the gases react, show that the effect of the intermolecular forces is expressed in the equation for chemical equilibrium by replacing the actual pressure p by a parameter p^* given by

$$RT \log p^*/p = Bp + \tfrac{1}{2}Cp^2 + \tfrac{1}{3}Dp^3.$$

[See H. Jones and A. R. Miller, *Proc. Roy. Soc.*, A, Vol. 194, p. 480 (1948)].

CHAPTER XIX

The Third Law of Thermodynamics

1 The Nernst Heat Theorem.

The third law of thermodynamics is intimately bound up with quantum statistics and the enumeration of distinct and accessible quantum states. It can be looked upon as a statement, in macroscopic terms, of the quantal behaviour of the individual atoms and molecules of an assembly. It had its origin, however, before the development of quantum statistics, in attempts to calculate the thermodynamical functions of substances from purely thermal measurements. In its original enunciation by Nernst it is called the *heat theorem*. Its significance and precise statement have given rise to much discussion, but it can no longer be denied the status of a fundamental law—the third law of thermodynamics.* Consider a reaction in which a quantity of heat ΔQ is absorbed. It can be shown that the first and second laws imply that as the temperature at which the reaction takes place approaches the absolute zero, the heat ΔQ vanishes, that is,

$$\text{Lim}_{T \to 0} \Delta Q = 0.$$

The Nernst heat theorem is a postulate about *how rapidly* ΔQ vanishes as the temperature falls. It says that not only ΔQ vanishes but, *in addition*, that $[\partial(\Delta Q)/\partial T]_{T=0}$ vanishes. This leads to the condition that entropy differences vanish as the absolute zero is approached. We must first consider the way in which this theorem arose.

In equations (14) and (19) of Chapter XVIII we have obtained expressions for the general conditions of equilibrium of a gaseous system in which a chemical reaction takes place. It has also been shown that in cases in which the actual equilibrium can be studied it is possible to determine the heat of reaction from the measured variation of the equilibrium condition with temperature.

It is natural to ask whether the converse problem can be solved, that is, is it possible from purely thermal measurements (such as specific-heat determinations, or measurements of heats of reaction) to determine the conditions of a chemical equilibrium, and thus to determine in which direction a chemical reaction will tend to proceed

* F. E. Simon, *Physica*, Vol. 4, p. 1089 (1937); *Year Book of the Physical Society*, London (1956) p. 1.

if the reagents are mixed in given proportions under given conditions? The attempts to solve this problem have led to results of fundamental importance; they provide the basis of Nernst's heat theorem.

Equation (13), Chapter XVIII, gives the equilibrium constant of a given reaction in terms of the Gibbs free energies of the reacting gases (or vapours) under specified conditons, and our problem is therefore solved if we can determine these Gibbs free energies from purely thermal measurements of the type mentioned. The difficulty arises on account of the arbitrary constants in the expressions for the entropy and the internal energy of a gram-molecule of a gas. From equation (13), Chapter XVIII, we have

$$RT \log K_c = -\sum \nu_j G_j$$
$$= -\sum \nu_j (U_j - TS_j + pV_j).$$

The expression on the right contains, as we have seen, two arbitrary constants for each gas, one in the expression for the internal energy, and the other in the expression for the entropy. The former can be eliminated by a determination of the heat of reaction; for the above equation can be written in the form

$$RT \log K_c = -\sum \nu_j (U_j + pV_j) + T \sum \nu_j S_j,$$

and a comparison with Chapter XVIII, Section 3, shows that [*]

$$H_p = -\sum \nu_j (U_j + pV_j),$$

so that the equilibrium constant is given by

$$RT \log K_c = H_p + T \sum \nu_j S_j, \quad \cdots \quad (1)$$

The expression on the right-hand side of this equation contains only one arbitrary constant for each gas, that is, that in the expression for the entropy. The Nernst heat theorem enables us to eliminate these constants. The theorem was originally stated [†] in the following way.

If a chemical change takes place between pure crystalline solids at the absolute zero, there is no change of entropy.

The theorem, together with the T^3 law for the specific heats of solids near the absolute zero, solves our problem. The lattice theory of specific heats (see Chapter XXII) shows that the quantity

---

[*] U_1 is the internal energy of a gram-molecule of the first gas in the mixture when its pressure is equal to p, the total pressure of the mixture, and V_1 is its volume under the same conditions, the temperature being T. Since the internal energy of a perfect gas is independent of its volume, and since pV is constant at constant temperature, the relation for H_p follows.

[†] Nernst, *Nachr. Ges. Wiss., Göttingen, Math.-physik*, p. 1 (1906).

$C_p{}^s/T$, where $C_p{}^s$ is the molecular heat of a solid, remains finite as T approaches zero, so that $\int_0^T \dfrac{C_p{}^s}{T} dT + S_0$, the entropy of a gram-molecule of a solid at temperature T, is a finite quantity.* S_0 is the entropy at absolute zero. If Λ is the molecular latent heat of vaporization of the solid at temperature T, the entropy of one gram-molecule of the vapour is given by

$$\int_0^T \frac{C_p{}^s}{T} dT + \frac{\Lambda}{T} + S_0,$$

and from this the entropy of the gas at higher temperatures can be determined from specific-heat measurements (for the detailed calculation, see Section 2). If we substitute the expression for the entropy so obtained in equation (1), the arbitrary constants can all be collected together in the expression $\Sigma \nu_j (S_j)_0$, and according to the Nernst heat theorem, this is equal to zero. Thus the arbitrary constants disappear.

Simon has pointed out that the term " pure crystalline solid " does not cover all the experimental evidence concerning the behaviour of entropy differences as the absolute zero is approached. He has suggested † that the theorem should be stated in terms of states of a system in internal thermodynamical equilibrium. A phase is in internal thermodynamical equilibrium if its state is completely determined by the pressure, temperature, and numbers of kinds of particles, and if the neighbouring states are less stable than the state under consideration. The system may be in internal thermodynamical equilibrium with respect to one factor specifying the system but not with regard to the others.‡ The third law of thermodynamics applies to all processes which involve only those factors with respect to which the system is in internal equilibrium. The third law can then be stated in the following way.

The contribution to the entropy due to each factor with respect to which the system is in internal thermodynamical equilibrium vanishes as the absolute zero is approached.

The advantage of such a formulation is that the restriction to systems in internal thermodynamical equilibrium is not a restriction

---

* Care must be taken that there are no specific-heat anomalies below the temperature to which measurements have been carried. These occur, for example, in hydrogen and in paramagnetic salts. Further, extrapolation must only be carried out below the temperature at which the true T^3 region of specific heats is reached. Most solids exhibit spurious T^3 specific-heat regions at temperatures up to ten times as great as the upper limit of the true T^3 region (see Section 14 of Chapter XXII).

† Simon, *Erg. ex. Naturwiss.*, Vol. 9, p. 235 (1930); *Physica*, Vol. 4, p. 1089 (1937).

‡ For example, a crystal could be in internal thermodynamical equilibrium with respect to the thermal vibrations and the crystallographic arrangement, but not with respect to the distribution of isotopes in the lattice.

invented *specially* for the third law; it is a condition that can be expected to be required for any thermodynamical law. While it is more restricted than " pure crystalline solid ", in that it takes into account the state of the constituents of the atoms, it is less restricted in that it also covers ordered mixed phases, frozen-in states, and systems like liquid helium.

An alternative statement of the law, which is equivalent to the preceding statement, can be given in the following way.

The differences in entropy between all those states of a system between which a reversible transition is possible in principle even at the lowest temperatures tend to zero as the temperature approaches the absolute zero.

The third law is often stated in the form that absolute zero is unattainable. Within the field of classical physics, specific heats are constant so that, as the temperature of a classical system approaches absolute zero, the entropy must approach minus infinity as shown in fig. 19.1. It is clear that for such a system absolute zero could not be reached in a finite number of operations. It is equally clear that the unattainability of absolute zero is trivial in this case. It is far otherwise when a quantal system is considered.

One of the earliest applications of Planck's hypothesis of a quantum of energy was made by Einstein to calculate specific heats (Chapter XXII, Section 1). He found that the specific heats of solids approach zero as the temperature falls. This means that within the context of quantum theory entropies must remain finite as the temperature approaches absolute zero. This is illustrated in fig. 19.2. Curves (*a*) show how the entropy of a quantal system would change at low temperatures if it violated the third law. The different curves correspond to different values of a parameter *x*, which could be the pressure in the case of a gas, the external magnetic field in the case of a paramagnetic salt, and so on. Curves (*b*) show the low-temperature variation of the entropy in accordance with the third law. It is clear in this latter case that, if a reversible transition is possible, the temperature of the system can be reduced by a sequence of reversible transitions, but it will never reach absolute zero in a finite

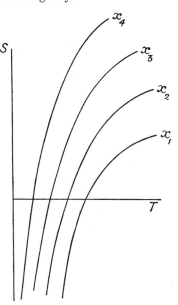

Fig. 19.1.—Entropy as a function of temperature for a classical system

number (no matter how large) of operations. On the other hand, if there were a system represented by the curves (a) of fig. 19.2, it would be a simple matter to reach absolute zero. This is illustrated by the curves in fig. 19.3 in which the operations are represented by the lines with arrows. Thus, the third law implies the unattainability of absolute zero. For all those processes which can be carried out at the lowest temperatures, the unattainability of absolute zero and the satisfaction of the third law go hand in hand. Amongst these are, for instance,

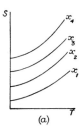 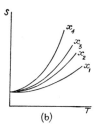

(a)   (b)

Fig. 19.2.—Entropy as a function of temperature for a quantal system. Curves (a) correspond to a violation of the third law and curves (b) to its satisfaction

volume changes of solids, processes depending on the transport of electrons in metals, the magnetic or electric polarization of crystals, the liquid-solid transition in helium, and the transition of a superconducting metal in a magnetic field (see Sections 5 to 9 below). All of these transitions can be carried out down to the lowest temperatures; and the violation of the third law in any of them would involve the possibility of reaching absolute zero; but no one has yet succeeded in using any of these transitions to reach absolute zero; and this in itself provides a formidable array of evidence in verification of the third law.

However, all of the transitions which are of interest are not of this character. Many of the transitions in which a prediction of the equili-

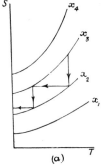 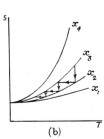

(a)   (b)

Fig. 19.3.—Curves (a) show how absolute zero would be reached if the third law were invalid and curves (b) show the unattainability of absolute zero

brium would be most valuable cannot be carried out at all at low temperatures. The violation of the third law in such a case would therefore not lead to a practicable way of reaching absolute zero. An example of this type of process is the graphite-diamond equilibrium. The transition takes place incredibly slowly at room temperature; at ordinary temperatures and pressures, graphite is the stable form and diamond exists under these conditions only on account of the extreme slowness of the transition. The specific heats of graphite and diamond have been measured, and from them, assuming that the entropy difference vanishes as $T \to 0$, the entropy differences between diamond and graphite have been determined over the temperature range of the measurements. The pressure-temperature curve for the graphite-diamond transition has been calculated * from these values and the specific volumes, using the Clausius-Clapeyron equation. The calculated transition curve indicates the pressure required to transform graphite to diamond at the high temperature required for the transition to proceed at a practicable rate. These predictions, based on the validity of the third law, have been recently confirmed by the successful synthesis of diamond.†

We now turn to consider further experimental verification of this law; it involves a detailed examination of experimental results on chemical reactions, and we close with an examination of the typical low-temperature phenomena in their bearing on the unattainability of absolute zero. These latter phenomena must now be regarded as providing the most striking experimental verification of the third law of thermodynamics.

2. The Proof of the Nernst Heat Theorem.

In order to establish the truth of the Nernst heat theorem it is necessary to appeal to experiment. A test is provided by any chemical reaction for which the equilibrium constant K_c can be measured, and for which we know also the heat of reaction H_p and the entropy changes of all the reacting substances from independent thermal measurements between the absolute zero and the temperature at which K_c is measured. We can then compare the observed reaction constant with that calculated from equation (1) by assuming the theorem true; or, what amounts to the same thing, we can use the measured value of the reaction constant, the heat of reaction, and all the entropies except one to determine this remaining entropy, and we may then compare the value so calculated with the entropy deduced from the direct thermal measurements.

* R. Berman and F. E. Simon, *Z. Elektrochem.*, Vol. 59, p. 333 (1955).

† F. P. Bundy, H. T. Hall, H. M. Strong, and R. H. Wentorf, *Nature*, Vol. 176, p. 51 (1955).

Since many of the equilibria for which the most accurate data are available involve reactions in which solids take part, we must consider the form which equation (1) takes for such reactions.

It is more convenient to deal with the equilibrium constant K referring to partial pressures and defined by equation (20), Chapter XVIII. Substituting in equation (1) from this equation, we obtain

$$RT \log K_p - RT \left(\Sigma \, \nu_j \right) \log p = H_p + T \, \Sigma \, \nu_j S_j.$$

In dealing with the question of reactions in which solids take part in Chapter XVIII, Sections 10–12, we found that it is necessary to distinguish carefully between those substances which are present in the gaseous state only and those which are present in the solid state as well as in the gaseous state. We shall use the letter p for the partial pressure of substances which are present in the gaseous state only, and the letter π for the partial (vapour) pressures of those substances which are present as solids. Further, we shall indicate under each Σ sign whether the summation is to extend over the substances which are present only in the gaseous state (Σ_g), or only over those which are present in the solid state (Σ_s), or over both (Σ_{g+s}). We shall indicate that H_p in the above equation refers to the heat of reaction between vapours and gases, and is not the measured heat of reaction—which includes latent heats of vaporization—by writing it $H_{p \text{(vapours)}}$.

Remembering that

$$K_p = p_1^{\nu_1} p_2^{\nu_2} p_3^{\nu_3} \ldots \pi_x^{\nu_x} \pi_y^{\nu_y} \ldots ,$$

the above equation becomes

$$RT \, \Sigma_g \, \nu_j \log p_j + RT \, \Sigma_s \, \nu_x \log \pi_x - RT \, \Sigma_{g+s} \, \nu_j \log p$$
$$= H_{p \text{(vapours)}} + T \, \Sigma_g \, \nu_j S_j + T \, \Sigma_s \, \nu_x S_{x \text{(vapours)}}.$$

We have further

$$H_{p \text{(measured)}} = H_{p \text{(vapours)}} + \Sigma_s \, \nu_x \Lambda_x,$$

where Λ_x is the molecular latent heat of vaporization of the solid of species x. The sign is right, because for each substance which disappears in the reaction ν_x is negative (see footnote on Chapter XVIII, Section 11).

Also, we have

$$S_{x \text{(vapour)}} = S_{x \text{(solid)}} + \frac{\Lambda_x}{T} + R \log \frac{\pi_x}{p},$$

in which the last term is included because $S_{x \text{(vapour)}}$ refers to the entropy of the vapour not at its actual partial pressure but at the pressure p.

Using these two results, our equation becomes

$$RT \, \Sigma_g \, \nu_j \log p_j + RT \, \Sigma_s \, \nu_x \log \pi_x - RT \, \Sigma_{g+s} \, \nu_j \log p$$
$$= H_{p \text{(meas.)}} - \Sigma_s \, \nu_x \Lambda_x + T \, \Sigma_g \, \nu_j S_j + T \, \Sigma_s \, \nu_x S_{x \text{(solid)}} + \Sigma_s \, \nu_x \Lambda_x$$
$$+ RT \, \Sigma_s \, \nu_x \log \pi_x - RT \, \Sigma_s \, \nu_x \log p.$$

Collecting terms, we obtain

$$RT \sum_g \nu_j \log p_j - RT \sum_g \nu_j \log p = H_{p \text{ (meas.)}} + T \sum_g \nu_j S_j + T \sum_s \nu_x S_x \text{ (solid)}. \quad (2)$$

In both terms on the left-hand side we consider only substances which are not present in the solid state (compare with Chapter XVIII, Section 11); and on the right-hand side we have the measured heat of reaction, and the entropies of the gases (at the pressure p) for those substances which are not present in the solid state, and for those substances which are present in the solid state, the entropies of the solids.

In order to test the Nernst heat theorem we shall apply this last equation to the dissociation of solid mercuric oxide * according to the equation

$$2HgO \rightarrow 2Hg + O_2.$$

Here we have $\nu_1 = -2$ (referring to solid mercuric oxide); $\nu_2 = +2$ (referring to mercury vapour); and $\nu_3 = +1$ (referring to oxygen). We calculate the entropy of oxygen from the equation, using the measured equilibrium constant, the entropy of mercury, and the entropy of mercuric oxide. The values of the last two quantities are obtained from purely calorimetric measurements on mercury and mercuric oxide; by the heat theorem the entropies at absolute zero of solid mercury and mercuric oxide can be replaced by that of oxygen. The value for the entropy of oxygen so obtained is compared (see (f) below) with that deduced from calorimetric measurements on oxygen itself. The agreement between the two values shows, at least to a first approximation, the correctness of the theorem.

(a) Taylor and Hulett † have measured the dissociation pressure at the boiling-point of mercury, (357° C.) 630° absolute, and found it to be 86 mm. of mercury. The vapour density shows that the amount of HgO in the vapour is negligible, so that the partial pressure of mercury is $\frac{2}{3} \times 86$ mm., and that of oxygen is $\frac{1}{3} \times 86$ mm. The total pressure p is, of course, 86 mm.

(b) The heat of the reaction

$$2HgO \text{ (solid)} \rightarrow 2Hg \text{ (liquid)} + O_2$$

has been determined by Varet ‡ and by Brønsted § at room temperature, 291° absolute. The former found −43,000 cals. and the latter −43,400 cals. We shall take the mean value of −43,200 cals. We require the heat of reaction between solid mercuric oxide, mercury *vapour*, and oxygen at a temperature of 630° abs. The heat of reaction between solid mercuric oxide, mercury (liquid), and oxygen at this temperature can be determined from the molecular heats

---

* The student is recommended to carry out the details of the calculations sketched out below. The unit of heat used in the calculations is the calorie.

† Taylor and Hulett, *Journ. Phys. Chem.*, Vol. 17, p. 565 (1913).

‡ Varet, *Ann. Chim. Phys.* (7), Vol. 8, p. 100 (1896).

§ Brønsted, *Zeits. f. phys. Chem.*, Vol. 65, pp. 84 and 744 (1909).

given below and from the measured value at 291° abs. by using equation (28), Chapter XVIII.

$$\text{Mol. Heat of HgO} = 9\cdot0 + 0\cdot006T;$$
$$\text{At. Heat of Hg (liq.)} = 6\cdot96 - 0\cdot0010T; *$$
$$\text{Mol. Heat of O}_2 \text{ (gas)} = 6\cdot50 + 0\cdot0010T.$$

We thus obtain for the heat of reaction between liquid mercury and the other substances at 630° abs.

$$-43,200 - \int_{291}^{630} (2\cdot42 - 0\cdot013T)\,dT,$$

or $-42,000$ cals.

The value of H_p, the heat of reaction between mercury *vapour* and the other substances at 630° abs., is therefore

$$H_p = -42,000 - 2\Lambda_{Hg},$$

where Λ_{Hg} is the atomic latent heat of vaporization of mercury at 630° abs. We do not need to know this quantity, as it disappears from the final equation.

(c) The entropy of solid mercuric oxide can be determined (see Chapter XXII, Section 8) from the accurate specific-heat measurements at low temperatures by Gunther.† Using these measurements Lewis and Randall have carried out the necessary integration, and find for the entropy of one gram-molecule of solid mercuric oxide at 298° abs., $16\cdot3 + (S_1)_0$.‡ From this figure and the molecular heat given in (b) above we obtain for the entropy at 630° abs. $25\cdot04 + (S_1)_0$ cal. deg.$^{-1}$.

(d) From the measurements, of the specific heat of solid and liquid mercury and from the latent heat of fusion Lewis and Randall obtain for the entropy of one gram-atom of liquid mercury at 298° abs., $17\cdot8 + (S_2)_0$. From this figure and from the value of the atomic heat of mercury given in (b) above we obtain for the entropy of one gram-atom of liquid mercury at 630° abs., $22\cdot68 + (S_2)_0$ cal. deg.$^{-1}$. The vapour pressure of mercury at this temperature is 760 mm. of mercury, and, if Λ_{Hg} is the atomic latent heat of vaporization of mercury at this temperature, the entropy of mercury vapour at 630° abs. and at a pressure of 760 mm. is $22\cdot68 + \Lambda_{Hg}/630 + (S_2)_0$. The entropy of a gram-atom of mercury vapour at 630° abs. and at a pressure of 86 mm. of mercury, which is the entropy required in the formula, is $22\cdot68 + R\log\dfrac{760}{86} + \dfrac{\Lambda_{Hg}}{630} + (S_2)_0$, where R equals $1\cdot986$ cal. deg.$^{-1}$. This is equal to

$$27\cdot01 + \frac{\Lambda_{Hg}}{630}.$$

(e) The entropy of oxygen we shall calculate by substituting the above values in equation (2). We obtain, since by the heat theorem $2(S_2)_0 + 2(S_3)_0 = 2(S_1)_0$,

$$R\log\frac{4}{27} = -\frac{42,000}{630} - \frac{2\Lambda_{Hg}}{630} + 2\left(27\cdot01 + \frac{\Lambda_{Hg}}{630}\right) + S_{(oxyg.)} - 2(S_3)_0 - 2 \cdot 25\cdot04,$$

---

* See Egerton, *Phil. Mag.*, Vol. 39, p. 8 (1920). The remaining data are taken from Lewis and Randall, *Thermodynamics and the Free Energy of Chemical Substances*, who have collected a large amount of experimental data.

† Gunther, *Ann. d. Physik*, Vol. 51, p. 828 (1916).

‡ We write $(S_1)_0$, $(S_2)_0$, and $(S_3)_0$ for the entropies at absolute zero of one gram-molecule of solid mercuric oxide, and one gram-atom of solid mercury and oxygen respectively.

where R must be put equal to $1 \cdot 986$, since we are using the calorie as the unit of energy. We thus obtain for the entropy of one gram-molecule of gaseous oxygen under the given conditions, that is, at $630°$ abs. and at a pressure of 86 mm. of mercury,

$$58 \cdot 9 + 2(S_3)_0 \text{ cal. deg.}^{-1}.$$

(f) In order to test the Nernst heat theorem we must compare this value for the entropy of oxygen with that deduced from the measurements on the specific and latent heats of oxygen. Using the experimental results of Eucken on the thermal constants of oxygen, Lewis and Randall obtain for the entropy of one gram-molecule of oxygen gas at a pressure of 760 mm. of mercury and at a temperature of $298°$ abs., $48 \cdot 2 + 2(S_3)_0$. Using the value of the molecular heat of oxygen given in (b) above, we obtain the entropy of one gram-molecule of oxygen at $630°$ abs. and a pressure of 760 mm. of mercury; and by adding to this $R \log(760/86)$, we obtained for the entropy at $630°$ abs. and at a pressure of 86 mm. of mercury,

$$57 \cdot 7 + 2(S_3)_0 \text{ cal. deg.}^{-1}.$$

The agreement between the two values $58 \cdot 9$ and $57 \cdot 7$ is sufficiently close to justify us in saying that in this particular case the Nernst heat theorem is *at least* approximately true.

Lewis and others have calculated the entropy of chlorine from four different reactions involving chlorides, and have obtained satisfactory agreement between the various values. Similarly they have calculated the entropy of iodine. The equilibrium constants in these calculations were determined from electromotive force measurements as described in the last chapter.*

Further evidence is given in Section 3.

3. The Chemical Constants.

In the last section we have carried out all our calculations in terms of the entropies of the reacting substances. We shall now show that it is possible to express these entropies in terms of the chemical constants of the substances, and that, therefore, the entropies can be eliminated from the equations, the chemical constants taking their place. It is very important to realize that there is no essential difference between the two methods of calculation; the method given in the last section shows up the underlying principles more clearly, while that about to be developed is numerically simpler once the chemical constants of the reacting substances have been calculated. Such calculations are made on account of the interest of the values of the constants themselves, so that the results are nearly always expressed in terms of them and not in the way illustrated in the preceding section.

* Lewis, Gibson and Latimer, *Journ. Amer. Chem. Soc.*, Vol. 44, p. 1008 (1922); we may note that these writers use a different notation from that usually employed, and that what they call the free energy is the Gibbs function.

We have already defined the chemical constant of a substance in Chapter VIII, Section 11, as the integration constant of the vapour-pressure formula. This formula may be written (see equation (3), Chapter VIII)

$$\frac{d \log \pi}{dT'} = \frac{\Lambda}{RT'^2},$$

where Λ is the molecular latent heat of vaporization, and π is the vapour pressure at temperature T': we assume that the vapour behaves as a perfect gas and that the volume of a given mass of the condensed substance is negligible compared with that of an equal mass of the vapour.

The molecular latent heat of vaporization may be written

$$\Lambda = \Lambda^0 + \tfrac{5}{2} RT' + \int_0^{T'} \{(C_{\text{int.}}) - (C_p{}^s)\} dT, \quad . \quad . \quad . \quad (3)$$

where Λ^0 is the molecular latent heat of vaporization at the absolute zero, and $(\tfrac{5}{2} R + C_{\text{int.}})$ and $C_p{}^s$ are the molecular heats of the vapour and solid respectively (see Chapter VIII, Section 11). The fact that by no conceivable process can we imagine the vaporization at the absolute zero carried out does not matter; we may for the present purpose regard Λ^0 as a constant defined by the above equation.

Substituting this value of Λ in the vapour-pressure formula and integrating, we obtain

$$\log \pi = - \frac{\Lambda^0}{RT'} + \tfrac{5}{2} \log T' + \int_0^{T'} \frac{dT}{RT^2} \int_0^{T} \{(C_{\text{int.}}) - (C_p{}^s)\} dT + i, \quad (4)$$

where i is an integration constant which we call the chemical constant of the substance considered.

In order to obtain the entropy S of a gram-molecule of gas at temperature T and pressure p, we shall commence with the solid at the absolute zero, where we shall suppose that its entropy is equal to S_0. We heat the solid to a certain temperature T', which is below the melting-point. At this temperature we vaporize the solid completely, the molecular latent heat of vaporization being Λ, and the vapour pressure π. We now heat the vapour at pressure π to the temperature T, and then expand it until its pressure is p. We thus obtain

$$S - S_0 = \int_0^{T'} \frac{C_p{}^s}{T} dT + \frac{\Lambda}{T'} + \int_{T'}^{T} \frac{C_{\text{int}}}{T} dT + \tfrac{5}{2} R \log \frac{T}{T'} + R \log \frac{\pi}{p}.$$

Substituting for Λ and for $\log \pi$ from equations (3) and (4), we obtain

$$S - S_0 = \int_0^{T} \frac{C_p{}^s}{T} dT + \tfrac{5}{2} R + \frac{1}{T'} \int_0^{T'} (C_{\text{int}} - C_p{}^s) dT + \int_{T'}^{T} \frac{C_{\text{int.}}}{T} dT$$

$$+ \tfrac{5}{2} R \log T + \int_0^{T'} \frac{dT}{T^2} \int_0^{T} (C_{\text{int.}} - C_p{}^s) dT + Ri - R \log p.$$

Rearranging terms and using the relation

$$\int_{T'}^{T} \frac{C_{\text{int.}}}{T} dT = \int_{0}^{T} \frac{C_{\text{int.}}}{T} dT - \int_{0}^{T'} \frac{C_{\text{int.}}}{T} dT,$$

we have

$$S - S_0 = 2 \cdot 5 \, R \log T + \int_{0}^{T} \frac{C_{\text{int.}}}{T} dT - R \log p + 2 \cdot 5 \, R + Ri$$

$$+ \int_{0}^{T'} \frac{C_p{}^s}{T} dT - \int_{0}^{T'} \frac{C_{\text{int.}}}{T} dT + \frac{1}{T'} \int_{0}^{T'} (C_{\text{int.}} - C_p{}^s) dT$$

$$+ \int_{0}^{T'} \frac{dT}{T^2} \int_{0}^{T} (C_{\text{int.}} - C_p{}^s) dT. \quad \ldots \ldots \quad (5)$$

The sum of the last four integrals in this expression is zero,* so that the expression for S assumes the very simple form

$$S - S_0 = 2 \cdot 5 \, R \log T + \int_{0}^{T} \frac{C_{\text{int.}}}{T} dT - R \log p + 2 \cdot 5 \, R + Ri. \quad (6)$$

We substitute this value for the entropy in equation (1). The arbitrary constants $(S_j)_0, \ldots$ can all be collected together in the term $\Sigma \nu_j (S_j)_0$, and, according to the Nernst heat theorem, this vanishes.

---

* The proof that the sum of the other terms in equation (5) is zero is as follows. The sixth and succeeding terms may be written

$$\left\{ \int_{0}^{T'} \frac{C_p{}^s}{T} dT - \frac{1}{T'} \int_{0}^{T'} C_p{}^s dT - \int_{0}^{T'} \frac{dT}{T^2} \int_{0}^{T} C_p{}^s dT \right\} - \left\{ \begin{array}{l} \text{an exactly similar set of terms} \\ \text{in which } C_{\text{int.}} \text{ replaces } C_p{}^s \end{array} \right\},$$

Each of these brackets vanishes identically, for we may write

$$C_p = \frac{dW}{dT},$$

and, therefore, also

$$\int_{0}^{T} C_p dT = W - W_0,$$

where W_0 is a constant and is the value of W when $T = 0$. Substituting from the first of these equations in the first term in the bracket, and from the second in the other two terms, and omitting the *dash* sign from T, we obtain

$$\int_{0}^{T} \frac{C_p}{T} dT - \frac{1}{T} \int_{0}^{T} C_p dT - \int_{0}^{T} \frac{dT}{T^2} \int_{0}^{T} C_p dT$$

$$= \int_{0}^{T} \frac{1}{T} \frac{dW}{dT} dT - \frac{1}{T}(W - W_0) - \int_{0}^{T} \frac{W - W_0}{T^2} dT = 0, \quad \cdot \quad (7)$$

the final result being obtained immediately by integrating by parts the integral

$$\int_{0}^{T} \frac{1}{T} \frac{dW}{dT} dT.$$

Thus the arbitrary constants all disappear, and the chemical constants remain; equation (1) becomes

$$\log K_c = \frac{H_p}{RT} + 2 \cdot 5(\Sigma \nu_j) \log T + \frac{1}{R}\Sigma \nu_j \int_0^T \frac{(C_{\text{int.}})_j}{T}\, dT$$
$$- (\Sigma \nu_j)\log p + \Sigma \nu_j(2 \cdot 5 + i_j),$$

or, from equation (20), Chapter XVIII,

$$\log K_p = \frac{H_p}{RT} + 2 \cdot 5(\Sigma \nu_j)\log T + \frac{1}{R}\Sigma \nu_j \int_0^T \frac{(C_{\text{int.}})_j}{T}\, dT + \Sigma \nu_j(2 \cdot 5 + i_j).$$

Now, if $H_p{}^0$ is the heat of reaction between the gases at the absolute zero,

$$H_p = H_p{}^0 - (\Sigma \nu_j)\, 2 \cdot 5\, RT - \Sigma \nu_j \int_0^T (C_{\text{int.}})_j\, dT; \quad . \quad (8)$$

actually $H_p{}^0$ cannot be measured directly, but it is a constant defined by equation (8). Substituting this value for H_p in the last equation, and using equation (7), we obtain

$$\log K_p = \frac{H_p{}^0}{RT} + 2 \cdot 5(\Sigma \nu_j)\log T + \Sigma \nu_j \int_0^T \frac{dT}{RT^2}\int_0^T (C_{\text{int.}})_j\, dT + \Sigma \nu_j i_j. \quad (9)$$

It is important to realize that this equation holds only if the Nernst heat theorem is true, for only in this case does the sum of the entropy constants of the substances involved in the reaction vanish.

An equation exactly similar to equation (9) can be obtained by direct integration of the equation of the isochore of reaction (equation (17), Chapter XVIII),

$$\frac{d \log K_p}{dT} = -\frac{H_p}{RT^2} = -\frac{H_p{}^0}{RT^2} + 2 \cdot 5(\Sigma \nu_j)\frac{1}{T} + \Sigma \nu_j \frac{1}{RT^2}\int_0^T (C_{\text{int.}})_j\, dT.$$

Integrating, we obtain

$$\log K_p = \frac{H_p{}^0}{RT} + 2 \cdot 5(\Sigma \nu_j)\log T + \Sigma \nu_j \int_0^T \frac{dT}{RT^2}\int_0^T (C_{\text{int.}})_j\, dT + I, \quad (10)$$

where I is a constant of integration.

Comparing equations (10) and (9), we see that, if the Nernst heat theorem is true, the constant of integration I in the equation of the isochore of reaction is equal to $\Sigma \nu_j i_j$, where $i_1, i_2, \ldots$ are the chemical constants of the reacting gases as determined from vapour-pressure measurements. It is for this reason that the constants $i_1, i_2, \ldots$ are called chemical constants. According to the Nernst heat theorem, a knowledge of the heat of reaction at one temperature, of the specific heats of the reacting gases, and of the chemical constants of the gases, suffices to determine the equilibrium condition at any temperature completely.

A comparison of the values of I, deduced from equilibrium measurements and measurements of heats of reaction, with values of $\Sigma\nu_j i_j$ for the gases concerned, therefore, furnishes a test of the Nernst heat theorem. Eucken * has collected data for such a comparison for a number of reactions. In deducing the chemical constants the best data on the specific heats of the condensed gases have been used, and corrections have been made for the departure of the gases from the perfect gas laws. From the probable errors in the various values he obtains the probable limits between which the values of I lie. His values of I and values of $\Sigma\nu_j i_j$ based on his figures are given in the first three columns of Table I.

TABLE I

Reaction	I (from chemical equilibrium) between	$\Sigma\nu_j i_j$ (from vapour pressure)	$\Sigma\nu_j i_j$ corrected for zero point entropy of hydrogen
Homogeneous.			
$3H_2 + N_2 = 2NH_3$	$+ 6.94$	$+ 7.14$	$+ 8.21$	$+ 7.14$
$2H_2 + O_2 = 2H_2O$	$+ 2.35$	$+ 2.55$	$+ 2.97$	$+ 2.25$
$H_2 + Cl_2 = 2HCl$	$+ 0.92$	$+ 1.32$	$+ 1.21$	$+ 0.85$
$H_2 + Br_2 = 2HBr$	$+ 0.8$	$+ 1.7$	$+ 1.57$	$+ 1.21$
$H_2 + I_2 = 2HI$	$+ 1.38$	$+ 1.62$	$+ 1.91$	$+ 1.55$
$N_2 + O_2 = 2NO$	$+ 0.65$	$+ 1.25$	$+ 0.65$	
$2CO + O_2 = 2CO_2$	$+ 0.55$	$+ 1.05$	$+ 1.39$	
$H_2O + CO = H_2 + CO_2$	$- 0.75$	$- 0.90$	$- 0.78$	$- 0.42$
$4HCl + O_2 = 2H_2O + 2Cl_2$	$+ 0.06$	$+ 0.34$	$+ 0.51$	
$3H_2 + CO = CH_4 + H_2O$	$+ 5.95$	$+ 6.55$	$+ 7.22$	$+ 6.15$
$4H_2 + CO_2 = CH_4 + 2H_2O$	$+ 6.75$	$+ 7.25$	$+ 7.98$	$+ 6.35$
Heterogeneous.†			
$2CO = C + CO_2$	$+ 0.68$	$+ 1.03$	$+ 1.03$	
$C + 2H_2 = CH_4$	$+ 4.20$	$+ 4.70$	$+ 5.40$	$+ 4.68$
$2Hg\ (vapour) + O_2 = 2HgO$ ‡	$- 4.14$	$- 4.50$	$- 4.35$	
$CaO + H_2O = Ca(OH)_2$	$+ 1.85$	$+ 2.15$	$+ 1.94$	
$CuSO_4 + H_2O = CuSO_4 \cdot H_2O$	$+ 1.99$	$+ 2.23$	$+ 1.94$	
$CaO + CO_2 = CaCO_3$ §	$- 0.75$	$- 1.05$	$- 0.90$	
$H_2 + HgO = Hg + H_2O\ (solid)$	$+ 3.34$	$+ 3.54$	$+ 3.69$	$+ 3.33$
$2Ag + Cl_2 = 2AgCl$	$- 1.95$	$- 2.35$⎫		
$2Hg + Cl_2 = 2HgCl$	$- 1.20$	$- 2.00$⎬	$- 1.66$	
$Pb + Cl_2 = PbCl_2$	$- 1.75$	$- 2.25$⎭		

* Eucken, *Phys. Zeits.*, Vol. 30. p. 818 (1929); Vol. 31, p. 361 (1930).

† For the theory of heterogeneous reactions, see Section 4.

‡ From the measurements of Simon, *Zeits. f. phys. Chem.*, Vol. 107, p. 279 (1923), which are not the same as those used in Section 2.

§ See also Eucken, *Phys. Zeits.*, Vol. 31, p. 362 (1930).

That there is a very close correlation between the two sets of figures is at once evident. A difference of $1\cdot0$ between I and $\Sigma\nu_j i_j$ corresponds to a difference of about 20 joules per degree if we use the method of calculation of Section 2. Such a wide range of reactions is considered that we are certainly justified in regarding the Nernst heat theorem as being established as a first approximation.

We can at least say, therefore, that the entropy changes in re-actions between crystalline solids at the absolute zero are small and finite. Some of the differences between I and $\Sigma\nu_j i_j$ are outside the experimental error. These can be explained in terms of quantum statistics. Let us take the case of hydrogen, which is best understood. As we have seen in Chapter VI, Section 28, there are two different types of hydrogen molecule, ortho-hydrogen and para-hydrogen. At the absolute zero in the state of true thermodynamic equilibrium all the hydrogen is in the para-form. We shall assume * that, as far as hydrogen is concerned, reactions involving solid para-hydrogen at the absolute zero obey the Nernst heat theorem. Ordinary hydrogen at the absolute zero is a metastable mixture of three parts of ortho-hydrogen and one part of para-hydrogen. MacGillavry and Stern,† developing a method first used by Fowler,‡ have shown how to calcu-late statistically the entropy difference at the absolute zero between the ordinary metastable mixture and pure para-hydrogen. They show that, as far as comparisons between I and $\Sigma\nu_j i_j$ are concerned, the difference can be allowed for by adding $\frac{3}{4}\log_{10}3$ or $+0\cdot358$ to $-3\cdot685$, the measured chemical constant i of hydrogen (H_2). The latter is obtained on the assumption that the specific heat of solid hydrogen continues to obey a cubic law right down to the absolute zero. The values obtained for $\Sigma\nu_j i_j$ after this adjustment has been made are given in the last column of Table I, and it will be seen that on the whole these values agree better with the values of I and that all the large discrepancies have disappeared. Eucken considers that the experiments are not accurate enough for it to be stated with certainty that the remaining discrepancies are not due to experimental error. It is possible that some of them may be real and that some adjustment similar in type to that made in the case of hydrogen may be necessary with other substances. For a full discussion, reference should be made to Eucken's paper.§

* See Stern, *Proc. Roy. Soc.*, A, Vol. 130. p. 378 (1931).

† MacGillavry, *Phys. Rev.*, Vol. 36, p. 1398 (1930); Stern, *Proc. Roy. Soc.*, A, Vol. 130, p. 367 (1931); see also Ludloff, *Zeits. f. Physik*, Vol. 68, p. 433 (1931).

‡ Fowler, *Proc. Roy. Soc.*, A, Vol. 118, p. 52 (1928).

§ It should be mentioned that in this paper Eucken shows how accurate values of chemical constants can be obtained from spectroscopic data. See also Clusius and Teske, *Zeits. f. phys. Chem.*, B, Vol. 6, p. 135 (1929), for a comparison of calculated and measured values for carbon monoxide; Stern, *Proc. Roy. Soc.*, A, Vol. 131, p. 339 (1931), for a calculation of the chemical constant of chlorine.

This example of hydrogen illustrates a general precaution that has to be taken. In extrapolating the specific heat to absolute zero according to a cubic law, it is essential that the extrapolation should be carried out from the *true* T^3 region. Recent work on the specific heats of solids by Blackman * has shown that, generally speaking, T^3 regions found experimentally in the hydrogen temperature range are spurious. His theory shows that the true T^3 region only starts at much lower temperatures, and at very much lower temperatures than would be expected on Debye's theory of specific heats. The reason is that Debye's theory, unlike that by Born and v. Kármán and the more recent work of Blackman, is not based rigorously on the principles of crystal dynamics. The reader is referred to Chapter XXII for a discussion of this point. In the case of hydrogen, the extrapolation which is taken into account in the last column of Table I is from measurements of the specific heat of solid hydrogen between 14° and 20° K. More recent measurements by Simon, Mendelssohn, and Ruheman † have shown that, at these temperatures, solid hydrogen has not yet reached the true T^3 region, for they have found anomalies in the specific heat of solid ortho-hydrogen below 10° K. It must be emphasized that the specific heats of the *condensed* gases must be measured down to the true T^3 region of temperature. Only then is extrapolation to the absolute zero reliable. It should also be noted that an error in the extrapolation of the gas or vapour to the absolute zero affects I and $\Sigma \nu_j i_j$ equally, and is therefore of no importance for the present comparison.

4. Heterogeneous Reactions.

So far we have considered in detail the use of chemical constants in homogeneous gaseous reactions only. For heterogeneous reactions in which solids and vapours take part we start from equation (27), Chapter XVIII,

$$\frac{d \log K_p'}{dT} = - \frac{H_p}{RT^2}.$$

From equation (28), Chapter XVIII, we may write

$$H_p = H_p{}^0 - \Sigma_g \nu_j \, 2 \cdot 5 \, RT - \Sigma_g \nu_j \int_0^T (C_{\text{int.}})_j \, dT - \Sigma_s \nu_x \int_0^T (C_p{}^s)_x dT.$$

$H_p{}^0$ is a constant defined by this equation; we may look on it as the heat of reaction at the absolute zero and at the pressure p between the same solids and vapours, although in practice such a reaction and such conditions would be quite unrealizable.

---

* Blackman, *Proc. Roy. Soc.*, A, Vol. 159, p. 416 (1937). See Chapter XXII, Section 14.

† Simon, Mendelssohn, and Ruheman, *Naturwiss.*, Vol. 18, p. 34 (1930).

Using this value for H_p and integrating, we obtain

$$\log K_p' = \frac{H_p^0}{RT} + \Sigma_g \nu_j \, 2{\cdot}5 \log T + \Sigma_g \nu_j \int_0^T \frac{dT}{RT^2} \int_0^T (C_{\text{int.}})_j \, dT$$

$$+ \Sigma_s \nu_x \int_0^T \frac{dT}{RT^2} \int_0^T (C_p{}^s)_x \, dT + I, \qquad . \quad . \quad (11)$$

where I is a constant of integration. Remembering that

$$\log K_p' = \Sigma_g \nu_j \log p_j,$$

and commencing from equation (2), we may obtain another expression for $\log K_p'$. We substitute in equation (2) for the entropies of the gases from equation (6), and for the entropies of the solids we put

$$\Sigma_s \nu_x S_x = \Sigma_s \nu_x \int_0^T \frac{(C_p{}^s)_x}{T} \, dT + \Sigma_s \nu_x (S_x)_0.$$

By the heat theorem the entropy constants vanish. It is important to remember that, as always, the entropy of a reacting gas that must be used is its entropy under the pressure p (the total pressure) and not under its actual partial pressure in the mixture. In this way we obtain by using equation (7)

$$\log K_p' = \frac{H_p^0}{RT} + \Sigma_g \nu_j \, 2{\cdot}5 \log T + \Sigma_g \nu_j \int_0^T \frac{dT}{RT^2} \int_0^T (C_{\text{int.}})_j \, dT$$

$$+ \Sigma_s \nu_x \int_0^T \frac{dT}{RT^2} \int_0^T (C_p{}^s)_x \, dT + \Sigma_g \nu_j i_j. \qquad (12)$$

Comparing equations (11) and (12), we see that according to the Nernst heat theorem—on which (12) is based—the integration constant in this case is given by

$$I = \Sigma_g \nu_j i_j, \quad . \quad . \quad . \quad . \quad . \quad . \quad . \quad . \quad (13)$$

that is, we have to omit from the sum the chemical constants of the reacting substances which are present in the solid state. This is illustrated in Table I.

Simon carried out an extensive series of measurements on supercooled liquids and solutions.* He has shown that all the experimental facts can be accounted for by assuming that, for all states of a system which are in internal thermodynamical equilibrium, entropy differences vanish in the neighbourhood of the absolute zero. These experiments provide further confirmation of the third law of thermodynamics.

5. Low-temperature Phenomena.

Experimental verification of the third law of thermodynamics is also provided by phenomena in which a reversible change can be carried out between the states of the system in question even at the lowest temperatures. In these cases, the entropy differences can be measured directly. Non-vanishing entropy differences, in the neighbourhood of the absolute zero, for these phenomena would be a clear

* Simon, *Erg. ex. Naturwiss.*, Vol. 9, p. 235 (1930).

contradiction of the third law; and any such contradiction would provide a straightforward means of reaching the absolute zero. The specifically low-temperature phenomena are: the two states of liquid helium, the superconducting state of some metals, and experiments on the adiabatic demagnetization of paramagnetic salts. We shall consider each of these in turn.

6. Liquid Helium.

At the lowest temperatures which have been reached, helium (isotope of mass 4) remains liquid,* and can be solidified only under a pressure of about 25 atmospheres. The melting-pressure curve shows no tendency at all to meet the vapour-pressure curve; it has been concluded from this that helium 4 cannot be solidified under its equilibrium vapour pressure simply by reducing the temperature. Thus, both liquid and solid helium can exist at all temperatures as the absolute zero is approached. The melting-pressure curve shows a peculiarity at the lowest temperatures; its gradient changes very rapidly in the neighbourhood of the lambda point under pressure (1·78° K.). At a temperature just above this, the gradient of the melting-pressure curve is about 34 atmos./deg., and just below the lambda point under pressure the gradient is only 7 atmos./deg. Thus, at this temperature, the melting-pressure curve very rapidly becomes more nearly parallel to the temperature axis, that is, its gradient approaches zero much more rapidly than would otherwise be the case. If p is the pressure at which liquid and solid helium (isotope 4) are in equilibrium at a temperature T, equation (23) of Chapter XVI is

$$\frac{dp}{dT} = \frac{s_L - s_s}{v_L - v_s}, \qquad \ldots \ldots \quad (14)$$

where s_L and s_s are the entropies, and v_L and v_s are the specific volumes of the liquid and the solid respectively. The behaviour of the melting-pressure curve corresponds to the vanishing of the entropy difference between the solid and the liquid as the absolute zero is approached.†

Recent measurements by Simon and Swenson ‡ have shown how rapid is the flattening of the melting-pressure curve of helium in the neighbourhood of the lambda point. Above about 2° K., dp/dT varies approximately as $T^{0.55}$ (see Chapter V, Section 15). It should be noted that this vanishes with T, but more slowly even than linearly.§ At

* W. H. Keesom, *Leiden Comm.*, No. 184b (1926); W. H. Keesom and A. P. Keesom, *ibid.*, No. 224e (1933); Simon and Swenson, private communication (1949); see also Chapter V, Section 13 and fig. 5.8.

† Kaischew and Simon, *Nature*, Vol. 133, p. 460 (1934).

‡ F. E. Simon and C. A. Swenson, *Nature*, Vol. 165, p. 829 (1950).

§ The rate at which entropy differences vanish in the approach to absolute zero has been discussed by Schottky, *Naturwiss.*, Vol. 31, p. 400 (1943).

the lambda point this variation changes strikingly until below $1.4°$ K. dp/dT varies as T^7. The change in the behaviour of dp/dT can be seen in fig. 19.4, which is reproduced from the article by Simon and Swenson. This very rapid vanishing, as the temperature falls, of the difference of entropy between the liquid and the solid provides a striking proof of the third law. There is no more conclusive experimental verification of the third law of thermodynamics than that provided by the solid-liquid transition in helium at low temperatures.

For the entropy difference between the spatially disordered liquid and the crystalline solid to vanish, the liquid necessarily undergoes a phase transition to an ordered state, the order being one in momentum

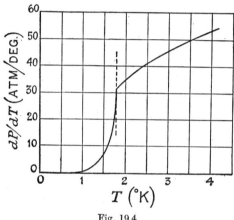

Fig. 19.4

space (see Section 2 of Chapter XVII). It is at this transition that the melting-pressure curve flattens out so that its gradient, and consequently the difference in entropy between the liquid and the solid, approaches zero, much more rapidly than would otherwise be the case, as the temperature approaches the absolute zero, in fact, from about $1.8°$ K. It is important to note that this behaviour is not simply a property of the system at $T = 0$, but in the neighbourhood of absolute zero. A transition to an ordered liquid state must be characteristic of any substance which remains liquid under its equilibrium vapour pressure to however low a value its temperature is reduced.* This is the fundamental significance of the low-temperature modification of the liquid helium isotope of mass 4. In this connexion, the third law of thermodynamics describes the macroscopic behaviour at low temperatures of a quantum statistical system which cannot be

* F. E. Simon, *Nature*, Vol. 133, p. 529 (1934); A. R. Miller, *ibid.*, Vol. 164, p. 325 (1949); F. E. Simon and C. A. Swenson, *ibid.*, Vol. 165, p. 829 (1950).

solidified under its own vapour pressure. For such a system, the third law implies the *existence* of a phase transition to an ordered liquid state, although it cannot describe the *character* and *properties* of the ordered state, nor specify the order of the transition.

Thus, the behaviour of dp/dT along the melting-pressure curve of the helium isotope of mass 4 as the temperature approaches the absolute zero implies that the entropy difference between the solid and liquid vanishes in the neighbourhood of $T = 0$. If this were not so, it would be possible to reach the absolute zero by means of volume changes of condensed helium. Furthermore, the rate at which the entropy difference vanishes increases very rapidly at the temperature of the phase transition in liquid helium. This indicates that the phase transition in liquid helium is fundamentally of thermodynamical import, and represents the response of the liquid to the requirements of the third law.

7. The Superconducting State.

It has been seen (Chapter XVII, Section 8) that the entropy difference between the normal and the superconducting states of a metal at a given temperature is proportional to the product of the magnetic threshold field at that temperature and its temperature coefficient. From measurements of the magnetic field necessary to destroy superconductivity at different temperatures, the magnetic threshold curve for the transition from the superconducting to the normal state can be determined. Using equation (20) of Chapter XVII, the entropy difference between the two states can be calculated. In all the metals which have been investigated, the gradient of the critical field curve falls as the temperature falls, so that the difference in entropy between the two states decreases. Further, as the temperature approaches the absolute zero, the gradient of the threshold curve approaches zero, so that the entropy difference between the two states vanishes in the limit. If this were not so, it would be possible to reach the absolute zero by an adiabatic reversible transition from the superconducting to the normal state.

8. Adiabatic Demagnetization.

We have already seen (Chapter V, Section 16) that there is a difference in entropy between the state of a paramagnetic salt in a magnetic field and its state in zero external field. In fact, the entropy at a given temperature when the salt is in a magnetic field is the same as that at a lower temperature in zero field. This is the basis of the method of adiabatic demagnetization for reaching low temperatures. If, however, these differences in entropy persisted for temperatures down to the absolute zero, it could have been reached without difficulty. Even at a temperature as high as 1° K., a field of about 100 gauss would produce a change of entropy of the order of magnitude of that due to the lattice vibrations. Thus, starting at a temperature of 1° K., absolute zero could be reached by an adiabatic demagnetization. All such experiments have shown, however, that even demagnetization from fields of forty or fifty thousand gauss does not make it possible to reach other than finite, though very low, temperatures. This indicates that as the temperature falls the entropy difference between the two states falls and approaches zero as the absolute zero is approached.

9. Each of the low-temperature processes which has been examined provides evidence that the entropy difference between the two possible states of the particular system considered vanishes as the absolute zero is approached. Thus, each provides a demonstration of the validity of the third law of thermodynamics. Each of these processes indicates in a very direct way that the third law of thermodynamics implies the unattainability of the absolute zero; and this can be regarded as a very convenient and comprehensive statement of the third law.

CHAPTER XX

Radiation

1. There are three methods by which the transfer of heat takes place: conduction, convection, and radiation. The first two require the presence of matter, while radiation takes place independently of it. It is the method by which heat reaches the earth from the sun. The fact that at an eclipse the heat and the light of the sun are cut off simultaneously indicates that radiant heat and light travel through space with the same velocity.

This suggests that radiant heat is of the same nature as light. Further evidence for this view is found in the fact that, if we pass the light from the sun through a prism of quartz or of rock salt (glass does not allow radiant heat to pass through it to any considerable extent) and examine the spectrum so produced with an instrument sensitive to heat (see Sections 3–5), we find that the spectrum extends beyond the red visible region. We conclude that the apparent difference between radiant heat and light is due only to our eyes.

Our study of radiant heat or of radiation therefore includes a study of light, but from a different point of view from that adopted in optics. We shall be concerned with radiation regarded as a flow of energy, and with the laws which govern its emission and absorption.

Instruments for the Detection and Measurement of Radiant Heat

2. There are three different types of instrument which can be used to detect or measure radiant heat.* They are (1) instruments of the bolometer type, (2) thermopiles, including the Boys radio-micrometer, (3) instruments of the type of Crookes's radiometer.

3. Bolometers.

The bolometer, which depends on the change of electrical resistance with temperature, was invented by Langley † in 1881. The apparatus has been improved by Abbot ‡ of the Mount Wilson observatory.

---

* For the instruments used to measure radiant heat in solar physics and in astrophysics, see *A Dict. of Applied Physics*, Vol. 3, pp. 699–719 (Macmillan, 1923); also Section 23.

† Langley, *Proc. Amer. Acad. Arts and Sciences*, Vol. 16, p. 342 (1881).

‡ Abbot, *Annals of the Astrophysical Observatory*, Vol. 2, p. 28 (1908).

The radiation falls on a fine strip of platinum 12 mm. long, 0·06 mm. wide, and 0·005 mm. thick. The strip is blackened in camphor smoke. This strip is in one arm of a Wheatstone bridge, and a similar strip which is sheltered from the radiation is in the opposite arm. The object of this symmetrical arrangement is to eliminate effects due to change in the temperature of the apparatus surrounding the receiving surface. The other two arms of the bridge consist of coils. The fine platinum strips may be prepared by soldering a piece of platinum foil to a considerably thicker piece of silver foil, and rolling the whole out until the platinum has the required thickness. A piece of the composite foil is then soldered to contacts mounted on a suitable frame, and the solder joints covered with a protecting film of lacquer. The silver is then dissolved from the exposed part with nitric acid, leaving the fine platinum strip.

4. Thermopiles.

A thermopile consists of a number of thermocouples connected in series. The radiation falls on one set of junctions, and the other set is protected from it. The electromotive force set up is measured. This type of instrument has been considerably developed by the work of Coblentz.* The thermocouples are usually made of bismuth and silver.

Under this head we may class the extremely sensitive instrument designed by Boys † called the radio-micrometer, which has but a single hot junction. Its distinctive feature is that it acts as its own galvanometer. Two very thin bars, one of antimony and the other of bismuth,‡ are soldered to a heat-receiving disc or strip two or three square millimetres in area. This is the hot junction. The other ends of the bars are soldered to the two ends of a copper loop and are protected from the radiation. Thus a complete circuit is formed. The copper loop is suspended in the field of a permanent magnet by a quartz fibre, which gives a very delicate control, so that the instrument is very sensitive. Between the quartz fibre and the copper loop is a fine glass rod or tube to which a small mirror is attached. The movements of the instrument are measured by observing the light reflected from the mirror with the usual lamp and scale arrangement. The object of the glass rod is to protect the thermocouple circuit against conduction of heat from the mirror. The sensitiveness is lost if there is any magnetic control. Since the thermocouple wires are magnetic,

* Coblentz, *Bull. Bur. of Standards*, Vol. 9, p. 7 (1913); Vol. 11, pp. 131, 613 (1915); Vol. 17, p. 725 (1922). See also Burger and van Cittert, *Zeits. f. Physik*, Vol. 66, p. 210 (1930); Cartwright, *Rev. Sci. Instr.*, Vol. 1, p. 592 (1930); Firestone, *Rev. Sci. Instr.*, Vol. 1, p. 630 (1930).

† For a detailed account of the method of constructing a radio-micrometer, see Boys, *A Dict. of App. Physics*, Vol. 3, p. 720 (Macmillan, 1923).

‡ Greater sensitiveness can be obtained by using suitable alloys of these metals; see Boys, *loc. cit.*, and also Witt, *Phys. Zeits.*, Vol. 21, p. 374 (1920).

they are placed as far as possible from the magnet and are surrounded by a protecting mass of soft iron. The copper circuit must be made non-magnetic. A method of doing this has been devised by Witt.* Ordinary copper wire is paramagnetic and electrolytic copper is diamagnetic. A loop of ordinary copper wire is taken and placed in nitric acid until it is nearly all dissolved away. On this slightly paramagnetic base diamagnetic electrolytic copper is deposited until the resultant loop is non-magnetic.

5. Radiometers.

Crookes discovered that a vane suspended in a partial vacuum and exposed to radiation on one side was acted on by a force, the nature of which has been explained in Chapter III, Section 22. The well-known Crookes radiometer depends on this force for its action.

Nichols has modified the Crookes radiometer and has made of it an instrument of precision. The vanes of very thin mica, blackened, are attached to the ends of an arm and suspended by a quartz fibre. One of the vanes is exposed to the radiation and the other is shielded. A small mirror is attached in order to measure the deflection.

Experiments to elucidate the details of the theory of the radiometer have been carried out by many investigators.†

General Theory of Emission and Absorption

6. Prévost's Theory of Exchanges.

Let us consider two bodies A and B, of which A is the hotter. The result of radiation between the two bodies is that the temperature of A falls while that of B rises; in other words, that heat is transferred from A to B by radiation. Prévost of Geneva pointed out in 1792 that the transfer must be regarded as a *net* transfer; that is, that each body radiates energy to and absorbs energy from the other. The hotter body radiates more energy than it absorbs, while the colder one absorbs more than it radiates.

Similarly, if a number of bodies all at the same temperature are enclosed in a space impervious to heat, each body continuously absorbs energy from and emits energy to the surrounding medium. The two processes balance each other exactly so that the temperature of each and all of the bodies remains constant.

This has an important practical application in thermometry. If a thermometer is so placed in a medium that it can radiate heat to surrounding bodies not at the same temperature as the medium, the temperature registered by the thermo-

---

* Witt, *loc. cit.*; see also Kapitza, *Proc. Roy. Soc.*, A, Vol. 102, p. 48 (1922).

† See Brüche and Littwin, *Zeits. f. Physik*, Vol. 67, p. 333 (1931), who give a summary of all earlier work and obtain many interesting results. For the physical basis of the theory, see Einstein, *Zeits. f. Physik*, Vol 27, p. 1 (1924).

meter is not necessarily that of the medium. This shows the importance of jacketing with steam the vessel containing the thermometer, as in the ordinary hypsometer, or of providing the thermometer with radiation shields, as in determining the sulphur point.

7. Emission and Absorption.

Some simple experiments with apparatus designed by Leslie throw considerable light on the processes of emission and absorption. For the emission experiments a Leslie cube is used. This is a cubical iron vessel which can be rotated about a vertical axis. The different faces are coated with different materials. One is blackened, another is highly polished, another is covered with paper, and another is left unpolished.

Fig. 20.1

The cube is filled with hot water, and the faces are turned successively towards some delicate detector of radiant heat. It is found that much more heat is radiated from the blackened surface than from any of the others, and that least heat is radiated from the highly polished surface. We describe this result by saying that a blackened surface has a high emissive power, and that a highly polished surface has a low emissive power.

For the absorption experiments the apparatus shown in fig. 20.1 is used. The glass bulbs C and D, which are the same size, are connected by a U-tube containing some non-volatile liquid such as sulphuric acid. The apparatus is mounted on a suitable stand. When the bulbs are at the same temperature the liquid stands at the same height in both sides of the U-tube. The bulb D is blackened, and C is covered with some highly polished substance such as silver foil. If the bulbs are placed at equal distances from a source of radiant heat, such as a vessel containing hot water, it is found that the liquid in the side D moves downwards. This shows that under similar conditions the blackened surface absorbs more heat than the polished surface. We describe this result by saying that a blackened surface has a high absorptive power, and that a polished surface has a low absorptive power.

A comparison of the results obtained with the two sets of apparatus gives the *qualitative* result that *surfaces with a high emissive power have a high absorptive power, and surfaces with a low emissive power have a low absorptive power.*

We shall now obtain a quantitative relation between the emissive and the absorptive power of a body.

8. Kirchhoff's Law.

If an isotropic body at temperature T emits into a vacuum in unit time per unit area an amount $e_\lambda d\lambda$ of energy in the form of radiation whose wave-length lies between the limits λ and $\lambda + d\lambda$, we shall define

e_λ as the *emissive power* of the body at temperature T for radiation of wave-length λ. We shall assume that e_λ depends only on the surface and its temperature and not on the temperature of surrounding bodies or on the radiation that falls on it. This assumption includes Prévost's law of exchanges. Phenomena such as phosphorescence which are not steady state phenomena are excluded. The radiation specified by the assumption is called *temperature radiation*.

If a given amount of radiant energy whose wave-length lies between the limits λ and $\lambda + d\lambda$ falls from a vacuum on an isotropic body at temperature T, and if a fraction a_λ of this energy is absorbed by the body, the remaining fraction $(1 - a_\lambda)$ being reflected or transmitted, we shall define a_λ as the *absorptive power* of the body at temperature T for radiation of wave-length λ.

We have to find a relation between e_λ and a_λ for a given body at a given temperature.

The first step is to show that the density of radiation of a given wave-length in a vacuous space, which is enclosed by walls maintained at a given temperature, depends only on the temperature and not on the nature of the walls or of any bodies that may be present in the enclosure.

Consider the radiation in the enclosure whose wave-length lies between the limits λ and $\lambda + d\lambda$. Equilibrium is established when the amount of radiation of this wave-length absorbed by the walls per second is equal to the amount emitted. The amount absorbed by the walls depends on the density of radiation of the given wave-length in the enclosure, and this density adjusts itself until the equilibrium condition is reached.

Let us suppose that we have two enclosures A and B of different materials, whose walls are at the same temperature T. We suppose further that the density of radiation whose wave-length lies between the limits λ and $\lambda + d\lambda$ depends on the nature of the walls as well as on the temperature, and that it is greater in A than in B. Let us now establish communication between A and B through a screen which is transparent only to radiation whose wave-length lies between the limits λ and $\lambda + d\lambda$. More of this radiation falls on the A side of the screen than on the B side; the net result is that A loses and B gains a certain amount of radiation of this wave-length. After a finite amount of radiation has been transferred, we close the screen. The density in B of the radiation of the given wave-length is greater than the equilibrium density, and the excess is absorbed by the walls. This causes their temperature to rise. Similarly the temperature of the walls of A falls. B can now be used as the source and A as the sink of heat in a heat engine, and work can be obtained while the bodies are being brought to the same temperature. The process can be repeated as often as we please, and is a contradition of the second law of thermodynamics. The assumption on which the possibility of its occurring is based is therefore false. We therefore conclude that *the density of radiation whose wave-length lies between the limits λ and $\lambda + d\lambda$ in an enclosure at temperature T depends only on T, and not on the nature of the walls of the enclosure or of any body that may be present in the enclosure.* The radiation inside an enclosure at temperature T is called *complete radiation*, and we may assign the temperature T to the radiation.

We now return to the problem of determining the relation between the emissive and absorptive powers of an isotropic body at temperature T. We suppose the body inside an enclosure at temperature T. The amount of radiant energy whose wave-length lies between the limits λ and $\lambda + d\lambda$, falling on unit area of the surface of the body in unit time, depends only on the density of radiation of this wave-length in the enclosure, and this depends only on the temperature of the enclosure and not on the nature of the body. We shall call this amount of radiant energy dQ. If a_λ is the absorptive power of the body for radiation of this wave-length, the amount absorbed per unit area by the body per second is

$$a_\lambda \, dQ.$$

The rest, $(1 - a_\lambda)dQ$, is reflected or transmitted. If e_λ is the emissive power of the body, the amount of energy of the given wave-length emitted by the body per unit area per second is

$$e_\lambda \, d\lambda.$$

The amount of radiant energy of the given wave-length which is restored to the enclosure by emission from the body must equal the amount absorbed. Otherwise the presence of the body would disturb the radiation equilibrium of the enclosure We have therefore

$$a_\lambda \, dQ = e_\lambda \, d\lambda,$$

or
$$\frac{e_\lambda}{a_\lambda} = \frac{dQ}{d\lambda}. \qquad \cdots \cdots \quad (1)$$

Since $dQ/d\lambda$ depends only on the temperature,

$$\frac{e_\lambda}{a_\lambda} = \text{constant} \qquad \cdots \cdots \quad (2)$$

for a given temperature. That is, *the ratio of the emissive power to the absorptive power for radiation of a given wave-length is the same for all bodies at the same temperature.* This is called *Kirchhoff's law.*

If we are dealing with a non-isotropic body, it is necessary to specify the direction of polarization of the radiation which is emitted or absorbed. The radiation in the enclosure must be isotropic, otherwise by using a screen which transmits only light polarized in one direction we can establish a difference of temperature between the two enclosures A and B considered above. Kirchhoff's law follows for this case exactly as for the case of an isotropic body. It is stated as follows: *The ratio of the emissive power to the absorptive power for radiation of a given wavelength polarized in a given direction is the same for all bodies at the same temperature.*

We have proved Kirchhoff's law for bodies in an enclosure. By Prévost's law of exchanges the radiation emitted by a body depends only on its temperature and not on its surroundings. Kirchhoff's law therefore applies under all conditions, and, if a body absorbs a given type of radiation strongly, it also emits a similar type of radiation strongly. Thus red glass, which appears red because it absorbs green light strongly, glows with a green light if heated to a high temperature. Green glass, which absorbs red light strongly, glows with a red light if heated to a high temperature. Tourmaline strongly absorbs light polarized in a given plane and is transparent to light polarized in a plane at right angles to this. If heated to a high temperature it emits plane polarized light, polarized in the same plane as the light which it absorbs.

In the above derivation of Kirchhoff's law we have taken no account of the fact that the emissive and absorptive powers of a body may depend on the angle of emergence or incidence of the radiation. For a detailed treatment of the case when this is taken into account, see Planck, *Wärmestrahlung*, 5th edition, pp. 23–49 (Barth, 1923).

9. The Full Radiator (Black Body) and Full (Black-body) Radiation.

The above considerations led Kirchhoff to define a *perfectly black body* or a *full radiator* as a body which at all temperatures absorbs completely all the radiation falling on it. For a full radiator

$$a_\lambda = 1$$

for all wave-lengths.

Substituting this value for a_λ in equation (1), we obtain the important result that the amount of energy emitted in a second in the form of radiation of a given wave-length from unit area of the surface of a full radiator at temperature T is equal to the amount of energy of radiation of the same wave-length that falls in 1 second on unit area of any body placed in an enclosure at the same temperature T. Thus, by studying the radiation emitted from a full radiator at a given temperature, we can learn all about the radiation inside an enclosure at the same temperature. If it were not for this fact, the radiation inside an enclosure would be entirely inaccessible to observation. For this reason *complete* or *full radiation* is sometimes called *black-body radiation*.

A full radiator is realized in practice as follows. Consider a large body A (fig. 20.2) maintained at a uniform temperature, and having a small opening B. Provided the inside of the walls of A are not perfectly reflecting, the opening B, if sufficiently small, is perfectly black. A ray of radiation falling on B passes inside the chamber and is reflected so many times on the inside surface before it again reaches B that it is completely absorbed. In practice the inside of A is usually coated with some black substance so that one reflection alone is sufficient to absorb practically all the radiation. In accurate work a small correction is necessary for the departure from perfect blackness with a hole of finite size.*

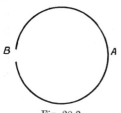

Fig. 20.2

10. The Principle of Detailed Balancing.

Kirchhoff's law has recently been extended and applied not only to the processes of the emission and absorption of radiation, but also to the processes which occur when atomic and electronic collisions take place. Such processes may or may not involve the simultaneous emission or absorption of radiation. The law so extended is called the *principle of detailed balancing*. It may be stated as follows.†

Every process of transformation or exchange of energy which occurs in a system in thermodynamical equilibrium is invariably accompanied by an analogous reverse process, and the two processes occur with equal frequency.

No formal proof of the principle can be given, but it accounts in a very simple and complete way for the general facts concerning systems in equilibrium. The laws of thermodynamics are believed to be of universal validity, and these laws lead to the result established in Section 8, that the distribution of radiant energy in an enclosure at a given temperature is independent of the nature of the matter present in the enclosure. Further, the laws of statistical mechanics, although not established with such certainty as the laws of thermodynamics, are, as far as they are developed, believed to be of universal validity. For example, the distribution of velocity among the free electrons in a space at a given tempera-ture is believed to be given by definite laws, and is independent of the nature of the matter present in the space. On the other hand, the *detailed* processes of emission and absorption of radiation or of electrons depend on the particular nature of the atoms and molecules present in the enclosure. If the detailed balance of such processes, postulated in the principle of detailed balancing, is maintained, the general balance required by thermodynamics and statistical mechanics is automatically maintained, whatever the nature of the matter in the enclosure. Without postulating the detailed balance, it seems impossible to account for the general balance.

The application of the principle of detailed balancing has led to the discovery of new processes occurring in nature. Klein and Rosseland applied the principle to the collisions between atoms and free electrons, and pointed out the necessity

---

* See Wien and Lummer, *Wied. Ann.*, Vol. 56, p. 451 (1895); Buckley, *Phil. Mag.*, Vol. 6, p. 447 (1928). For a slit-shaped opening, see Liebmann, *Zeits. f. techn. Physik*, Vol. 12, p. 433 (1931).

† See Fowler, *Phil. Mag.*, Vol. 47, pp. 257, 416 (1924); *Proc. Camb. Phil. Soc.*, Vol. 22, p. 253 (1924). In these papers the principle is applied to a particular problem and references are given to the earlier work. See also Eddington, *The Internal Constitution of the Stars*, p. 45 (Cambridge University Press, 1926).

for the existence of " superelastic " collisions or collisions of the second kind. Such collisions are the reverse of ordinary inelastic collisions, which occur when an electron with sufficient velocity collides with an atom and causes an electron in the atom to move from a given stationary state to one with higher energy. There is no emission or absorption of radiation in the process, the energy being supplied at the expense of the colliding electron. The reverse process, or super-elastic collision, is one in which an electron collides with an excited atom. The atom goes back to normal without the emission of radiation, and the whole of the superfluous energy goes to increase the kinetic energy of the colliding electron.

The Stefan-Boltzmann Law

We shall now obtain a relation between the total density of radiation in an enclosed space and the temperature.

11. Thermodynamical Deduction.

Suppose the radiation is enclosed in an evacuated space with perfectly reflecting walls and provided with a perfectly reflecting moving piston. The object of assuming perfectly reflecting walls is that no exchange of heat may take place between the radiation and the walls, so that the thermal capacity of the latter does not enter into the calculation. We shall suppose, however, that at one point in the wall there is a small speck of ordinary matter, by means of which heat from outside can reach the radiation. If T is the temperature of this speck of matter, the radiation in the enclosure will be that corresponding to temperature T. The speck of matter is supposed to be so small that its heat capacity can be neglected in comparison with that of the radiation.

If E is the energy density of the radiation, E is a function of T only. Maxwell's electromagnetic theory of light shows that isotropic radiation of density E exerts a pressure p given by

$$p = \tfrac{1}{3}E. \qquad \cdots \cdots \cdots (3)$$

If V is the volume of the enclosure, the total energy of the radiation in it is EV.

Let us now suppose that we allow a small amount of heat dQ to flow into the enclosure from outside, and at the same time allow the volume to change by a small amount dV so that the temperature, and therefore E, changes by an infinitesimal amount. The change is to be reversible but neither adiabatic nor isothermal. dQ is equal to the increase in the internal energy EV *plus* the external work done, $p\,dV$, that is,

$$dQ = d(EV) + p\,dV = (E + p)\,dV + V\,dE. \quad \cdots (4)$$

The change in entropy dS is equal to dQ/T, that is,

$$dS = \frac{E + p}{T}\,dV + \frac{V}{T}\,dE.$$

But dS is a perfect differential. Therefore

$$\left(\frac{\partial S}{\partial V}\right)_E = \frac{E + p}{T}$$

and

$$\left(\frac{\partial S}{\partial E}\right)_V = \frac{V}{T}.$$

Differentiating the first of these equations with respect to E, and the second with respect to V, and equating the results, we obtain

$$\left(\frac{\partial}{\partial E}\right)_V \left(\frac{E + p}{T}\right) = \left(\frac{\partial}{\partial V}\right)_E \left(\frac{V}{T}\right).$$

Putting $p = \frac{1}{3}E$, and carrying out the differentiation, we obtain

$$\frac{dE}{E} = 4\frac{dT}{T}.$$

Integrating this, we have

$$\log E = 4 \log T + \text{constant},$$

or $\hspace{4em} E = aT^4, \hspace{1em} \ldots \ldots \ldots \hspace{1em} (5)$

where a is a constant.

We shall now obtain the relation between the temperature and the volume in an adiabatic change. In equation (4) we substitute the value of p from equation (3), the value of E from equation (5), and we put $dQ = 0$, obtaining

$$\frac{dV}{V} = -3\frac{dT}{T}.$$

Integrating this, we have

$$\log V = -3 \log T + \text{constant},$$

or $\hspace{4em} VT^3 = \text{constant}. \hspace{1em} \ldots \ldots \hspace{1em} (6)$

12. The Total Emissive Power of a Full Radiator.

In Section 9 we have shown that the amount of energy emitted from unit area of a full radiator in 1 second is equal to the amount of energy falling from one side on unit area of any body placed in an enclosure at temperature T. We shall now deduce the value of this quantity from equation (5).

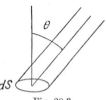

Fig. 20.3

If a small area dS (fig. 20.3) is placed in a space containing isotropic radiation, the amount of radiation which crosses dS in a direction making an angle θ with the normal to dS is proportional to the "opening" presented by dS to the radiation; that is, it is proportional to

$$dS \cos \theta.$$

Now consider the radiation propagated through any one point in dS from below to above. The amount propagated into a small solid angle $d\omega$ is proportional to $d\omega$. Consider the small solid angle lying between the directions θ and $\theta + d\theta$, and ϕ and $\phi + d\phi$, where ϕ specifies the direction of the radiation in azimuth. For this solid angle, $d\omega$ is given by

$$d\omega = \sin\theta\, d\theta\, d\phi.$$

The amount of radiation propagated through any point in the area in directions lying between θ and $\theta + d\theta$, and ϕ and $\phi + d\phi$, is therefore proportional to

$$\sin\theta\, d\theta\, d\phi.$$

Combining the results of the last two paragraphs, we obtain for the amount of radiant energy propagated in time dt through the whole area dS in directions lying between θ and $\theta + d\theta$, and ϕ and $\phi + d\phi$,

$$K\, d\omega \cos\theta\, dS\, dt, \qquad \ldots \ldots \ldots \text{(7)}$$

or
$$K \sin\theta \cos\theta\, d\theta\, d\phi\, dS\, dt, \qquad \ldots \ldots \text{(8)}$$

where K is a constant.

The total amount of energy propagated through the area dS from below to above in time dt is obtained by integrating the expression (8) from $\theta = 0$ to $\theta = \pi/2$, and from $\phi = 0$ to $\phi = 2\pi$. That is, it is given by the expression

$$K\, dS\, dt \int_0^{2\pi} d\phi \int_0^{\pi/2} \sin\theta \cos\theta\, d\theta$$

or
$$\pi K\, dS\, dt. \qquad \ldots \ldots \ldots \ldots \text{(9)}$$

We must now obtain the relation between the constant K and E, the density of the radiation. Consider a very small volume v inside the enclosure (fig. 20.4). From some point O inside v, draw a sphere of radius r, which is large compared with the linear dimensions of v. Each ray of radiation that passes through the volume v must come from some point on the sphere.

Consider the radiation which passes through v coming from an infinitesimal area dS on the sphere. The linear dimensions of dS are to be taken as infinitely small compared with those of v. Divide the small solid angle subtended by v at dS into a large number of infinitesimal cones each of solid angle $d\omega$, one of which is shown in the figure. If f is the area of cross-section of one of the divisions at a distance r from dS, we have

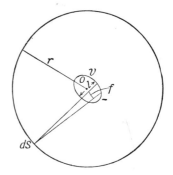

Fig. 20.4

$$d\omega = f/r^2.$$

If l is the length of the infinitesimal cone which is cut off by the volume v, a ray takes a time τ, given by

$$\tau = l/c,$$

to travel through the volume v; c is the velocity of light. The energy coming from dS which is at any instant contained in the part of the infinitesimal cone cut off by the volume v is obtained by putting $dt = \tau = l/c$, and $d\omega = f/r^2$ in equation (7). As the linear dimensions of v are small compared with r, $\cos\theta = 1$ and this gives

$$K\frac{dS}{cr^2}fl.$$

The amount of energy coming from dS, which is at any instant contained in the whole volume v, is obtained by summing this expression for all the infinitesimal cones, and is therefore equal to

$$K\frac{dS}{cr^2}\Sigma fl,$$

since $K\,dS/cr^2$ has the same value for all the infinitesimal cones drawn from dS. It will be seen from the figure that Σfl is equal to v. The above expression is therefore equal to

$$K\frac{dS}{cr^2}v.$$

To obtain the total amount of energy contained in the volume v at any instant we have simply to integrate this expression over the whole sphere of which dS is an element. This gives

$$\frac{4\pi K}{c}v.$$

Therefore, if E is the energy density, we have

$$E = \frac{4\pi K}{c}. \qquad \ldots \ldots \ldots \quad (10)$$

This is the required relation between E and K for isotropic radiation.

By equation (9) the amount of energy which in 1 second falls on unit area of a body placed in an enclosure at temperature T is equal to πK. Substituting the value of K from equation (10), we obtain

$$\pi K = \tfrac{1}{4}Ec. \qquad \ldots \ldots \ldots \quad (11)$$

By section 9 this is the amount of energy emitted from unit area of a full radiator in 1 second.

Using the value for E given by equation (5), we obtain for the total emissive power of a full radiator

$$\tfrac{1}{4}acT^4 \quad \text{or} \quad \sigma T^4, \qquad \ldots \ldots \ldots \quad (12)$$

where

$$\sigma = \tfrac{1}{4}ac. \qquad \ldots \ldots \ldots \quad (13)$$

This is called the *Stefan-Boltzmann law*, and σ is called the *Stefan-Boltzmann constant*. If the value of σ is measured, the value of a can be deduced, since the value of c is known. Thus from a measurement of the Stefan-Boltzmann constant we can determine the density of the total radiation in an enclosure at any given temperature.

13. The Experimental Proof of the Stefan-Boltzmann Law and the Determination of the Stefan-Boltzmann Constant.

The essential parts of the apparatus for the direct determination of the Stefan-Boltzmann constant (the same apparatus is used to prove the Stefan-Boltzmann law) are shown diagrammatically in fig. 20.5. The radiation from the radiator, which is a full radiator and is maintained at a high temperature, passes through the small hole cd in the screen and falls on the receiver ab. The receiver is also a full radiator and absorbs all the radiation falling on it. The amount of radiation falling on the receiver in 1 second is measured. The principle of the method is as follows.

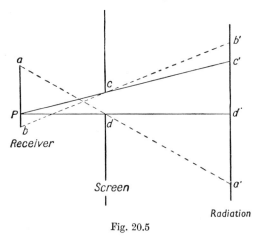

Fig. 20.5

In the first place it is essential that the lines ad and bc produced intersect the radiator. If this condition is fulfilled, the radiation received by any and every point on the receiver is the same as it would be if the radiator had the same area as the aperture cd in the screen and were situated in the plane of the aperture. To prove this, consider the radiation received by an infinitesimal area at the point P on the receiver. As far as the point P is concerned, the only part of the radiator which is effective is that represented by $c'd'$. If A_1 is the area of cd, and A_1' that of $c'd'$,

$$\frac{A_1}{A_1'} = \frac{(Pc)^2}{(Pc')^2};$$

that is, the areas are proportional to the squares of their distances from the point P. But the intensity of radiation from a source falls off inversely as the square of the distance from the source. Since it is also proportional to the area of the source, the increase in area compensates for the increased distance, and the radiation at P from the surface $c'd'$ is the same as the radiation from a surface of the size of cd situated in the plane of the screen would be.

The experiment consists essentially in measuring the difference between the amount of radiation received by the receiver, (1) when the hole in the screen is closed by a *black* water-cooled shutter at temperature T_1, and (2) when the hole in the shutter is open.

If Q is the measured difference between the amount of energy received by the receiver per second with cd open and closed, D is the distance of the receiver from cd, A_1 is the area of the aperture cd, and A_2 that of the receiver; and if T_1 is the temperature of the shutter and T_2 that of the radiator,

$$Q = \frac{\sigma(T_2{}^4 - T_1{}^4)A_1A_2}{\pi D^2}. \qquad \ldots \ldots \quad (14)$$

This follows directly from equation (7) by putting

$$K = \sigma T^4/\pi \quad \text{(from equations (10), (5), and (13))},$$
$$d\omega = A_2/D^2, \quad \cos\theta = 1, \quad dS = A_1, \quad dt = 1 \text{ second}.$$

Equation (14) can be used to determine the value of σ. For the proof of the Stefan-Boltzmann law it is only necessary to show that Q is proportional to $(T_2{}^4 - T_1{}^4)$ for various values of T_2.

Actually equation (14) is strictly accurate only if the linear dimensions of all the apertures and surfaces are small compared with the distances between them. In practice, this condition can be fulfilled approximately.*

We shall now consider the actual apparatus used by Coblentz.†

(a) The screen (fig. 20.5) consisted of two water-cooled tanks 25 cm. in diameter. The one X which was nearer the radiator was 1·5 cm. thick, and the more important one Y which was nearer the receiver was 3 cm. thick. The hole in Y (*cd* in fig. 20.5) was an accurately cut knife-edge hole in a brass disc. Various discs were used with holes varying in diameter from 2 to 5·5 mm. The shutter which closed this hole was water-cooled and slid in guides on the side of the screen Y remote from the receiver. Thus, when the shutter was opened there was no change in the disposition of the screens facing the receiver except the opening of the hole *cd*. The surface of the shutter was blackened. Its temperature, T_1 in equation (14), was determined by a mercury thermometer in the water flowing through it. A slight departure from full-radiator conditions in the shutter was unimportant since $T_1{}^4$ was very small compared with $T_2{}^4$.

(b) The radiator is shown in fig. 20.6. It consisted of three concentric porcelain tubes, A, B, and C. The inner tube A was uniformly wound with a platinum ribbon 0·02 mm. thick. The ribbon was 20 mm. wide in the centre and tapered to 10 mm. wide at the ends. Thus extra heating was provided at the ends to make up for the heat lost by radiation. The middle tube B was wound with a platinum ribbon 10 mm. wide and 0·02 mm. in thickness. The ends were wound more closely than the middle. By regulating the current through these two platinum strips the interior of the tube A could be heated to a uniform tempera-

* For the small corrections due to departure from this condition, see Gerlach, *Ann. d. Physik*, Vol. 38, p. 1 (1912); Christiansen, *Wied. Ann.*, Vol. 19, p. 268 (1883); Keene, *Proc. Roy. Soc.*, A, Vol. 88, p. 49 (1913); Hoare, *Phil. Mag.*, Vol. 13, p. 388 (1932).

† See Coblentz, *A Dict. of Applied Physics,* Vol. 4, p. 541 (Macmillan, 1923). This article contains a complete bibliography.

ture through the greater part of its length.* The walls of A and the front of the
radiating diaphragm d were painted with a mixture of chromium oxide and
cobalt oxide. The actual radiating cavity was between the diaphragms d and a.
The temperature of this cavity was determined by the thermocouple shown in
the figure. At temperatures above 1200° C. the oxide paints become electrically
conducting. The thermocouple was therefore enclosed in a small porcelain tube.
At these high temperatures alternating current should be used in the furnace
windings.

(c) The receiver was a modified Ångström pyrheliometer.† It consisted of
a strip of manganin blackened with lamp black or platinum black. A thermopile,
consisting of a number of elements of bismuth and silver and having a continuous
receiving surface, was placed behind the central part of the manganin receiving
surface and close to it. The thermopile was heated by radiation from the manganin surface. With the aperture cd (fig. 20.5) closed the manganin strip was heated
electrically to the same temperature as it attained when the shutter was open

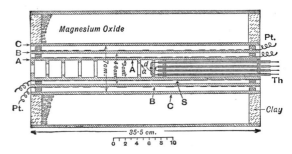

Fig. 20.6

and it was exposed to radiation from the hot radiator. Q in equation (14) was
obtained by measuring the electrical energy supplied. The whole of the surface
of the manganin strip receiver was exposed to the radiation, but measurements
were made only on the central portion between two potential terminals of fine
wire from 0·003 to 0·025 mm. in diameter which accurately defined the length
of the portion on which measurements were made. This procedure eliminated
the effect of losses by conduction along the heavy current terminals.

A blackened manganin strip does not completely absorb all the radiation
which falls on it, and a correction is necessary for this. The amount of diffuse
reflection from the strip was determined by carrying out absorption experiments
both with and without a hemispherical mirror in front of the absorbing surface.
The surface was placed at the centre of curvature of this mirror, and the radiation was admitted through a hole in it. It was found to be inadvisable to use this
" blackening " device in the actual experiments on the determination of the
Stefan-Boltzmann constant, because it introduced complications into the electrical
part of the measurements.

Coblentz obtained the value $\sigma = 5·72 . 10^{-5}$ erg cm.$^{-2}$ sec.$^{-1}$ deg.$^{-4}$.

* See Waidner and Burgess, *Bull. Bur. Stand.*, Vol. 3, p. 163 (1907). For a summary
with complete bibliography of methods of heating furnaces up to 3000° C., see Cohn,
Zeits. f. tech. Physik, Vol. 9, p. 110 (1928).

† Ångström, *Phys. Rev.*, Vol. 1, p. 365 (1893); *Ann. d. Phys.*, Vol. 67, p. 663 (1899).

Hoare * has made a determination by a method similar to that of Coblentz, but using a Callendar radio-balance as receiver.

The radiation was received in a small copper cup 3 mm. in diameter and 8 mm. long, and its heating effect was balanced by the Peltier cooling effect in a thermocouple which was soldered to the bottom of the cup and through which a measured current was passed. The temperature of the cup was measured by a thermopile.

Two such cups mounted in the same enclosure were used in these experiments, in order to compensate for any change in the temperature of the surroundings. The measuring thermopiles of the two cups were connected in opposition and the circuit completed through a sensitive galvanometer. The Peltier junctions soldered to the bottoms of the cups were also connected in opposition and this circuit was completed through a source of electric supply, a variable resistance, some means of measuring the current accurately, and a reversing switch.

One cup of the receiver was exposed to the radiation from the hot full radiator and the current through the Peltier junctions was adjusted so that the temperature difference between the cups (that is, the galvanometer deflection) was as nearly zero as possible. The small residual galvanometer deflection was read. The second cup was then exposed to the radiation and the first one was shielded. At the same time the Peltier current was reversed but unaltered in magnitude. The radiant energy E incident in either cup per second was given by

$$E = 2PC + Ds \text{ microwatts,}$$

where P was the value of the Peltier coefficient in millivolts (for the measurement of P, see below) and C the current in milliamperes passed through the Peltier junctions; D was the change in the galvanometer deflection on transferring the radiation from cup 1 to cup 2, and this was called positive if the deflection was in the direction of the deflection that would have been produced if the radiation had been transferred from cup 1 to cup 2 with no Peltier balancing current; s was the scale sensitivity of the galvanometer and was measured by shielding both cups from radiation and measuring the galvanometer deflection D' when a known current of C' milliamperes passing through the junctions was reversed, s being given by the equation

$$s = 2PC'/D'.$$

The value of P was determined by placing in each cup a small manganin heating coil, the two coils having the same resistance. A measured current was passed through the coil in cup 1 and also through a pair of dummy leads in the other cup so that any heating effect in the leads was compensated. A current C'' was passed through the Peltier junctions so as to make the temperature difference between the cups as small as possible. The same current was now passed through the coil in cup 2 and the Peltier current was reversed. Let W be the heat generated in either coil in microwatts (W could be accurately measured) and let D'' be the change in the galvanometer deflection on transferring the heating from cup 1 to cup 2; then

$$W = 2PC'' + D''s.$$

P was determined from this equation.

This method had the great advantage that both the source and the receiver were full radiators. It was used with the source at 100° C. and at temperatures

* Hoare, *Phil. Mag.*, Vol. 6, p. 828 (1928); Vol. 13, p. 386 (1932); Vol. 14, p. 445 (1932).

between 700° and 1000° C., the latter temperatures being measured with a platinum thermometer. The results obtained at the different temperatures agreed, the mean value being $5.73_6 \cdot 10^{-5}$ erg cm.$^{-2}$ sec.$^{-1}$ deg.$^{-4}$.

We shall now consider another method of determining the value of the Stefan-Boltzmann constant which has been used by Shakespear,[*] Todd [†] (in a slightly modified form), and Westphal.[‡] A small highly polished body of area A is suspended in a large evacuated enclosure. The body is heated electrically to a temperature T, and the walls of the enclosure are maintained at temperature T_0. The energy emitted from the body in 1 second is equal to

$$A \epsilon_1 \sigma T^4,$$

where ϵ_1 is the ratio of the total emissive power of the body to that of a full radiator. ϵ_1 is called the *emissivity* of the body. The density of radiation in the enclosure is that corresponding to the temperature T_0 of the walls, and the amount of energy falling in 1 second on a body of area A placed in the enclosure is $A \sigma T_0^4$. Of this, a fraction ϵ_1 is absorbed (Kirchhoff's law). The net loss of energy per second by radiation is therefore

$$A \epsilon_1 \sigma (T^4 - T_0^4).$$

If $f(T, T_0)$ represents the loss of heat by conduction along the leads the total energy W_1 that must be supplied is given by

$$W_1 = A \epsilon_1 \sigma (T^4 - T_0^4) + f(T, T_0).$$

The experiment is now carried out with all the conditions the same except that the surface of the body is blackened so that its emissivity is ϵ_2. If W_2 is the electrical energy supplied in this case,

$$W_2 = A \epsilon_2 \sigma (T^4 - T_0^4) + f(T, T_0).$$

Subtracting these equations, we obtain

$$\sigma = \frac{W_2 - W_1}{A(\epsilon_2 - \epsilon_1)(T^4 - T_0^4)}.$$

The emissivities ϵ_1 and ϵ_2 are determined by comparing the total emission from the body with that from a full radiator by bringing the bodies in turn in front of some form of radiometer.

The close agreement between the values of the Stefan-Boltzmann constant determined by Coblentz using a high-temperature source, by

---

* Shakespear, *Proc. Roy. Soc.*, A, Vol. 86, p. 180 (1912).

† Todd, *Proc. Roy. Soc.*, A, Vol. 83, p. 19 (1909).

‡ Westphal, *Verh. d. deuts. phys. Ges.*, Vol. 15, p. 897 (1913). For a modification of this method and a very full discussion of possible errors, see Mendenhall, *Phys. Rev.*, Vol. 34, p. 502 (1929).

Hoare using both high- and low-temperature sources, and by Westphal using this method at ordinary temperatures, gives a particularly striking confirmation of the truth of the Stefan-Boltzmann law.

Wien's Displacement Law

14. So far we have considered only the total radiation and have not been concerned with the distribution of the energy among different wave-lengths. We deal with the distribution problem as follows.

(1) We show thermodynamically that, if complete radiation contained in a chamber with perfectly white walls * is compressed adiabatically, the radiation remains complete. The energy density and therefore the temperature of the radiation is changed by the compression.

The proof of this is as follows. Consider the adiabatic compression of an evacuated cylinder with perfectly reflecting walls filled with complete radiation at temperature T. Reflection at the moving piston changes the direction as well as the wave-length of a ray falling on it. This may make the radiation anisotropic. This is avoided by having the walls *perfectly white*, that is, impervious to radiation and reflecting diffusely according to the cosine law. Suppose that the effect of the adiabatic compression is to make the radiation no longer complete, and that it consists of incomplete radiation whose total density is the same as that of complete radiation of temperature T_1. Now introduce a small speck of matter whose thermal capacity is negligibly small compared with that of the radiation in the enclosure and whose temperature is T_1. The radiation is transformed so that it becomes complete, but its total amount is unaltered. This change is irreversible and therefore involves an increase of entropy. Now leave the speck of matter in the enclosure, and expand it adiabatically to its original volume. The work gained depends only on the total energy density and not on its distribution, and is therefore the same as that expended in the compression. The density of the complete radiation is exactly the same at the beginning as at the end. If the speck of matter is removed, the whole system has returned exactly to its original state and its entropy and energy are the same as at the beginning. The changes in the entropy and energy of the speck of matter are infinitesimal. The net result of the process is that we have reversed exactly an irreversible change without doing any work on the system and without any heat leaving or entering it. This is impossible, and therefore the assumption that complete radiation enclosed in an evacuated vessel with perfectly reflecting walls does not remain complete, when it is adiabatically compressed, is false. This is what we had to prove. It will be seen that essentially the proof rests on the fact that the presence of an infinitesimal speck of matter is sufficient to convert any amount of incomplete isotropic radiation into complete radiation with the same total density.

(2) We now calculate from purely mechanical considerations the change in the distribution of energy which is caused by the adiabatic compression of radiation contained in a vessel with perfectly reflecting walls. The change in the temperature is obtained from the Stefan-Boltzmann law connecting the total density and the temperature. We thus obtain

---

* It is important to realize that in a chamber with fixed perfectly white walls *any* distribution of radiation is permanently stable. We use " perfectly white " in the sense introduced by Wien, namely, as impervious to radiation and reflecting the incident radiation diffusely according to the cosine law.

a relation between the distribution of energy among the different wave-lengths at two different temperatures. As we shall see, this enables us to determine the general form of the function expressing the distribution of energy as a function of the wave-length at a given temperature. The calculation is somewhat lengthy and occupies the part of this Section 14 between equations (15a) and (29). The following analysis, ending with equation (15a), does not form part of the main argument; in it we merely deduce an expression for the Doppler effect with which the reader may not be familiar, and which concerns the change in wave-length when radiation is reflected from a moving mirror. We calculate the change in distribution caused by adiabatic compression, using this expression for the Doppler effect.

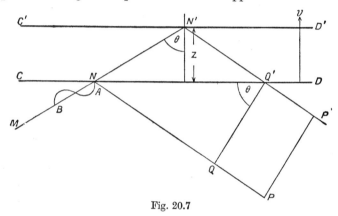

Fig. 20.7

The Doppler effect may be calculated as follows. Consider radiation moving in the direction MN (fig. 20.7), and being reflected at the mirror CD, which moves away from the direction from which the light comes with velocity v perpendicular to its own plane. We consider the reflection of the beginning A and the end B of a wave, and we shall calculate the interval of time between their arrival at P and P' respectively. PP' is perpendicular to NP and $N'P'$. The distance AB is equal to λ, the wave-length of the radiation before reflection.

The time taken for A to reach P is equal to

$$NP/c, \qquad \qquad \text{(i)}$$

where c is the velocity of radiation in the medium.

The time taken for B to reach P' is equal to

$$(\lambda + NN' + N'Q' + Q'P')/c.$$

We have $\qquad NN' = N'Q' = z/\cos\theta,$

and $\qquad Q'P' = QP = NP - 2z \sin^2\theta/\cos\theta.$

The time taken for B to reach P' is therefore

$$\frac{1}{c}\left(NP + \lambda + \frac{2z}{\cos\theta} - \frac{2z\sin^2\theta}{\cos\theta}\right) = \frac{1}{c}(NP + \lambda + 2z\cos\theta). \qquad \text{(ii)}$$

The difference between (ii) and (i) gives the interval of time between the arrival of successive wave beginnings at P and P' respectively as

$$(\lambda + 2z \cos \theta)/c.$$

If ν' is the frequency of the reflected radiation, ν' is equal to the reciprocal of this interval of time, that is,

$$\nu' = \frac{c}{\lambda + 2z \cos \theta}. \qquad \cdots \cdots \cdots \text{(iii)}$$

We must now obtain the value of z, the distance travelled by the mirror in the interval of time between the arrival of A and B at its surface.

Equating the time taken for the mirror to move a distance z and for the light to move from B to N', we have

$$\frac{z}{v} = \frac{\lambda + (z/\cos \theta)}{c}.$$

Thus z is given by

$$z = \frac{\lambda v}{c - (v/\cos \theta)}.$$

Substituting this in (iii), and using $\nu\lambda = c$, we obtain

$$\nu' = \frac{c}{\lambda + \dfrac{2\lambda v \cos \theta}{c - (v/\cos \theta)}} = \frac{\nu}{1 + \dfrac{2v \cos \theta}{c - (v/\cos \theta)}}. \qquad \cdots \text{(iv)}$$

In applications to radiation problems v is always negligibly small compared with c, so that equation (iv) becomes

$$\nu' = \nu\left(1 - \frac{2v \cos \theta}{c}\right), \qquad \cdots \cdots \cdots \text{(15)}$$

or

$$\lambda' = \lambda\left(1 + \frac{2v \cos \theta}{c}\right); \qquad \cdots \cdots \cdots \text{(15a)}$$

it is important to remember that v is the velocity of the mirror in a direction *away from* that of the oncoming radiation.

Let us now return to the problem in hand, the consideration of the adiabatic expansion of radiation in an enclosure with perfectly white walls.

Larmor * has shown that the geometrical calculations are greatly simplified if we suppose the radiation enclosed in a *sphere* which is uniformly expanded. For the sake of generality we shall suppose that the sphere reflects perfectly and diffusely; that is, we shall suppose that its surface is made up of a very large number of very small perfectly reflecting mirrors whose surfaces are orientated in random directions. The sphere expands uniformly and infinitely slowly with velocity v, so that

$$v = \frac{dR}{dt}$$

* Larmor, *Brit. Assoc. Report, Bradford*, p. 657 (1900); *Collected Papers*, Vol. 2, p. 217; see also Westphal, *Verh. d. deuts. phys. Ges.*, Vol. 16, p. 93 (1914). In his original demonstration, Wien (*Litz kön. preuss. Akad. Wiss.*, Vol. 55, 1893) considered a cylindrical cavity; see also Richardson, *The Electron Theory of Matter*, Cambridge University Press (1916), pp. 339–42.

is infinitesimal compared with c, the velocity of light. In this case the radiation undergoes a reversible adiabatic change of volume.

We now calculate the change of wave-length which a monochromatic ray undergoes when it is reflected at one of the very small planes. If the normal to this plane makes an angle ψ with the radius of the sphere, and if η is the angle of incidence of the ray (that is, the angle between the ray and the normal to the plane), and v the velocity with which the radius of the sphere increases, $v \cos \psi$ is the velocity of the small plane in the direction of its normal, and the change of wave-length of the ray on reflection is by equation (15a) given by

$$\lambda' = \lambda \left(1 + 2 \frac{v}{c} \cos \psi \cos \eta \right). \quad \ldots \ldots \quad (16)$$

If now θ_1 and θ_2 are the angles between the incident and emergent rays repectively and the radius of the sphere,

$$2 \cos \psi \cos \eta = (\cos \theta_1 + \cos \theta_2).^* \quad \ldots \ldots \quad (17)$$

Substituting this in equation (16), we obtain

$$\lambda' = \lambda \left\{ 1 + \frac{v}{c} (\cos \theta_1 + \cos \theta_2) \right\}. \quad \ldots \ldots \quad (18)$$

If s_1 is the length of the chord which makes an angle θ_1 with the radius at the point of contact with the sphere, and s_2 the corresponding quantity for θ_2, then

$$\cos \theta_1 = \frac{s_1}{2R}, \quad \cos \theta_2 = \frac{s_2}{2R},$$

* The proof of this is as follows. Take the point of incidence on the small plane as origin, and the perpendicular to the plane through this point as the z axis. Take the x axis as the line in which the plane of incidence cuts the small reflecting plane, and take the y axis in the small reflecting plane and perpendicular to the x axis.

The direction cosines of the incident ray are

$$\sin \eta, \quad 0, \quad \cos \eta;$$

those of the emergent ray are $-\sin \eta, \quad 0, \quad \cos \eta;$

and those of the radius are $l, \quad m, \quad \cos \psi,$

where l and m are not fixed by a knowledge of η and ψ.

The angle θ between two lines whose direction cosines are l_1, m_1, n_1, and l_2, m_2, n_2, is given by

$$\cos \theta = l_1 l_2 + m_1 m_2 + n_1 n_2.$$

Therefore for θ_1, the angle between the incident ray and the radius, we have

$$\cos \theta_1 = l \sin \eta + \cos \eta \cos \psi,$$

and for θ_2, the angle between the emergent ray and the radius,

$$\cos \theta_2 = -l \sin \eta + \cos \eta \cos \psi.$$

Adding these two equations, we obtain

$$\cos \theta_1 + \cos \theta_2 = 2 \cos \eta \cos \psi,$$

which is the required relation.

where R is the radius of the sphere. Substituting these values in equation (18), we obtain

$$\lambda' = \lambda\left(1 + \frac{v}{c}\frac{s_1 + s_2}{2R}\right) \quad \ldots \ldots \quad (18a)$$

for one reflection.

For n successive reflections we have

$$\lambda' = \lambda\left(1 + \frac{v}{c}\frac{s_1 + s_2}{2R}\right)\left(1 + \frac{v}{c}\frac{s_2 + s_3}{2R}\right)\cdots\left(1 + \frac{v}{c}\frac{s_n + s_{n+1}}{2R}\right),$$

on the assumption that, during the time occupied by the n reflections, the change in R is small compared with R itself. Since v/c is infinitesimal, this equation may be written

$$\lambda' = \lambda\left(1 + \frac{v}{c}\frac{s_1 + 2s_2 + 2s_3 + \ldots + 2s_n + s_{n+1}}{2R}\right).$$

If the number of reflections is large, the difference between s_1 and s_{n+1} is negligible compared with the sum of the s_p, so the equation becomes

$$\lambda' = \lambda\left(1 + \frac{v}{cR}\sum_{p=1}^{p=n} s_p\right).$$

If τ is the time occupied by the dilation, $\sum_1^n s_p$ is the distance travelled by the ray in time τ, so that

$$\sum_1^n s_p = c\tau.$$

If ΔR is the increase in the radius in the time τ,

$$v = \Delta R/\tau.$$

Using these two results, the last equation becomes

$$\lambda' = \lambda\left(1 + \frac{\Delta R}{R}\right),$$

or, introducing the volume V,

$$\lambda' = \lambda\left(1 + \frac{\Delta V}{3V}\right). \quad \ldots \ldots \ldots \quad (19)$$

This equation may be written in the form

$$\frac{\Delta\lambda}{\lambda} = \frac{\Delta V}{3V}. \quad \ldots \ldots \ldots \quad (20)$$

If ν is the frequency,

$$\Delta\lambda = \frac{d\lambda}{d\nu}\Delta\nu = -\frac{c}{\nu^2}\Delta\nu. \quad \ldots \ldots \quad (21)$$

Substituting for λ and $\Delta\lambda$ in equation (20), it becomes

$$\frac{\Delta\nu}{\nu} = -\frac{\Delta V}{3V}. \quad \ldots \ldots \ldots \quad (22)$$

Integrating this equation, we obtain

$$\nu^3 V = \text{constant},$$

or if ν is the frequency before the expansion, and ν' the frequency after the expansion, and V and V' are the corresponding volumes,

$$\nu'^3 V' = \nu^3 V. \qquad \ldots \ldots \ldots \quad (23)$$

This formula holds for finite or infinitesimal changes of volume. It is the formula giving the change in the frequency of *monochromatic* radiation contained in a perfectly reflecting chamber which is expanded adiabatically. The remaining part of the deduction of Wien's law is merely the algebraic development of this result.

Suppose that we now consider radiation consisting not of a single frequency ν, but of a group of frequencies lying between the limits ν and $\nu + d\nu$. If this radiation is contained in a perfectly white enclosure which is adiabatically expanded, not only are the actual frequencies of all the constituent rays altered, but the extent $d\nu$ of the range is also altered.

Consider the individual radiations at the extreme ends of the group. Their frequencies before the expansion are ν and $\nu + d\nu$. After the expansion, let them be respectively ν' and $\nu' + d\nu'$. Applying equation (23), we have

$$\nu'^3 V' = \nu^3 V,$$

and $$(\nu' + d\nu')^3 V' = (\nu + d\nu)^3 V.$$

Subtracting these equations, we obtain

$$V'\nu'^2 d\nu' = V\nu^2 d\nu. \qquad \ldots \ldots \ldots \quad (24)$$

We shall now apply these results to obtain Wien's law.

Consider a perfectly reflecting enclosure of volume V filled with complete radiation at a temperature T. As we have already proved, the radiation remains complete if adiabatic expansion takes place. It can also be shown * that the change of angle with the normal, on reflexion with the moving wall, is compensated by the change of radius between reflexions. From this, it follows that the energy of any infinitesimal range of frequencies is altered in the same ratio as that of any other range of frequencies. Thus, during the adiabatic expansion, the distribution in direction is maintained. Let $u_\nu d\nu$ be the energy per unit volume of the radiation with frequencies lying between the limits ν and $\nu + d\nu$. Our object is to determine u_ν.

The energy in the volume V is

$$V u_\nu d\nu.$$

If the enclosure is expanded adiabatically, any change that takes place in this particular radiation is quite independent of the presence or absence of radiation of other frequencies. We may therefore for the moment assume that this is the

* Hercus, *Nature*, Vol. 162, p. 143 (1948).

only radiation present in the enclosure. The pressure p exerted by the radiation on the walls of the enclosure is given by

$$p = \tfrac{1}{3} u_\nu \, d\nu.$$

If the volume increases by an amount ΔV, the work done by the radiation is $p \Delta V$. Since the change is adiabatic, this work is done at the expense of the internal energy. The internal energy after the expansion is therefore

$$V u_\nu \, d\nu - p \Delta V,$$

or

$$V u_\nu \, d\nu - \tfrac{1}{3} u_\nu \, d\nu \, \Delta V.$$

We may therefore write

$$V u_\nu \, d\nu - \tfrac{1}{3} u_\nu \, d\nu \, \Delta V = V' u'_{\nu'} \, d\nu'. \quad \dots \dots \quad (25)$$

Substituting from equation (24) for $V' d\nu'$, this becomes

$$V u_\nu \, d\nu - \tfrac{1}{3} u_\nu \Delta V \, d\nu = \frac{\nu^2}{\nu'^2} V u'_{\nu'} \, d\nu,$$

or dividing through by $d\nu$,

$$V u_\nu - \tfrac{1}{3} u_\nu \Delta V = V u'_{\nu'} \frac{\nu^2}{(\nu + \Delta \nu)^2} = V u'_{\nu'} \left(1 - \frac{2 \Delta \nu}{\nu}\right).$$

Substituting from equation (22), this becomes

$$V u_\nu - \tfrac{1}{3} u_\nu \Delta V = V u'_{\nu'} + \tfrac{2}{3} u'_{\nu'} \Delta V. \quad \dots \dots \quad (26)$$

This is as far as we can go by considering the single group of radiations alone. Since u_ν is a *continuous* function of ν, we have

$$u'_{\nu'} = u_\nu + \left(\frac{\partial u_\nu}{\partial \nu}\right)_V \Delta \nu + \left(\frac{\partial u_\nu}{\partial V}\right)_\nu \Delta V.$$

Eliminating $\Delta \nu$ by substituting its value from equation (22), we obtain

$$u'_{\nu'} = u_\nu - \frac{\nu}{3V} \left(\frac{\partial u_\nu}{\partial \nu}\right)_V \Delta V + \left(\frac{\partial u_\nu}{\partial V}\right)_\nu \Delta V.$$

Substituting this value of $u'_{\nu'}$ in equation (26) and collecting terms, we obtain

$$\frac{\nu}{3} \left(\frac{\partial u_\nu}{\partial \nu}\right)_V - V \left(\frac{\partial u_\nu}{\partial V}\right)_\nu - u_\nu = 0. \quad \dots \dots \quad (27)$$

The solution of this equation is

$$u_\nu = \nu^3 F(\nu^3 V), \quad \dots \dots \dots \quad (28a)$$

where F is an undetermined function. The correctness of this solution can be proved by differentiation.

We now introduce the temperature by using the result, given in equation (6), that in an adiabatic change of volume $V T^3 = $ constant. Substituting this in equation (28a), we have

$$u_\nu = \nu^3 f_1 \left(\frac{\nu}{T}\right), \quad \dots \dots \dots \quad (28b)$$

where f_1 is an undetermined function. This is *Wien's displacement law*.

Wien's law enables us to deduce the curve connecting u_ν and ν for any desired temperature once the curve has been determined experimentally for one particular temperature. This is as far as thermodynamics alone can carry us. We cannot deduce the form of the function f_1.

In practice we generally use wave-lengths and not frequencies. This changes the form of the distribution law slightly. Let $E_\lambda d\lambda$ be the energy per unit volume of the radiation whose wave-length lies between the limits λ and $\lambda + d\lambda$, the corresponding frequencies being ν and $\nu + d\nu$. We have

$$E_\lambda d\lambda = u_\nu d\nu,$$

or, since $\nu = \dfrac{c}{\lambda}$, $\qquad E_\lambda = u_\nu \dfrac{d\nu}{d\lambda} = -\dfrac{c}{\lambda^2} u_\nu.$

Substituting from the last two equations in equation (28b), we obtain

$$E_\lambda = \frac{1}{\lambda^5} f(\lambda T), \qquad \ldots \ldots \quad (29)$$

where f is another undetermined function. This is the most convenient form of Wien's law.

We may determine by experiment at a given temperature T_0 the curve in which values of E_λ are plotted as ordinates and values of λ as abscissæ. The curve for any higher temperature T is obtained by shortening each λ in the ratio T_0/T, so that λT (and therefore also $f(\lambda T)$) has the same value as before, and lengthening the corresponding E_λ in the ratio $(T/T_0)^5$, because of the term λ^5 in the denominator of equation (29). It will be seen that the maximum ordinate of the first curve becomes the maximum ordinate of the second curve. Therefore, if λ_m is the wave-length corresponding to the maximum, we have

$$\lambda_m T = \text{constant}, \qquad \ldots \ldots \quad (30)$$

and, if E_m is the length of the maximum ordinate,

$$E_m = \text{constant} \cdot T^5. \qquad \ldots \ldots \quad (31)$$

15. Planck's Formula.

All these deductions from Wien's displacement law have been accurately verified by experiment. The actual form of the distribution curve which has been deduced from theoretical considerations by Planck represents the experimental results with an error which is less than the uncertainty of the measurements. Planck's formula is consistent with Wien's law, so that an experimental verification of Planck's formula is the same thing as an experimental verification of Wien's law. It is more convenient to consider some of the properties of

Planck's formula before dealing with the experimental work. This formula (see equation (10), Chapter XXI) is

$$E_\lambda = \frac{8\pi hc}{\lambda^5(e^{hc/k\lambda T} - 1)}, \qquad \cdots \quad (32)$$

where h is Planck's constant, c is the velocity of light, and k is Boltzmann's constant, that is, $k = R/N_0$. The curve is shown in fig. 20.8.

The wave-length λ_m corresponding to the maximum of the distribution curve is obtained from the equation

$$\left(\frac{dE_\lambda}{d\lambda}\right)_{\lambda=\lambda_m} = 0.$$

Carrying out the differentiation of equation (32), this gives, if we write for short

$$\frac{hc}{k\lambda_m T} = \beta,$$

$$e^{-\beta} + \beta/5 - 1 = 0.$$

The solution of this equation is

$$\beta = 4\cdot9651,$$

so that we have

$$\lambda_m T = \frac{ch}{4\cdot9651k}. \qquad \cdots \quad (33)$$

Thus from an experimental determination of the value of $\lambda_m T$ the value of ch/k, which is usually written C_2, can be determined. Writing

$$C_2 = \frac{ch}{k}, \qquad \cdots \quad (34)$$

Planck's radiation formula becomes

$$E_\lambda = \frac{8\pi hc}{\lambda^5(e^{C_2/\lambda T} - 1)}. \qquad \cdots \quad (35)$$

The value of the Stefan-Boltzmann constant σ may be deduced from Planck's radiation formula by integrating equation (32) over all values of λ.* This gives the value of a in equation (5). The relation between σ and a is given in equation (13). In this way we obtain †

$$\sigma = \frac{2\pi^5 k^4}{15c^2 h^3}. \qquad \cdots \quad (36)$$

* Putting $\xi = \frac{hc}{k\lambda T}$, we obtain a multiple of the integral whose value is given in equation (11), Chapter XXII.

† See Planck, *Wärmestrahlung*, 5th edition, Section 162 (Barth, 1923).

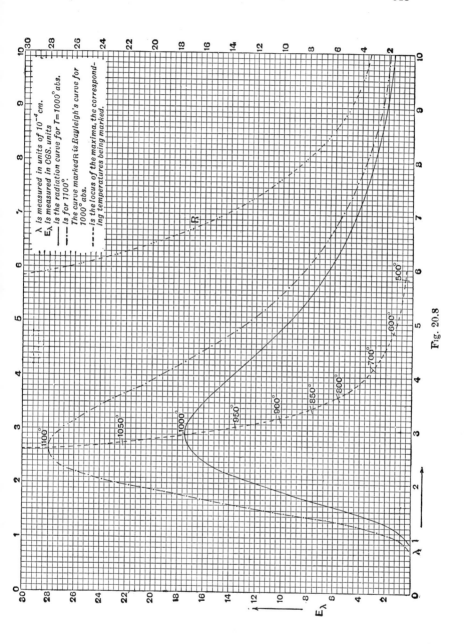

λ is measured in units of 10⁻⁴ cm.
E_λ is measured in CGS. units
——— is the radiation curve for T=1000° abs.
—·— is for 1100°.
The curve marked R is Rayleigh's curve for 1000° abs.
---- is the locus of the maxima, the corresponding temperatures being marked.

Fig. 20.8

An experimental determination of the values of C_2 and σ enables us to determine the values of both h and k, for we have, from equations (34) and (36),

$$h = \frac{15\sigma C_2{}^4}{2\pi^5 c^2}, \quad \cdots \cdots \cdots \quad (37)$$

and

$$k = \frac{15\sigma C_2{}^3}{2\pi^5 c}. \quad \cdots \cdots \cdots \quad (38)$$

Thus, values of the constants h and k can be found from radiation measurements. The values found in this way can be compared with those found by direct methods and are in good agreement with them. From the value of k and the known value of the gas constant, a value for Avogadro's number can be determined; it agrees closely with that given in Chapter III, Section 7.

The experimental data on the radiation constants have been examined critically by Wensel.* For *direct* determinations of the radiation constants (as distinct from their calculation from measured values of the atomic constants) he gives the following values:

$$C_2 = 1 \cdot 436 \text{ cm. deg.,}$$
$$\sigma = 5 \cdot 69 \times 10^{-5} \text{ erg cm.}^2 \text{ sec.}^{-1}.$$

Using these values in equations (37) and (38), we obtain

$$h = 6 \cdot 598 \times 10^{-27} \text{ erg sec.}$$
$$k = 1 \cdot 377 \times 10^{-16} \text{ erg deg.}^{-1}.$$

Taking the value $\quad R = 8 \cdot 314 \times 10^7 \text{ erg deg.}^{-1}$

for the gas constant, we obtain for Avogadro's number

$$N_0 = 6 \cdot 036 \times 10^{23}.$$

The accepted best values † of these atomic constants are

$$h = 6 \cdot 625 \times 10^{-27} \text{ erg sec.,}$$
$$k = 1 \cdot 380 \times 10^{-16} \text{ erg deg.}^{-1},$$
$$N_0 = 6 \cdot 025 \times 10^{23}.$$

Here, for the purposes of comparison, we have given the values to the same number of significant figures as the values which have been calculated from the radiation constants. It can be seen that the agreement is very close indeed. The importance of accurate values of the radiation constants is that they are used in the Planck radiation formula from which temperatures on the international temperature

---

* Wensel, *Bull, Res. Bur. Stand.*, Washington, Vol. 22, p. 375 (1939); see also *Procès Verbaux des Séances du Comité International des Poids et Mesures*, p. 21 (1948).

† Birge, *Rev. Mod. Phys.*, Vol. 1, p. 1 (1929); *Reports on Progress in Physics*, Vol. 8, p. 131 (1914); J. A. Bearden and J. S. Thomsen, *Nuovo Cimento*, Supplemento al Vol. 5, p. 338 (1957).

scale are calculated from optical pyrometric measurements at temperatures above the gold point (see Chapter I, Section 22). From the comparison we have already made of the values of the atomic constants calculated from the measured radiation constants, it will be clear that, if the radiation constants are calculated from the measured atomic constants, the values which are obtained confirm the directly measured values very closely. Since the atomic constants are known more accurately than most other data, this is the best way to determine accurate values of the radiation constants for use in thermometry. For the purposes of the international temperature scale the value of C_2 is taken as 1·438 cm. deg. Wensel (*loc. cit.*) has given a full comparison of the values of the radiation constants determined by different methods and has discussed their use in optical pyrometry. The values of the radiation constants calculated from the atomic constants are given by Bearden and Thomsen (*loc. cit.*) as

$$C_1 = 8\pi hc = (4 \cdot 9920 \pm 0 \cdot 0002) \times 10^{-15} \text{ erg cm.,}$$
$$C_2 = 1 \cdot 43879 \pm 0 \cdot 00003 \text{ cm. } °\text{K.,}$$
$$\sigma = (5 \cdot 6696 \pm 0 \cdot 0004) \times 10^{-5} \text{ erg cm.}^{-2} \text{ sec.}^{-1} °\text{K.}^{-4}$$

16. The Experimental Verification of Wien's Law and the Determination of the Constant C_2 in Planck's Radiation Formula.

The apparatus for the experimental verification of Wien's law and for the determination of the value of the constant C_2, which (see equations (33) and (34)) involves the determination of the position of the

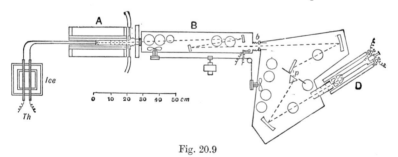

Fig. 20.9

maximum of the distribution curve, is shown in fig. 20.9.* The radiations from the full radiator A are focused on the spectrometer slit b by means of silvered mirrors placed in an air-tight box B. The spectrum is produced by a fluorite or quartz prism p. The radiometer (a vacuum bolometer) for measuring the spectral intensities is shown at D.

* See Coblentz, " Radiation ", A *Dict. of App. Physics*, Vol. 4, p. 554. A bibliography and account of earlier work are given in this article. See also H. A. Wilson. *Modern Physics* (Blackie), 4th edition 1960, Chapter V.

The temperature of the full radiator is measured by a thermocouple, as in the determination of the Stefan-Boltzmann constant.

In making measurements, the furnace is kept at a constant temperature and the intensities are measured in different parts of the spectrum. A correction is necessary for the fact that, with a slit of fixed width, the range of wave-lengths included in a given length of the spectrum is not constant at different parts of the spectrum.*

RADIATION PYROMETRY

17. The Temperature Scale at High Temperatures.

Even under ideal conditions the difficulties and uncertainties in the use of gas thermometers at temperatures above the melting-point of gold (1063° C.) are so great that the most accurate way of establishing the thermodynamic scale of temperature is to use the radiation laws.

For a full radiator at temperature T the energy emitted from unit area in the form of radiation of wave-length between λ and $\lambda + d\lambda$ is $E_\lambda \, d\lambda$, where (see equation (32)) E_λ is given by

$$E_\lambda = \frac{C_1}{\lambda^5 (e^{C_2/\lambda T} - 1)},$$

where C_1 and C_2 are constants. Experiment shows (see Sections 15 and 16) that C_2 is about 1·44 if all quantities are measured in c.g.s. units, and for red light (which is generally used) $\lambda = 6·58 \times 10^{-5}$ cm. If we put $T = 4000°$ K. as the upper limit of temperature with which we are likely to be concerned in radiation pyrometry, we have

$$e^{C_2/\lambda T} = 230,$$

which is large compared with unity. Under these conditions Planck's radiation formula can be written with close approximation in the form

$$E_\lambda = C_1 \lambda^{-5} e^{-C_2/\lambda T}. \qquad \ldots \ldots (39)$$

This is commonly called Wien's radiation formula, since it was proposed by Wien before Planck discovered his theoretical formula.†

Let E_1 and E_2 be the radiant energies per unit wave-length interval at wavelength λ, emitted per unit time by unit area of a full radiator at temperature T_1 and $T_2°$ K. respectively. Then we have, from equation (39),

$$\frac{E_2}{E_1} = \exp\left\{\frac{C_2}{\lambda}\left(\frac{1}{T_1} - \frac{1}{T_2}\right)\right\}. \qquad \ldots \ldots (40)$$

The actual methods of measuring E_λ will be considered in the next section. Provided the measure of one temperature on the thermodynamic scale and the value of the constant C_2 are known, equation (40) can be used to determine any other temperature on the thermodynamic scale.

* See Coblentz, *Bull. Bur. Stand.*, Vol. 10, p. 7 (1913).

† Wien's formula must be carefully distinguished from Wien's law. The former is admittedly approximate and of limited application, the latter is believed to be rigorously true.

To realize the international temperature scale, the standard temperature is taken as the gold point, $t_{Au}°$ C., and the exact form of Planck's radiation formula, equation (32), is used. Any other temperature on the international scale is then given by

$$\frac{E_t}{E_{Au}} = \frac{e^{C_2/\lambda(t_{Au} + T_0)} - 1}{e^{C_2/\lambda(t + T_0)} - 1}, \qquad \cdots \cdots \quad (41)$$

where T_0 is the thermodynamic temperature of the ice point, E_{Au} is the radiant energy per unit wave-length interval at wave-length λ emitted per unit time by unit area of a full radiator at the temperature of the gold point, and C_2 is taken as 1·438 cm. degree. This is the best representation of the thermodynamic scale at temperatures above the gold point.

18. Optical Pyrometers.

The quantities E_2 and E_1, or rather their ratio, can be measured with an optical pyrometer.

(a) *The disappearing filament pyrometer.* The simplest form of optical pyrometer is the disappearing filament pyrometer. This is

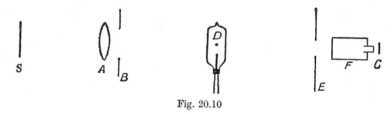

S   A   B   D   E   F   C

Fig. 20.10

shown diagrammatically in fig. 20.10. An image of the source S is formed by the objective A in the plane in which the filament D of the lamp lies. The eye-piece F is focused on D, and G is a piece of red glass which transmits only a very narrow band of wave-lengths. B and E are diaphragms. The current through D is carefully adjusted until D is invisible against the image of the source S. If the current through D is too great, the filament stands out brightly against the image of the source, while, if the current is too small, the filament appears black.* The current is measured on a sensitive ammeter.

The method of using the pyrometer is as follows. The pyrometer is sighted on a full radiator at various temperatures up to the melting-point of gold, the temperatures being measured on a standard thermocouple as described in Chapter I, Section 28 (for the method of taking the observations at the melting-point, see Section 22). In this way a curve is drawn up showing the relation between filament current and the temperature of the full radiator on which the pyrometer is sighted for temperatures up to the melting-point of gold.

In measuring temperatures above the melting-point of gold the light from the full radiator is cut down by means of a rotating sector. This is a piece of metal in the shape of a sector of a circle which is rapidly rotated about its centre. It is placed between the full-radiator source and the pyrometer. The rate of rotation

* For details, see Fairchild and Hoover, *Journ. Opt. Soc. Amer.*, Vol. 7, p. 543 (1924).

must be such that there are at least 30 or 40 alternations per second. If θ is the angle of the opening in the sector, the energy falling on the pyrometer is exactly $\theta/2\pi$ times what it would be if the sector were absent.

With the sector rotating between the source and the pyrometer,* the filament current is adjusted until a match is obtained. Let T_1 be the apparent temperature obtained from the calibration curve of the pyrometer—the sector should be so chosen that T_1 lies as near as possible to the melting-point of gold. If we assume that the light transmitted by the glass in the pyrometer is strictly monochromatic, E_2/E_1 of equation (41) is given by

$$\frac{E_2}{E_1} = \frac{2\pi}{\theta}.$$

Thus we have from equation (40), retaining only the first power in $1/T$,

$$\log_e \left(\frac{2\pi}{\theta}\right) = \frac{1 \cdot 438}{\lambda} \left(\frac{1}{T_1} - \frac{1}{T}\right),$$

and if λ is known T can be obtained.

Actually the red glass ordinarily used transmits a comparatively wide range of wave-lengths, so that the radiation cannot be treated as monochromatic. The result is that the effective wave-length which must be used in the above equation varies with the temperature, because the distribution of energy in the band of wave-lengths transmitted by the glass varies with the temperature of the source.† This difficulty can be avoided by using a spectral pyrometer or the combination of glass filters selected by Egerton and Milford,‡ which transmits a very narrow range of wave-lengths of green light.

Full details of the use of rotating sectors with optical pyrometers are given in a paper by Roeser, Caldwell and Wensel § on the melting-point of platinum.

(b) *The polarizing optical pyrometer.*—Another type of optical pyrometer is sometimes used. A matt glass surface is illuminated by an electric lamp which is run at constant intensity by always passing the same current through it; the lamp is from time to time compared with a standard amyl acetate lamp in order to avoid errors due to variations in the lamp filament. The light from this surface and that from the hot source are both passed through a polarizing prism so that each is split up into two beams polarized in planes at right angles to each other. One of each of these beams is chosen and the others are screened out. The choice is made in such a way that the plane of polarization of the beam from the hot source is at right angles to that of the beam from the matt surface. The beams are viewed in juxtaposition through a Nicol prism which can be rotated, an eye-piece, and a piece of red glass. The Nicol prism is set to the position in which the beams appear of equal intensity. The setting of the prism is a measure of the intensity of the light from the hot source, and thus of its temperature. The calibration of the instrument is similar to that of the disappearing filament pyrometer.

* An alternative is to use a piece of neutral absorbing glass which has been calibrated against a sector.

† For details of this correction, see Fairchild, Hoover and Peters. *Bur. Stand. Journ. Res.*, Vol. 2, p. 930 (1929).

‡ Egerton and Milford, *Proc. Roy. Soc.*, A, Vol. 130, p. 111 (1931). These authors have designed a magnifying optical pyrometer which can be used to measure the temperature of small bodies such as hot wires. See also Milford, Bracey, Cunnold and Egerton, *J. Sci. Inst.*, Vol. 12, p. 80 (1935); Cunnold, *Proc. Roy. Soc.*, A, Vol. 152, p. 64 (1935).

§ Roeser, Caldwell, and Wensel, *Bur. Stand. Journ. Res.*, Vol. 6, p. 1123 (1931).

19. The Total-radiation Pyrometer.

Another type of pyrometer called the total-radiation pyrometer is often used. In this type the total energy of radiation of all wavelengths is measured. The most convenient form of total-radiation pyrometer is that designed by Féry. The instrument is illustrated diagrammatically in fig. 20.11.

M is a concave mirror, usually of copper plated with nickel or gold. D is a small diaphragm placed immediately in front of the small blackened receiving surface T. One junction of a thermocouple is attached to T. The mirror M can be moved by means of a rack and pinion so as to focus an image of the furnace on to the aperture in D. In order to enable the observer to tell whether focusing is accurate, the diaphragm D is polished to form a mirror, and is made in two halves which are inclined at a small angle to each other. D is viewed through the

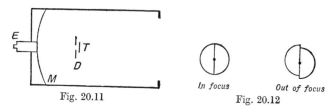

Fig. 20.11

In focus   Out of focus

Fig. 20.12

eyepiece E. The appearance through the eyepiece is shown in fig. 20.12. Only when the image of the furnace is formed on the surface of D do the two halves of the image of the furnace in E appear undisplaced relative to each other.

Provided the aperture in D is filled by the image of the furnace, the reading of the thermocouple is independent of the distance from the furnace. The reason for this is that the reading of the thermocouple depends only on the intensity of the image. If the distance from the furnace is doubled, the total amount of energy received by the mirror M is reduced to one-fourth; but the area of the image is simultaneously reduced to one-fourth, so that the intensity of the image remains constant. With the furnace at a given distance, the size of furnace aperture necessary to fill the aperture in D completely can be calculated from the geometry of the instrument. If, as is usually the case, the aperture in D is 0·15 cm. in diameter and the focal length of M is 7·6 cm., the following table gives the necessary diameter of the source at various distances.

Distance of source Centimetres		Diameter of source Centimetres
70	....	1·2
100	....	1·8
200	....	3·8
300	....	5·8
500	....	9·7

Calibration.—If T is the temperature of the source and T_0 that of the receiving surface, it is not possible to assume that the deflections of the galvanometer of a radiation pyrometer are proportional to $(T^4 - T_0^4)$, or, since T is large compared with T_0, to the fourth power of the temperature of the source. It is therefore necessary to calibrate the instrument directly at a number of points by sighting on to a furnace of the type shown in fig. 20.6, the temperature of which is measured by a standard thermocouple if below 1063° C. or for higher temperatures by an optical pyrometer as in Section 18. The range of the instrument can be extended beyond the calibration limit by the use of a rotating sector. It is assumed that the total radiation obeys the Stefan-Boltzmann law, so that if T_1 is the apparent temperature as read on the calibrated instrument and θ is the sector opening and if T is the true temperature, $T_1{}^4 = \dfrac{\theta}{2\pi} T^4$.

There are several reasons why the deflection of the instrument is not proportional to the fourth power of the temperature of the source. They are as follows:*

1. The electromotive force generated by the thermocouple is not strictly proportional to the temperature difference between the hot and cold junctions. When the rise of temperature of the receiving disc above the surroundings is of the order of eighty degrees, this factor has an appreciable influence.

2. The receiving surface and diaphragm D are enclosed in a small cell. Stray reflections from the walls falling on the receiving surface produce disturbances.

3. The rate of loss of heat from the junction is not strictly proportional to its temperature excess.

4. Conduction of heat along the thermocouple wires produces a temperature rise in the cold junction.

5. The galvanometer is usually a millivoltmeter; the readings of such an instrument are subject to error.

20. Comparison of Total-radiation and Optical Pyrometers.

It is a most important test of both total-radiation and optical pyrometers and of the radiation laws to compare the scales obtained by extrapolation using both types. Such a comparison has been made by Mendenhall and Forsythe,† who have measured with both a total-radiation and a disappearing-filament pyrometer the temperature of a full-radiator furnace outside the range in which standard thermocouples can be used. The results are shown in Table I. The agree-

TABLE I

Number of comparisons	Temperature (°C.)	$T_{\text{opt.}} - T_{\text{tot. rad.}}$	Range of observations
9	1750	Less than 0·5 deg.	—
7	2200	Less than 2 deg.	2 deg.
3	2500	About 2 deg.	4 deg.
4	2820	About 4 deg.	7 deg.

ment is within the experimental error, and is a satisfactory confirmation of the general principles on which radiation pyrometry is based. The differences, however, show a definite trend with temperature. To bring the two scales into agreement it is only necessary to assume

* See Griffiths, *Methods of Measuring Temperature* (Griffin, 1925).
† Mendenhall and Forsythe, *Phys. Rev.*, Vol. 4, p. 69 (1914).

a slightly different C_2 or λ; a change in the latter from 6·58 to
6·57 . 10^{-5} cm. would accomplish the result, and this change is less
than the uncertainty with which the wave-length is known.

21. Emissivity and Temperature of Radiators other than Full Radiators.

The *emissivity* of a surface is defined as the ratio of the emissive power to that of
a full radiator for a given wave-length and at the same temperature. The methods
of measuring emissivities will be understood from the discussion in the next
section of the measurement of high-temperature melting-points. They differ
considerably from unity and, if an optical pyrometer is sighted on a metal surface, the apparent temperature given by the pyrometer (usually called the brightness temperature) is not the same as the true temperature. This is shown by the
results for various surfaces * given in Table II.

TABLE II

True temperature	Brightness temperature for $\lambda = 6\cdot65 \times 10^{-5}$ cm.			
	Mo	Ni	Pt	W
1000	958	956	950	966
1200	1139	1137	1124	1149
1400	1316	1315	1296	1330
1600	1489		1466	1509
1800	1658		1634	1684
2000	1824		1800	1857
2500	2220			2274
3000				2673

A considerable amount of work has been done on the total emissivity of various
surfaces, i.e. the ratio of the total emissive power for all wave-lengths and that
of a full radiator.† One way of representing the results, which was first used by
Lummer, is to assume a law for total emissive power similar to the Stefan-Boltzmann law and of the form $\sigma' T^n$. The constants σ' and n are determined empirically.‡ Such an expression only holds over a limited range of temperatures. A
more satisfactory expression of the form

$$(1 - e^{-\alpha T})\sigma T^4,$$

where σ is the Stefan-Boltzmann constant and the constant α is determined
empirically, has been suggested by Helfgott.§ He has shown that a formula of
this type fits the experimental results for a considerable number of metals. In

* For further results and tables from which true temperatures can be obtained
from apparent temperatures, also for a full bibliography on emissivity, see *International Critical Tables*, Vol. 5, pp. 237–47. For a general discussion of brightness
temperature, see Forsythe, *Phys. Rev.*, Vol. 38, p. 1247 (1931). It may be mentioned
that optical pyrometers are less affected by departure from blackness in the radiator
than are total-radiation pyrometers.

† See reference to *International Critical Tables* given in the last footnote.

‡ See e.g. Utterback, *Phys. Rev.*, Vol. 34, p. 785 (1929).

§ Helfgott, *Zeits. f. Physik*, Vol. 49, p. 555 (1928).

general it may be noted that the higher the temperature the more nearly does the total emissive power approach that of a full radiator.*

22. Optical Pyrometers and the Determination of High-temperature Melting-points.

The most satisfactory way of measuring the melting- or freezing-point of a metal with an optical pyrometer is to immerse a small hollow sight tube or full radiator in the molten metal and, during the freezing of the metal, to take observations on this full radiator with an optical pyrometer. Accurate determinations by this method have been made of the freezing-points of nickel, palladium and platinum.† Another method used by Jenkins and Gayler ‡ in a determination of the melting-point of iron is to sight on a bubble blown at the end of a tube dipping in the molten liquid. These methods can also be used to measure the emissivity of the surface by sighting on both the immersed full radiator and the surface of the metal.

If a strip of metal is folded into a wedge of small angle and electrically heated, the inside of the wedge approximates closely to a full radiator.§ A pyrometer can be sighted on the inside of the wedge and the full-radiator temperature measured when the metal just begins to melt. If a pyrometer is also sighted on the outside the emissivity may be obtained. A similar method has been used by Worthing ‖ for tungsten and platinum. A hollow cylindrical filament of the metal was mounted in a lamp bulb and heated by a current. The filament was perforated with small holes, each hole being an approximate full radiator. A comparison between the light emitted from the holes and that from the neighbouring metal surface enables the emissivity to be measured, the temperature being obtained from the light emitted by the hole. Corrections were necessary for (1) the departure from full-radiator conditions caused by the presence of the hole, (2) the

---

* It should be mentioned here that Griffiths and Awbery (*Proc. Roy. Soc.*, A, Vol. 123, p. 401 (1929)) have made a careful study of various methods of measuring flame temperatures. One method used was to heat a platinum wire placed in the flame by an electric current. In general when conditions are steady the heat generated by the current is carried away from the wire in three ways: (1) radiation to distant cold objects, (2) conduction along the wire to its supports, (3) transference to the hot gases composing the flame. If the wire is at the temperature of the flame (3) cannot take place, so that all the heat generated is lost by (1) and (2). With the same wire similarly mounted and placed in a vacuum exactly the same conditions prevail, i.e. all the heat is lost by (1) and (2). Thus if the point is found at which both the current and the temperature are the same for the wire in the flame and in a vacuum and the temperature of the wire is measured, this temperature will be the flame temperature. The results obtained in this way agreed with those given by Kirchhoff's method of spectrum line reversal, which was also studied in detail. The latter method has also been used above 3000° K. by Henning and Tingwaldt, *Zeits. f. Physik*, Vol. 48, p. 805 (1928). For a full discussion of the application of the line-reversal method to determine internal-combustion engine temperatures, see Brevoort, *Rev. Sci. Inst.*, Vol. 7, p. 342 (1936).

† Schofield, *Proc. Roy. Soc.*, A, Vol. 125, p. 517 (1929); Wensel and Roeser, *Bur. Stand. Journ. Res.*, Vol. 5, p. 1309 (1930); Roeser, Caldwell and Wensel, *Bur. Stand. Journ. Res.*, Vol. 6, p. 1119 (1931). See also Kanolt, *Bull. Bur. Stand.*, p. 295 (1914), who determined the melting-points of lime, magnesia, aluminium oxide and chromium oxide. It may be mentioned here that Liebmann, *Zeits. f. Physik*, Vol. 63, p. 404 (1930), has made a careful study of the temperature radiation from colourless oxides which are of considerable technical importance. He has shown how their temperature can be accurately measured, and gives a full bibliography.

‡ Jenkins and Gayler, *Proc. Roy. Soc.*, A, Vol. 129, p. 91 (1930).

§ Mendenhall, *Astrophys. Journ.*, Vol. 33, p. 91 (1911). See also Egerton and Milford, *Proc. Roy. Soc.*, A, Vol. 130, p. 111 (1930), for a general discussion.

‖ Worthing, *Phys. Rev.*, Vol. 10, p. 377 (1917).

difference between the temperature of the inside of the filament and that of the surface, (3) the effect of the hole in causing an unsymmetrical distribution of the heating current.*

Another method is to observe a full-radiator furnace which is brought to the melting-point of the metal. The metal is welded between the ends of two thermo-couple wires and placed in the furnace, which is gradually heated. At the melting-point the E.M.F. of the thermocouple remains steady for a short time and then the wire breaks and the E.M.F. ceases.†

The following melting-points are accurately known on the international scale. The values obtained by Day and Sosman are given for comparison, although they are known to be in error owing to the extreme difficulty of using gas ther-mometers at these temperatures.

Metal	International‡ scale (°C.)	Day and Sosman (Gas thermometer)
Nickel	1453	1452
Palladium ..	1552	1549
Platinum ..	1769	1752
Tungsten ..	3380	

One of the main difficulties of working at high temperatures is to maintain a uniform temperature over an appreciable volume. This problem and a number of other practical problems have been discussed in a useful review by Sosman.§

23. The Temperature of the Sun.

By sighting a total-radiation pyrometer on the sun we may deter-mine its effective or full-radiator ‖ temperature; it is about 6000°.

An important quantity in connexion with solar radiation is the *solar constant*. This is the amount of energy which, in the absence of the atmosphere, would be absorbed per minute per unit area by a perfectly absorbing surface at the mean distance of the earth from the sun, and so placed that the solar radiation falls normally on it. For details, reference should be made to *Annals of Astrophys. Observatory of Smithsonian Inst.*, Vol. 3, Chapters I, III, V; Vol. 4, Chapter VI.

---

* Hyde, Cady, and Forsythe, *Phys. Rev.*, Oct. (1917), also Hyde, *Gen. Elect. Rev.*, Vol. 22, pp. 10, 819 (1917), have drawn up tables showing the relation between true and apparent temperatures for tungsten filaments. They have also developed a method of determining the temperatures of tungsten filaments by matching the *colour* of the light which they emit with that emitted by a full radiator, the temperature of which is measured. For further data concerning tungsten filaments, see Langmuir, MacLane, and Blodgett, *Phys. Rev.*, Vol. 35, p. 478 (1930); H. A. Jones and Langmuir, *Gen. Elect. Rev.*, Vol. 30, pp. 310, 354, 408 (1927).

† For a discussion of this method, see Fairchild, Hoover and Peters, *Bur. Stand. Journ. Res.*, Vol. 2, p. 931 (1929).

‡ The values for platinum and palladium have since been confirmed by Schofield, *Proc. Roy. Soc.*, A, Vol. 146, p. 792 (1934); Vol. 155, p. 301 (1936).

§ Sosman, *Ind. and Engin. Chemistry*, Vol. 23, p. 1369 (1931).

‖ For a discussion as to whether the sun can be regarded as a full radiator, see Eddington, *The Internal Constitution of the Stars*, Chapter XII (Cambridge University Press, 1926).

CHAPTER XXI

Planck's Radiation Formula

1. Thermodynamics alone can carry us no farther than the deduction of Wien's displacement law. If we wish to obtain the actual form of the function f in equation (29), Chapter XX, we must use the methods of statistical mechanics.

Statistical mechanics is concerned with the application of the laws of mechanics and of probability to determine the state of a system. Let us take a simple example, into which the laws of mechanics do not enter, of the use of the laws of probability. Suppose that we have N exactly similar articles and s similar boxes. We shall suppose at first that each of the articles has a mark so that it can be distinguished. The articles are placed at random in the boxes. The probability that a particular article is in a specified box is $1/s$. And the probability that article number 1 is in a specified box, and that at the same time article number 2 is in a specified box, article number 3 is in a specified box, and so on for the whole N articles, is s^{-N}.

We shall suppose that in this particular arrangement box number 1 contains N_1 articles, box number 2 contains N_2, and so on. We have obviously

$$N_1 + N_2 + N_3 + \ldots + N_s = N.$$

Now the total number of different ways in which N articles can be arranged in s boxes so that box 1 contains N_1 articles, box 2 contains N_2 articles, and so on, is

$$\frac{N!}{N_1! \, N_2! \, N_3! \ldots N_s!}.$$

The probability of each particular one of these arrangements is s^{-N}. Therefore, if the articles are distributed at random, the probability W that there will be N_1 articles in the first box, N_2 articles in the second box, and so on, is given by

$$W = \left(\frac{1}{s}\right)^N \frac{N!}{N_1! \, N_2! \, N_3! \ldots N_s!}.$$

This means that, if we examine a large number of different random distributions of the articles, we shall find that in a fraction W of the total number the articles are distributed so that box 1 contains N_1 articles, box 2 contains N_2 articles, and so on.

The most probable distribution is that for which W is a maximum. It can be shown that the condition for this is

$$N_1 = N_2 = N_3 = \ldots = N/s.$$

Further, if N, N_1, N_2, ... are all very large numbers, it can be shown that the probability of an *appreciable* departure from the equal distribution is infinitesimal.

The simplest application of these ideas is to the molecules of a gas in a closed vessel. We suppose the vessel divided into a large number of cells of equal volume, which correspond to the boxes, and assume that, independently of the presence of other molecules, any given molecule is just as likely to be in any one cell as in any other. The probability of a given arrangement gives in this case the fraction of the total time during which the given arrangement persists. In dealing with molecules, the numbers N, N_1, N_2, ... are all large, and therefore, if we examine the distribution of the molecules in the vessel for a time t, we shall find an equal distribution (that is, equality of density) for all but an infinitesimal fraction of the time.

Exactly the same considerations apply to the distribution of energy among the units of a physical system. The most probable distribution is simply that which can occur in the maximum number of different ways, subject of course to the condition that the total amount of energy remains fixed. It can be shown by considerations which are similar in principle to those outlined above that, if we have a large number of independent " plane-polarized " simple harmonic vibrations of the same frequency, the most probable distribution is that in which the number whose energy lies between the limits E and $E + dE$ is equal to *

$$Ae^{-E/kT} dE, \quad \ldots \ldots \quad (1)$$

where A is a constant depending on the total number of vibrators, and T is the absolute temperature.† $k (= R/N_0)$ is Boltzmann's constant. If the number of vibrators is sufficiently large, the probability of an appreciable departure from this distribution, which is usually referred to as Boltzmann's law, is infinitesimal.

* See Jeans, *Dynamical Theory of Gases*, 4th edition, Section 105 and equation 936 (1925).

† The temperature is introduced by finding the condition that, if the system under consideration is placed so that an exchange of energy can take place between it and a perfect monatomic gas, no net exchange does take place. The gas and the system under consideration are then at the *same* temperature. The condition which is so found involves the mean energy of translation of the gas molecules. The relation between this mean energy of translation and the temperature is known by equation (8), Chapter III. We substitute for the mean energy of translation the expression $\frac{3}{2}kT$ given by this equation, and thus introduce the absolute temperature into our various relations.

18

Let us examine expression (1). Imagine that small equal ranges of energy dE are marked out surrounding the values $E = 0$, $E = \epsilon$, $E = 2\epsilon$, and so on. By expression (1) the numbers of vibrators whose energy lies within these ranges will stand in the ratios

$$1 : e^{-\epsilon/kT} : e^{-2\epsilon/kT} : \ldots, \qquad \cdots \cdots (2)$$

so that if N have energy lying in the range dE around zero, the numbers having energies lying in the ranges dE around ϵ, 2ϵ, $\ldots$ will be $Ne^{-\epsilon/kT}$, $Ne^{-2\epsilon/kT}$, $\ldots$. The total number of vibrators will be

$$N(1 + e^{-\epsilon/kT} + e^{-2\epsilon/kT} + e^{-3\epsilon/kT} + \ldots) = \frac{N}{1 - e^{-\epsilon/kT}}. \quad (3)$$

The total energy of all the vibrators is

$$N(\epsilon e^{-\epsilon/kT} + 2\epsilon e^{-2\epsilon/kT} + \ldots) = \frac{N\epsilon}{e^{\epsilon/kT}(1 - e^{-\epsilon/kT})^2}. \quad (4)$$

Dividing the total energy of the vibrators by the total number, we obtain for the mean energy

$$\frac{\epsilon}{e^{\epsilon/kT} - 1}. \qquad \cdots \cdots \cdots (5)$$

If, as in classical mechanics, all values are possible for the energy of one of the vibrators, the mean energy is obtained by finding the limit to which expression (5) approaches when $\epsilon \to 0$. This limit is

$$kT. \qquad \cdots \cdots \cdots (6)$$

This expression is in accordance with the principle of the equipartition of energy, which we have used in Chapters VI and VII, for the expression for the energy of each vibrator contains two squared terms, one depending on the kinetic and one on the potential energy.

2. Number of Independent Vibrations of a Continuous Medium.

In applying this result to the radiation problem, we must first determine the number of independent vibrations of which a continuous medium is capable. To illustrate the nature of the problem let us consider a familiar acoustical case—the vibration of a stretched string. The string can vibrate in one segment, giving out its fundamental note. At the same time it can vibrate in two, three, four, or more segments, giving out notes whose frequencies are respectively two, three, four, $\ldots$ times that of the fundamental note. Each of these stationary vibrations is independent; that is, the energy of each can be varied independently of all the others. Similar considerations apply to the various stationary vibrations of which a continuous medium is capable.

Let us first take a plane wave of wave-length λ moving between two parallel boundaries and at right angles to them as in fig. 21.1(a). If there are n_1 nodal planes N_1, N_2, ... parallel to the boundaries, and if l is the distance between the boundaries, we have

$$n_1 \frac{\lambda}{2} = l.^*$$

If the wave is moving in such a direction that the normal to the wave-front makes an angle θ with the normal to the boundaries, we have the case shown in fig. 21.1(b). The path difference between the reflected and oncoming waves at

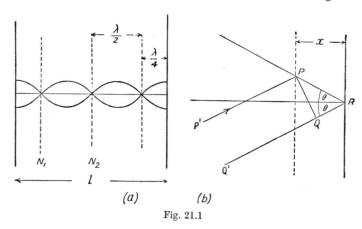

(a)   (b)

Fig. 21.1

the point P is equal to QR + RP, that is, to $x(\cos 2\theta + 1)/\cos\theta$, or to $2x\cos\theta$, where x is the distance of P from the surface. If P lies on a nodal plane, this path difference must be an odd multiple of $\lambda/2$; that is, for a nodal plane we have

$$2x\cos\theta = (2n + 1)\frac{\lambda}{2}.$$

The distance between successive nodal planes is, therefore, $\lambda/2\cos\theta$, and the distance of the first nodal plane from a surface is $\lambda/4\cos\theta$. If, therefore, we have a stationary vibration with n_1 nodal planes between two surfaces separated by a distance l, comparison with fig. 21.1(a) shows that we must have

$$n_1 \frac{\lambda}{2} = l\cos\theta.$$

If, therefore, we have a plane wave, of which the normal to the wave-front makes angles θ_1, θ_2, θ_3 with the normals to the three pairs of faces of a cube of side l, and if there are n_1, n_2, n_3 nodal planes parallel to the first, second, and third pairs of faces respectively, we have

$$n_1 \frac{\lambda}{2} = l\cos\theta_1, \quad n_2 \frac{\lambda}{2} = l\cos\theta_2, \quad n_3 \frac{\lambda}{2} = l\cos\theta_3.$$

* If there is a change of phase on reflection, the same treatment applies if we consider the loops in place of the nodes.

Remembering that $(\cos^2\theta_1 + \cos^2\theta_2 + \cos^2\theta_3) = 1$, we have

$$\frac{\lambda}{2}\sqrt{n_1{}^2 + n_2{}^2 + n_3{}^2} = l.$$

And if c is the velocity of the waves in the medium and ν is their frequency (in what follows we shall assume c independent of ν), this becomes

$$\nu = \frac{c}{2l}\sqrt{n_1{}^2 + n_2{}^2 + n_3{}^2}. \quad \ldots \ldots \quad (7)$$

We may note here that n_1, n_2, and n_3 must all be integral numbers.

If now we wish to reckon the number of possible stationary vibrations for frequencies lying between the limits ν and $\nu + \Delta\nu$, we must reckon up the number of all the possible combinations of values of n_1, n_2, and n_3 such that

$$\nu < \frac{c}{2l}\sqrt{n_1{}^2 + n_2{}^2 + n_3{}^2} < \nu + \Delta\nu.$$

We may carry out the reckoning as follows: Let us plot on three rectangular axes the values of $n_1 c/2l$, $n_2 c/2l$, and $n_3 c/2l$ respectively, thus obtaining a simple cubic lattice. ν is the distance of any point from the origin. We have only to consider positive values of the n's, and the total number of combinations of the n's, for which the above relation is fulfilled, is the number of points lying in one octant between spheres of radii ν and $\nu + \Delta\nu$. Provided $\Delta\nu$ is not too small, this number is the ratio of one-eighth of the total volume between the two spheres to the volume of an elementary cube of the lattice; that is, it is equal to

$$\tfrac{1}{8}(4\pi\nu^2\Delta\nu)\Big/\left(\frac{c}{2l}\right)^3.$$

This is the number of independent vibrations of a volume l^3 for waves of frequencies between ν and $\nu + \Delta\nu$.

The number of independent vibrations per unit volume for waves whose frequencies lie between ν and $\nu + d\nu$ is therefore

$$4\pi\frac{1}{c^3}\nu^2 d\nu. \quad \ldots \ldots \ldots \quad (8)$$

We have obtained this result for a cube; Weyl* has shown that the same result is obtained for a body of any shape.

For radiation there are two independent vibrations in any given direction, corresponding to radiation polarized in planes at right angles to one another. Expression (8) applies to each of these. Thus, the number of independent modes per unit volume for radiation of frequencies between ν and $\nu + d\nu$ is

$$(8\pi\nu^2/c^3)\,d\nu.$$

For the vibrations of a gas, which only transmits longitudinal sound waves, expression (8) applies as it stands. For an elastic solid which can transmit three independent vibrations in any given direction, namely, two transverse vibrations polarized in planes at right angles to one another and a longitudinal wave, the

---

* Weyl, *Math. Ann.*, Vol. 71, p. 441 (1911); *Crelle's Journ.*, Vol. 141, p. 163 (1912); Vol. 143, p. 177 (1914). See also Laue, *Ann. d. Physik*, Vol. 44, p. 1210 (1914); Flamm, *Phys. Zeits.*, Vol. 19, p. 116 (1918).

expression becomes $4\pi \left(\dfrac{2}{c_t^3} + \dfrac{1}{c_l^3} \right) \nu^2 d\nu$, where c_t is the velocity of transverse waves and c_l that of longitudinal waves.

Remembering that $\nu = \dfrac{c}{\lambda}$, and that therefore $d\nu = -\dfrac{c}{\lambda^2}d\lambda$, we can easily obtain from the above results the number of independent vibrations per unit volume of a medium, when the vibrations are classified according to wave-length.

The results are summarized in Table I. Those in λ hold whether c depends on λ or not. Those in ν hold only for a non-dispersive medium.

TABLE I

Medium	Vibrations per unit volume for waves whose frequencies lie between the limits ν and $\nu + d\nu$, or whose wave-lengths lie between the limits λ and $\lambda + d\lambda$	
Gas	$4\pi \dfrac{1}{c^3} \nu^2 \, d\nu$	$4\pi\lambda^{-4} \, d\lambda$
Radiation ..	$8\pi \dfrac{1}{c^3} \nu^2 \, d\nu$	$8\pi\lambda^{-4} \, d\lambda$
Elastic solid ..	$4\pi \left(\dfrac{2}{c_t^3} + \dfrac{1}{c_l^3} \right) \nu^2 \, d\nu$	$12\pi\lambda^{-4} \, d\lambda$

3. Rayleigh's Radiation Formula.

Applying the result given in expression (6) to radiation in equilibrium with matter at temperature T, we obtain for the energy per unit volume of the vibrations whose wave-lengths lie between the limits λ and $\lambda + d\lambda$,

$$8\pi k T \lambda^{-4} d\lambda. \qquad \ldots \ldots \ldots (9)$$

This is Rayleigh's radiation formula, and is the result to which we are inevitably led by the application of classical dynamics to the radiation problem. It is approximately true for very long wave-lengths, but is hopelessly wrong for shorter wave-lengths, since it predicts that for infinitely short wave-lengths the energy becomes infinite (see Chapter XX, Section 15, fig. 20.8).

4. The Quantum Theory.

The failure of classical mechanics to give the correct solution to the radiation problem (that is, the distribution of energy in the spectrum of a full radiator) led Planck to the discovery of the quantum. The justification for the quantum theory is its success in many branches of physics.

In one method of applying the quantum theory to the radiation problem the essential postulates are:

(1) The only possible energies * of a simple harmonic vibration of frequency ν are

$$(n + \tfrac{1}{2})h\nu$$

where n is a whole number or zero, and h is a universal constant called Planck's constant.

(2) By analogy with classical mechanics the partition of energy is given by the expression (2).

(3) The number of independent vibrations of radiation is that given by Table I.

The first of these postulates is the most important. It is in complete contradiction to classical mechanics, since it states that energy cannot vary continuously but only in jumps or quanta. This means that radiant energy is absorbed or emitted by matter in whole quanta (and possibly that the conservation of energy between matter and radiation is only statistical). The quantum theory has been successfully applied to absorption and emission in the explanation of the photoelectric effect by Einstein, and in Bohr's theory of spectra.

The second postulate is equivalent to assuming that the number of vibrations, whose energy would according to equation (1) lie between the limits $nh\nu$ and $(n + 1)h\nu$, all have the energy $(n + \tfrac{1}{2})h\nu$. This assumption actually rests on the more fundamental one that *a priori* all the quantum states are equally probable, or that the statistical weights of the various states are equal;† this means that at infinite temperature, where there is no restriction on the total energy, the vibrators are equally divided between the various states.

The third postulate means that although the processes of emission and absorption might suggest that the radiant energy is done up in bundles, yet the discontinuity applies only to the processes of emission and absorption (that is, to the interaction of radiation and matter). Otherwise, the radiation behaves, as in classical mechanics, as if it consisted of continuous waves.

The analysis from equations (1) to (5) applies to this case, and the mean energy of a vibration is given by equation (5), where ϵ is not equal to zero as in classical mechanics, but is equal to $h\nu$ or hc/λ, where c is the velocity of light. Thus the mean energy of a vibration of wavelength λ at temperature T is

$$\frac{hc/\lambda}{e^{hc/k\lambda T} - 1}. \qquad \cdots \quad \cdots \quad (10)$$

---

* The later developments of quantum mechanics show that the eigenvalues of the energy for a harmonic oscillator are actually $(n + \tfrac{1}{2})h\nu$, but this does not alter the essential fact that energy can only change in jumps of $h\nu$.

† Compare Fowler, *Statistical Mechanics*, 2nd edition, Cambridge University Press (1936), Chapter I.

Since the total number of vibrations per unit volume for radiation whose wave-lengths lie between the limits λ and $\lambda + d\lambda$ is $8\pi\lambda^{-4}d\lambda$, the energy per unit volume of radiation whose wave-length lies between the limits λ and $\lambda + d\lambda$ is obtained by multiplying expression (10) by $8\pi\lambda^{-4}d\lambda$. This gives

$$\frac{8\pi hc\lambda^{-5}}{e^{hc/k\lambda T} - 1}\, d\lambda. \qquad \cdots \cdots \quad (11)$$

This is Planck's radiation formula. It gives the partition of energy in the spectrum of a full radiator, and is in full accord with experiment. The formula has been discussed in Chapter XX, Sections 15–17.*

* For a further discussion of Planck's radiation formula, see H. A. Wilson, *Modern Physics*, Chapter V (Blackie), 4th edition, 1960.

CHAPTER XXII

Theory of the Specific Heats of Solids

1. Introduction of Quantum Theory by Einstein.

Classical mechanics leads quite definitely to the theory of the equipartition of energy and therefore to the result given in Chapter VII, Section 6, that the atomic heat of a monatomic solid should be equal to $3R$, that is, to 24·9 joules per degree. As we have seen in Chapter VII, this result is not in accord with experiment. Einstein suggested that the quantum theory should be applied to this problem.

He made the simplest possible assumptions, that the atoms in a solid are all independent, and that each atom acts as a simple harmonic oscillator with a common frequency ν. Thus, the energy of each linear oscillator is given by

$$\epsilon = nh\nu,$$

where ν is the natural frequency and n can take integral values. This gives a system of non-degenerate energy levels. The probability that an oscillator will have an energy

$$\epsilon_i = n_i h\nu$$

is given by

$$p_i = \exp(-\epsilon_i/kT)/\sum_i \exp(-\epsilon_i/kT),$$

where the summation is to be carried out over all the levels. This gives

$$p_i = e^{-n_i h\nu/kT}/(1 - e^{-h\nu/kT}). \qquad \ldots \quad (1)$$

The mean energy of an oscillator is given by

$$\bar{\epsilon} = \sum_i p_i \epsilon_i,$$

which leads to

$$\bar{\epsilon} = \frac{h\nu}{e^{h\nu/kT} - 1}. \qquad \ldots \ldots \quad (2)$$

It follows that the molar specific heat, for the Einstein energy spectrum, is given by

$$C_v = \frac{\partial}{\partial T}(3N_0\bar{\epsilon}) = 3RE(x), \qquad \ldots \ldots \quad (3)$$

where N_0 is Avogadro's number, and the Einstein function is defined by

$$E(x) = x^2 e^x/(e^x - 1)^2, \qquad \ldots \ldots \quad (4)$$

where x has been written for $h\nu/kT$. If the parameter ν is adjusted to give agreement with the room-temperature values of the specific heat, it is generally of the order of magnitude of an infra-red frequency. It should be noted that for high temperatures the Einstein function approaches unity, and the specific heat approaches the classical (Dulong and Petit) value $3R$. The Einstein specific-heat curve agrees fairly well with the experimental data for high temperatures, but although it approaches zero as $T \to 0$, it does so far too rapidly. In fact, equation (3) indicates that as $T \to 0$,

$$C_v \sim 3R(h\nu/kT)^2 \exp(-h\nu/kT),$$

while the experimental results show a variation as T^3.

An empirical formula was put forward by Nernst and Lindemann [*] to fit the results better. They suggested that the Einstein spectrum of a single line frequency should be replaced by two lines of equal weights and having frequencies $\nu/2$ and ν. The specific-heat function deduced from this assumption was successful over a wide range of temperatures, but still failed at the lowest temperatures. Recent work on the energy spectrum of cubic crystals [†] makes it clear why such a spectrum of two lines is so successful.

2. Frequency Spectrum.

Almost simultaneously, Born and v. Kármán [‡] and Debye [§] suggested that instead of considering each atom to oscillate with the same frequency, a distribution of frequencies should be considered. In all, there will be three modes of oscillation per atom, and this can be used to fix the range of the frequency distribution. If there is such a distribution of frequencies, then the mean energy of the system of N_0 oscillators is given by

$$\bar{E} = \sum_i h\nu_i/(e^{h\nu_i/kT} - 1), \quad \ldots \ldots \quad (5)$$

where the summation is to be carried out over all the $3N_0$ possible frequencies. When the distribution of wave numbers or of frequencies can be represented by an integrable function, this sum can be replaced by an integral. Thus

$$\bar{E} = \int_0^{\nu_m} \frac{h\nu}{e^{h\nu/kT} - 1} g(\nu)d\nu, \quad \ldots \ldots \quad (5')$$

where $g(\nu)d\nu$ is the number of modes with frequencies which lie between ν and $\nu + d\nu$. The lattice theory of specific heats (Sections 6

[*] Nernst and Lindemann, *Zeits. Elektrochem.*, Vol. 17, p. 817 (1911).
[†] Blackman, *Proc. Roy. Soc.*, A, Vol. 159, p. 416 (1937); see below, Section 11.
[‡] Born and v. Kármán, *Phys. Zeit.*, Vol. 13, p. 297 (1912); Vol. 14, p. 15 (1913).
[§] Debye, *Ann. d. Physik*, Vol. 39, p. 789 (1912).

and 11 below) shows that the total number of modes of vibration should be used to specify a cut-off *wave number*; thus, equation (5′) would be better written as

$$\bar{E} = \int_0^{\nu = \sigma_m c} \frac{h\nu}{e^{h\nu/kT} - 1} g(\nu) \, d\nu,$$

where σ_m is the maximum wave number and c is the velocity of the wave. In the case in which there are different velocities for transverse and longitudinal waves, the corresponding equation for the mean energy would be

$$\bar{E} = \sum_i \int_0^{\nu = \sigma_m c_i} \frac{h\nu}{e^{h\nu/kT} - 1} g(\nu) \, d\nu,$$

where c_i is the velocity of the wave corresponding to the mode i of vibration. The corresponding expression for the specific heat is

$$C_v = \int_0^{\nu = \sigma_m c} g(\nu) \left[\frac{(h\nu/kT)^2 \, e^{h\nu/kT}}{(e^{h\nu/kT} - 1)^2} \right] d\nu.$$

The part of the integrand contained within square brackets is the specific heat of a simple oscillator, and is a monotonic, increasing function of the temperature for all wave numbers. It follows that the specific heat C_v of the assembly must also be a monotonic, increasing function; it increases steadily from zero at the absolute zero to the classical value $3R$ per gram-molecule at high temperatures. This is a direct consequence of the primitive assumption that the energy of the assembly can be represented as the sum of the energies of a number of atomic systems. The important point is that the specific heat associated with the normal modes of vibration of any lattice increases steadily with the temperature.

Born and v. Kármán suggested that the total number of modes of vibration should be used to specify a cut-off *wave number*. This concept follows necessarily from their idea that the distribution function should be determined by a detailed examination of the dynamics of the crystal lattice of atoms. Debye failed to realize the primacy of the wave number over the frequency (compare equation (7) below). He suggested that the total number of modes of vibration should be used to specify a cut-off *frequency*, and also assumed that the distribution law for long wave-lengths (that is, for a continuous elastic medium) could be extrapolated right up to the cut-off frequency. These two specifications are not in general identical. That this is so, can be seen from fig. 22.1, in which the frequency ν is plotted against the wave number σ. The two full lines represent the two kinds of polarization. Debye selected the $3N$ possible modes of vibration by choosing all the waves which have a frequency less than ν_m. Thus, the transverse modes with wave numbers in the range σ_t to σ_l are excluded, whereas the corresponding longitudinal modes are included. This constitutes a serious objection to Debye's theory. Born selected the $3N$ modes by choosing all those with a wave number less than σ_m. The

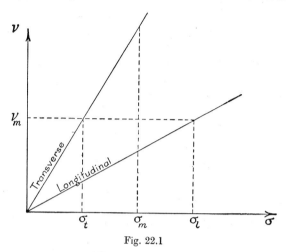

Fig. 22.1

Born and v. Kármán theory is more firmly based on rigorous principles of atomic dynamics than is the Debye treatment, and is accordingly to be greatly preferred to it. We shall now consider these theories.

3. Debye's Theory.

It has already been seen (Chapter XXI, Section 2) that for a continuous elastic solid the number of modes of vibration with frequencies between ν and $\nu + d\nu$ is

$$4\pi \left(\frac{1}{c_l{}^3} + \frac{2}{c_t{}^3} \right) \nu^2 d\nu, \quad \ldots \ldots \quad (6)$$

where c_l and c_t are the velocities of the waves for longitudinal and transverse vibrations. In this treatment, a cut-off frequency is determined by the number of independent modes of vibrations of the atoms, their interactions being neglected. Also, it is assumed that the frequency distribution (6) can be extrapolated up to the cut-off frequency. Thus, ν_m in equation (5′) is determined by

$$4\pi V \left(\frac{1}{c_l{}^3} + \frac{2}{c_t{}^3} \right) \int_0^{\nu_m} \nu^2 d\nu = 3N_0. \quad \ldots \quad (7)$$

Equation (7) gives on integration

$$\left(\frac{1}{c_l^3} + \frac{2}{c_t^3}\right) = \frac{9N_0}{4\pi V}\frac{1}{\nu_m^3}.$$

Using this result with expressions (2) and (6), we obtain for the total energy of the body

$$9N_0\frac{1}{\nu_m^3}\int_0^{\nu_m}\frac{h\nu^3}{e^{h\nu/kT}-1}\,d\nu. \quad \cdot \quad \cdot \quad \cdot \quad \cdot \quad (8)$$

Differentiating this expression with respect to T, we obtain for C_v, the atomic heat at constant volume,

$$C_v = \frac{9N_0}{\nu_m^3}\int_0^{\nu_m}\frac{\dfrac{h^2\nu^4}{kT^2}e^{h\nu/kT}}{(e^{h\nu/kT}-1)^2}\,d\nu.$$

In this equation we substitute for simplicity

$$\left.\begin{array}{l} \xi = h\nu/kT \\ x = h\nu_m/kT \end{array}\right\},$$

and it becomes, remembering that $d\nu = kT\,d\xi/h$,

$$C_v = 9N_0k\frac{1}{x^3}\int_0^x\frac{\xi^4 e^\xi}{(e^\xi-1)^2}\,d\xi. \quad \cdot \quad \cdot \quad \cdot \quad \cdot \quad (9)$$

This equation may be integrated by parts, for we have

$$\int\frac{\xi^4 e^\xi}{(e^\xi-1)^2}\,d\xi = -\int\xi^4\frac{d}{d\xi}\left(\frac{1}{e^\xi-1}\right)d\xi$$

$$= -\xi^4\frac{1}{e^\xi-1} + \int\frac{1}{e^\xi-1}\frac{d\xi^4}{d\xi}\,d\xi$$

$$= -\xi^4\frac{1}{e^\xi-1} + 4\int\frac{\xi^3}{e^\xi-1}\,d\xi.$$

Using this result and remembering that $N_0k = R$, equation (9) becomes

$$C_v = 9R\left[\frac{4}{x^3}\int_0^x\frac{\xi^3}{e^\xi-1}\,d\xi - \frac{x}{e^x-1}\right]. \quad \cdot \quad \cdot \quad (10)$$

4. Comparison with Experiment.

We may first note that this equation is in accord with the important experimental result (Chapter VII, Section 7 and fig. 7.5) that

$$C_v = F\left(\frac{T}{\Theta}\right),$$

where Θ is a constant for a given substance and F is the same function for all substances. According to equation (10), C_v is a function of x, which is equal to $h\nu_m/kT$; and, since h and k are universal constants, this may be written in the form Θ/T, where

$$\Theta = \frac{h\nu_m}{k}. \quad \ldots \ldots \ldots \quad (11)$$

The Debye function of equation (10) is that plotted in Chapter VII, fig. 7.6, and we have already seen that the curve closely represents the experimental results for a large number of simple substances. The values of Θ are given in Chapter VII, Table III. We may mention here that the integral in equation (10) cannot be evaluated in finite terms, but Debye * has evaluated it numerically. We give in Table I the values of C_v for various values of Θ/T. Using the values of Θ given in Chapter VII, Table III, we can obtain the value of C_v for any of the substances in that table at any given temperature.

TABLE I

Values of C_v for values of $\dfrac{\Theta}{T}$ from 0 to 30, using Debye's formula †

$\frac{\Theta}{T}$	0·0	0·1	0·2	0·3	0·4	0·5	0·6	0·7	0·8	0·9	1·0
0	5·955	5·95	5·94	5·93	5·91	5·88	5·85	5·81	5·77	5·72	5·67
1	5·670	5·61	5·55	5·48	5·41	5·34	5·26	5·18	5·09	5·01	4·92
2	4·918	4·83	4·74	4·64	4·54	4·45	4·35	4·25	4·15	4·05	3·95
3	3·948	3·85	3·75	3·63	3·56	3·46	3·36	3·27	3·18	3·09	3·00
4	2·996	2·91	2·82	2·74	2·65	2·57	2·50	2·42	2·34	2·27	2·20
5	2·197	2·13	2·06	1·99	1·93	1·87	1·81	1·75	1·69	1·63	1·58
6	1·582	1·53	1·48	1·43	1·39	1·34	1·30	1·26	1·21	1·18	1·14
7	1·137	1·100	1·065	1·031	0·998	0·966	0·935	0·906	0·878	0·850	0·823
8	0·823	0·798	0·774	0·750	0·727	0·704	0·683	0·662	0·642	0·623	0·604
9	0·604	0·588	0·570	0·552	0·537	0·521	0·507	0·492	0·478	0·465	0·452
10	0·452	0·439	0·427	0·415	0·404	0·394	0·383	0·373	0·363	0·353	0·345
11	0·345	0·335	0·324	0·319	0·310	0·302	0·295	0·287	0·280	0·273	0·267
12	0·267	0·260	0·254	0·248	0·242	0·237	0·231	0·226	0·221	0·216	0·211
13	0·211	0·206	0·202	0·197	0·193	0·188	0·184	0·180	0·176	0·172	0·169
14	0·169	0·165	0·162	0·159	0·155	0·152	0·149	0·146	0·143	0·140	0·137
15	0·137	0·135	0·132	0·130	0·127	0·125	0·122	0·120	0·118	0·116	0·113

$\frac{\Theta}{T}$	C_v	$\frac{\Theta}{T}$	C_v	$\frac{\Theta}{T}$	C_v
16	0·113	21	0·0502	26	0·0264
17	0·0945	22	0·0436	27	0·0236
18	0·0796	23	0·0382	28	0·0212
19	0·0677	24	0·0336	29	0·0190
20	0·0581	25	0·0298	30	0·0172

* Debye, *Ann. d. Physik*, Vol. 39, p. 789 (1912).

† See Nernst, *Die Grundlagen des neuen Wärmesatzes*.

A comparison of equations (11) and (7) shows that the value of Θ for a given substance can be calculated directly from the elastic constants, since c_l and c_t are known in terms of these constants. Such a calculation involves no thermal measurements, and the agreement of the values deduced in this way with the values required by the specific-heat measurements would indicate the validity of the Debye theory. We give in Table II the corresponding numbers for the substances for which sufficiently accurate values of the elastic constants are available. In compiling the table * the following values have been used:

$$h = 6\cdot55 \,.\, 10^{-27} \text{ erg sec.}; \quad k = 1\cdot347 \,.\, 10^{-16} \text{ erg deg.}^{-1};$$

$$h/k = 4\cdot863 \,.\, 10^{-11} \text{ sec. deg.}; \quad N_0 = 6\cdot17 \,.\, 10^{23}.$$

TABLE II

Values of Θ deduced from specific-heat measurements, and from elastic constants

Substance	Specific heat	Elastic constants
Pb	88	75
Cd	168	174
Ag	215	220
KCl	230	227
NaCl	281	305
Cu	315	341
Al	398	413
Fe	453	484
CaF_2	474	510
FeS_2	645	696

In compiling this table the values of the elastic constants at ordinary temperatures have been used. At first sight we should expect better agreement if the values of the elastic constants at vanishingly low temperatures were employed. Eucken,[†] however, has shown that this is not so and that the agreement using such constants is considerably worse. Eucken suggests that this is because metals are not truly isotropic and that the properties of an aggregate of small crystals held together by intercrystalline layers are not the same as those of a single crystal. The experiments of Kaye and Roberts ‡ on the thermal conductivity of single crystals of bismuth, of Griffiths § on the thermal conductivity of a crystal

* Schrödinger, *Phys. Zeits.*, Vol. 20, p. 476 (1919).

† Eucken, *Verh. d. deuts. phys. Ges.*, Vol. 15, p. 571 (1913).

‡ Kaye and Roberts, *Proc. Roy. Soc.*, A, Vol. 104, p. 98 (1923); see also Kannuluik and Laby, *Proc. Roy. Soc.*, A, Vol. 121, p. 640 (1928). Eucken and Kuhn, *Zeits. f. phys. Chem.*, Vol. 134, p. 193 (1928), find differences in a few isolated cases. See also Eucken, *Phys. Zeits.*, Vol. 29, p. 563 (1928).

§ Ezer Griffiths, *Proc. Roy. Soc.*, A, Vol. 115, p. 236 (1927).

of aluminium, and of Roberts * on the thermal expansion of single crystals of bismuth, indicate, however, that the thermal properties of an aggregate mass of small crystals do not differ appreciably from those of a single crystal of the same substance. Against Eucken's criticism it may be pointed out that we would not necessarily expect the agreement to be improved by using the values of the elastic constants at low temperatures. The value of C_v deduced by using equation (14), Chapter XIII, does not give the specific heat with the volume remaining constant throughout at the volume occupied at the lowest temperatures, but it gives the specific heat when the volume remains constant at the volume occupied under atmospheric pressure at the given temperature.

5. The T^3 Law.

An important result is obtained when we consider the form which the Debye function takes at very low temperatures. From the definition of x it will be seen that, when T becomes small, x becomes large. We have †

$$\lim_{x \to \infty} \int_0^x \frac{\xi^3}{e^\xi - 1}\, d\xi = \frac{\pi^4}{15}, \quad \cdots \quad (12)$$

and, when x is large, the second term on the right-hand side of equation (10) vanishes in comparison with the first. We may, therefore, write as an approximate formula for small (T/Θ)

$$C_v \simeq \frac{12}{5}\pi^4 R \frac{T^3}{\Theta^3}. \quad \cdots \cdots \quad (13)$$

This result has been tested experimentally for a large number of substances. Evidence was collected by Schrödinger,‡ who gave a table of values for ten substances. The results for calcium fluoride and for iron sulphide are in good agreement with the theory over a range of temperature from $\Theta/25$ to $\Theta/12$; the constancy of C_v/T^3 in this temperature range is almost perfect for these two salts. For other salts it is not nearly so good. For instance, for aluminium the value of C_v/T^3 in the range 19–35° K. changes by about 25 per cent; for sodium chloride in the temperature range 10–20° K., the value of C_v/T^3 changes by about 20 per cent; for lithium in the temperature range 15–30° K., it changes by about 30 per cent. Analysis of careful measurements of the specific heats of silver and zinc § shows that for temperatures less than 20° K., there are similar divergences in the value of C_v/T^3. Furthermore, it should be noted that, even for the two salts

* Roberts, *Nature*, Vol. 113, p. 275 (1924); *Proc. Roy. Soc.*, A, Vol. 106, p. 385 (1924).

† For the evaluation of the integral, see Wilson, *Modern Physics*, 3rd edition (1948), p. 85.

‡ Schrödinger, *Phys. Zeits.*, Vol. 20, p. 498 (1919).

§ Clusius and Harteck, *Z. phys. Chem.*, Vol. 134, p. 243 (1928); W. H. Keesom and van den Ende, *Proc. Acad. Sci., Amsterdam*, Vol. 35, p. 143 (1932); W. H. Keesom and Kok, *ibid.*, Vol. 35, p. 301 (1932).

for which C_v/T^3 is very nearly constant over a wide range of temperature, the values of Θ calculated from the specific-heat data are some 5 per cent lower than the values which are obtained from measurements of the elastic constants at room temperature; and the discrepancy would be increased considerably if low-temperature values of the elastic constants were used. This is important, as the existence of a T^3 region would require that the thermal and elastic values of Θ be equal. The experimental evidence for the existence of a T^3 region, *as predicted by Debye,* is therefore weak. We shall see below that a *true* T^3 region can exist only at very much lower temperatures than suggested by Debye's theory, and that many substances which exhibit an apparent T^3 region at about 20° K. show specific-heat anomalies at lower temperatures. In fact, the Debye theory is seriously in error concerning the temperatures at which it predicts the T^3 region to begin.* This does not, however, detract from the faithfulness with which the Debye theory describes the experimental results at higher temperatures. We have already seen (Chapter VII, fig. 7.6) that the measured specific heats of a large number of substances fit a Debye curve over a wide range of temperatures. This good agreement does not extend to low temperatures. The lattice theory of specific heats which will be considered below (Section 11) throws some light on this point.

6. Born's Theory.

We have already mentioned that Born's theory is based on the principles of the dynamics of a lattice of particles, and introduces a cut-off wave number determined by the number of normal modes. It starts from a consideration of the modes of vibration of a lattice of atoms to determine the frequency spectrum.† This is a problem which has been solved in detail only fairly recently. Without working out the detailed spectrum for a three-dimensional lattice, Born and v. Kármám constructed an approximate spectrum by analogy with the (one-dimensional) case of a linear chain. The distribution function has the form

$$g(\nu) = \frac{72N}{\pi^3 \nu_0} \frac{\{\sin^{-1}(\nu/\nu_0)\}^2}{\{1 - \nu^2/\nu_0^2\}^{1/2}}. \quad \cdot \quad \cdot \quad \cdot \quad (14)$$

This reduces to the same form as for an elastic continuum for small values of ν/ν_0. Both expression (14) and the resulting specific-heat function are more complicated than the corresponding functions on Debye's theory, and have consequently been somewhat neglected.

---

* Eucken and Werth, *Z. anorg. Chem.*, Vol. 188, p. 152 (1930); Blackman, *Reports on Progress in Physics*, Vol. 8, p. 11 (1941).

† Born and v. Kármán, *Phys. Zeits.*, Vol. 13, p. 297 (1912). See also, E. Fisher, *J. Chem. Phys.*, Vol. 19, p. 632 (1951).

It must, however, be emphasized that the general theory on which it was based has become part of the lattice theory of vibrations, which is the basis of the most recent work on the specific heat of crystalline solids.

An interesting calculation, based on Born's theory, was made by Thirring.* He showed that the specific heat at high temperatures could be worked out without finding an explicit form for the spectrum and without any further approximations. The method is to expand the mean energy of an oscillator in powers of $h\nu/kT$. The result is

$$\bar{\epsilon} = kT \left\{ 1 - \sum_{n=1}^{\infty} (-1)^n \frac{B_n}{(2n)!} \left(\frac{h\nu}{kT} \right)^{2n} \right\}, \quad \cdot \quad \cdot \quad \cdot \quad (15)$$

where the B_n are the Bernoulli numbers.† The heat capacity of the linear oscillator is then given by

$$C_v = \frac{d\bar{\epsilon}}{dT} = k \left\{ 1 + \sum_{n=1}^{\infty} (-1)^n \frac{B_n(2n-1)}{(2n)!} \left(\frac{h}{kT} \right)^{2n} \nu^{2n} \right\}. \quad (16)$$

This series, in even powers of ν, is convergent for $h\nu/kT < 2\pi$. The sum of expression (16) for the $3N$ frequencies of vibration of the lattice of atoms gives the lattice specific heat. Born's theory gave an expression for the frequencies of vibration of a crystal lattice in the form of a determinant ‡ involving ν^2. Thirring showed that, for small values of n, the sum in (16) could be worked out quite simply from this determinant. Thus, he was able to work out fully the implications of the theory of Born and v. Kármán. Results were obtained for a number of crystals; the values for sodium chloride are given in Table III.

TABLE III

Specific heat of sodium chloride calculated by Thirring
on the Born and v. Kármán theory

Temperature, $T°$ K. ..	83·4	81·4	69·0	67·0
Specific heat { observed	3·75	3·54	3·13	3·06
calculated	3·71	3·67	3·09	3·02

It has already been pointed out that the Born and v. Kármán theory depends on the calculation of the frequency spectrum from the dyna-

---

* Thirring, *Phys. Zeits.*, Vol 14, p. 867 (1913); *ibid.*, Vol. 15, pp. 127, 180 (1914).

† See, for example, Whittaker, *Modern Analysis*, Cambridge University Press (1902), Section 63, p. 97.

‡ This is simply the case of free vibrations of a system of particles about an equilibrium position, and is dealt with in standard textbooks on sound. See, for example, Rayleigh, *The Theory of Sound*, 2nd edition, Macmillan, London and New York (1894), Vol. 1, Section 84.

mics of the crystal lattice. It is the achievement of the lattice theory of specific heats, chiefly in the hands of Blackman, to have solved this problem. We defer further consideration of this approach until we examine the modern theory in Section 11. It has already been re-marked that, since the examination of the dynamics of the crystal lattice leads to a cut-off wave number, it is quite indefensible to use a cut-off frequency as Debye did. The different modes of vibration should be treated separately, so that, for example, equation (7) should be replaced by

$$\frac{4\pi V}{c_l^3} \int_0^{\nu = \sigma_m c_l} \nu^2 d\nu + \frac{8\pi V}{c_t^3} \int_0^{\nu = \sigma_m c_t} \nu^2 d\nu = 3N_0. \qquad . \quad (7')$$

It is then convenient to carry out the analysis in terms of the momentum p.

7. Extension of the Theory.

We should expect these theories to apply only to a strictly iso-tropic body, and to one in which all the atoms were the same. The theory has been extended by Born and others * to apply to crystals and to bodies containing more than one type of atom. These theories take into account the fact that the body is not continuous but consists of atoms arranged on a lattice. The general results of the theory are that for non-isotropic bodies the specific heat is expressed as a sum of three Debye terms with different values of Θ; and that for crystalline bodies containing atoms of different types the specific heat is the sum of three Debye terms and of a number of terms arising out of single frequencies, which we now consider. The idea of single frequencies and their contribution to the specific heat derives from the original application, by Einstein, of the ideas of quantum theory to this prob-lem, which we have considered in Section 1.

Following the earlier work of Born and v. Kármán, the general theory of the vibrations of a crystal was worked out.† It was shown that the modes of vibration of a lattice of atoms could be divided into $3s$ groups, where there are s particles in a unit cell of the crystal. Of these, three represent low-frequency vibrations which are asymptoti-cally identical with the vibrations of an elastic continuum. These are termed acoustical vibrations. The remaining $(3s - 3)$ vibrations have frequencies generally in the optical region, and they are termed optical frequencies. Born worked out the general equations which determine these frequencies in the case of central forces, but the determination of the spectrum was too laborious and complicated to be attempted.

---

* See Schrödinger, *loc. cit.*, p. 500; see also Born, *Atomtheorie des festen Zustandes* (*Dynamik der Kristallgitter*), 2nd edition, pp. 643–52.

† Born, *Atomtheorie des festen Zustandes*, Leipzig (1923).

The specific-heat data were therefore given only in an approximate form. The simplest formulation is to represent each of the acoustical vibrations by a Debye spectrum, and each of the optical vibrations by an Einstein (single-line) spectrum; then the specific heat is represented by

$$C_v = \frac{1}{3s}\left[\sum_{s=1}^{3} D(\Theta_s) + \sum_{s=4}^{3s} E(\Theta_s)\right], \quad \cdots \quad (17)$$

where $D(\Theta)$ has been written for the function on the right-hand side of equation (10), and $E(\Theta)$ for the Einstein function which was introduced in equation (2).

This work by Born showed that at *sufficiently low* temperatures the specific heat must follow a cubic law; but the general theory leaves any specification of what is a sufficiently low temperature undefined. It can be worked out from case to case once the equations for the frequencies are known, but it depends very much on the forces between the particles in the crystal. It is therefore not surprising that the Debye theory, which completely neglects the interatomic interactions, should be far out in its specification of the T^3 region. The fact that at the lowest temperatures, specifically in the neighbourhood of the absolute zero, the specific heat of all crystalline solids vanishes as T^3 is a result of the greatest importance.

8. The Entropy of Solids.

The entropy S of a gram-atom of a pure solid at temperature T is given by

$$S - S_0 = \int_0^T \frac{C_v}{T}dT + \int_0^T \frac{C_p - C_v}{T}dT.$$

The second correction term can be dealt with simply by graphical methods or by using an approximation formula giving the dependence of $(C_p - C_v)$ on T (see Chapter VII, Section 5). The evaluation of the first term when C_v is a Debye or an Einstein function is of considerable importance in thermodynamics.

Writing
$$E = \int_0^T C_v dT,$$

and therefore
$$C_v = \frac{dE}{dT},$$

we have
$$\int_0^T \frac{C_v}{T}dT = \int_0^T \frac{1}{T}\frac{dE}{dT}dT = \frac{E}{T} + \int_0^T \frac{E}{T^2}dT.$$

Values of C_v, $\frac{E}{T}$, and of $\int_0^T \frac{E}{T^2}dT$ $\left(\text{which Nernst calls } \frac{F}{T}\right)$ are tabulated by Nernst for Einstein and Debye functions.*

* See Nernst, *Die Grundlagen des neuen Wärmesatzes*, 2nd edition, pp. 200–9 (1924).

9. Specific Heats at High Temperatures.

The above theories all give the result that at high temperatures atomic heats at constant volume converge towards the value given by the law of Dulong and Petit. In general this is confirmed by experimental results at moderate temperatures except in the case of substances, such as sodium and ice, which have low melting-points. With these substances anomalies appear as the melting-point is approached.*

The experiments that have been carried out at the highest temperatures all indicate a systematic departure from the law of Dulong and Petit. The atomic heats increase as the temperature is raised and reach values considerably above the limiting value 24·9 joules predicted by the law. The explanation of this is undoubtedly that all the theories are based on the assumption that the oscillations considered in the various cases are strictly harmonic: in other words, that Hooke's law is strictly obeyed. Actually this cannot be the case, and the departures from Hooke's law become greater as the amplitude of oscillation increases. Born and others † have extended the theory, taking into account the fact that the oscillations are not harmonic.

At high temperatures the contribution to the specific heat of a metal from the free electrons begins to be appreciable.‡

10. The Energy of an Oscillator at the Absolute Zero.

By equation (5), Chapter XXI, the energy of an oscillator of frequency ν at temperature T is equal to

$$kT \frac{h\nu/kT}{e^{h\nu/kT} - 1}.$$

We have

$$e^{h\nu/kT} = 1 + \frac{h\nu}{kT} + \tfrac{1}{2}\left(\frac{h\nu}{kT}\right)^2 + \ldots.$$

Substituting this in the expression for the energy of the oscillator, we obtain

$$kT/(1 + h\nu/2kT + \ldots).$$

For very large values of T this becomes

$$kT - \frac{h\nu}{2};$$

all other terms contain T in the denominator and can be neglected.

The result is that at high temperatures the energy of an oscillator does not converge towards the value kT predicted by classical mechanics, but towards the value $kT - h\nu/2$. In order to make it converge towards the value kT it is necessary to assume that an oscillator of frequency ν has an amount of energy $h\nu/2$ at the absolute zero.§ This is called the zero-point energy.

* Carpenter and Stoodley, *Phil. Mag.*, Vol. 10, p. 249 (1930), have made a careful study of the specific heat of mercury in the neighbourhood of the melting-point and have shown that anomalies occur in this case also.

† See Born, *Atomtheorie des festen Zustandes*, p. 698; also Waller, *Ann. d. Physik*, Vol. 83, p. 180 (1927).

‡ See Chapter XI, Section 20.

§ It is important to remark that the principles of statistical mechanics do not necessarily require that at high temperatures the quantum and classical values should converge and become identical, but that their ratio should converge to unity. The latter condition is satisfied whether there is or is not an energy term at the absolute zero.

The existence or non-existence of the energy term at the absolute zero does not affect specific heats at all, since the term disappears on differentiating with respect to the temperature.

The most striking effects of zero-point energy are obtained from a comparison of the properties of the hydrogen isotopes where the large mass ratio 2 : 1 makes the differences large. For example, the molecular heat of sublimation at the absolute zero is 274·0 for D_2 and 183·4 for H_2.*

Evidence in favour of the existence of zero-point energy in crystals may be obtained from a study of the temperature variation of the intensity of reflection of X-rays by crystals.† The theory of the variation of intensity of scattering with variation of temperature, that is, with a known *variation* of the heat energy of the atoms in the crystal, is in accord with experiment over a wide range of temperatures. Thus, from the measured scattering at the lowest temperature at which experiments are available, the theory of temperature variation may with reasonable confidence be used to extrapolate and obtain the intensity of scattering if the atoms were at rest. Different results are obtained in this way for the "measured" intensity with the atoms at rest according to whether it is assumed that the atoms at the lowest temperature of experiment have (a) the heat-energy corresponding to this temperature *plus* zero-point energy, or (b) only the heat energy. The scattering for the atoms at rest may also be independently calculated from the known distribution of charge in the sodium and chlorine ions (rock-salt is the substance for which experimental results are available). It is found that the theoretical value so obtained agrees much better with the measured intensity deduced with the assumption of the existence of zero-point energy than with that deduced with the assumption of no zero-point energy.

11. Blackman's Lattice Theory of Specific Heats.

From the results which have been collected in this chapter, it is evident that the theory which has been developed so far gives a general account of the specific heats of solids except at low temperatures. Blackman ‡ has considered the values which are obtained for Θ_D on the Debye theory, and has shown that it varies widely with temperature. From these results it appears that it is unsatisfactory to treat the crystal as a continuum, and that the specific crystal properties are of much greater significance than had been appreciated previously. The vibrational spectrum of a crystal lattice can differ very much from that of an elastic solid. To account for these properties, the detailed particle dynamics have to be calculated on the lines first suggested by Born and v. Kármán. Calculation of the vibrational spectrum of a two-dimensional lattice by Blackman § showed that it differed greatly from that assumed by Debye. This was confirmed

---

* See Eucken, *J. de Physique*, Vol. 7, p. 287 (1936), where a number of other differences are given.

† See James, Waller, and Hartree, *Proc. Roy. Soc.*, A, Vol. 118, p. 334 (1928); see also Claus, *Phys. Rev.*, Vol. 38, p. 604 (1931), who has studied the effect of temperature on the diffuse scattering of X-rays and has obtained results in accord with the theory including zero-point energy.

‡ Blackman, *Proc. Roy. Soc.*, A, Vol. 148, pp. 365, 384 (1935); Vol. 149, pp. 107, 126 (1935).

§ Blackman, *Proc. Roy. Soc.*, A, Vol. 148, p. 384 (1934).

by the calculation of the spectrum of a simple cubic lattice.* Black-man took account of the interactions between the closest neighbour particles on the lattice and also between next nearest neighbour particles. Forces of a quasi-elastic type were assumed and, for purposes of calculation, the latter were taken to be one-twentieth of the former.

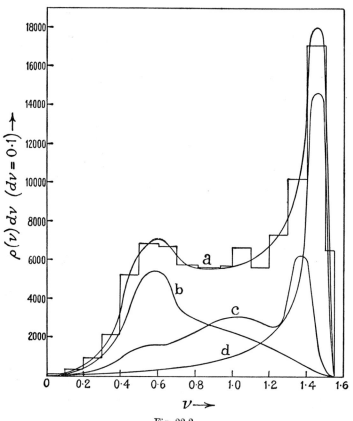

Fig. 22.2

The vibrational spectrum calculated in this case is shown by curve (a) in fig. 22.2. The most striking feature of the spectrum is the heaping up of frequencies at somewhat less than half the maximum frequency. At low frequencies, the distribution function varies as ν^2, but then rises to a maximum; the density then remains nearly constant until optical frequencies are reached, where there is a rapid increase. The distribution follows that for the two-dimensional case very closely.

* Blackman, *Proc. Roy. Soc.*, A, Vol. 159, p. 416 (1937); *Proc. Cambridge Phil. Soc.*, Vol. 33, p. 94 (1937).

The shape of the distribution curve with its two maxima and their relative positions indicates how the Nernst-Lindemann spectrum of two single lines gave such a good representation of the experimental data. Curves (b), (c), and (d) of fig. 22.2 correspond to the three frequency branches which arise from the three modes of vibration obtained by interchanging the phase differences of neighbouring particles along the three axes. On the basis of this model, which approximates to a potassium chloride crystal, Blackman calculated the specific heat of the crystal and from it the corresponding Debye Θ_D. This is shown plotted as a function of temperature in fig. 22.3.

Similar calculations have been made by Fine * for a body-centred cubic lattice, with the atomic force constants chosen so that the model

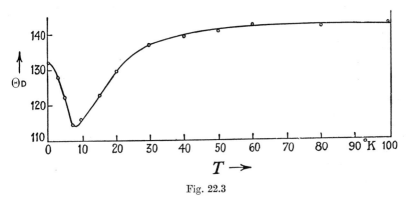

Fig. 22.3

would represent tungsten. Kellermann † has made careful calculations for sodium chloride using ionic and repulsive forces between the particles.

These calculations show that the density of normal vibrations, which starts off as a ν^2 law, rises faster than ν^2 as soon as the continuum region is passed. This appears to be a consequence of lattice theory, and to be a property of all lattices in which short-range forces are assumed, although no general proof has yet been given. This property of the spectrum ensures that C_v/T^3 will rise as the temperature increases. In terms of the Debye theory,‡ this means that the value of Θ_D will fall, but the amount by which it falls will depend very much on the particular properties of the spectrum. It is this effect which moves the true T^3 region to temperatures less than $\Theta_D/100$. Most of

* Fine, *Phys. Rev.*, Vol. 56, p. 355 (1939).

† Kellerman, *Phil. Trans. Roy. Soc.*, A, Vol. 238, p. 513 (1940); *Proc. Roy. Soc.*, A, Vol. 178, p. 17 (1941).

‡ For a general discussion of the relation of Debye theory to lattice theory, see Blackman, *Proc. Roy. Soc.*, A, Vol. 181, p. 58 (1942).

the limited temperature regions over which a cubic variation of specific heat has been observed are spurious and due to a fortuitous combination of circumstances.

The Debye function depends on only one parameter, and it appears clear from lattice theory that a one-parameter representation cannot, in general, give a valid representation of specific-heat data. The specific heats at high and at low temperatures depend on different combinations of the forces between particles. In the high-temperature region, the specific heat is controlled by the normal vibrations of the crystals, and the low-frequency end of the spectrum plays a negligible part in determining it. On the other hand, the specific heat at low temperatures is controlled by the low-frequency end of the spectrum. In particular cases, this can be varied a great deal (by varying the forces between the particles) without altering the high-frequency end appreciably.

To understand the details of the variation of the specific heat of solids with temperature, it would appear to be necessary to make a detailed calculation of the frequency spectrum in each case. In view of the complications which occur in the lattice theory of specific heats, the Debye theory is remarkable, not in that it fails badly in some cases, but because it gives as good a description as it does for most crystals except at low temperatures.

The calculation of the vibrational spectrum has thrown an important new light on the theory of the specific heats of solids. The vibrational spectrum is of a quite different character from that assumed by Debye. This represents a vindication of the method originally proposed by Born and v. Kármán. The detailed properties of the vibrational spectrum explain the deviations from Debye theory which are observed at low temperatures, and indicate that a true T^3 region can exist only at helium and demagnetization temperatures.

12. Anomalies in the Specific Heats of Solids.

We have seen that the specific heat associated with the normal modes of any lattice is a monotonic, increasing function of the temperature. It is dangerous to regard any part of a specific-heat curve as anomalous unless it contradicts this theorem. If, however, this theorem fails, and there is a region of the specific-heat curve over which $dC_v/dT \leqslant 0$, then there is certainly a true anomaly for which an explanation outside the straightforward lattice theory must be found.* The interesting anomalies are those for which there are departures from the law of steadily increasing specific heat at low temperatures, and over more or less strictly limited temperature ranges. We shall consider three main types of specific-heat anomalies.

Simon and his co-workers † have discovered that over limited ranges of tem-

---

* Fowler, *Proc. Roy. Soc.*, A, Vol. 151, p. 1 (1935).

† Simon, *Ann. d. Physik*, Vol. 68, p. 241 (1922); F. E. Simon, C. von Simson, and M. Ruhemann, *Zeits. f. phys. Chem.*, A, Vol. 129, p. 339 (1927). For other references, see Simon and Bergmann, *Zeits. f. phys. Chem.*, B, Vol. 8, p. 225 (1930).

perature the specific heats and other properties of many solids show anomalies. These are of several different types.

The general nature of one type of anomaly is illustrated in fig. 22.4. The mole-

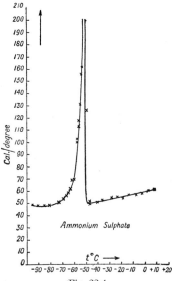

Fig. 22.4

cular heat of ammonium sulphate measured by Crenshaw and Ritter * is plotted as a function of the temperature. Similar effects have been found for other ammonium salts, and these are summarized in Table IV.

TABLE IV

Ammonium salt	Temperature of anomaly	Total energy of anomaly in cal. per gm.-ion of NH_4
Fluoride ..	$-30.7°$ C.	16
Chloride ..	-30.4	200
Bromide ..	-38.0	80
Iodide ..	-42.5	69
Sulphate ..	-50.7	485
Nitrate ..	-60.4	530

Volume changes are associated with these anomalies † and Hettner and Simon ‡ have also found temperature variations in the transparency of the salts to infrared light. The results for ammonium chloride are shown in fig. 22.5. The full line shows the energy content measured calorimetrically, the dotted line the trans-

* Crenshaw and Ritter, *Zeits. f. phys. Chem.*, B, Vol. 16, p. 143 (1932).

† See Simon and Bergmann, *loc. cit.*

‡ Hettner and Simon, *Zeits. f. phys. Chem.*, B, Vol. 1, p. 293 (1928).

parency for light of wave-length $5 \cdot 55\mu$, and the broken line the transparency for light of wave-length $7 \cdot 98\mu$—all as a function of the temperature. With the effect shown is associated a slight shift of the maximum of the absorption band when the temperature changes. Similar changes in transparency were found in

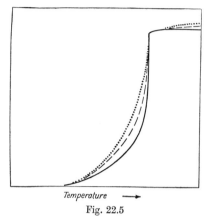

Temperature ⟶

Fig. 22.5

ammonium sulphate, and, as described above, specific-heat anomalies at the same temperature have since been found by Crenshaw and Ritter.

In the above cases the anomalies are presumably due to the ammonium ion. Other workers have since found similar specific-heat anomalies in other substances.*

There are certain orientations of the molecules in a crystal for which the potential energy is a minimum. These orientations correspond to equilibrium positions. In general, the difference in potential energy between two equilibrium orientations will be large compared with kT, so that the molecules will execute small oscillations about an equilibrium orientation. The specific-heat anomalies observed in these ammonium salts correspond to a transition from one equilibrium orientation to another. That the re-orientation of the ammonium radicals, and not the onset of free rotation, is responsible has been demonstrated by Lawson,† who has determined the thermodynamical functions in the neighbourhood of the transition point very carefully. Lawson's experimental work thus supports Frenkel's ‡ hypothesis rather than that of Pauling,§ who, following Fowler's work ‖ on the rotation of molecules in crystals, attempted to explain these anomalies as due to the onset of free rotation. Observations on nuclear magnetic resonance ¶ support the view that the molecules do not rotate freely above the transition temperature. The important point, however, is that the anomaly is due to a transition from one state to another, which occurs as a result of the interactions between the molecules of the crystal lattice. Essentially, we are concerned here with a co-operative effect, in that the behaviour at the transition point is dominated by the coupling between the molecules, and this shows itself as a specific-heat anomaly.

Other cases of specific-heat anomalies associated with co-operative action between systems of the assembly are also well known. The classical example is that of ferromagnetism. Another case is that of alloys which show an order-disorder transition at a critical temperature. In each of these cases, the specific-heat anomaly can be associated with a more fundamental physical change which it accompanies, and which occurs at the same temperature. A statistical theory

* Clusius, *Zeits. f. phys. Chem.*, B, Vol. 3, p. 41 (1929), in methane; Giauque and Wiebe, *Journ. Amer. Chem. Soc.*, Vol. 50, pp. 101, 2193 (1928); Vol. 51, p. 1441 (1929), in HCl, HBr and HI. See also Bridgman, *Phys. Rev.*, Vol. 38, p. 182 (1931), who has studied the effect of pressure on the volume anomalies; A. J. C. Wilson, *Phys. Rev.*, Vol. 54, p. 1103 (1938).

† Lawson, *Phys. Rev.*, Vol. 57, p. 417 (1940).

‡ Frenkel, *Acta Physicochemica*, Vol. 3, p. 23 (1935).

§ Pauling, *Phys. Rev.*, Vol. 36, p. 430 (1930).

‖ Fowler, *Proc. Roy. Soc.*, A, Vol. 118, p. 52 (1928); Vol. 149, p. 1 (1935).

¶ N. L. Alpert, *Phys. Rev.*, Vol. 75, p. 398 (1949); H. T. Gutowsky and G. E. Pake, *J. Chem. Phys.*, Vol. 18, p. 162 (1950).

of the more fundamental effect provides a free-energy contribution which accounts, at least qualitatively, for the anomalous specific heat. Below the Curie point, the specific heat of a ferromagnetic substance begins to increase steadily, until there is an excess specific heat of several joules per degree per mole. This excess specific heat falls discontinuously to zero on passing through the Curie temperature. In the case of metallic alloys, there is a critical temperature below which the alloy exhibits a super-lattice structure, due to regular alternations of the atoms of the components of the alloys. The state of order at any temperature depends on the state of order already existing in the lattice; this assumption introduces the essentially co-operative nature of the process that is envisaged. In this way, the interaction energy of the lattice varies more rapidly than linearly with the parameter which specifies the degree of order. This establishes the existence of a transition temperature and a specific-heat excess which gradually increases as the transition temperature is approached from below, and then falls discontinuously on passing through the transition point. This gives the essential features of the order-disorder theory originally proposed by Bragg and Williams,* to explain the discontinuities in the physical properties of alloys which occurred at the temperature at which the super-lattice lines disappeared in X-ray photographs of the alloy.

The specific-heat anomalies which occur at the phase transitions in liquid helium, and at the onset of superconductivity in some metals, have already been mentioned.† The specific-heat anomalies in these two cases have the same general character as those which we have been considering in alloys, ferromagnetics, and some ammonium crystals. Although there is no accepted theory to account for the anomalies in these two cases, it is fairly clear that they are also due to co-operative action. In fact, the remarkable low-temperature properties in each of these transitions are an example of quantal effects on a macroscopic scale. The quantal conditions impose an intensely strong coupling between the systems of the assembly.

The second type of specific-heat anomaly occurs in a transition between two solid phases; a typical example is the transition from white to grey tin. In these cases, the specific heat of the two modifications may have different values on the two sides of the transition point, corresponding to the different crystal lattices, but does not extend over a wide range of temperature on the low-temperature side, as in the case of anomalies due to co-operative effects. In these cases, the different geometries of the lattice structures imply, from energy considerations, that the change cannot take place on a molecular scale; the distortion of the lattice is too great. A *small* bit of the second lattice cannot be embedded in the first lattice without the expenditure of a very large amount of distortional energy; in short, for a *reasonable* expenditure of energy we can only create large blocks of the second lattice. Either the whole lattice must change over to the other modification or there can be no change at all. This explains the sharpness of such a transition, of which the melting of a solid is one of the most striking examples.‡

There is another class of specific-heat anomaly which is characterized by the fact that the excess specific heat has a maximum at a definite temperature, and falls away gradually on either side. This type of anomaly is more difficult to recognize, and there are some specific-heat curves which have been thought to be

* Bragg and Williams, *Proc. Roy. Soc.*, A, Vol. 145, p. 699 (1934); Vol. 151, p. 540 (1935); Williams, *Proc. Roy. Soc.*, A, Vol. 152, p. 231 (1935); see also the references to Sections 5 and 6 of Chapter XVII.

† Chapter XVII, Sections 2 and 7–9 respectively.

‡ Compare Mott, *Proc. Roy. Soc.*, A, Vol. 146, p. 465 (1934), who has shown that the formal theory of a transition between two crystal lattices may be applied for some purposes even when one of the " lattices " is a liquid.

anomalous * but which are probably quite normal. The explanation of this type of anomaly is that each atom in the lattice has two possible states of known weights ϖ_1, ϖ_2, and energy difference ε, and the lattice states are independent of which state each atom is in. Schottky showed that such an assumption gives a specific-heat anomaly of the kind which we are now considering. The distribution of the energy between these two states is given by the partition function

$$\varpi_1 + \varpi_2 e^{-\varepsilon/kT}.$$

The corresponding contribution to the free energy of N such atoms is

$$-NkT \log (\varpi_1 + \varpi_2 e^{-\varepsilon/kT}).$$

The resultant total energy and the specific heat are

$$\bar{E} = N\varpi_2 \varepsilon/(\varpi_1 e^{\varepsilon/kT} + \varpi_2),$$

$$C_v = Nk \left(\frac{\varepsilon}{kT}\right)^2 \frac{\varpi_1 \varpi_2 e^{\varepsilon/kT}}{(\varpi_1 e^{\varepsilon/kT} + \varpi_2)^2}. \qquad \cdots \cdots \quad (18)$$

On the high-temperature side, the excess specific heat falls off as $1/T^2$. The anomalous specific heat of gadolinium sulphate † below 4° K. can be explained in this way. The Gd^{+++} ion, when free, has a lowest state, ^8S, of eight-fold degeneracy, due to the eight possible spin orientations. This spin is almost, but not quite, unaffected by the fields of the surrounding ions in the lattice, and the state is split by the crystalline field of the lattice into a number of less degenerate states with small energy separations. The splitting of the state of a particular ion is practically independent of the states of the neighbouring ions, so that the effects for all the ions can be summed. Physically, the excess specific heat corresponds to the energy required to raise the ions from their state of lowest orientational energy and to distribute them over the other states. This theory reproduces the observed specific-heat anomaly of gadolinium sulphate, and similar explanations can be advanced with regard to the specific-heat anomalies shown by other paramagnetic salts at very low temperatures. Such specific-heat anomalies are important in connexion with cooling by adiabatic demagnetization (see Chapter V, Section 16).

It has more recently been shown ‡ that the interactions between the lattice vibrations and the conduction electrons in a metal modify the properties of a metal at low temperatures. This effect has been adduced to explain the peaks observed in the specific heats of sodium and beryllium at low temperatures. Reasonable agreement with the observations is obtained.

---

* The measurements of the specific heat of lithium by Simon and Swain, *Z. phys. Chem.*, B, Vol. 28, p. 189 (1935), have often been held to indicate an anomaly in the region of 200° K. However, Blackman's work on specific heats indicates that the subsidiary maxima in the frequency spectrum make the Debye temperature variable, and in a way that depends on the details of the crystal structure. Also, this variation can extend to surprisingly low temperatures and even for the simplest lattices there can be regions of spurious constancy of Θ_D when it is near a turning value, and these can be mistaken for the true constant Θ_D region which extends to the absolute zero. The observed variation of Θ_D for lithium is not unlike that calculated by Blackman. In the absence of definite evidence of anomalous behaviour, it must be presumed to be normal. See Fowler, *Proc. Roy. Soc.*, A, Vol. p. 8 (1935).

† Kürti, *Z. phys. Chem.*, B, Vol. 20, p. 305 (1933).

‡ M. J. Buckingham, *Nature*, Vol. 168, p. 281 (1951).

CHAPTER XXIII

The Equation of State for Solids

1. In obtaining the equation of state for solids we shall use a general theorem due to Clausius * and called the virial law. We shall first deduce this law.

2. The Virial Law of Clausius.

Let the co-ordinates of any atom be x, y, z, and let the components of the force acting on it parallel to the three axes of x, y, z, in the directions of x, y, z increasing, be respectively X, Y, Z. If μ is the mass of an atom and t is the time, we have

$$\mu \frac{d^2x}{dt^2} = X. \qquad \ldots \ldots \ldots \quad (1)$$

By differentiation of x^2 with respect to t we obtain

$$\frac{d^2}{dt^2}(x^2) = 2\frac{d}{dt}\left(x\frac{dx}{dt}\right) = 2\left(\frac{dx}{dt}\right)^2 + 2x\frac{d^2x}{dt^2}. \quad \ldots \ldots \quad (2)$$

Substituting in (1) the value of d^2x/dt^2 given by (2), we obtain

$$\tfrac{1}{2}\mu\left(\frac{dx}{dt}\right)^2 = \tfrac{1}{4}\mu\frac{d^2(x^2)}{dt^2} - \tfrac{1}{2}xX.$$

Taking mean values of all three quantities over an interval of time τ, we have

$$\frac{\mu}{2\tau}\int_0^\tau \left(\frac{dx}{dt}\right)^2 dt = \frac{\mu}{4\tau}\left[\frac{d(x^2)}{dt}\right]_0^\tau - \frac{1}{2\tau}\int_0^\tau xX\,dt. \quad \ldots \ldots \quad (3)$$

If τ is made sufficiently large, the two terms involving integrals remain finite and do not vary appreciably. The first term on the right-hand side of the equation, however, becomes vanishingly small, since it contains τ in the denominator and since the quantity dx^2/dt fluctuates only between certain specified limits. We have therefore

$$\text{time mean value of } \tfrac{1}{2}\mu\left(\frac{dx}{dt}\right)^2 = \text{time mean value of } (-\tfrac{1}{2}xX).$$

Similar relations apply to the motion parallel to the axes of y and z. Thus, the time mean values of

$$\tfrac{1}{2}\mu\left\{\left(\frac{dx}{dt}\right)^2 + \left(\frac{dy}{dt}\right)^2 + \left(\frac{dz}{dt}\right)^2\right\} \quad \text{and} \quad -\tfrac{1}{2}\{xX + yY + zZ\}$$

are equal.

* Clausius, *Phil. Mag.*, August, 1870.

The quantity $\left\{ \left(\dfrac{dx}{dt}\right)^2 + \left(\dfrac{dy}{dt}\right)^2 + \left(\dfrac{dz}{dt}\right)^2 \right\}$ is the square of the resultant velocity c of the atom. Summing over all the atoms in the system, we obtain

time mean value of $\sum \frac{1}{2}\mu c^2 = $ time mean value of $-\frac{1}{2} \sum \{xX + yY + zZ\}$.   (4)

The quantity on the right-hand side of this equation is called the *virial* of the system. Equation (4) may therefore be stated: *The mean kinetic energy of a system is equal to its virial.* This is the virial law of Clausius.

The virial depends only on the forces acting on the atoms and not on their motion. The case which is of importance for our purpose is that in which the forces included in the virial are of two kinds: (1) the mutual forces between the atoms themselves, and (2) a uniform external pressure on the surface of the body under consideration. We shall consider these separately.

We may assume that the force $f(r)$ between two atoms depends only on the distance r between them. $f(r)$ is to be reckoned positive if the force is repulsive. The force acts along the line joining the particles. If the centres of the atoms are at x, y, z and x', y', z' respectively, and if the components of the forces acting on them due to their mutual reaction are X, Y, Z and X', Y', Z', then

$$X = f(r)\,\frac{x - x'}{r}, \ \ X' = f(r)\,\frac{x' - x}{r},$$

with similar relations for the y and z components. The contribution to ΣxX made by the forces between these two particles is

$$xX + x'X' = \frac{f(r)}{r}(x - x')^2.$$

The contribution to $\Sigma(xX + yY + zZ)$ is therefore

$$\frac{f(r)}{r}\{(x - x')^2 + (y - y')^2 + (z - z')^2\} = rf(r). \quad . \quad . \quad . \quad (5)$$

The contribution to the virial which arises from interatomic forces is therefore

the time mean value of $-\frac{1}{2}\sum rf(r)$, ...   (6)

where each pair of molecules is to be reckoned once in taking the sum.

We now reckon the contribution to the virial due to a uniform pressure p acting over the surface of the body. Consider an element dS of the surface of the body, and let the direction cosines of the outward-drawn normal from this element be l, m, n. The total force exerted by the ν atoms which strike the element of area in unit time is $p\,dS$; the force is directed along the normal. The components of this force are $lp\,dS$, $mp\,dS$, $np\,dS$. The components of the total force exerted by the pressure on the ν atoms of the body which strike dS in unit time are $-lp\,dS$, $-mp\,dS$, $-np\,dS$. The time mean value of ΣX contributed by the pressure p acting over the area dS is therefore

$$-lp\,dS,$$

and similar relations hold for ΣY and ΣZ.

If x, y, z are the co-ordinates of the element of area dS, the virial of the forces due to the pressure exerted over the element dS is therefore given by

$$-\tfrac{1}{2}(-lpx\,dS - mpy\,dS - npz\,dS),$$

or $$\tfrac{1}{2}p(lx\,dS + my\,dS + nz\,dS).$$

To find the total contribution of the external pressure to the virial we have to integrate this expression over the whole surface, obtaining

$$\tfrac{1}{2}p\left(\iint lx\,dS + \iint my\,dS + \iint nz\,dS\right). \quad \dots \quad (7)$$

If $\mathbf{V}$ is the volume of the body,

$$\iint lx\,dS = \iint my\,dS = \iint nz\,dS = \mathbf{V}.$$

Expression (7) is therefore equal to

$$\tfrac{3}{2}p\mathbf{V}. \quad \dots \dots \dots \quad (8)$$

The virial due to the interatomic forces and to the uniform external pressure p is obtained by combining expressions (6) and (8), and is therefore equal to

$$-\tfrac{1}{2}\sum\overline{rf(r)} + \tfrac{3}{2}p\mathbf{V}, \quad \dots \dots \dots \quad (9)$$

where the bar signifies that the time mean value is to be taken. Substituting this in equation (4), we obtain

$$\sum\overline{\tfrac{1}{2}\mu c^2} = -\tfrac{1}{2}\sum\overline{rf(r)} + \tfrac{3}{2}p\mathbf{V}. \quad \dots \dots \quad (10)$$

The summation of $rf(r)$ is to be taken so that each *pair* of molecules is considered once. This is the relation that we shall require below.*

The Theory of the Solid State

3. In order to apply equation (10) to solids we must first consider in some detail the behaviour of the atoms in a solid. Our ultimate object is to evaluate the term on the left and the first term on the right-hand side of the equation.†

X-ray examination has shown that the atoms of a solid are arranged on a space lattice. We shall consider the simplest form of solid, in which all the atoms are identical. Further, we shall suppose that the atoms are arranged in the simplest possible way, that is, at the corners of a cubic lattice. The theory for other cubic lattices (face-centred or body-centred) differs from that for the simple cubic lattice only through the introduction of numerical constants; the theory given below can therefore be applied to any monatomic solid which crystallizes in the regular system.

For such a lattice, if $\bar{r}$ is the mean distance between two neighbouring atoms on the lattice, and if V is the volume of, and N_0 the number of atoms in, a gram-atom,

$$N_0\bar{r}^3 = V. \quad \dots \dots \dots \dots \quad (11)$$

We shall suppose that the atoms are held in position on the lattice through the agency of attractive and repulsive forces which they exert on one another. In the equilibrium position these forces exactly balance one another.‡ In order

---

* For the application of this relation to gases, see Jeans, *Dynamical Theory of Gases*, 3rd edition, p. 131. If the molecules are far enough apart to be outside the sphere of one another's attractions, the first term on the right vanishes and we have the relation: $p\mathbf{V}$ equal to two-thirds of the total kinetic energy.

† See Grüneisen, *Ann. d. Physik*, Vol. 39, p. 257 (1912).

‡ This idea was first introduced by Mie, *Ann. d. Physik*, Vol. 11, p. 657 (1903).

to account for the elastic properties of solids it is necessary to suppose that, with increase of the distance between two atoms, the repulsive force falls off much more rapidly than the attractive force.* We shall suppose further that both the attractive † and the repulsive forces obey simple inverse power laws as regards the distance between them, and that, apart from a constant, the potential energy θ of two atoms separated by a distance r is given by

$$\phi = \lambda r^{-s} - \mu r^{-t}, \quad \dots \dots \dots \quad (12)$$

where λ and μ are constants. The first term arises from the attractive and the second from the repulsive force; s is greater than t.

The force $f(r)$ between two atoms, reckoned positive if repulsive, is equal to $-d\phi/dr$; that is,

$$f(r) = \frac{s\lambda}{r^{s+1}} - \frac{t\mu}{r^{t+1}}. \quad \dots \dots \dots \quad (13)$$

4. The Total Potential Energy of the Atoms in a Gram-atom.

Let us first consider a solid under zero external pressure, and at the absolute zero where we assume the atoms completely at rest. The atoms are held in their equilibrium positions by the attractive and repulsive forces. If r_0 is the distance between neighbouring atoms and V_0 is the volume occupied by a gram-atom, then by equation (11)

$$N_0 r_0^3 = V_0. \quad \dots \dots \dots \dots \quad (14)$$

The simplest way of obtaining the potential energy is to regard half the potential energy θ of two atoms separated by a distance r (see equation (12)) as being the potential energy of *one* atom due to its proximity to the other.

We shall now estimate the value of ϕ_0, the potential energy of a single atom arising from the *attractive* forces of the other atoms in the lattice. A certain known number ν_λ of atoms will be separated from the given atom by a distance $k_\lambda r_0$, and we have

$$\phi_0 = -\tfrac{1}{2}\mu \sum \frac{\nu_\lambda}{(k_\lambda r_0)^t}. \quad \dots \dots \dots \quad (15)$$

The sum is to be taken for all values of λ so as to include all the atoms in a gram-atom, but may be stopped if we reach a distance outside which the atoms do not produce an appreciable change in the potential energy.

Similarly the potential energy χ_0 of a single atom due to the *repulsive* forces of the other atoms in the lattice is given by

$$\chi_0 = +\tfrac{1}{2}\lambda \sum \frac{\nu_\lambda}{(k_\lambda r_0)^s}. \quad \dots \dots \dots \quad (16)$$

We now write the factors which depend only on the nature of the lattice and on the exponents t and s in the forms

$$\sum \frac{\nu_\lambda}{(k_\lambda)^t} = \sigma(t), \quad \text{and} \quad \sum \frac{\nu_\lambda}{(k_\lambda)^s} = \sigma(s).$$

* For a discussion of the forces between atoms and molecules, see Lennard-Jones in Chapter X of Fowler's *Statistical Mechanics*, 2nd edition, Cambridge University Press (1936); also Lennard-Jones, *Physica*, Vol. 4, p. 941 (1937).

† The leading term in the van der Waals (attractive) energy must be of the form $-\mu r^{-6}$. See Lennard-Jones, *Proc. Phys. Soc.*, Vol. 43, p. 461 (1931), and F. London, *Zeits. f. phys. Chem.*, Vol. 11, p. 222 (1930).

We thus obtain for the potential energy of the given atom due to both attractive and repulsive forces

$$\phi_0 + \chi_0 = -\tfrac{1}{2}\frac{\mu\sigma(t)}{r_0{}^t} + \tfrac{1}{2}\frac{\lambda\sigma(s)}{r_0{}^s}. \quad \ldots \ldots \quad (17)$$

The total potential energy Ω_0 of the atoms in a gram-atom at the absolute zero and under zero pressure is obtained by multiplying this by N_0, giving

$$\Omega_0 = \Phi_0 + X_0 = -\tfrac{1}{2}\frac{N_0\mu\sigma(t)}{r_0{}^t} + \tfrac{1}{2}\frac{N_0\lambda\sigma(s)}{r_0{}^s}, \quad \ldots \ldots \quad (18)$$

where we have written Φ_0 for $N_0\phi_0$ and X_0 for $N_0\chi_0$. Introducing the volume V_0 by using equation (14), we obtain

$$\Omega_0 = -\frac{1}{2}\frac{N_0{}^{1+t/3}\mu\sigma(t)}{V_0{}^{t/3}} + \frac{1}{2}\frac{N_0{}^{1+s/3}\lambda\sigma(s)}{V_0{}^{s/3}}.$$

This may be written

$$\Omega_0 = \frac{A}{V_0{}^m} - \frac{B}{V_0{}^n}, \quad \ldots \ldots \ldots \quad (19)$$

where

$$\left. \begin{aligned} A &= \tfrac{1}{2}N_0{}^{1+s/3}\lambda\sigma(s), \\ B &= \tfrac{1}{2}N_0{}^{1+t/3}\mu\sigma(t); \end{aligned} \right\} \quad \ldots \ldots \quad (20)$$

and

$$n = t/3, \quad m = s/3. \quad \ldots \ldots \quad (21)$$

A and B are constants depending on the law of force between the atoms and on the structure of the lattice, but independent of the volume.

At any higher temperature T the mean separation of the atoms increases, and the atoms oscillate about their mean positions. The expression for Ω, the instantaneous value of the potential energy of the atoms in a gram-atom, is

$$\Omega = \Phi + X = -\tfrac{1}{2}\mu \Sigma \left(\frac{1}{r_{\xi\rho}}\right)^t + \tfrac{1}{2}\lambda \Sigma \left(\frac{1}{r_{\xi\rho}}\right)^s, \quad \ldots \ldots \quad (22)$$

where $r_{\xi\rho}$ is the instantaneous separation of the ξth atom from the ρth atom, and where, in taking the sum, ξ and ρ both have all values from 1 to N_0.

$\bar{\Omega}$, the time mean value of Ω, is equal to the sum of the potential energies which the atoms in a gram-atom would possess if they were at rest at their various centres of oscillation, *plus* the time mean value of the *potential* energy of oscillation of all the atoms. The former is obtained immediately from equation (19) by substituting V, the volume occupied by a gram-atom at temperature T, for V_0; we thus have

$$\frac{A}{V^m} - \frac{B}{V^n}. \quad \ldots \ldots \ldots \quad (22a)$$

The latter is obtained as follows. We assume that the oscillations of the atoms are undamped harmonic oscillations, and that the total energy E of these oscillations is given by

$$E = \int_0^T C_v \, dT, \quad \ldots \ldots \ldots \quad (23)$$

where C_v is the atomic heat at constant volume. The energy of oscillation is half kinetic and half potential, so that the potential energy of oscillation is

$$\tfrac{1}{2}E \quad \text{or} \quad \tfrac{1}{2}\int_0^T C_v \, dT. \quad \ldots \ldots \ldots \quad (23a)$$

We have therefore for $\overline{\Omega}$, the time mean value of the potential energy of the atoms in a gram-atom,

$$\overline{\Omega} = \frac{A}{V^m} - \frac{B}{V^n} + \tfrac{1}{2}E. \quad \ldots \ldots \ldots \quad (24)$$

We have now to determine how much of $\tfrac{1}{2}E$ arises from attractive and how much from repulsive forces. This requires a detailed consideration of the oscillations of the atoms.

5. Atomic Oscillations.

In order to calculate the frequency of the atomic oscillations it is necessary to determine the restoring force which acts on an atom displaced from its mean position in the lattice. In carrying out the calculations we shall make the simplifying assumption that only one atom is displaced and that all the other atoms in the lattice are in their mean positions.*

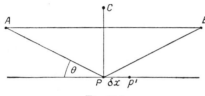

Fig. 23.1

Let the atom P under consideration be displaced a distance δx to P′ along one of the lines of the lattice, i.e. directly towards one of its immediate neighbours. Consider the effect on the displaced atom of two atoms A and B which are mirror images of each other in the plane drawn at right angles to the direction of the displacement δx. If $AP = r$, $AP' = r + \delta x \cos\theta$, and $BP' = r - \delta x \cos\theta$. If $f(r)$ is the repulsive force between two atoms, the force due to A on P′ is $f(r + \delta x \cos\theta)$ along the line AP′, or

$$f(r + \delta x \cos\theta) \cos\theta$$

in the direction PP′. That due to B on P′ is

$$-f(r - \delta x \cos\theta) \cos\theta$$

in the same direction. The total force due to the two atoms is

$$\cos\theta \{f(r + \delta x \cos\theta) - f(r - \delta x \cos\theta)\},$$

or
$$2f'(r)\,\delta x \cos^2\theta, \quad \ldots \ldots \ldots \ldots \quad (25)$$

since, for ε small, $\qquad f(r + \varepsilon) = f(r) + \varepsilon f'(r).$

The force in a direction at right angles to δx due to A and B is exactly balanced by that due to the two atoms which are symmetrical with A and B about the point P.

By equation (13),
$$f(r) = -\frac{t\mu}{r^{t+1}} + \frac{s\lambda}{r^{s+1}},$$

so that
$$f'(r) = \frac{t(t+1)\mu}{r^{t+2}} - \frac{s(s+1)\lambda}{r^{s+2}}. \quad \ldots \ldots \quad (26)$$

---

* For the case in which this assumption, which leads to Einstein's specific-heat formula, is not made, see Born and v. Kármán, *Phys. Zeits.*, Vol. 14, p. 15 (1913).

Substituting this in equation (25), we obtain for the force, due to the two atoms considered, acting on the displaced atom in the direction of δx increasing,

$$2\,\delta x\left\{\frac{t(t+1)\mu\cos^2\theta}{r^{t+2}} - \frac{s(s+1)\lambda\cos^2\theta}{r^{s+2}}\right\}. \quad \ldots \quad (27)$$

This formula may be applied to all the pairs of atoms which do not lie in the plane through P at right angles to δx.

The force acting on P' in the direction of δx increasing due to an atom C in this place is equal to

$$\delta x\,\frac{f(r)}{r},$$

or to

$$2\,\delta x\left\{-\frac{\frac{1}{2}t\mu}{r^{t+2}} + \frac{\frac{1}{2}s\lambda}{r^{s+2}}\right\}. \quad \ldots \ldots \quad (28)$$

In order to obtain the total force acting on the displaced atom we must sum the effects of all the atoms. If $\bar{r}$ is the distance between the mean position of two neighbouring atoms on the lattice, we may write for r, the distance between the λth atom and the displaced atom,

$$\boldsymbol{r} = k_\lambda\,\bar{r},$$

where k_λ is a numerical factor.

Reference to expressions (27) and (28) shows that the effect of the N_0 atoms in a gram-atom on the displaced atom may be written in the form

$$2\,\delta x\,\Sigma\left\{\frac{q_\lambda t(t+1)}{k_\lambda^{t+2}}\frac{\mu}{\bar{r}^{t+2}} - \frac{q_\lambda' s(s+1)}{k_\lambda^{s+2}}\frac{\lambda}{\bar{r}^{s+2}}\right\}, \quad \ldots \quad (29)$$

where λ has all values from 1 to $(N_0 - 1)$, and where for atoms which do not lie in the plane through P at right angles to δx

$$q_\lambda = q_\lambda' = \tfrac{1}{2}\cos^2\theta$$

(the factor $\frac{1}{2}$ occurring because in obtaining equation (27) the atoms are considered in pairs), and for atoms which lie in this plane

$$q_\lambda = -\frac{1}{2(t+1)} \quad \text{and} \quad q_\lambda' = -\frac{1}{2(s+1)}.$$

Now the sums $\Sigma\dfrac{q_\lambda t(t+1)}{k_\lambda^{t+2}}$ and $\Sigma\dfrac{q_\lambda' s(s+1)}{k_\lambda^{s+2}}$ depend only on the form of the lattice and on the law of force between the atoms, and are independent of the distance $\bar{r}$, that is, of the specific volume. We shall therefore write

$$\left.\begin{aligned}\Sigma\,\frac{q_\lambda t(t+1)}{k_\lambda^{t+2}} &= \psi(t)\\[6pt]\Sigma\,\frac{q_\lambda' s(s+1)}{k_\lambda^{s+2}} &= \psi(s)\end{aligned}\right\} \quad \ldots \ldots \quad (30)$$

and

Substituting in expression (29), it becomes

$$2\,\delta x\left\{\frac{\mu\psi(t)}{\bar{r}^{t+2}} - \frac{\lambda\psi(s)}{\bar{r}^{s+2}}\right\}. \quad \ldots \ldots \quad (31)$$

This is the force acting on a displaced atom in the direction of δx increasing.

The *restoring* force acting on the displaced atom may be written in the form $D\,\delta x$, where, by equation (31),

$$D = 2 \left\{ \frac{\lambda \psi(s)}{\bar{r}^{s+2}} - \frac{\mu \psi(t)}{\bar{r}^{t+2}} \right\}. \qquad \dots \dots (32)$$

It is important to note that $\psi(t)$ and $\psi(s)$ do not depend on the specific volume, and that for a simple cubic lattice D is the same for displacements in three mutually perpendicular directions, so for any displacement.

If μ is the mass of the displaced atom, it oscillates about its mean position with frequency ν given by

$$\nu = \frac{1}{2\pi} \sqrt{\frac{D}{\mu}}. \qquad \dots \dots \dots (33)$$

Equation (32) shows which part of the factor D, which determines the restoring force, arises from attractive forces (t) and which from repulsive forces (s). It thus enables us to determine which part of the potential energy of oscillation arises from the attractive forces and which from repulsive forces. Let us write

$$D_s = 2 \frac{\lambda \psi(s)}{\bar{r}^{s+2}},$$

and

$$D_t = 2 \frac{\mu \psi(t)}{\bar{r}^{t+2}}. \qquad \dots \dots \dots (34)$$

Then

$$D = D_s - D_t. \qquad \dots \dots \dots (35)$$

The part of the potential energy of oscillation, $\frac{1}{2}E$, which is due to repulsive forces is $\frac{1}{2}D_sE/D$, and that due to attractive forces is $-\frac{1}{2}D_tE/D$; the latter is a negative quantity.

If $\overline{\Phi}$ is the time mean value of the *total* potential energy due to attractive forces, and $\overline{X}$ is the time mean value of the total potential energy due to repulsive forces, we have, from equation (24),

$$\overline{\Phi} = -\frac{B}{V^n} - \frac{1}{2}\frac{D_sE}{D}$$

$$\overline{X} = \frac{A}{V^m} + \frac{1}{2}\frac{D_tE}{D} \qquad \dots \dots \dots (36)$$

The first term on the right-hand side of each of these equations is the potential energy which the atoms would possess if they were at rest in their mean positions, and the second is the potential energy of oscillation.

6. Change of Frequency with Volume.

Let us define the quantity γ (not to be confused with the ratio of the specific heats) by the relation

$$\gamma = -\frac{d \log \nu}{d \log V}. \qquad \dots \dots \dots (37)$$

From equation (33) we have $\log \nu = \text{constant} + \frac{1}{2} \log D$. Therefore

$$\frac{d \log \nu}{d \log V} = \frac{1}{2} \frac{d \log D}{d \log V}$$

$$= \frac{1}{2} \frac{d \log D}{d \log \bar{r}} \frac{d \log r}{d \log V}$$

$$= \frac{1}{6} \frac{d \log D}{d \log \bar{r}},$$

since from equation (11) $\dfrac{d \log \bar{r}}{d \log V} = \dfrac{1}{3}$. We therefore have

$$\gamma = -\frac{d \log \nu}{d \log V} = -\frac{1}{6} \frac{d \log D}{d \log \bar{r}}. \qquad \ldots \ldots \quad (38)$$

But

$$\frac{d \log D}{d \log \bar{r}} = \frac{\bar{r}}{D} \frac{dD}{d \bar{r}}.$$

Differentiating equation (32) and using equations (34), we obtain

$$\gamma = -\frac{d \log \nu}{d \log V} = \frac{1}{6} \left\{ \frac{(s+2) D_s - (t+2) D_t}{D} \right\}, \qquad \ldots \quad (38a)$$

a relation which we shall need below.

For small changes of volume γ does not vary appreciably.

7. The Equation of State for Solids.

We are now in a position to obtain the equation of the solid state. Considering a gram-atom, we shall apply the virial law of Clausius (equation 10):

$$\Sigma \overline{\mu c^2} + \Sigma \overline{r f(r)} = 3pV. \qquad \ldots \ldots \ldots \quad (10)$$

The first term on the left is *twice* the time mean value of the kinetic energy of the atoms. It is therefore equal to E, the energy of oscillation of the atoms, which is half kinetic energy and half potential energy. We have therefore

$$E + \Sigma \overline{r f(r)} = 3pV. \qquad \ldots \ldots \ldots \quad (39)$$

Using the value of $f(r)$ given in equation (13), the instantaneous value of $\Sigma r f(r)$ is given by

$$\Sigma r f(r) = -\tfrac{1}{2} t \Sigma \frac{a}{r_{\xi\rho}{}^t} + \tfrac{1}{2} s \Sigma \frac{b}{r_{\xi\rho}{}^s},$$

where $r_{\xi\rho}$ is the instantaneous separation of the ξth atom from the ρth atom, and where, in taking the sum, ξ and ρ both have all values from 1 to N_0, so that each pair of atoms occurs twice. The factor $\frac{1}{2}$ occurs because, in taking the sum $\Sigma r f(r)$, each pair of atoms is to be taken once (see Section 2). Comparison with equation (22) shows that

$$\Sigma r f(r) = t\Phi + sX,$$

where Φ is the instantaneous potential energy of all the atoms due to attractive forces, and X is that due to repulsive forces. Taking time mean values, we have

$$\Sigma \overline{r f(r)} = t\overline{\Phi} + s\overline{X}.$$

The values of $\overline{\Phi}$ and $\overline{X}$ are given in equation (36). Using these values, we obtain

$$\Sigma \overline{rf(r)} = t\,\frac{A}{V^m} - s\,\frac{B}{V^n} + \frac{sD_s - tD_t}{2D}\,E.$$

Substituting this in equation (39), and remembering that $n = t/3$, $m = s/3$, and that $D = D_s - D_t$, we obtain

$$pV - m\,\frac{A}{V^m} + n\,\frac{B}{V^n} = \frac{1}{6}\,\frac{(s+2)D_s - (t+2)D_t}{D}\,E. \quad . \quad . \quad (40)$$

If $W(V)$ is the potential energy per gram-atom of the crystal when the atoms are at rest in their mean positions, we have from expression (22a)

$$W(V) = \frac{A}{V^m} - \frac{B}{V^n}. \quad . \quad . \quad . \quad . \quad . \quad . \quad (41)$$

Let us define $G(V)$ by the relation

$$G(V) = V\,\frac{d}{dV}\,W(V). \quad . \quad . \quad . \quad . \quad . \quad . \quad (42)$$

We have then

$$G(V) = -\,m\,\frac{A}{V^m} + n\,\frac{B}{V^n}. \quad . \quad . \quad . \quad . \quad . \quad (43)$$

Substituting this in equation (40), and also using equation (38), we have

$$pV + G(V) = \gamma E = -\,\frac{d\log \nu}{d\log V}\,E. \quad . \quad . \quad . \quad . \quad (44)$$

This is the *equation of state for solid bodies*. It will be seen that with $G(V)$ defined by (42) it does not depend on the exact form of the potential law.[*]

8. The Direct Measurement of the Value of γ.

If we heat a solid at constant volume, we have, from equation (44), since $G(V)$ is constant,

$$V\left(\frac{\partial p}{\partial T}\right)_V = \gamma C_v.$$

Since further

$$\left(\frac{\partial p}{\partial T}\right)_V = -\left(\frac{\partial V}{\partial T}\right)_p \Big/ \left(\frac{\partial V}{\partial p}\right)_T,$$

we obtain

$$\gamma = -\,\frac{V}{C_v}\left(\frac{\partial V}{\partial T}\right)_p \Big/ \left(\frac{\partial V}{\partial p}\right)_T. \quad . \quad . \quad . \quad . \quad (45)$$

Thus γ can be determined from measurements of thermal expansion and compressibility.[†]

---

[*] It can, in fact, be obtained in other ways (see Section 10).

[†] Simon and Kippert (*Zeits. f. phys. Chem.*, Vol. 135, p. 113 (1928)) have measured $(\partial p/\partial T)_V$ directly for condensed gases by enclosing the solid gas in a metal cylinder and altering the temperature, the pressure change being obtained from the change of resistance of a manganin coil. Bridgman has shown that this is a convenient way of measuring pressures. They discuss the possible effect of the variation of ν with volume on the specific-heat temperature curve.

9. Thermal Expansion: Grüneisen's Law.

If the external pressure is zero, equation (44) becomes

$$G(V) = \gamma E. \qquad \ldots \ldots \ldots \quad (46)$$

In order to obtain the law of thermal expansion we have to determine V as a function of E, and thus of T. In order to do this we develop the left-hand side as a series of increasing powers of $(V - V_0)$, where V_0 is the volume at absolute zero and under zero pressure. We have

$$G(V) = G(V_0) + (V - V_0)\frac{d}{dV_0}G(V_0) + \frac{(V - V_0)^2}{2!}\frac{d^2}{dV_0{}^2}G(V_0) + \ldots \ldots \quad (47)$$

We have to consider, then, $G(V_0)$ and its differential coefficients at $V = V_0$.

We have from equation (42)

$$G(V_0) = V_0 \frac{d}{dV_0} W(V_0). \qquad \ldots \ldots \ldots \quad (48)$$

Therefore

$$\frac{d}{dV_0} G(V_0) = V_0 \frac{d^2}{dV_0{}^2} W(V_0) + \frac{d}{dV_0} W(V_0), \qquad \ldots \quad (48a)$$

and

$$\frac{d^2}{dV_0{}^2} G(V_0) = V_0 \frac{d^3}{dV_0{}^3} W(V_0) + 2 \frac{d^2}{dV_0{}^2} W(V_0). \qquad \ldots \quad (48b)$$

The differential coefficients of $W(V_0)$ are as follows:

$$W(V_0) = \frac{A}{V_0{}^m} - \frac{B}{V_0{}^n}; \qquad \ldots \ldots \ldots \ldots \quad (49)$$

$$\frac{d}{dV_0} W(V_0) = -\frac{mA}{V_0{}^{m+1}} + \frac{nB}{V_0{}^{n+1}}; \qquad \ldots \ldots \ldots \quad (49a)$$

$$\frac{d^2}{dV_0{}^2} W(V_0) = \frac{m(m+1)A}{V_0{}^{m+2}} - \frac{n(n+1)B}{V_0{}^{n+2}}; \qquad \ldots \ldots \quad (49b)$$

$$\frac{d^3}{dV_0{}^3} W(V_0) = -\frac{m(m+1)(m+2)A}{V_0{}^{m+3}} + \frac{n(n+1)(n+2)B}{V_0{}^{n+3}}. \quad (49c)$$

These can be simplified from the consideration that at the absolute zero and under zero external pressure the atoms are completely at rest and are in equilibrium. The criterion for this equilibrium is that the differential coefficient of the potential energy with respect to the specific volume shall be zero.* We have, therefore,

$$\frac{d}{dV_0} W(V_0) = \frac{mA}{V_0{}^{m+1}} - \frac{nB}{V_0{}^{n+1}} = 0,$$

or

$$nB = mA V_0{}^{n-m}. \qquad \ldots \ldots \ldots \quad (50)$$

* For the application of this criterion to obtain the laws of force between atoms from the measured dimensions and structure of crystals, see Lennard-Jones and Dent, *Proc. Roy. Soc.*, A, Vol. 112, p. 230 (1926), and earlier papers. If there is zero-point energy the criterion cannot be applied.

Substituting this value in equations (49), we obtain

$$\frac{d}{dV_0} W(V_0) = 0; \quad \ldots \ldots \ldots \ldots \quad (51)$$

$$\frac{d^2}{dV_0^2} W(V_0) = m(n - m) \frac{A}{V_0^{m+2}}; \quad \ldots \ldots \ldots \quad (51a)$$

$$\frac{d^3}{dV_0^3} W(V_0) = -m(n - m)(m + n + 3) \frac{A}{V_0^{m+3}}$$

$$= -\frac{(m + n + 3)}{V_0} \frac{d^2}{dV_0^2} W(V_0). \quad \ldots \ldots \quad (51b)$$

Using these results in equations (48), we have

$$G(V_0) = 0; \quad \ldots \ldots \ldots \ldots \ldots \quad (52)$$

$$\frac{d}{dV_0} G(V_0) = V_0 \frac{d^2}{dV_0^2} W(V_0); \quad \ldots \ldots \ldots \quad (52a)$$

$$\frac{d^2}{dV_0^2} G(V_0) = -(n + m + 1) \frac{d^2}{dV_0^2} W(V_0). \quad \ldots \quad (52b)$$

We now obtain a relation between K_0, the compressibility at the absolute zero and at zero pressure, and the second differential coefficient of $W(V_0)$. We have

$$K_0 = -\frac{1}{V_0} \left(\frac{\partial V_0}{\partial p} \right)_T.$$

Consider an isothermal change at the absolute zero in which the volume is changed from V_0 to V by increasing the pressure from 0 to δp. We have

$$W(V) = W(V_0) + (V - V_0) \frac{d}{dV_0} W(V_0) + \frac{(V - V_0)^2}{2!} \frac{d^2}{dV_0^2} W(V_0) + \cdots.$$

By equation (51) the second term on the right vanishes. We have therefore

$$W(V) - W(V_0) = \tfrac{1}{2}(V - V_0)^2 \frac{d^2}{dV_0^2} W(V_0).$$

But $W(V) - W(V_0)$, the *increase* in the potential energy, is equal to the mean pressure $\tfrac{1}{2}\delta p$, multiplied by the *diminution* of volume, $(V_0 - V)$. That is,

$$W(V) - W(V_0) = -\tfrac{1}{2}\delta p(V - V_0).$$

Equating the two values for the increase in the potential energy, we obtain

$$\frac{d^2}{dV_0^2} W(V_0) = -\frac{\delta p}{V - V_0}.$$

Further, we have $$V - V_0 = \frac{\partial V_0}{\partial p} \delta p = -V_0 K_0 \delta p.$$

Using this, we obtain $$V_0 \frac{d^2}{dV_0^2} W(V_0) = \frac{1}{K_0}. \quad \ldots \ldots \ldots \quad (53)$$

Finally, using this result, equations (52) become

$$G(V_0) = 0; \quad \ldots\ldots\ldots\ldots \quad (54)$$

$$\frac{d}{dV_0} G(V_0) = \frac{1}{K_0}; \quad \ldots\ldots\ldots\ldots \quad (54a)$$

$$\frac{d^2}{dV_0{}^2} G(V_0) = -(n + m + 1)\frac{1}{V_0 K_0}. \quad \ldots\ldots \quad (54b)$$

Substituting from equations (54) in equation (47), and using the result so obtained in equation (46), we have

$$\frac{V_T - V_0}{K_0}\left\{1 - \frac{n + m + 1}{2}\frac{V_T - V_0}{V_0} + \ldots\right\} = \gamma E. \quad \ldots \quad (55)$$

From this equation we may deduce Grüneisen's law, which was first established experimentally, and for which the experimental evidence is given in Chapter X, Table I. The thermal expansion of solids is always small, so that $\frac{n + m + 1}{2}\frac{V_T - V_0}{V_0}$ is always small compared with unity. Neglecting it (the error involved never amounts to more than a few per cent), equation (55) becomes

$$V_T - V_0 = \gamma K_0 E. \quad \ldots\ldots\ldots \quad (56)$$

Differentiating with respect to T, we have

$$\frac{\partial V}{\partial T} = \gamma K_0 \frac{\partial E}{\partial T} = \gamma K_0 C_v, \quad \ldots\ldots \quad (57)$$

from equation (23). It follows immediately from equation (57) that for a given substance the coefficient of expansion is proportional to the atomic (or specific) heat at constant volume. This is Grüneisen's law.*

10. Debye's Deduction of the Equation of State.†

The following method of deriving the equation of state is more general than that used by Grüneisen. It depends on thermodynamics and on the formula for the specific heat developed by Debye, that is, on thermodynamics and on statistical mechanics modified to include the quantum theory. The assumption of the potential law and of the non-existence of zero-point energy used by Grüneisen is unnecessary. Also it is not assumed that, when one atom is displaced, all around it remain undisturbed.

The free energy F of a gram-molecule of a body is given by the relation

$$F = U - TS.$$

We shall take the condition of the body at the absolute zero of temperature and under zero external pressure as the standard state from which the various thermodynamic quantities are measured; in this condition we shall put U and S, and consequently F, equal to zero.

---

* The figures given in Chapter X, Table I, and the statement of Grüneisen's law in Chapter X, Section 5, refer to the specific heat at constant pressure. To a first approximation this makes no important difference, since the variation from unity of the ratio of C_p to C_v is small (see Chapter VII, Table II). For the experimental proof of the more exact relation contained in equation (55), reference should be made to Grüneisen, *Ann. d. Physik*, Vol. 39, p. 257 (1912).

† Debye, *Phys. Zeits.*, Vol. 14, p. 259 (1913).

Let us take the gram-molecule of solid at the absolute zero and under zero pressure, where its volume is V_0, and heat it at constant volume to temperature T. The internal energy U is given by

$$U = \int_0^T C_v \, dT;$$

while the entropy S is given by

$$S = \int_0^T \frac{C_v}{T} \, dT$$

$$= \int_0^T \frac{1}{T} \left(\frac{\partial U}{dT}\right)_v \partial T$$

$$= \frac{U}{T} + \int_0^T \frac{U}{T^2} \, dT.$$

The last result follows by integrating by parts, and from the fact that U/T vanishes as the absolute zero is approached. The free energy is therefore given by

$$F = -T \int_0^T \frac{U}{T^2} \, dT. \quad \cdots \cdots \cdots \quad (58)$$

We have to evaluate this integral using the Debye expression for U. We have from equations (5) and (7), Chapter XXII,

$$U = 9N_0 kT \left(\frac{T}{\Theta}\right)^3 \int_0^{\Theta/T} \frac{\xi^3}{e^\xi - 1} \, d\xi, \quad \cdots \cdots \quad (59)$$

where Θ, the characteristic temperature of the body, is defined by equation (11), Chapter XXII. Further, we have from equation (10), Chapter XXII,

$$\left(\frac{\partial U}{\partial T}\right)_v = C_v = 36N_0 k \left(\frac{T}{\Theta}\right)^3 \int_0^{\Theta/T} \frac{\xi^3}{e^\xi - 1} \, d\xi - \frac{9N_0 k\Theta/T}{e^{\Theta/T} - 1}.$$

From this last expression we obtain

$$9N_0 k \left(\frac{T}{\Theta}\right)^3 \int_0^{\Theta/T} \frac{\xi^3}{e^\xi - 1} \, d\xi = \frac{1}{4} \left\{ \left(\frac{\partial U}{\partial T}\right)_v + \frac{9N_0 k\Theta/T}{e^{\Theta/T} - 1} \right\}.$$

Substituting this in the equation for U, we have

$$U = \frac{1}{4} \left\{ T \left(\frac{\partial U}{\partial T}\right)_v + \frac{9N_0 kT\Theta/T}{e^{\Theta/T} - 1} \right\}.$$

Putting this value of U in the expression on the right-hand side of equation (58), we have

$$-T \int_0^T \frac{U}{T^2} \, dT = -\frac{T}{4} \left\{ \int_0^T \frac{1}{T} \left(\frac{\partial U}{\partial T}\right)_v \, dT + \int_0^T \frac{9N_0 k}{T} \frac{\Theta/T}{e^{\Theta/T} - 1} \, dT \right\}$$

$$= -\frac{T}{4} \left\{ \frac{U}{T} + \int_0^T \frac{U}{T^2} \, dT - 9N_0 k \int_\infty^{\Theta/T} \frac{1}{e^{\Theta/T} - 1} \, d\left(\frac{\Theta}{T}\right) \right\}.$$

This result follows by integrating by parts the first integral on the right, and by transforming the second integral using the relation

$$dT = -\frac{T^2}{\Theta} \, d\left(\frac{\Theta}{T}\right).$$

Taking the term $-\dfrac{T}{4}\displaystyle\int_0^T \dfrac{U}{T^2}\,dT$ to the left-hand side, and multiplying through by 4/3, we obtain

$$-T\int_0^T \frac{U}{T^2}\,dT = F = -\frac{U}{3} + 3N_0 kT \int_\infty^{\Theta/T} \frac{1}{e^{\Theta/T}-1}\,d\left(\frac{\Theta}{T}\right).$$

Substituting the value of U given in equation (59), and putting $N_0 k = R$, we obtain

$$F = 3RT\left\{-\left(\frac{T}{\Theta}\right)^3 \int_0^{\Theta/T} \frac{\xi^3}{e^\xi - 1}\,d\xi + \int_\infty^{\Theta/T} \frac{1}{e^\xi - 1}\,d\xi\right\}. \qquad . \quad (60)$$

This is the free energy of a gram-molecule of the solid at temperature T and occupying the volume V_0.

To determine the free energy of a gram-molecule at temperature T and occupying any other volume V, we proceed as follows. Compress the solid at the absolute zero from volume V_0 to volume V. Let the increase in the potential energy be Φ (not to be confused with the Φ of Sections 4–7, or with the thermodynamic potential). Φ is the work done by the external forces during the compression, and is therefore the increase in the free energy in passing from the volume V_0 to the volume V. Φ is actually equal to $\{W(V) - W(V_0)\}$ (see Section 9), but in the present treatment we do not specify the form of the function W. We now heat the solid at the constant volume V to temperature T. The increase in the free energy is given by equation (60), provided we use the value of Θ appropriate to the volume V, and not that appropriate to the volume V_0. The free energy F of a gram-molecule at temperature T and occupying the volume V is therefore given by *

$$F = \Phi + 3RT\left\{-\left(\frac{T}{\Theta}\right)^3 \int_0^{\Theta/T} \frac{\xi^3}{e^\xi - 1}\,d\xi + \int_\infty^{\Theta/T} \frac{1}{e^\xi - 1}\,d\xi\right\}. \qquad (61)$$

Now by equation (61), Chapter XVI, we have for the pressure

$$p = -\left(\frac{\partial F}{\partial V}\right)_T.$$

Differentiating equation (61) with respect to V at constant T, and remembering that then

$$\frac{\partial}{\partial V} = \frac{\partial(\Theta/T)}{\partial V}\frac{\partial}{\partial(\Theta/T)} = \frac{1}{T}\frac{d\Theta}{dV}\frac{\partial}{\partial(\Theta/T)},$$

we obtain

$$p = -\frac{d\Phi}{dV} - 9RT\frac{1}{T}\frac{d\Theta}{dV}\left(\frac{T}{\Theta}\right)^4 \int_0^{\Theta/T} \frac{\xi^3}{e^\xi - 1}\,d\xi.$$

We have further

$$\frac{d\Theta}{dV} = \frac{\Theta}{V}\frac{d\log\Theta}{d\log V}.$$

---

* For a discussion of the thermodynamical functions of a crystal which makes use of the methods of statistical mechanics, see Tolman, *Principles of Statistical Mechanics*, Oxford University Press (1938), pp. 587–95, and Moelwyn-Hughes, *Physical Chemistry*, Pergamon Press (1957), pp. 558–63. It is interesting to note that the entropy calculated on Debye's theory of the normal modes of the vibration of a crystal differs only negligibly from that calculated on Einstein's theory (see Moelwyn-Hughes, *Physical Chemistry*, Cambridge University Press (1940), p. 618, equations (57) and (55a)).

Substituting this in the last equation, and multiplying through by V, we obtain

$$pV + V\frac{d\Phi}{dV} = -\frac{d\log\Theta}{d\log V}9RT\left(\frac{T}{\Theta}\right)^3\int_0^{\Theta/T}\frac{\xi^3}{e^\xi-1}\,d\xi. \quad . \quad . \quad (62)$$

This is the equation of state, and it is essentially identical with equation (44). $G(V)$ and $V\,d\Phi/dV$ have precisely the same meaning; by equation (11), Chapter XXII,

$$\frac{d\log\Theta}{d\log V} = \frac{d\log\nu_{max.}}{d\log V}$$

and this corresponds to $d\log\nu/d\log V$ of equation (44); finally, comparison with equation (59) shows that the expression

$$9RT\left(\frac{T}{\Theta}\right)^3\int_0^{\Theta/T}\frac{\xi^3}{e^\xi-1}\,d\xi$$

is the " thermal energy " of the body at temperature T and at the volume V, where Θ has the value appropriate to the volume V: this expression is therefore equal to the quantity E in equation (44).

From equation (62) Grüneisen's law can be deduced as a first approximation.

Debye's method of deducing the equation of state shows very clearly the connexion between the thermal expansion and the fact that Θ varies with the volume.

11. The Thermal Expansion of Anisotropic Bodies.

The theory has been extended by Grüneisen and Goens * to apply to anisotropic (hexagonal) crystals, and has been used to interpret the results of their measurements of the thermal expansion and elastic properties of zinc and cadmium crystals at low temperatures. The expansions of zinc parallel and perpendicular to the axis of symmetry are shown in fig. 23.2. The broken curves show the experimental values, and the full curves the values calculated from the theory, using the measured elastic constants. The agreement between the theoretical and experimental values is good. Particularly striking is the agreement below about 80° absolute, where both theory and experiment indicate a negative coefficient perpendicular to the axis of symmetry. Qualitatively the explanation of this is as follows. The elastic deformability parallel to the axis is large. This corresponds to a low value for ν_m, the limiting frequency, and therefore to a low characteristic temperature Θ. Perpendicular to the axis the elastic deformability is small, and the characteristic temperature is high. At the absolute zero the atoms are all at rest.† At first, as the crystal is heated, nearly all the energy goes into oscillations parallel to the axis on account of the low value of Θ. The thermal expansion depends on the amplitude of oscillation of the atoms. At the lowest temperatures, therefore, the expansion parallel to the axis is appreciable, while that perpendicular to the axis is negligible. The expansion parallel to the axis is accompanied by an elastic contraction perpendicular to the axis, the magnitude of which is given by Poisson's ratio. This elastic contraction is more than sufficient to balance the small thermal expansion, and thus we get the negative coefficient.

* Grüneisen and Goens, *Zeits. f. Physik*, Vol. 29, p. 141 (1924).

† The existence of zero-point energy does not affect the argument.

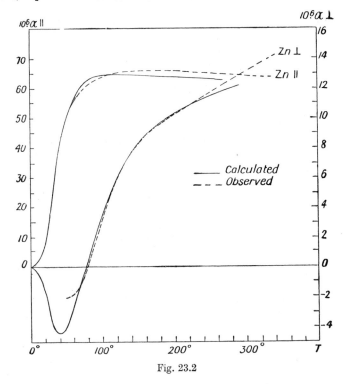

Fig. 23.2

12. The Latent Heat of Vaporization at the Absolute Zero.

We now return to the Grüneisen theory. If $W(V)$ is the potential energy which the atoms would possess if they were at rest in their mean positions, and the total volume of a gram-molecule is V, the latent heat of vaporization at the absolute zero Λ_0 is given by

$$\Lambda_0 = [W(V)]_{V=\infty} - [W(V)]_{V=V_0}.$$

From equation (41) we have
$$\Lambda_0 = \frac{B}{V_0{}^n} - \frac{A}{V_0{}^m},$$

since $[W(V)]_{V=\infty}$ is zero. From equation (50)

$$A = \frac{n}{m} B V_0{}^{m-n}.$$

Substituting this in the above expression, we obtain

$$\Lambda_0 = \frac{B}{V_0{}^n} \left(\frac{m-n}{m} \right).$$

From equation (53)
$$\frac{1}{K_0} = V_0 \frac{d^2 W(V_0)}{d V_0{}^2},$$

K_0 being the compressibility at the absolute zero and under zero external pressure. From equation (51a) we obtain

$$\frac{1}{K_0} = n(m-n)\frac{B}{V_0^{n+1}},$$

or

$$\frac{B}{V_0^n} = \frac{V_0}{n(m-n)K_0}.$$

Substituting this in the expression for Λ_0, we have

$$\Lambda_0 = \frac{1}{mn}\frac{V_0}{K_0}. \qquad \ldots \ldots \ldots (63)$$

Finally, from equation (57) we have for α, the coefficient of expansion,

$$\alpha = \frac{\gamma K_0}{V_0}C_v.$$

Using this in equation (63), we obtain

$$\Lambda_0 = \frac{\gamma}{mn}\frac{C_v}{\alpha}. \qquad \ldots \ldots \ldots (64)$$

This is Grüneisen's expression for the latent heat of vaporization of a solid at the absolute zero.

C_v/α is a constant for a given substance (Grüneisen's law) which can easily be determined by experiment. Grüneisen * evaluates approximately the factor γ/mn as follows. On the assumption that, as far as the oscillations of the atoms are concerned, the effect of repulsive forces is very great compared with that of attractive forces, he obtained the result (see equation (38a)) that γ is approximately equal to $(3m+2)/6$. He assumes $n=1$, that is, $t=3$, which is equivalent to assuming that the attractive force between two atoms falls off as the inverse fourth power of the distance. Using these values we have

$$\frac{\gamma}{mn} = \frac{3m+2}{6m}.$$

This factor varies very slightly with the value of m. For example, if $m=2$, it has the value 0.67; while, if $m=\infty$, it has the value 0.5. Grüneisen assumes a mean value 0.6, so that equation (64) becomes

$$\Lambda_0 \sim 0.6\frac{C_v}{\alpha}. \qquad \ldots \ldots \ldots (65)$$

This equation is in satisfactory agreement with experiment, as Table I shows.†

TABLE I

Metal	Λ_0 (experimental)	Λ_0 (from equation (65))
Copper	76,000 calories	75,000 calories
Silver	61,000 „	65,000 „
Lead	48,000 „	46,000 „

* Grüneisen, *Ann. d. Physik*, Vol. 39, p. 289 (1912).
† See Grüneisen, *Verh. d. deuts. phys. Ges.*, Vol. 10, p. 322 (1912).

13. The Energy of Crystalline Salts.

As we have seen in the last section, the potential energy of a gram-atom of a metal at the absolute zero can be determined directly by calculating the latent heat of vaporization at the absolute zero; this last quantity can be deduced from the measured latent heat of vaporization at the melting-point if the specific heat of the solid metal is known and if we assume that the vapour has the atomic heat of a monatomic gas (see Chapter VIII, Section 13).

In the case of a salt crystal such as NaCl, which is built up of Na^+ ions and Cl^- ions, what we wish to determine is the difference between the potential energy at the absolute zero of a gram-molecule of the salt crystal and the sum of the potential energies of a gram-atom of each of the *ions* when they are in the form of an infinitely extended gas. We shall denote this difference by $-U_{MX}$. To determine it we employ the following method first used by Born.*

Let us imagine that at the absolute zero we carry out the cyclical process illustrated in the diagram (fig. 23.3). M is a metallic atom and X is a halogen atom.

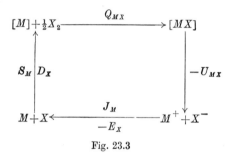

Fig. 23.3

A substance in the gaseous state is indicated by the chemical formula written in the ordinary way, while a substance in the solid state is indicated by the chemical formula enclosed in square brackets. The heat *evolved* in each stage is written at the centre of the arrow indicating the direction of the process.

Q_{MX} is the heat of formation of the solid salt from the solid metal and the gaseous halogen. The measurement of this quantity is considered in Chapter XVIII, and the reduction to the absolute zero in Chapter XVIII. S_M is the heat of sublimation of the metal at the absolute zero (see Chapter VIII). J_M is the energy of ionization of an atom of the metallic vapour. This is known from spectroscopic data and the Bohr theory of the atom.

D_X is the heat of dissociation of the halogen. This can be determined from the variation with temperature of the dissociation equilibrium constant as explained in Chapter XVIII, and reduced to the absolute zero as explained in Chapter XIX. The equilibrium constant has been determined by Bodenstein † by measurements of density and pressure at various temperatures. Wohl ‡ has determined the heat of dissociation of chlorine and of hydrogen using Pier's explosion method (see Chapter VI, Section 6). Actually, however, in the present case D_X is eliminated from the final result together with E_X.

---

* See Born, *Atomtheorie des festen Zustandes*, p. 748 (1923); see also Fajans and Schwartz, *Zeits. f. phys. Chem.*, Bodenstein Festband, p. 717 (1931).

† Bodenstein, *Zeits. f. Elektrochemie*, Vol. 16, p. 961 (1910); Vol. 22, p. 327 (1916); see also v. Wartenberg and Henglein, *Ber. d. deuts. chem. Ges.*, Vol. 55, p. 1003 (1922).

‡ Wohl, *Zeits. f. Elektrochemie*, Vol. 30, pp. 36, 49 (1924).

E_X is the work that is necessary to remove the superfluous electron from the halogen ion X^-. This cannot be determined at present and is eliminated from the final result.

Applying the first law of thermodynamics to the cycle, we obtain

$$U_{MX} = Q_{MX} + S_M + J_M + D_X - E_X.$$

We can eliminate D_X and E_X by considering a second cyclical process involving the dissociation of the corresponding gaseous hydrogen halide into a hydrogen ion and a halide ion. The process is shown in the diagram (fig. 23.4).

Q_{HX} is the heat of formation of gaseous HX from the gases. U_{HX} is the energy required to ionize the gaseous hydrogen halide. It is determined by the method of electron collisions.* J_H is the energy of ionization of the hydrogen atom, which is determined from spectroscopic data. D_H is the heat of dissociation of hydrogen. This can be determined from the temperature variation of the equilibrium constant of dissociation of hydrogen. The degree of dissociation at various temperatures can be determined by the method used by Langmuir † which depends on

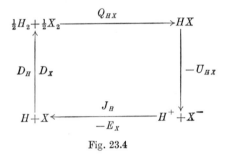

Fig. 23.4

the loss of heat from an electrically heated tungsten wire in hydrogen. The heat of dissociation can also be determined directly by the method of electron collisions.‡

Applying the first law of thermodynamics, we have

$$U_{HX} = Q_{HX} + D_H + J_H + D_X - E_X.$$

Subtracting this equation from the equation for U_{MX}, we obtain

$$U_{MX} = U_{HX} + Q_{MX} - Q_{HX} + S_M + J_M - D_H - J_H.$$

All the quantities on the right-hand side of this equation are directly measurable, as explained above. The equation therefore enables us to determine the value of U_{MX}, which is what was required.

Numerical values collected by Born for carrying out the calculation are given in Table II. The unit of energy is the kilocalorie. Using these values, we obtain for the crystal energy of 1 gram-mol. NaCl 183 kilocalories, and for that

* See Foote and Mohler, *Journ. Amer. Chem. Soc.*, Vol. 42, p. 1832 (1914); Knipping, *Zeits. f. Physik*, Vol. 7, p. 328 (1921).

† Langmuir, *Journ. Amer. Chem. Soc.*, Vol. 34, p. 860 (1912); Vol. 36, p. 708 (1914); Vol. 37, p. 417 (1915).

‡ See Franck, Knipping, and Kruger, *Verh. d. deuts. phys. Ges.*, Vol. 21, p. 728 (1919).

TABLE II

Q_{MX}	Na	K	Rb	Q_{HX}	U_{HX}
Cl	99	104	105	22	313
Br	90	97	99	12	299
I	77	85	87	1	290
S_M	26	21	20	$D_H = 40$	—
J_M	117	99	95	$J_H = 310$	—

of KCl 165 kilocalories. These may be compared with the values 179 and 161 respectively, which have been calculated by Lennard-Jones and Taylor * from the force constants between the ions and from the crystal dimensions. For the method of determining the force constants reference must be made to the paper of Lennard-Jones and Taylor. The agreement is very satisfactory.†

THE THEORY OF FUSION

14. When a crystal is heated to a sufficiently high temperature, the lattice breaks down and the crystal melts. Lindemann ‡ assumed that this takes place when the amplitude of oscillation of the atoms becomes so great that direct collisions take place between neighbouring atoms, or rather between the outer parts of their structure. When this takes place the nature of the motion is entirely changed.

Let σ be the diameter of an atom, or rather of its sphere of action, and let r be the distance between the mean positions of two neighbouring atoms. Let

$$\sigma = r(1 - \rho),$$

where ρ is a fraction. The shortest distance between the spheres of action of two neighbouring atoms which are at rest in their mean positions is $r\rho$. In order that the atoms may make a direct collision, the amplitude of oscillation of each from the mean position must be $r\rho/2$. The kinetic energy L of the atom in passing through the mean position is given by

$$L = \int_0^{r\rho/2} Dx\,dx = \tfrac{1}{8}Dr^2\rho^2,$$

where Dx is the restoring force acting on an atom displaced a distance x from the mean position. The frequency of oscillation ν is given by

$$\nu = \frac{1}{2\pi}\sqrt{\frac{D}{\mu}} = \frac{1}{2\pi}\sqrt{\frac{8L}{\mu r^2 \rho^2}},$$

where μ is the mass of an atom.

We shall assume that the melting-point T_s is sufficiently high for the laws

---

* Lennard-Jones and Taylor, *Proc. Roy. Soc.*, A, Vol. 109, p. 502 (1925).

† Compare also Mayer and Wintner, *J. Chem. Physics*, Vol. 6, p. 301 (1938).

‡ Lindemann, *Phys. Zeits.*, Vol. 11, p. 609 (1910).

of classical mechanics to be applicable. In this case the energy L of a single linear oscillator is given by

$$L = kT_s.$$

Note that L, the total energy of the oscillator, is equal to the kinetic energy in passing through the mean position. Substituting this value for L in the expression for ν, we obtain

$$\nu = \frac{\sqrt{2}}{\pi\rho}\frac{1}{r}\sqrt{\frac{kT_s}{\mu}}.$$

If we assume the atoms arranged on the simple lattice described in Section **3**, we have

$$N_0 r^3 = V,$$

where V is the atomic volume. Further, we have

$$k = \frac{R}{N_0}, \quad \text{and} \quad \mu = \frac{M}{N_0},$$

where M is the atomic weight in grams. Substituting these values in the above equation, we obtain

$$\nu = \frac{\sqrt{2}}{\pi\rho} R^{1/2} N_0^{1/3} M^{-1/2} V^{-1/3} T_s^{1/2}.$$

If we assume that ρ has the same value for all substances, we have

$$\nu = C M^{-1/2} V^{-1/3} T_s^{1/2}, \quad \ldots \ldots \ldots \quad (66)$$

where C is a constant. This is Lindemann's formula connecting the atomic frequency ν with the melting-point T_s.

The value of the constant C may be found by using the known value of the Einstein single frequency ν for a substance like platinum. Using the value of C thus determined, the single frequencies for other elements may be deduced from the melting-points. The values so calculated may then be compared with those obtained from specific-heat measurements (Einstein's formula). The agreement between calculated and observed values is shown in Table III. The value $C = 2 \cdot 06 \cdot 10^{12}$ has been used to obtain the calculated values.

TABLE III

Element	Value of ν from specific-heat measurements	Value of ν from melting-point formula
Lead	$1 \cdot 2 \cdot 10^{12}$	$1 \cdot 4 \cdot 10^{12}$
Tin	$2 \cdot 7$	$1 \cdot 8$
Cadmium ..	$2 \cdot 7$	$2 \cdot 1$
Antimony ..	$3 \cdot 1$	$2 \cdot 3$
Platinum ..	$3 \cdot 1$	$3 \cdot 1$
Silver	$3 \cdot 3$	$3 \cdot 2$
Zinc	$3 \cdot 7$	$3 \cdot 1$
Magnesium ..	$5 \cdot 1$	$5 \cdot 4$
Copper ..	$5 \cdot 3$	$4 \cdot 7$
Aluminium ..	$6 \cdot 8$	$5 \cdot 6$

Similar agreement may be obtained between the values of $\nu_{max.}$, the maximum frequency in the Debye specific-heat formula, deduced from specific-heat measurements and those deduced from equation (66), using an appropriate value of C.

It may be mentioned here that Goetz and Hergenrother * have brought forward evidence to show that in the process of melting the so-called secondary structure breaks down first. For a general discussion of this and related questions, particularly the importance of impurities, reference should be made to a paper by Webster.†

15. Recent Theories of Melting and of Liquids.

More recent theories of melting and of the liquid state are based on the application of the results of statistical mechanics. A useful and clear summary of a number of the important statistical results required has been given by Guggenheim,‡ whose treatment we shall follow closely. If we are considering an assembly of molecules, the statistical problem is to determine the average properties of the assembly subject to certain general conditions. If we have a given amount of some substance in a given specified form (for example, liquid, solid or vapour), the macroscopic state of the substance is defined by two suitable variables; for example, the internal energy U and the volume V, or the pressure p and the temperature T, and so on.

Thus, in order to fix the macroscopic state, we must specify in all four quantities which we may take as the energy U, the volume V, the number of molecules N, and a quantity ξ which defines the amount that is in the liquid form, the amount that is in the vapour form, and so on.§ Let us consider an assembly of molecules whose macroscopic condition is so specified. According to the quantum theory this assembly will be able to exist in a number of stationary states. To each such state there corresponds one proper function. ‖ The statistical problem is in part to count up for a given type of system the number of such proper functions. Let $\Omega(U, V, N, \xi)$ be this number. It can be shown that the change in the quantity $k \log \Omega$ is the same as the change in the entropy S, and we can therefore put

$$S(U, V, N, \xi) = k \log \Omega(U, V, N, \xi), \quad \ldots \ldots (67)$$

where k is Boltzmann's constant.

$\Omega(U, V, N, \xi)$ is called a partition function, and Guggenheim proposes that this particular partition function should be called the *weight*.

Now consider an assembly of specified V, N, and ξ. Let Ω_0 be the weight for a total energy U_0, and Ω_1 for a total energy U_1, and so on. We define a function $z(T, V, N, \xi)$ by the relation

$$z(T, V, N, \xi) = \Omega_0 e^{-U_0/kT} + \Omega_1 e^{-U_1/kT} + \ldots = \sum_r \Omega_r e^{-U_r/kT}, \quad . \ (68)$$

where T is the absolute temperature. The function z is called the *ordinary partition function*. It can be shown that changes in the quantity $-kT \log z$ are the

---

* Goetz and Hergenrother, *Phys. Rev.*, Vol. 38, p. 2075 (1931); Vol. 40, p. 643 (1932).

† Webster, *Proc. Roy. Soc.*, A, Vol. 133, p. 170 (1931).

‡ Guggenheim, *J. Chem. Physics*, Vol. 7, p. 103 (1939). The standard work on this subject is R. H. Fowler, *Statistical Mechanics* (Cambridge University Press (1936)).

§ For other examples of what ξ may specify, see Guggenheim's discussion.

‖ Also called *eigenfunction*.

same as changes in the Helmholtz free energy F, and we can therefore put

$$F(T,\ V,\ N,\ \xi) = -kT \log z(T,\ V,\ N,\ \xi),\ \ \ \ \ \ \ (69)$$

and, since $\left(\dfrac{\partial F}{\partial T}\right)_V = -S$, we have

$$S = kT\ \frac{\partial}{\partial T} \log z + k \log z.\ \ \ \ \ \ \ \ (70)$$

If the system consists of N independent mass points of mass m occupying a volume V, and if the temperature is high enough for the separation of the characteristic energies to be small in comparison with kT, it can be shown that

$$z = \frac{1}{N!} \left[\frac{(2\pi mkT)^{3/2}}{h^3}\ V\right]^N.\ \ \ \ \ \ \ (71)$$

Theory of the Liquid State.

We shall first outline the theory of the liquid state due to Lennard-Jones and Devonshire.* In their theory, the partition function for the liquid is written as the product of N identical factors. Each factor arises from the motion of a single molecule in the potential field which exists when each neighbouring particle is fixed in the centre of its cell. In this model each particle is treated as independent, the other particles in the liquid merely providing a smoothed potential field in which the particle under consideration moves. Thus, no account is taken of the correlation of the motions of the particles in the neighbouring cells. The partition function derived by Lennard-Jones is

$$z = \lambda^{-3N} \exp\left(-\phi_0/kT\right)\vartheta^N$$

where ϕ_0 is the potential energy when all the molecules are placed at the centres of their cells and λ has been written for $(2\pi mkT)^{1/2}/h$.

To apply this result to an ideal gas, we must put ϕ_0 equal to zero and each molecule can move in a cell of volume

$$\vartheta = V/N.$$

Thus, the Lennard-Jones theory gives

$$[z_{\text{ideal}}]_{LJ} = \lambda^{-3N} V^N/N^N$$

for an ideal gas. However, the partition function for an ideal gas of N non-interacting particles can be evaluated exactly. It is

$$z_{\text{ideal}} = \lambda^{-3N} V^N/N!.$$

* J. E. Lennard-Jones and A. F. Devonshire, *Proc. Roy. Soc.*, A, Vol. 165, p. 1 (1938). See also, J. G. Kirkwood, *Journ. Chem. Phys.*, Vol. 18, p. 380 (1950); W. J. Taylor, *ibid.*, Vol. 24, p. 454 (1956); J. S. Dahler, J. O. Hirschfelder, and H. C. Thacher. *ibid.*, Vol. 25, p. 249 (1956).

The Lennard-Jones partition function is thus too small, in this case, by a factor

$$N^N/N! \approx e^N,$$

and it can be assumed that the Lennard-Jones expression for the partition function of a system of N interacting particles is likewise too small by a factor of the same order of magnitude. This factor arises from the fact that in the theory of Lennard-Jones each cell is occupied by one molecule at a time, whereas in an actual fluid the total volume V is shared by the N molecules. Corresponding to this factor $N^N/N!$ in the partition function there is an additional term R per gram-molecule in the expression for the entropy. This additional term is referred to as the " communal entropy " of the fluid.

The omission of this term is probably the main defect in the theory of Lennard-Jones. It has been shown by de Boer * that this short-coming can be rectified by taking account of the correlation of the motions of the particles in the neighbouring cells. He does this by considering not only the motion of single molecules in single cells, but also that of pairs of molecules in a cell-cluster of two neighbouring cells, of groups of three molecules in cell-clusters of three adjacent cells, and so on for larger clusters. The contributions arising from these successive clusters can be written as correction terms to the expression for the partition function obtained in the Lennard-Jones theory.

The partition function in de Boer's theory can be evaluated exactly in the one-dimensional case. It leads to a partition function larger by a factor e^N than that given by the Lennard-Jones theory. Corresponding to this factor there is an extra term R per gram-molecule in the expression for the entropy.

In the two- and three-dimensional cases, the partition function cannot be evaluated exactly in de Boer's theory. However, the methods which have been used in the theory of order-disorder phenomena can be applied to determine an approximate value for the combinatory factor in the partition function. The results obtained in this way are satisfactory, in that de Boer finds that even when only clusters of two cells are taken into account the correction term to the expression for the entropy obtained by Lennard-Jones is already of the order of magnitude of the total correction R. For details of recent developments in the theory of liquids, the student should consult the original papers which have been cited above, the account † of a discussion on the theory of liquids held by the Royal Society, and a review of the theory of monatomic liquids ‡ by de Boer.

We shall now consider the theory of fusion.

Theory of Fusion.

Hirschfelder, Stevenson and Eyring § have discussed the process of fusion, starting from the following simple analogy and using equation (71) above. Suppose a container of volume V is partitioned into N equal parts, each of volume V/N, and that each partition contains one mass point. The ordinary partition

* J. de Boer, *Physica*, Vol. 20, p. 655 (1954); E. G. D. Cohen, J. de Boer, and Z. W. Salsburg, *ibid.*, Vol. 21, p. 137 (1955).

† *Proc. Roy. Soc.*, A, Vol. 215, p. 1 (1952).

‡ J. de Boer, *Nuovo Cimento*, Supplemento al Vol. 10, p. 225 (1953).

§ Hirschfelder, Stevenson and Eyring, *J. Chem. Phys.*, Vol. 5, p. 896 (1937).

function for each such particle is

$$\frac{(2\pi mkT)^{3/2}}{h^3} \frac{V}{N},$$

and from the definition of z in equation (68) it can be seen that for the whole system the ordinary partition function z is

$$z = \left[\frac{(2\pi mkT)^{3/2}}{h^3} \frac{V}{N}\right]^N.$$

If the partitions, which are assumed to be of negligible volume, are removed, so that each particle has access to the whole volume, the ordinary partition function z' is

$$z' = \frac{1}{N!} \left[\frac{(2\pi mkT)^{3/2}}{h^3} V\right]^N.$$

If we take $N! = (N/e)^N$, the expression for z' becomes

$$z' = \left[\frac{(2\pi mkT)^{3/2}}{h^3} \frac{eV}{N}\right]^N.$$

The increase in the entropy of the system when the partitions are removed is

$$kT \frac{\partial}{\partial T} \log \frac{z'}{z} + k \log \frac{z'}{z}.$$

Since $z'/z = e^N$, this increase of entropy is Nk or R for 1 gm.-mol. This is called the communal entropy.

The removal of the partitions may be taken as a representation of what happens when a solid melts. For the simple model considered, the " entropy of fusion " would be R or 2 cal. deg.$^{-1}$ per mol. This may be compared with the experimental results collected in Chapter IX, Section 7, which show that the measured values vary from 1·2 to 3·4 cal. deg.$^{-1}$ per mol. The above simple calculation treating the atoms as mass points gives the maximum contribution that can arise from the communal entropy. It is evident, however, that the atoms cannot be treated as mass points and that some account must be taken of the forces between them and of energy changes which accompany the volume changes which occur on melting. We shall not consider further the methods used by Hirschfelder, Stevenson and Eyring to take account of these factors, but shall pass on to the recent development of the theory by Lennard-Jones and Devonshire,* who have aimed at giving a detailed theory applicable in the first place to simple substances like the rare gases, and have taken into account more accurately the effect of the indefiniteness of position of the atoms when melting takes place, and have included the effect of volume changes.

* Lennard-Jones and Devonshire, *Proc. Roy. Soc.* A, Vol. 169, p. 317 (1939); Vol. 170, p. 464 (1939).

We shall begin by considering the behaviour of a solid as the temperature is raised. When it is at the absolute zero the motion of the constituent atoms is a minimum, and the zero-point vibrations take place about points which are fixed in definite relative positions in space. As the temperature is raised, the amplitude of the oscillations increases and thus each atom requires more room and the whole solid expands. The atoms, however, continue to oscillate about fixed relative positions. As the process is continued and the amplitude becomes greater and greater, a point will ultimately be reached at which a new phenomenon will occur: an atom will occasionally move so far from its centre of oscillation that it will not return to it, but its place will be taken by another atom. In other words, there will be local rearrangement of the atoms on the centres of oscillation. When these rearrangements occur with sufficient frequency the solid will melt.

For the sake of definiteness let us consider a two-dimensional lattice as in fig. 23.5, the sites or centres of oscillation being shown by the small full circles. Suppose the atom normally on site A moves into P, which is not normally a lattice point at all. The atoms on B, C, D will presumably move out so that they are

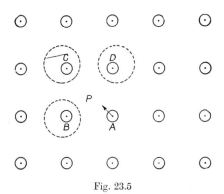

Fig. 23.5

oscillating within the dotted circles with centres not exactly on the normal centres of oscillation, and the site A may or may not be occupied by another atom. The energy of such configurations will be high. If we consider the solid at comparatively low temperatures, when nearly all the atoms remain on their normal sites and the number migrating at any instant is very small, the occurrence of a configuration of this type would appear to be a necessary step before migration can occur; that is, there must momentarily be a configuration with the atom A at P, which is not a lattice site at all and which is on the line joining two lattice sites. The configuration illustrated may then be regarded as a sort of transition state in the process of migration. The number of such configurations may be taken as a measure of the amount of migration or the extent to which melting has proceeded and the solid structure has broken down.

The first problem that arises is to obtain statistically an expression for this number. In doing this we must treat atoms as either on normal lattice sites or on sites like P, and further, we must suppose that, when an atom is in a P-position it remains there sufficiently long to make a number of oscillations about it before the local configuration breaks up. In assuming that atoms are to be assigned definitely either to lattice sites or to P-positions we are obviously simplifying what actually occurs, but it is a simplification that is justified as a first approximation which enables the statistical problem to be solved by the direct application of the methods that have been developed by Bragg and Williams and others in connexion with order-disorder problems in alloys. Similar considerations will apply to three-dimensional lattices and in particular to the face-centred cubic lattices in which the rare gases crystallize when they are solid.

We shall, for convenience, refer to the normal lattice sites as α-sites and to sites like P in fig. 23.5 as β-sites. For the sake of definiteness we shall consider a face-centred cubic lattice. In it there are six β-sites adjacent to any α-site and six α-sites adjacent to any β-site. The β-sites are situated at the centres of the cubes and at the centres of the cube edges. There is one α-site per atom and also one β-site. If the N atoms are all in a state of perfect order, i.e. all on α-sites, the ordinary partition function can be taken as

$$\left[(2\pi mk)T^{3/2} \frac{v_f{}^*}{h^3} e^{-\Phi/NkT} \right]^N, \quad \ldots \ldots \quad (72)$$

where $v_f{}^*$ is an average volume swept out by an atom in its " cell ", and is obtained by weighting each element of volume in the cell by a Boltzmann factor appropriate to the energy measured relative to the energy at the centre of the cell. Φ is the energy of the system when all the atoms are in their equilibrium positions. Lennard-Jones and Devonshire have calculated $v_f{}^*$ and Φ in terms of interatomic forces.[†] In obtaining $v_f{}^*$ it was assumed that the atoms surrounding a given atom were all fixed in their equilibrium positions, and the potential of the given atom at various points in its cell was calculated. In using this partition function effects of the quantization of the motion of the atom are neglected.

We now consider how the partition function is affected when disorder sets in and some of the atoms are on β-sites. The degree of order of any configuration may be specified in terms of the number N_α of atoms vibrating about α-sites and the number $N_\beta = N - N_\alpha$ vibrating about β-sites, and is usually defined as $(N_\alpha - N_\beta)/N$. When $N_\alpha = N_\beta$ the degree of order is zero, when $N_\beta = 0$ it is unity, and when $N_\alpha = 0$ it is -1. If we define a quantity Q by

$$Q = \frac{N_\alpha}{N}, \quad \ldots \ldots \ldots \quad (73)$$

the degree of order is $2Q - 1$. We assume that for any value of Q the atoms are distributed in such a way that the state of disorder is homogeneous throughout the assembly, that is, that if the average number of β-sites adjacent to any α-site is z the number of occupied β-sites near any one atom on an α-site is $z(1 - Q)$. Similarly the number of occupied α-sites near any atom on an α-site is Qz.

We have to find an expression for the energy in the disordered state in terms of Q. When all the atoms are in their equilibrium positions on α-sites the energy is Φ. Suppose that the interaction energy between two atoms on α-sites is ϕ if the sites are neighbouring α-sites and is negligible if the sites are farther away. Suppose, further, that to each α-site there are z' neighbouring α-sites. We have then

$$\Phi = z' \frac{N}{2} \phi.$$

† It should be mentioned here that Lennard-Jones and Devonshire have used calculations of $v_f{}^*$ and Φ in a discussion of evaporation and critical phenomena.

In the disordered state there will be QN atoms on α-sites. Each such atom will on the average be surrounded by Qz' occupied neighbouring α-sites and the interaction energy will be

$$QN \times Qz' \frac{\phi}{2}.$$

There will be $(1 - Q)N$ atoms on β-sites and each such atom will on the average be surrounded by $(1 - Q)z'$ occupied neighbouring β-sites. Since the α- and β-lattices are similar, the interaction energy between atoms on β-sites will be

$$(1 - Q)N \times (1 - Q)z' \frac{\phi}{2}.$$

If the interaction energy between each pair of atoms on α- and β-sites is χ, the total energy due to interactions between atoms on α-sites with atoms on neighbouring β-sites will be

$$QN \times (1 - Q)z\chi.$$

The total energy in the disordered state is therefore

$$Nz' \frac{\phi}{2}(1 - 2Q + 2Q^2) + zN\chi Q(1 - Q),$$

or

$$\Phi + (zN\chi - 2\Phi)Q(1 - Q). \quad \ldots \ldots \quad (74)$$

The number of ways $\gamma(Q)$ of choosing N_α of the α-sites and N_β of the β-sites is given by

$$\gamma(Q) = \frac{N!}{(N - N_\alpha)! \, N_\alpha!} \times \frac{N!}{(N - N_\beta)! \, N_\beta!}. \quad \ldots \quad (75)$$

If we now assume that the motion of an atom in its cell is the same whether it is on an α-site or a β-site, the ordinary partition function in the disordered state for a given value of Q is

$$\iota = \gamma(Q)\left[(2\pi mkT)^{3/2} \frac{v_f^*}{h^3} \exp(-\Phi/NkT) \exp\left\{-z(\chi - 2\Phi/zN)Q(1 - Q)/kT\right\}\right]^N. \quad (76)$$

The Helmholtz free energy F is given by

$$F = -kT \log z, \quad \ldots \ldots \ldots \quad (77)$$

and for a given T, χ and Φ the equilibrium value Q_m of Q will be that which makes F a minimum, that is, that which makes z a maximum. This is given by

$$2Q_m - 1 = \tanh \frac{z\left(\chi - \frac{2}{z}\frac{\Phi}{N}\right)(2Q_m - 1)}{4kT}. \quad \ldots \quad (78)$$

This equation is always satisfied by $Q_m = \frac{1}{2}$, but when $z\left(\chi - \frac{2}{z}\frac{\Phi}{N}\right)\big/4kT > 1$ there will be another root greater than $\frac{1}{2}$. When this other root exists, it corresponds to the maximum value of z. When it does not exist, $Q_m = \frac{1}{2}$ corresponds to the maximum value. When $z\left(\chi - \frac{2}{z}\frac{\Phi}{N}\right)\big/4kT$ is very large, Q_m is nearly unity and the order is nearly perfect, but when it is much less than one, $Q_m = \frac{1}{2}$ and there is complete disorder.

Substituting the value of Q_m from (78) in (77), we obtain for the partition function

$$z = z_1 z_2, \qquad \ldots \ldots \ldots \quad (79)$$

where

$$z_1 = \left[(2\pi m k T)^{3/2} \frac{v_f^*}{h^3} \exp(-\Phi/NkT) \right]^N, \qquad \ldots \ldots \quad (80)$$

$$z_2 = \gamma(Q_m) \exp\{-zN(\chi - 2\Phi/zN)Q_m(1 - Q_m)/kT\}. \quad \ldots \quad (81)$$

The Helmholtz free energy F is given by

$$F = -kT \log z_1 - kT \log z_2 = F_1 + F_2. \quad \ldots \ldots \quad (82)$$

Comparison with (80), (81) and (72) shows that the term F_1 is the free energy that the system would have if all the atoms remained in their ordered positions and F_2 is the additional free energy due to disorder. The entropy divides up into two terms in a similar way.

The pressure p is given by $-\left(\dfrac{\partial F}{\partial V}\right)_T$. Thus we can write

$$p = p_1 + p_2, \qquad \ldots \ldots \ldots \quad (83)$$

where

$$p_1 = -\left(\frac{\partial F_1}{\partial V}\right)_T = kT \left(\frac{\partial \log z_1}{\partial V}\right)_T, \qquad \ldots \ldots \quad (84)$$

and

$$p_2 = -\left(\frac{\partial F_2}{\partial V}\right)_T = -zNQ_m(1 - Q_m)\frac{\partial}{\partial V}\left(\chi - \frac{2\Phi}{zN}\right). \quad \ldots \quad (85)$$

We assume * that

$$\left(\chi - \frac{2\Phi}{zN}\right) = B_0 \left(\frac{V_0}{V}\right)^4, \qquad \ldots \ldots \ldots \quad (86)$$

where V_0 is the volume that N atoms would occupy if they were at a distance apart which would make the potential energy of an isolated pair a minimum,

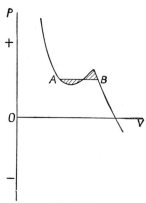

Fig. 23.6

and B_0 is a constant. For a given B_0 and T the pressure p can be calculated as a function of V. To do this Q_m is calculated for a given V from (78), Φ and χ being known if V is known; z_1 is obtained from (80) and z_2 from (81), and then p_1 and p_2 from (84) and (85). The type of curve obtained is shown in fig. 23.6. For convenience we take T as the ordinary melting-point. The melting pressure for the given B_0 is the pressure corresponding to the line AB which makes the two shaded areas equal. The correct value of B_0, which is regarded as an adjustable constant, is that which makes the melting pressure zero.

Once B_0 has been determined in this way, the entropy of melting can be calculated and is in good agreement with the observed value for argon. Lennard-Jones and Devonshire also consider other properties, for example, the volume change on melting, and they discuss the significance of Lindemann's relation from the point of view of their theory.

Mott and Gurney † have formulated the problem of calculating the entropy

* See Lennard-Jones and Devonshire, *loc. cit.*

† Mott and Gurney, *Trans. Faraday Soc.*, Vol. 35, p. 364 (1939).

change on melting by considering the process as one in which the solid breaks down into a polycrystalline mass of gradually decreasing crystal size. It is difficult to set up the theory in detail, but the preliminary examination made by Mott and Gurney shows that in a general way it gives the correct behaviour.

In conclusion mention must be made of Eyring's theory of holes in liquids.* He shows that the energy necessary to make a hole in a liquid just large enough to accommodate a single molecule is the same as the energy required to vaporize a molecule leaving no hole, and further that to a first approximation the entropy of a molecule in the vapour is for the same volume the same as the entropy of a hole in the liquid. This leads to the law of rectilinear diameters of Cailletet and Mathias, and the fact that the entropies are not quite the same accounts for the observed inclination of the line of mean density of liquid and vapour.

Reference

For a complete treatment of the questions dealt with in an elementary way in the earlier part of this chapter, reference should be made to Born, *Atomtheorie des festen Zustandes* (*Dynamik der Kristallgitter*), 2nd edition (Teubner, 1923).

* Eyring, *J. Chem. Physics*, Vol. 4, p. 284 (1936).

Appendix

THERMODYNAMIC RELATIONS AND THE THERMODYNAMIC PROPERTIES OF STEAM

1. There are a great many relations between the differential coefficients of the various quantities used in thermodynamics. Some of the most important are collected below.* The student should prove each of these relations for himself by the methods described in Chapter XIII, and in Chapter XVI, Section 9, where some of the relations have already been given.

Pressure $= p$.

Volume of one gram $= \text{v}$.

Temperature $= T$.

Internal energy of one gram $= \text{u}$.

Entropy of one gram $= \text{s}$.

Total heat of one gram $= \text{H} = \text{u} + p\text{v}$.

Thermodynamic potential of one gram $= \text{G} = \text{u} - T\text{s} + p\text{v}$.

Free energy of one gram $= \text{F} = \text{u} - T\text{s}$.

$$d\text{u} = T\,d\text{s} - p\,d\text{v}. \qquad \dots \dots \quad (1)$$

$$d\text{H} = T\,d\text{s} + \text{v}\,dp. \qquad \dots \dots \quad (2)$$

$$d\text{G} = \text{v}\,dp - \text{s}\,dT. \qquad \dots \dots \quad (3)$$

$$d\text{F} = -p\,d\text{v} - \text{s}\,dT. \qquad \dots \dots \quad (4)$$

$$\left(\frac{\partial T}{\partial \text{v}}\right)_\text{s} = -\left(\frac{\partial p}{\partial \text{s}}\right)_\text{v}. \qquad \dots \dots \quad (5)$$

$$\left(\frac{\partial T}{\partial p}\right)_\text{s} = \left(\frac{\partial \text{v}}{\partial \text{s}}\right)_p. \qquad \dots \dots \quad (6)$$

$$\left(\frac{\partial \text{v}}{\partial T}\right)_p = -\left(\frac{\partial \text{s}}{\partial p}\right)_T. \qquad \dots \dots \quad (7)$$

$$\left(\frac{\partial p}{\partial T}\right)_\text{v} = \left(\frac{\partial \text{s}}{\partial \text{v}}\right)_T. \qquad \dots \dots \quad (8)$$

$$\left(\frac{\partial \text{H}}{\partial \text{s}}\right)_p = T = \left(\frac{\partial \text{u}}{\partial \text{s}}\right)_\text{v}. \qquad \dots \dots \quad (9)$$

$$\left(\frac{\partial \text{H}}{\partial p}\right)_\text{s} = \text{v} = \left(\frac{\partial \text{G}}{\partial p}\right)_T. \qquad \dots \dots \quad (10)$$

$$\left(\frac{\partial \text{F}}{\partial \text{v}}\right)_T = -p = \left(\frac{\partial \text{u}}{\partial \text{v}}\right)_\text{s}. \qquad \dots \dots \quad (11)$$

* This list of the most important relations has been collected by Ewing in *Thermodynamics for Engineers*. Further relations are given in an appendix to Callendar's *Properties of Steam*. A convenient " shorthand " summary has been devised by Bridgman, *Phys. Rev.*, Vol. 3, p. 273 (1914).

$$\left(\frac{\partial F}{\partial T}\right)_{v} = -s = \left(\frac{\partial G}{\partial T}\right)_{p}. \quad \ldots \ldots \ldots \quad (12)$$

$$ds = \frac{c_{v}}{T} dT + \left(\frac{\partial p}{\partial T}\right)_{v} dv. \quad \ldots \ldots \ldots \quad (13)$$

$$\left(\frac{\partial c_{v}}{\partial v}\right)_{T} = T \left(\frac{\partial^{2} p}{\partial T^{2}}\right)_{v}. \quad \ldots \ldots \ldots \quad (14)$$

$$ds = \frac{c_{p}}{T} dT - \left(\frac{\partial v}{\partial T}\right)_{p} dp. \quad \ldots \ldots \ldots \quad (15)$$

$$\left(\frac{\partial c_{p}}{\partial p}\right)_{T} = -T \left(\frac{\partial^{2} v}{\partial T^{2}}\right)_{p}. \quad \ldots \ldots \ldots \quad (16)$$

$$c_{p} - c_{v} = T \left(\frac{\partial p}{\partial T}\right)_{v} \left(\frac{\partial v}{\partial T}\right)_{p}. \quad \ldots \ldots \quad (17)$$

$$c_{v} = T \left(\frac{\partial s}{\partial T}\right)_{v}. \quad \ldots \ldots \ldots \quad (18)$$

$$c_{p} = T \left(\frac{\partial s}{\partial T}\right)_{p}. \quad \ldots \ldots \ldots \quad (19)$$

$$\frac{c_{v}}{T} \left(\frac{\partial T}{\partial v}\right)_{s} = -\left(\frac{\partial p}{\partial T}\right)_{v}. \quad \ldots \ldots \ldots \quad (20)$$

$$\frac{c_{p}}{T} \left(\frac{\partial T}{\partial p}\right)_{s} = \left(\frac{\partial v}{\partial T}\right)_{p}. \quad \ldots \ldots \ldots \quad (21)$$

$$\gamma = \frac{c_{p}}{c_{v}} = \left(\frac{\partial v}{\partial p}\right)_{T} \left(\frac{\partial p}{\partial v}\right)_{s}. \quad \ldots \ldots \quad (22)$$

$$\left(\frac{\partial U}{\partial T}\right)_{v} = c_{v}. \quad \ldots \ldots \ldots \quad (23)$$

$$\left(\frac{\partial U}{\partial v}\right)_{T} = T \left(\frac{\partial p}{\partial T}\right)_{v} - p. \quad \ldots \ldots \quad (24)$$

$$dU = c_{v} dT + \left\{T\left(\frac{\partial p}{\partial T}\right)_{v} - p\right\} dv. \quad \ldots \ldots \quad (25)$$

$$\left(\frac{\partial H}{\partial T}\right)_{p} = c_{p}. \quad \ldots \ldots \ldots \quad (26)$$

$$\left(\frac{\partial H}{\partial p}\right)_{T} = v - T \left(\frac{\partial v}{\partial T}\right)_{p}. \quad \ldots \ldots \quad (27)$$

$$dH = c_{p} dT + \left\{v - T\left(\frac{\partial v}{\partial T}\right)_{p}\right\} dp. \quad \ldots \ldots \quad (28)$$

$$\left(\frac{\partial T}{\partial p}\right)_{H} = \frac{1}{c_{p}} \left\{T\left(\frac{\partial v}{\partial T}\right)_{p} - v\right\} = -\frac{1}{c_{p}} \left(\frac{\partial H}{\partial p}\right)_{T}. \quad \ldots \quad (29)$$

$$\left(\frac{\partial T}{\partial p}\right)_{H} = -\frac{1}{c_{p}} \left\{\left(\frac{\partial U}{\partial p}\right)_{T} + \left(\frac{\partial(pv)}{\partial p}\right)_{T}\right\}. \quad \ldots \quad (30)$$

$$\left(\frac{\partial T}{\partial v}\right)_{U} = -\frac{1}{c_{v}} \left\{T\left(\frac{\partial p}{\partial T}\right)_{v} - p\right\} = -\frac{1}{c_{v}} \left(\frac{\partial U}{\partial v}\right)_{T}. \quad \ldots \quad (31)$$

$$\left(\frac{\partial H}{\partial s}\right)_{T} = T + v \left(\frac{\partial p}{\partial s}\right)_{T} = T - v \left(\frac{\partial T}{\partial v}\right)_{p}. \quad \ldots \ldots \quad (32)$$

$$\left(\frac{\partial H}{\partial s}\right)_v = T + v\left(\frac{\partial p}{\partial s}\right)_v = T - v\left(\frac{\partial T}{\partial v}\right)_s. \quad \ldots \ldots \quad (33)$$

$$\left(\frac{\partial T}{\partial s}\right)_H = -\frac{T}{v}\left(\frac{\partial T}{\partial p}\right)_H = \frac{T}{c_p}\left\{1 - \frac{T}{v}\left(\frac{\partial v}{\partial T}\right)_p\right\} = \frac{T}{c_p} - \frac{T^2}{v}\left(\frac{\partial v}{\partial H}\right)_p. \quad (34)$$

$$\left(\frac{\partial H}{\partial p}\right)_v = v + c_v\left(\frac{\partial T}{\partial p}\right)_v = v - T\left(\frac{\partial v}{\partial T}\right)_s. \quad \ldots \ldots \quad (35)$$

$$\left(\frac{\partial U}{\partial p}\right)_T = -T\left(\frac{\partial v}{\partial T}\right)_p - p\left(\frac{\partial v}{\partial p}\right)_T. \quad \ldots \ldots \quad (36)$$

$$\left(\frac{\partial H}{\partial v}\right)_p = T\left(\frac{\partial p}{\partial T}\right)_s. \quad \ldots \ldots \quad (37)$$

THE PROPERTIES OF STEAM

2. An important application of thermodynamics and of the above relations is the correlation of the various measured properties of a substance. We shall take the case of steam as an example. This substance has been very fully dealt with by Callendar.*

Although the specific heat of steam varies considerably with both temperature and pressure, Callendar has shown by experiments in which the temperature and pressure of the steam in the cylinder of a steam-engine were measured, that, over a considerable range of temperatures and pressures, the adiabatic law for steam is (compare Chapter VI, Section 13)

$$\frac{p}{T^{n+1}} = \text{constant}, \quad \ldots \ldots \quad (38)$$

where n is a constant independent of the temperature and pressure. This rather remarkable result for a vapour which departs very considerably from the perfect gas laws can be explained if its internal energy U can be expressed in the form †

$$U = np(v - b) + \beta, \quad \ldots \ldots \quad (39)$$

where b and β are constants. Further, if the internal energy can be so expressed, it follows immediately that the equation of state is of the general form

$$\frac{p(v - b)}{T} = \text{a function of } \left(\frac{p}{T^{n+1}}\right). \ddagger \quad \ldots \ldots \quad (40)$$

Our knowledge of the properties of gases and vapours (see Chapters III and IV) suggests that the simplest assumption that we could make as to the form of the unknown function in equation (40) would be to suppose the function a constant and equal to r, where

$$r = \frac{R}{M},$$

R being the gas constant and M the molecular weight. This assumption is too simple and is not in accord with the experimental facts. The assumption next in simplicity is to write

$$\frac{p(v - b)}{T} = r - \frac{ap}{T^{n+1}}, \quad \ldots \ldots \quad (46)$$

* Callendar, *Properties of Steam* (Arnold, 1920).

† In this appendix it is assumed that all quantities of energy are measured in ergs.

‡ See footnote on next page.

where a is a constant. We shall show that this equation, which is Callendar's equation of state, is in accord with the experimental facts for steam. The term b (compare Chapter IV) is taken as representing the effect of the size of the molecules, and the second term on the right-hand side is taken as representing the effect of the tendency of the molecules to form clusters and includes the effect of molecular attractions. The numerical values of the constants are determined as follows:

b is taken as equal to the volume occupied by one gram when the molecules are nearly in contact, that is, in the liquid state, and is 1 c.c. per gram.

r is determined from the known value of the gas constant (see Chapter I) and from the molecular weight of unassociated H_2O molecules.

n is determined as follows. Equation (43) shows that at zero pressure (infinite dilution) the specific heat at constant volume is given by

$$(c_v)_0 = \lim_{p \to 0} c_v = nr. \qquad \ldots \ldots \ldots \quad (47)$$

From the value of r and from that of $\lim c_v$, obtained by extrapolation of experimental results, the value of n can be deduced. Extrapolation from specific-heat experiments indicates that, over the range of temperatures which are important in steam-engines, $\lim c_v$ does not vary appreciably, and that n has the value $\frac{10}{3}$.

‡ The proof of these various results is as follows (see Callendar, *loc. cit.*, p. 53). If

$$\upsilon = np(v - b) + \beta, \qquad \ldots \ldots \ldots \quad (41)$$

the fundamental assumption, then the total heat H is given by

$$H = (n + 1)p(v - b) + bp + \beta, \qquad \ldots \ldots \ldots \quad (42)$$

an expression which contains no new arbitrary constant. Applying equations (26) and (23), we obtain

$$c_p = (n + 1)p \left(\frac{\partial v}{\partial T}\right)_p$$

and

$$c_v = n(v - b) \left(\frac{\partial p}{\partial T}\right)_v \qquad \ldots \ldots \ldots \quad (43)$$

and from these two equations

$$c_p - c_v = (n + 1)p \left(\frac{\partial v}{\partial T}\right)_p - n(v - b)\left(\frac{\partial p}{\partial T}\right)_v. \qquad \ldots \ldots \quad (44)$$

Equating this expression for the difference between the specific heats to that given in equation (17), we obtain a differential equation of state, namely,

$$T = (n + 1)p \left(\frac{\partial T}{\partial p}\right)_v - n(v - b)\left(\frac{\partial T}{\partial v}\right)_p. \qquad \ldots \ldots \quad (45)$$

The solution of this equation is equation (40) of the text. The solution can be verified by differentiation.

For an adiabatic change we have from equation (21)

$$\left(\frac{\partial p}{\partial T}\right)_s = \frac{c_p}{T}\left(\frac{\partial T}{\partial v}\right)_p.$$

Substituting the value of $c_p\left(\frac{\partial T}{\partial v}\right)_p$ from equation (43), we obtain for an adiabatic change

$$\frac{dp}{p} = (n + 1)\frac{dT}{T}.$$

The solution of this equation is equation (38) in the text.

The limiting value of the specific heat at constant pressure $(c_p)_0$ is given by

$$(c_p)_0 = (n + 1)r. \quad \ldots \ldots \ldots \quad (48)$$

a is determined from measurements of the Joule-Kelvin effect. The theory is as follows. If the characteristic equation has the simple form given in equation (46), the expression for v becomes (see equation (39)) in terms of p and T (which are more convenient and, in general, more easily measurable variables than p and v)

$$v = nrT - n\frac{a}{T^n}p + \beta. \quad \ldots \ldots \quad (49)$$

The total heat (see equation (42)) is given by

$$H = (n + 1)rT - (n + 1)\frac{a}{T^n}p + bp + \beta. \quad \ldots \quad (50)$$

Further, we have by differentiating equation (50)

$$c_p = \left(\frac{\partial H}{\partial T}\right)_p = (n + 1)r + n(n + 1)\frac{a}{T^{n+1}}p. \quad \ldots \quad (51)$$

Now for the Joule-Kelvin effect, $\left(\frac{\partial T}{\partial p}\right)_H$, we have from the thermodynamic equation (29)

$$c_p \left(\frac{\partial T}{\partial p}\right)_H = -\left(\frac{\partial H}{\partial p}\right)_T,$$

and thus, differentiating equation (50),

$$c_p \left(\frac{\partial T}{\partial p}\right)_H = (n + 1)\frac{a}{T^n} - b. \quad \ldots \ldots \quad (52)$$

Substituting the value of c_p from equation (51), we obtain

$$\frac{a}{T^n} = \frac{r\left(\frac{\partial T}{\partial p}\right)_H + \frac{b}{n+1}}{1 - \frac{np}{T}\left(\frac{\partial T}{\partial p}\right)_H}. \quad \ldots \ldots \ldots \quad (53)$$

Callendar and Nicolson have measured the Joule-Kelvin effect for steam at temperatures between 120° and 180° C. and at pressures ranging from about 1 to 8 atmospheres. All the other quantities on the right-hand side of equation (53) are known, and therefore, from each measurement of the Joule-Kelvin effect, a value of the constant a can be deduced. The values so obtained all agree within the limits of experimental error. This is an important check of the accuracy of Callendar's equation of state.

3. Steam Tables.

We shall now consider how the various quantities tabulated in steam tables are calculated, when the equation of state and the constants occurring in it have been determined in the manner described above.

(1) The *total heat* at various temperatures and pressures is calculated from the expression on the right-hand side of equation (50), namely,

$$H = (n + 1)rT - (n + 1)\frac{a}{T^n}p + bp + \beta.$$

The constant β, which depends on the zero from which H is measured, is deter-mined from a measurement of H at one particular temperature and pressure. The most convenient condition to choose is that of saturated steam under stan-dard atmospheric pressure, i.e. at a temperature of 100° C. The zero condition in measuring all quantities is taken as the condition of water at the freezing-point and under its saturation vapour pressure. The total heat of *water* under saturation pressure at 100° C. is determined by ordinary calorimetric methods. The total heat of saturated steam at the same temperature is obtained by adding the measured latent heat of vaporization at 100° C. to the total heat of water. In this way the value of β is determined, and thus the total heat of steam, whether saturated, superheated, or supercooled, can be determined under any given conditions from the above equation.

That the results obtained in this way are in accord with experimental facts has been proved by Callendar as follows. The total heat of steam at 100° C. and under atmospheric pressure is known (see above). Callendar and others, using the method of continuous electrical heating (see Chapter VI, Section 10), have determined the specific heat of steam under constant atmospheric pressure over a wide range of temperatures. From these measurements and from the value of the total heat of steam at 100° C. and under atmospheric pressure, the total heat of steam under atmospheric pressure and at any temperature within the range of specific-heat measurements can be deduced. If now we wish to deter-mine experimentally the total heat of steam in any other condition which we shall call A, we pass steam in condition A through a throttle or porous plug so that the pressure of the steam after passing through the throttle is atmospheric. It is only necessary to measure the temperature of the steam after throttling to determine its total heat, since it is at atmospheric pressure. But, as was explained in Chapter XIII, Sections 5 and 6, the total heat is not altered by throttling. Therefore the measurement of the total heat after throttling gives directly the total heat before throttling. Experimental values of the total heat determined in this way agree closely with those deduced from Callendar's equation, and this is a further proof of the accuracy and usefulness of his equation of state.

(2) The *entropy* is determined as follows. Let s_{100} be the entropy of saturated steam at 100° C. and under atmospheric pressure, which for convenience we shall call T_{100} and p_{100}. The value of s_{100} may be obtained directly from experiment; for if λ_{100} is the latent heat of vaporization at 100° C., s_{100} is equal to λ_{100}/T_{100} *plus* the entropy of water under saturation pressure at 100° C., and the latter quantity can be deduced directly from measurements of the specific heat of water (see Callendar, *loc. cit.*, p. 135). The entropy s at any other temperature T and pressure p can be deduced from s_{100}, using the equation of state. First imagine the steam heated at constant pressure p_{100} from temperature T_{100} to temperature T: the change of entropy is equal to $\int_{T_{100}}^{T} c_p/T\, dT$. Using the value of c_p given in equation (51), we obtain for the change of entropy

$$(n+1)r \log_e \frac{T}{T_{100}} - np_{100}\frac{a}{T^{n+1}} + np_{100}\frac{a}{T_{100}^{n+1}}.$$

Now compress the steam at constant temperature T from pressure p_{100} to pressure p. Using equation (7), the change in entropy is equal to $-\int_{p_{100}}^{p} (\partial v/\partial T)_p dp$. The value of $(\partial v/\partial T)_p$ may be deduced from equations (43) and (51), and, using this value in the integral, the change in the entropy becomes

$$-r \log_e \frac{p}{p_{100}} - np\frac{a}{T^{n+1}} + np_{100}\frac{a}{T^{n+1}}.$$

Collecting these two results, we obtain for $(s - s_{100})$, the net change of entropy in passing from T_{100} and p_{100} to T and p,

$$s - s_{100} = (n + 1)r \log_e \frac{T}{T_{100}} - r \log_e \frac{p}{p_{100}} - np \frac{a}{T^{n+1}} + np_{100} \frac{a}{T_{100}^{n+1}}. \quad (54)$$

The entropy s at any temperature and pressure is calculated from this equation.

(3) Callendar obtains the *equation of the vapour-pressure curve* by similar methods which may be briefly described as follows.

Equation (54) applies to steam at any point on the saturation curve. For such a point we have also

$$s_{steam} = s_{water} + \frac{\lambda}{T},$$

where λ is the latent heat of vaporization. Substituting this in equation (54), we have for saturated steam

$$s_w - (s_w)_{100} + \frac{\lambda}{T} - \frac{\lambda_{100}}{T_{100}} = (n+1)r \log_e \frac{T}{T_{100}} - r \log_e \frac{p}{p_{100}} - na \left(\frac{p}{T^{n+1}} - \frac{p_{100}}{T_{100}^{n+1}} \right), \quad (55)$$

where the subscript w refers to water. This gives an equation between the vapour pressure p and the absolute temperature T. It may be simplified as follows.

Experiments on the specific heat of water show that H_w, the total heat of water, can be represented by the empirical expression

$$H_w = \sigma t + T v_w \left(\frac{\partial p}{\partial T} \right)_{sat.},$$

where t is the celsius temperature (ice-point = zero), and where the subscript *sat.* refers to changes along the saturation curve. σ is a constant which depends only on the unit of heat. It follows from this that s_w, the entropy of water under saturation pressure, is given by the equation

$$s_w = \sigma \log_e \frac{T}{T_0} + v_w \left(\frac{\partial p}{\partial T} \right)_{sat.},$$

where T_0 is the temperature of the ice-point on the absolute scale.* But by the Clausius-Clapeyron equation

$$\left(\frac{\partial p}{\partial T} \right)_{sat.} = \frac{\lambda}{T(v_s - v_w)},$$

where the subscript s refers to steam. Substituting this result in the last two equations, we obtain

$$H_w = \sigma t + \frac{v_w}{v_s - v_w} \lambda, \quad \cdot \;\cdot\;\cdot\;\cdot\;\cdot\;\cdot\;\cdot \quad (56)$$

and

$$s_w = \sigma \log_e \frac{T}{T_0} + \frac{v_w}{v_s - v_w} \frac{\lambda}{T}. \quad \cdot \;\cdot\;\cdot\;\cdot\;\cdot\;\cdot \quad (57)$$

λ at any temperature is given by the relation

$$\lambda = H_s - H_w.$$

* Neither of these expressions vanishes exactly when $T = T_0$, but the terms $T_0(v_w)_0 (\partial p/\partial T)_0$ and $(v_w)_0 (\partial p/\partial T)_0$ are so small that for practical purposes they can be neglected. For the deduction of the expression for the entropy, see Callendar, *loc. cit.*, pp. 134–6.

Substituting from equations (50) and (56), we obtain

$$\frac{\mathbf{v}_s}{\mathbf{v}_s - \mathbf{v}_w} \lambda = (n+1)rT - \sigma t - (n+1)a\frac{p}{T^n} + bp + \beta. \quad . \quad (58)$$

Substituting the value of s_w from equation (57) and the value of λ from equation (58) in equation (55), the equation of the saturation vapour-pressure curve, we obtain after some reduction in which β is eliminated by substituting its value obtained by applying equation (58) at 100° C.

$$r \log_e \frac{p}{p_{100}} = L_{100}\left(\frac{1}{T_{100}} - \frac{1}{T}\right) + \{(n+1)r - \sigma\}\left\{\left(\log_e \frac{T}{T_{100}}\right) - \left(1 - \frac{T_{100}}{T}\right)\right\}$$

$$+ \left[\left(\frac{a}{T^n} - b\right)\frac{p}{T}\right]_{T_{100}}^{T}, \quad . \quad . \quad . \quad . \quad . \quad . \quad (59)$$

where

$$L_{100} = \frac{(\mathbf{v}_s)_{100}}{(\mathbf{v}_s)_{100} - (\mathbf{v}_w)_{100}} \lambda_{100} + (n+1)a\frac{p_{100}}{T_{100}^n} - bp_{100}.$$

The value of L_{100} is determined by measurement of the latent heat of vaporization at 100° C., the other terms in it being known. An approximate value of p may be used to determine the value of the last term on the right-hand side of equation (59).

Substituting the value of p_{100} (viz. 1 atmosphere), equation (59) represents the relation between the pressure and temperature with extraordinary accuracy, as the following figures show. Remembering that the equation does not contain a single adjustable constant, this is a very striking proof of the accuracy of Callendar's equation and of the second law of thermodynamics, on which the theory is based.

VAPOUR PRESSURE OF STEAM IN MILLIMETRES OF MERCURY

Temperature, °C.	Callendar's equation	Experiments of Holborn and Henning and of Thiesen and Scheel
0	4·62	4·58
20	17·59	17·51
40	55·38	55·13
60	149·38	149·19
80	355·1	355·1
120	1409·5	1488·9
140	2715·3	2709·5
160	4646	4633
180	7532	7514
200	11,653	11,647

INDEX

Abbey and Barlow, measurement of speed of sound VI, 17.

Abbot bolometer XX, 3.

Aberdeen and Laby, thermal conductivity of powders XI, 21.

Abraham, Osborne, D. W., and Weinstock, vapour pressure of helium 3 IV, 7.

Abraham, see *Osborne, D. W.*

Absolute temperature, and root mean square velocity III, 6 — defined in terms of efficiency of reversible engine XII, 6 — determination of, from measurements in terms of empirical scale XIII, 8 — equivalent to gas scale XII, 7 — scale I, 4, 34, 36.

Absolute zero I, 35; XII, 7 — unattainability of XIX, 1, 6–9.

Absorption XX, 7.

Absorptive power XX, 8.

Accommodation coefficient, defined and measured values XI, 11 — use of in study of adsorbed monolayers VIII, 27.

Activity, defined XVIII, 14 — to determine equilibrium conditions XVIII, 16 — variation with pressure XVIII, 15.

Adams, calibration of thermocouples I, 30.

Adiabatic, changes VI, 12, 16 — equation of, for perfect gas VI, 13 — equation of, for actual gas VI, 14 — defined I, 2.

Adiabatic demagnetization, methods of heating salt V, 17 — double, of paramagnetic salt V, 18 — nuclear V, 19 — relation between magnetic and thermodynamic temperature V, 17 — theory of method V, 16 — unattainability of absolute zero XIX, 8 — to reach low temperatures V, 1, 16–19.

Adiabatic vacuum calorimeter VII, 3; VIII, 16.

Adsorption, on solid surfaces VIII, 26 — kinetic considerations VIII, 27.

Ahlberg, see *Simon.*

Aldrich and Nier, relative abundance of the helium isotopes XVIII, 8.

Alexander and Lambert, vibrational specific heat VI, 29.

Allen, E. T., see *Day.*

Allen, J. F., and Jones, H., properties of liquid helium V, 14 — fountain effect in liquid helium XVII, 2.

Allen, J. F., and Reekie, thermomechanical effect in liquid helium XVII, 2.

Alpert, nuclear magnetic resonance and reorientation of molecules in solids XXII, 12.

Alty, condensation coefficient of water VIII, 7.

Aluminium, freezing-point I, 22.

Amagat, compressibility of gases IV, 10 — mercury manometer IV, 10.

Ambler and Hudson, distribution of ions over quantum states in adiabatic demagnetization V, 16 — measurements on chromium methyl ammonium sulphate V, 17.

Ammonia equilibrium, reaction constant of XVIII, 17.

Ammonium salts, specific heat anomalies XXII, 12.

Andreewa, see *Bennewitz.*

Andrews, compression of carbon dioxide IV, 3; (apparatus) VIII, 2.

Angell, thermal conductivity of metals at high temperatures XI, 17.

Angström, pyrheliometer XX, 13.

Antimony, freezing-point I, 22.

Apparent temperature, of radiating surface XX, 21 — of tungsten filament XX, 22.

Archer, see *Gregory.*

Arnold, see *Yarnell.*

Arzybyschew and Parfianowitsch, thermal conductivity at low temperatures XI, 22.

Ashmead, helium liquefier V, 6 — magnetic and thermal properties below 1° K. V, 17 — water-cooled magnet V, 16.

Assmann, adiabatic changes in gases VI, 15.

Aston, isotopes VIII, 25.
Atmosphere, standard, defined I, 22.
Avogadro's law I, 38; III, 1 — obeyed by perfect gas III, 4.
Avogadro's number, defined and experimental determination III, 7 — value from radiation laws XX, 15.
Awbery, measurement of latent heat of vaporization VIII, 15 — see *Griffiths, Ezer.*
Awbery and Griffiths, Ezer, continuous-flow method of measuring latent heat of vaporization VIII, 19 — latent heat of fusion of metals IX, 5.

Bacon, theory of heat II, 2.
Balamuth, Wolfe and Zemansky, temperature concept I, 1.
Ball, see *Ginnings.*
Barber, see *Hall.*
Barber and Hall, size of degree I, 4 — unit of heat II, 5.
Barieau, see *Giauque.*
Barlow, see *Abbey.*
Barnes, see *Callendar.*
Bartels, see *Eucken.*
Bartoli and Stracciati, specific heat of water II, 17.
Bates and Kirschman, composition of vapour phase in contact with hydrochloric acid XVIII, 25.
Bateucas, gas constant I, 38.
Baumann, see *Holborn.*
Bearden and Thomsen, fundamental constants I, 38; III, 7; XVIII, 22; XX, 15.
Beattie, constant-volume nitrogen thermometer I, 7 — ice point I, 35.
Beattie, Benedict, and Blaisdell, sulphur-point determination I, 18.
Beattie, Benedict, Blaisdell, and Kaye, J., comparison of international and thermodynamic scales I, 22.
Beattie, Jacobus, Gaines, Benedict and Blaisdell, constant-volume nitrogen thermometer I, 7.
Becker, expansion of crystals by X-ray methods X, 6.
Beeck, see *Stevenson.*
Behn and Geiger, velocity of sound VI, 20.
Bendt, see *Yarnell.*
Benedict, see *Beattie.*
Bennewitz, condensation coefficient VIII, 7.
Bennewitz and Andreewa, measurement of total heat of steam IV, 12.

Benoit, expansion of Iceland spar X, 6.
Benzoic acid, triple point I, 22.
Benzophenone, boiling-point I, 19 — condensing point of vapour I, 22.
Bergmann, ultrasonics VI, 29 — see *Simon.*
Berman and Simon, diamond-graphite equilibrium XIX, 1.
Berry, see *Soddy.*
Berthelot, equation of state IV, 4 — equation of state and adiabatic path VI, 14 — equation of state and Boyle temperature IV, 6 — equation of state and calculation of chemical constant VIII, 24 — equation of state and difference between specific heats VI, 3 — equation of state and gas thermometer corrections I, 14 — equation of state and second virial coefficient IV, 6 — equation of state and velocity of sound in gases VI, 16 — heat of reaction XVIII, 26 — latent heat of vaporization VIII, 18.
Bertram, see *Eucken.*
Bichowsky and Wilson, E. B., molecular effusion III, 21.
Bidwell, thermal conductivity of metals XI, 13.
Biermasz, see *De Haas.*
Birge, atomic constants XX, 15 — Avogadro's number III, 7 — gas constant I, 38 — ice point I, 35 — recalculation of mechanical and electrical equivalents II, 16 — the faraday XVIII, 22.
Birge and Jenkins, gas constant I, 38.
Bjerrum, measurement of equilibrium constants XVIII, 17 — specific heats of gases VI, 6 — vibrational specific heat VI, 29.
Black, latent heat II, 3 — specific heat II, 4.
Black body, definition XX, 9 — emissive power of XX, 12 — partition of energy XXI, 4 — see *Radiator, full.*
Black-body furnace XX, 13.
Black-body radiation XX, 9 — Planck's law of XX, 15; XXI, 4 — Stefan-Boltzmann law of XX, 11–12 — Wien's law of XX, 17.
Black-body source, thermometer shield as I, 18 — wedge as XX, 22.
Black-body temperature, comparison of by different methods XX, 20 — of filament XX, 22 — of metallic surface XX, 21 — of sun XX, 23 — see *Brightness temperature.*

Blackett, Henry, P. S. H., and Rideal, specific heat of gases VI, 11.

Blackman, calculation of Θ_D for lithium XXII, 12 — cubic variation of specific heat only at much lower temperatures than predicted by Debye's theory XXII, 5 — explanation of success of two-line spectrum for specific heat of solids XXII, 1 — lattice theory of specific heats XIX, 3; XXII, 11 — relation of lattice theory to Debye's theory XXII, 11.

Blaisdell, see Beattie.

Blaisdell and Kaye, J., measured values of sulphur point I, 18.

Blaisse, see De Boer.

Bleaney, heating by γ-rays V, 17.

Bleaney and Hull, verification of temperature scale V, 11.

Bleaney and Simon, 1937 scale thermodynamically inconsistent V, 11.

Blodgett, see Langmuir.

Bodenstein, measurement of equilibrium constants XVIII, 17; XXIII, 13.

Bohr, microscopic reversibility III, 23 — quantization of angular momentum VI, 28.

Boiling-point, defined VIII, 1 — effect of pressure on I, 17; XVI, 8 — of water I, 4; I, 17 — see Latent heat — see particular substances.

Boks, see Onnes.

Bolland and Melville, conductivity and gas analysis VI, 28.

Bolometer XX, 3.

Boltzmann, distribution of velocities III, 8 — law XXI, 1.

Boltzmann's constant, defined, and measurement of III, 6 — value from radiation laws XX, 15.

Bonhoeffer, Farkas and Harteck, ortho- and para-hydrogen conversion VI, 28.

Borelius, see Wilner.

Born, chemical constant VIII, 23 — concept of heat II, 6, 18 — energy of crystalline salts XXIII, 13 — general theory of specific heats, cubic law at sufficiently low temperatures XXII, 7 — internal energy II, 18 — moment of inertia of molecules VI, 28 — second law of thermodynamics XII, 12 — specific heat of crystals containing more than one type of atom XXII, 7 — specific heats at high temperatures XXII, 9 — temperature concept I, 3.

Born and v. Kármán, crystal dynamics XXII, 6; XXIII, 5 — frequency spectrum for atoms in crystal XXII, 2, 6 — lattice theory of specific heats XIX, 3; XXII, 6.

Bound energy XVI, 3.

Bousfield and Bousfield, electrical equivalent II, 13.

Bowden and Tabor, skiing on snow XVI, 8.

Bowers, see Daunt.

Boyle temperature, defined IV, 5 — for different equations of state IV, 6 — ratio to critical temperature IV, 6.

Boyle's law, I, 9; III, 1 — departures from I, 14; XIII, 6 — obeyed by perfect gas III, 2, 5; XII, 7.

Boys, radio-micrometer XX, 4.

Bracey, see Milford.

Bradley and Jay, superlattice lines XVII, 5.

Bragg and Williams, co-operative phenomena XVII, 6 — order-disorder phenomena in alloys XVII, 5; XXII, 12; XXIII, 15.

Braun, linear expansion of solids X, 2.

Brevoort, measurement of high temperatures in internal combustion engines XX, 21.

Brickwedde, comparison of different platinum thermometers I, 23 — sulphur point determination I, 18 — see Scott.

Bridges for thermometric work I, 29.

Bridgman, compressibility of liquids IV, 10 — different kinds of ice XVI, 14 — second-order transitions XVII, 1 — specific-heat anomalies XXII, 12 — thermal conductivity of liquids XI, 12 — thermodynamic relations, Appendix.

Brightness temperature, XX, 21.

Brinkley, complete description of a phase XVI, 10.

Brinkworth, specific heat of hydrogen at low temperatures VI, 27.

Broderson, adiabatic changes in a gas VI, 15.

Brønsted, dissociation of water vapour XVIII, 25 — heat of reaction XIX, 2.

Brønsted and Hevesy, separation of isotopes VIII, 25.

Brown, see Richardson.

Brüche and Littwin, radiometer XX, 5 — thermal conductivity of krypton XI, 9.

Buckingham, intermolecular law of force IV, 7 — see Halpern.

Roman figures refer to chapters, and Arabic figures to sections within these chapters

Buckingham, Hamilton, Massey, and Corner, second virial coefficient of helium IV, 6.

Buckley, correction for finite hole in black body XX, 9.

Buffington, see *Giauque*.

Buisson, see *Fabry*.

Bundy, Hall, Strong, and Wentorf, synthesis of diamond XIX, 1.

Bunsen ice calorimeter VIII, 17; IX, 3.

Burdon, adsorption on liquid surfaces VIII, 26.

Burger and van Cittert, thermopile XX, 4.

Burgess, international temperature scale I, 18; I, 23 — see *Waidner*.

Cadmium, freezing-point I, 22.

Cady, see *Hyde*.

Cailletet and Colardeau, critical phenomena IV, 13.

Cailletet and Mathias, law of rectilinear diameters IV, 11; XXIII, 15.

Caldwell, see *Roeser*.

Callendar, bridge for use in thermometry I, 29 — critical phenomena in water IV, 12 — discharge through nozzles XIV, 16 — enthalpy-pressure diagram XIV, 10 — equation of state IV, 4 — platinum thermometry I, 23 — properties of steam, Appendix, 2 — specific heat of water II, 5, 17 — steam tables XIV, 9; Appendix, 3 — thermal conductivity of liquids XI, 12 — thermal conductivity of metals XI, 13, 15.

Callendar and Barnes, determination of electrical equivalent II, 13 — specific heat of water II, 17.

Callendar and Griffiths, E. H., bridge for use in thermometry I, 29 — sulphur point I, 18.

Callendar and Moss, expansion of liquids X, 9.

Callendar and Nicolson, Joule-Kelvin effect for steam, Appendix, 2.

Callendar, Hartree and Porter, heat losses in calorimetry II, 8.

Caloric theory, account II, 2 — contradictions involved in explanation of experiments of Rumford and Davy II, 3 — Joule's experiments decisive against II, 6.

Calorie, exact definition II, 7 — formerly used as unit of heat II, 5 — ratio of mean to standard II, 7; VIII, 20.

Calorimeter, adiabatic vacuum VII, 3;

VIII, 16 — bomb VI, 6 — to measure heat of reaction XVIII, 26 — ice, of Bunsen VIII, 13, 17; IX, 3 — Nernst VII, 2 — steam, of Joly VI, 4; VIII, 20.

Calorimetry, continuous-flow VI, 11; VIII, 19 — heat losses in II, 8; VI, 11; VIII, 15 — method of mixtures II, 4, 20; VII, 8 — method of mixtures and latent heat of fusion of ice IX, 2 — method of mixtures and latent heat of fusion of metals IX, 5.

Carathéodory, temperature concept I, 3.

Carathéodory's principle XII, 12.

Carbon dioxide, freezing-point I, 22 — isotherms IV, 3.

Carlton-Sutton, measurement of latent heat of vaporization VIII, 20.

Carman, see *Kannuluik*.

Carnot cycle, definition and efficiency of XII, 3 — for perfect gas XII, 7; XIV, 17 — for saturated vapour XIV, 3.

Caro and Martin, velocity of sound VI, 17.

Carpenter and Stoodley, specific heats at high temperatures XXII, 9.

Cartwright, thermopile XX, 4.

Cascade process (of liquefaction) V, 2.

Casimir, effect of size of specimen on specific thermal resistance XI, 23 — ice point I, 36 — microscopic reversibility III, 23 — magnetism at very low temperatures V, 16 — see *Gorter*.

Casimir and de Haas, magnetic and thermodynamic temperatures V, 17.

Casimir and Gorter, thermodynamical functions of a superconductor XVII, 9.

Casimir, de Haas and de Klerk, magnetic and thermal properties below 1° K. V, 17.

Cells, reversible electric XVIII, 18–24.

Celsius temperature scale I, 4.

Centésimale, see *Celsius*.

Centigrade, see *Celsius*.

Chandrasekhar, temperature concept I, 3.

Chapman, specific heat of gases VI, 11 — thermal diffusion III, 24.

Chapman and Cowling, theory of non-uniform gases III, 24.

Chappuis, expansion of liquids X, 9 — gas thermometry I, 14 — sulphur point I, 18.

Chappuis and Harker, gas thermometer corrections I, 15 — sulphur point I, 18.

Characteristic function, for different choices of independent variables XVI, 12.

Characteristic temperature, of nuclear interactions V, 19.

Charles's law I, 34; III, 1.

Chemical compounds, specific heats, law of VII, 6.

Chemical constant, calculation of VIII, 24 — deduction from spectroscopic data XIX, 3 — defined VIII, 11 — theoretical, and comparison with measured values VIII, 23 — verification of third law XIX, 3.

Chemical potential, see *Partial potential*.

Chowdri and Kothari, mechanical equivalent, modification of method of Laby and Hercus II, 11.

Christiansen, measurement of Stefan-Boltzmann constant XX, 13.

Chromium methyl ammonium sulphate V, 17.

Clark and Katz, measurement of ratio of specific heats VI, 15; XIII, example 7.

Classical system, entropy as function of temperature XIX, 1.

Claude, liquefaction of gases V, 4.

Claus, zero-point energy of crystals XXII, 10.

Clausing, cosine law III, 17 — streaming through narrow tubes III, 18.

Clausius, equation of state IV, 4 — virial law XXIII, 1.

Clausius-Clapeyron equation, analogue of, for second-order phase transition XVII, 1, 8 — derived XVI, 8 — integration of VIII, 8 — use to interpret vapour-pressure measurements VIII, 9.

Clement, temperature scale below 5° K. V, 11 — see *Day*.

Clement and Désormes, cooling effect of sudden expansion of gas V, 4 — ratio of specific heats VI, 15.

Clusius, measurement of chemical constants VIII, 23 — specific-heat anomalies XXII, 12 — see *Eucken* — see *Keesom*.

Clusius and Dickel, separation of isotopes III, 24.

Clusius and Hiller, specific heat of hydrogen at low temperatures VI, 28.

Clusius and Perlick, specific heat anomaly in methane XVII, 1.

Clusius and Riccoboni, latent heat of solidified permanent gases, IX, 7 — measurement of chemical constants VIII, 23.

Clusius and Teske, chemical constants XIX, 3.

Clusius, Harteck and Vaughan, specific heats of solids VII, 7.

Clusius, Kruis and Konnertz, measurements of chemical constants VIII, 23.

Cobalt, freezing-point I, 22.

Coblentz, experimental verification of Wien's law XX, 16 — measurement of Stefan-Boltzmann constant XX, 13 — thermopile XX, 4.

Cockcroft, performance of helium liquefier V, 6.

Coefficient of expansion, see *Expansion*.

Coefficient of pressure, see *Pressure*.

Coexistence curves IV, 12.

Cohen, see *Hutchison*.

Cohen, E. G. D., de Boer, and Salsburg theory of liquids XXIII, 15.

Cohn, furnaces at high temperatures XX, 13 — linear expansion of solids X, 4.

Colardeau, see *Cailletet*.

Collins, C. B., see *Thode*.

Collins, S. C., helium liquefier V, 6.

Colour of filament, variation with temperature XX, 22.

Compensating leads, in resistance thermometry I, 26.

Complete radiation, see *Black-body radiation*.

Compressibility, defined IV, 8 — relations between coefficients measured under different conditions IV, 8; VI, 14; XIII, example 8.

Compressibility of gases, see *Gases*.

Compressibility of liquids, see *Liquids*.

Compton, see *Coster*.

Condensation coefficient VIII, 7, 27.

Conduction, transfer of heat by XI, 1 — see *Thermal conductivity*.

Conductivity, ratio of thermal and electric XI, 18.

Conservation of energy II, 21.

Constant-pressure and constant-volume thermometers, see *Thermometer*.

Constant-temperature bath I, 4, 20; V. 12.

Continuity of state IV, 2.

Continuous-flow methods, latent heat of vaporization VIII, 19 — thermal conductivity of liquids XI, 12 — specific heat of gases VI, 7, 10, 11.

Convection, defined XI, 24 — forced, experimental results compared with theory XI, 27 — forced, law of cooling II, 8 — natural, experimental results compared with theory XI, 26 — transfer of heat by XI, 1 — treated by dimensional methods XI, 24, 25, 27.

Cooke, heating by γ-rays V, 17 — see *Scott*.

Cooke, Meyer, and Wolf, magnetic cooling V, 17.

Co-operative assemblies XVII, 6; XXII, 12.

Copper, freezing-point I, 22.

Corbino, specific heats of metals VII, 8.

Corner, intermolecular energy of inert elements in solid state IV, 6 — see *Buckingham*.

Correlation of motion of particles in neighbouring cells XXIII, 15.

Corresponding states, applied to frozen rare gases IV, 7 — law of IV, 7 — quantum basis of IV, 7.

Cosine law, experimental test III, 19–20 — statement III, 17.

Coster, Smyth, and Compton, test of velocity distribution law III, 13.

Cragoe, gas constant I, 38 — isotherms of oxygen I, 38 — isotherms of rare gases; IV, 1 — see *Osborne, N. S.*

Crank and Nicolson, numerical integration of heat-conduction equation XI, 28.

Crenshaw and Ritter, specific heat of ammonium salts XXII, 12.

Critical coefficient IV, 3.

Critical data, for inorganic substances IV, 3, 11.

Critical point, defined IV, 3, 12 — effect of dissolved air on IV, 12.

Critical temperature, defined IV, 2 — for Dieterici's equation IV, example 6 — for Van der Waals' equation IV, 3 — helium, liquid at temperature ten times higher than V, 15 — ratio of, to Boyle temperature IV, 6.

Crommelin, see *Onnes*.

Crookes, radiometer XX, 5.

Crystalline electric field, in demagnetization experiments V, 16.

Crystalline salts, energy of XXIII, 13 — specific heat of XXII, 7.

Crystals, properties of single and of aggregates of small XXII, 4.

Cunnold, optical pyrometer XX, 18 — see *Milford*.

Dahler, Hirschfelder, and Thacher, theory of liquids XXIII, 15.

Dalton's law of partial pressures, obeyed by perfect gas III, 5 — statement III, 1.

Dammers, see *Keesom*.

Daniell cell XVIII, 20.

Darby, Hatton, Rollin, Seymour, and Silsbee, two-stage demagnetization V, 18.

Darrow, conduction in metals XI, 20.

Däumichen, specific heat of hydrogen VI, 28.

Daunt and Heer, superconductor as thermal switch XVII, 7.

Daunt and Johnston, helium liquefier V, 6.

Daunt and Mendelssohn, expansion liquefier V, 6.

Daunt, Mendelssohn and Bowers, transfer of liquid helium films XVII, 2.

Daunt, Miller, Pippard, and Shoenberg, temperature variation of penetration depth in a superconductor XVII, 7.

Davis, method of dimensions, use in studying convection XI, 24, 27.

Davy, nature of heat II, 3.

Day and Clement, measurement of melting-points at high temperatures I, 20.

Day and Sosman, high-temperature gas thermometry XX, 22 — measurement of melting-points at high temperatures I, 21 — sulphur point I, 18.

Day, Sosman and Allen, high-temperature melting-points I, 21.

Dead-space correction I, 6.

De Boer, implication of existence of liquid state down to $0°$ K. XVII, 2 — properties of helium 3 and helium 4 calculated IV, 7 — quantum basis of law of corresponding states IV, 7 — theory of helium XVII, 2 — theory of liquids XXIII, 15 — see *Cohen, E. G. D.*

De Boer and Blaisse, quantum calculation of properties of gaseous elements IV, 7.

De Boer and Michels, A., law of corresponding states IV, 7.

Debye, comparison of specific heat theory with experiment XXII, 4, 5 — criticism of theory of specific heats XIX, 3; XXII, 2, 5, 7 — equation of state for solids XXIII, 10 — expression for entropy of solid differs negligibly from that of Einstein XXIII, 10 —frequency spectrum for atoms in crystal XXII, 2 — heat conduction in crystals XI, 23 — predicts T^3 region at too high temperatures XXII, 5 — principle of magnetic cooling V, 16 — specific heats of solids XXII, 3.

Debye function, table of values XXII, 4.
Degeneration of gases VI, 27.
Degree, definition of I, 4 — size of I, 4, 34; III, 6 — different in size on thermodynamical and international scales I, 37.
De Groot, thermomolecular pressure III, 23.
De Haas, see *Casimir*.
De Haas and Biermasz, effect of size of specimen on specific thermal resistance XI, 23 — thermal conductivity at low temperatures XI, 22.
De Haas and de Noble, thermal conductivity of bismuth XI, 19.
De Haas and Wiersma, magnetic and thermodynamic temperatures V, 17.
De Haas, Wiersma and Kramers, data on paramagnetic salts V, 16.
De Klerk, see *Casimir*.
De Klerk and Hudson, magnetic cooling equipment at Washington V, 16.
De Klerk, Hudson, and Pelham, explanation of properties of liquid helium on Landau theory XVII, 2.
De Klerk, Steenland and Gorter, magnetic cooling V, 17.
Demagnetization, adiabatic V, 16–19 — in relation to third law XIX, 8 — nuclear V, 19 — two-stage V, 18.
Dennison, specific heat of hydrogen VI, 28.
De Noble, see *De Haas*.
Dent, see *Lennard-Jones*.
Désormes, see *Clement*.
Detailed balancing, principle of XX, 10.
Deuterium VI, 28; XXII, 10 — critical constants of IV, 11.
Dewar, effect of pressure on melting-point of ice XVI, 8 — liquefaction of hydrogen V, 3 — production of high vacua by adsorption on charcoal VIII, 26.
Diameter and free path of gas molecules, see *Free path*.
Diamond, synthesis of XIX, 1.
Diamond-graphite equilibrium, as experimental evidence of third law XIX, 1.
Diathermic I, 2.
Dickel, see *Clusius*.
Dickinson, Harper and Osborne, N. S., latent heat of fusion of ice IX, 4.
Diesel cycle XIV, 19.
Diesselhorst, see *Jaeger*.
Dieterici, critical constants IV, example 6

— equation of state IV, 8 — latent heat of vaporization VIII, 17.
Dimensional methods, used to examine convection XI, 24–27.
Dingle, theory of liquid helium XVII, 2.
Dirac, degeneration of gases VI, 27 — see *Fermi-Dirac statistics*.
Dispersion in gases, observed VI, 29 — theory VI, 30.
Dispersion, ultrasonic VI, 29.
Dissociation, heat of XXIII, 13 — of ammonium sulphide XVIII, 10 — of halogens XXIII, 13 — of hydrogen XXIII, 13 — of mercuric oxide XIX, 2, 3 — of water vapour XVIII, 17, 24.
Distribution of pressure in vertical column of gas III, 7.
Distribution of velocities III, 8, 13, 19, 20.
Dixon, correction of velocity of sound in tube VI, 18 — measurement of velocity of sound VI, 22 — see *Rodebush*.
Dodge, see *Larson*.
Domb, co-operative assemblies XVII, 6.
Doppler effect XX, 14.
Dorsey, linear expansion of solids X, 3.
Dorsman, see *Onnes*.
Douglas, see *Ginnings*.
Drude, postulate of free electrons XI, 18.
Dulong and Petit, law of specific heat VII, 6, 7 — measurement of absolute expansion of liquids X, 9.
Duncan, thermal conductivity of metals XI, 15.
Durieux, see *van Dijk*.
Dust figure, to measure velocity of sound VI, 20.

Ebert, relation between thermal conductivity and specific heat of solid X, 5.
Eddington, departure of sun from black body XX, 23 — detailed balancing XX, 10.
Edmondson and Egerton, measurement of chemical constants VIII, 23 — vapour pressure of metals VIII, 5.
Edwards, see *Simon*.
Efficiency, brake XIV, 11 — definition XII, 3 — of reversible engine XII, 5 — stage XIV, 15.
Egerton, atomic heat of mercury XIX, 2 — effusion method to measure vapour pressure of metals VIII, 5 — measurement of chemical constants VIII, 23 — vapour pressure of mercury VIII, 4, 9 — see *Edmondson* — see *Milford*.

Egerton and Lee, separation of isotopes VIII, 25.

Egerton and Milford, disappearing filament pyrometer XX, 18 — optical pyrometer to measure melting-points XX, 22.

Egerton and Ubbelohde, constant-temperature baths V, 12.

Ehrenfest, thermodynamic functions for a second-order transition XVII, 1.

Ehrenfest-Afanassjewa, second law of thermodynamics XII, 12 — temperature concept I, 3.

Ehrenfest and Trkal, theory of chemical constant VIII, 23.

Einstein, quantum theory applied to emission and adsorption of radiation XXI, 4 — radiometer XX, 5 — specific heats of solids XXII, 1, 7 — thermal conductivity of non-metallic crystals XI, 23.

Eldridge, test of velocity distribution law III, 13.

Electrical standards, check on accuracy II, 12, 16.

Electrochemical equivalent of silver XVIII, 22.

Electrode, chlorine XVIII, 25 — gas XVIII, 24, 25 — hydrogen XVIII, 24 — reversible XVIII, 19.

Electromotive force, relation to equilibrium constant XVIII, 19 — reversible XVIII, 20, 21.

Electronic charge III, 7.

Emissive power XX, 8.

Endo Yositosi, thermal conductivity of non-metallic crystals XI, 23.

Energy, conservation of II, 18, 19 — equipartition of VI, 25; XXI, 1 — intermolecular IV, 7 — zero-point XVII, 3; XXII, 10.

Energy spectrum of liquid helium XVII, 2.

Engine, Diesel XIV, 19 — internal-combustion XIV, 17–20 — Otto XIV, 18 — reciprocating XIV, 3.

Enskog, thermal diffusion III, 24.

Enthalpy, and Joule-Kelvin effect XIII, 6 — characteristic function XVI, 12 — defined VIII, 10; XIII, 6 — effect of dissolved air on IV, 12 — measurement of, for steam IV, 12 — measurement of, using ice calorimeter IX, 3.

Enthalpy-entropy diagram XIV, 10.

Entropy, as function of temperature in classical and quantum systems XIX, 1

— change in a Carnot cycle XII, 9 — change in any reversible cycle XII, 10 — change on melting XXIII, 15 — communal XXIII, 15 — defined XII, 8 — function of state XII, 10 — of crystalline solids XXII, 8 — of crystalline solids, on Debye theory differs negligibly from that calculated on Einstein theory XXIII, 10 — of mixture of perfect gases XV, 3, 4; XVIII, 1 — of perfect gas XV, 2 — properties of XII, 11.

Entropy-temperature diagram XIV, 5.

Equation of state, of solids XXIII, 7, 10 — see Gases — see Virial expansion.

Equilibrium, between two states of a substance XVI, 8, 15 — general condition XVI, 13 — internal thermodynamic XIX, 1 — in heterogeneous reactions involving condensed material XVIII, 10 — in mixture of reacting gases XVIII, 2, 16 — stable, unstable and metastable XVI, 5 — under adiabatic conditions XVI, 6 — under isothermal conditions XVI, 7 — use of activity XVIII, 16.

Equilibrium constant, defined XVIII, 2 — from electromotive force of a cell XVIII, 19, 24–5 — in terms of partial pressures XVIII, 7 — measurement of XVIII, 17 — relation between at different pressures and temperatures XVIII, 18 — variation with pressure XVIII, 5 — variation with temperature XVIII, 4.

Equilibrium state I, 2; XVI, 5–8, 13, 15; XVIII, 2.

Equipartition of energy VI, 25.

Erickson and Roberts, L. D., temperature scale below 5° K. V, 11.

Escribano, see Moles.

Esselson, see Lasarew.

Estermann, see Volmer.

Estermann, Frisch and Stern, molecular diffraction by crystal lattice III, 17 — test of velocity distribution law III, 13.

Ethylene, coexistence curves of liquid and vapour IV, 12.

Eucken, characteristic temperature and elastic constants XXII, 4 — chemical constant VIII, 23 — specific heat of deuterium at low temperatures VI, 28 — specific heat of hydrogen at low temperatures VI, 5, 27; VIII, 24 — test of third law XIX, 3 — thermal conductivity at low temperatures XI, 22 — thermal conductivity of metals XI, 19 — thermal measurements at low temperatures VII, 2 — values of specific heats of gases VI, 26.

Eucken and Bartels, calculations using Berthelot's equation of state VI, 3.

Eucken and Berger, Joule-Kelvin effect XIII, 5.

Eucken and Bertram, accommodation coefficient XI, 11.

Eucken and Hiller, specific heat of hydrogen at low temperatures VI, 5, 28.

Eucken and Kuhn, thermal conductivity at low temperatures XI, 22 — thermal conductivity of single crystals and aggregates XXII, 4.

Eucken and Schwers, specific heat of solids VII, 2.

Eucken and Werth, cubic variation of specific heat only at temperatures much lower than predicted by Debye's theory XXII, 5.

Eucken, Clusius and Berger, Joule-Kelvin effect XIII, 5.

Eucken, Karwat and Fried, calculation of chemical constant VIII, 24.

Eucken, Lüde and Hoffman, measurement of ratio of specific heats VI, 15.

Eumorfopoulos, gas thermometry I, 14 — sulphur point I, 18.

Eumorfopoulos and Rai, Joule-Kelvin effect XIII, 4.

Evaporation, rate of VIII, 7, 27.

Exchange gas, as thermal switch V, 18.

Exchanges, extension to atomic processes XX, 10 — theory of XX, 6.

Expansion coefficient, and specific heat of solids X, 5; XXIII, 9, 11 — apparent X, 8 — defined I, 35; X, 1 — of anisotropic crystals X, 6 — of fused silica X, 8 — of liquids X, 8–10 — of perfect gas I, 35 — of water near melting-point X, 10.

Expansion of anisotropic crystals X, 6; XXIII, 11.

Expansion of liquids, effect of pressure on X, 9 — measurement by absolute methods X, 9 — measurement by weight thermometer X, 8.

Expansion of solids, measurement by comparator methods X, 2 — measurement by Fizeau's method X, 3 — measurement by optical lever method X, 4.

Explosion method, of measurement of specific heat VI, 6.

Eyres, Hartree, Ingham, Jackson, Sarjant and Wagstaff, numerical integration of heat-conduction equation XI, 28.

Eyring, theory of liquids XXIII, 15 — see Hirschfelder.

Fabry and Buisson, breadth of spectral lines and temperature variation of velocity distribution III, 13.

Fairbairn and Tate, measurement of vapour density VIII, 22.

Fairchild, Hoover and Peters, disappearing filament pyrometer XX, 18 — measurement of high melting-points XX, 22.

Fajans and Schwartz, energy of crystalline salts XXIII, 13.

Falkenstein, measurement of equilibrium constants XVIII, 17.

Faraday (unit), defined XVIII, 22.

Farkas, ortho- and para-hydrogen conversion VI, 28 — see Bonhoeffer.

Fenning and Whiffen, molecular heats of gases VI, 6.

Ferguson and Miller, J. T., specific heats of liquids VII, 9.

Fermi, degeneration of gases VI, 27.

Fermi-Dirac statistics, for electrons XI, 20.

Feynman, wave functions for liquid helium XVII, 2.

Feynman and Cohen, M., energy spectrum of liquid helium XVII, 2.

Filament, apparent and true temperatures of XX, 21.

Fine, lattice theory of specific heats XXII, 11.

Fiock, see Rodebush.

Firestone, thermopile XX, 4.

Fixed points, at low temperatures V, 7 — constant-temperature baths I, 20 — defined I, 15-22 — measurement of freezing-points I, 20-1 — on international scale I, 22.

Fizeau, linear expansion of solids X, 3.

Flame temperatures XX, 21.

Flamm, independent vibrations of continuous medium XXI, 2.

Flow method, for conductivity of liquids XI, 12.

Flow of gases through narrow tubes and small openings III, 19–21.

Foote and Mohler, ionization energy XXIII, 13.

Forbes, conductivity of metals XI, 13.
Forcrand, latent heat of vaporization and boiling-point VIII, 21.
Forsythe, brightness temperature XX, 21 — see *Hyde* — see *Mendenhall*.
Fourier, thermal conductivity XI, 2.
Fowler, co-operative assemblies XVII, 6 — detailed balancing XX, 10 — distribution of ions over quantum states in adiabatic demagnetization V, 16 — entropy differences between different mixtures of ortho- and para-hydrogen XIX, 3 — para- and ortho-hydrogen VI, 28; XIX, 3 — rotation of molecules in crystals XXII, 12 — specific-heat anomalies XXII, 12 — " Statistical Mechanics " III, 8; IV, 5; VI, 28; VIII, 23; XI, 20; XVII, 6; XXI, 4; XXIII, 15 — statistical weights of atoms in different states of aggregation VIII, 23 — theory of metals XI, 20 — weight of statistical states XXI, 4.
Frank, Knipping and Kruger, degree of dissociation XXIII, 13.
Fransden, see *Rossini*.
Free energy, see *Gibbs* — see *Helmholtz*.
Free path, mean, and molecular diameters XI, 10 — and number of collisions III, 15 — defined III, 14 — from thermal conductivity and viscosity XI, 10 — probability of given length III, 16.
Freedom, degrees of, defined VI, 24 — rotational VI, 29 — vibrational VI, 24, 29.
Freezing-point, see *Melting-point*.
Frenkel, specific-heat anomalies in ammonium salts XXII, 12.
Fricke, ultrasonic dispersion in carbon dioxide VI, 30.
Fried, see *Eucken*.
Frisch, see *Estermann*.
Fundamental constants, values of I, 35, 38; II, 16; III, 7; XIII, 9; XVIII, 22; XX, 15.
Furnace, uniformly heated black body XX, 13.
Fusion, latent heat of II, 3; IX, 1–7 — theories of XXIII, 14–15.

Gaede, specific heat of solids VII, 1.
Gaines, see *Beattie*.
Galvanic cell, relation between electromotive force and equilibrium constant of reaction XVIII, 19 — reversible and irreversible XVIII, 20.

Gamma-rays, to supply energy to paramagnetic salt V, 17.
Gannon, see *Schuster*.
Gardiner, see *Kurti*.
Garner, see *Yost*.
Garrett, magnetic cooling V, 16 — Mollier diagram for paramagnetic salt V, example 7.
Gas constant I, 38; III, 6; VI, 25.
Gas electrode, see *Electrode*.
Gas thermometry, constant-pressure I, 6 — constant-volume I, 7 — general I, 5–8 — identity of constant-pressure and constant-volume scales I, 8–10 — identity of scales for different gases I, 8, 10, 12 — numerical values of corrections I, 14 — theory of corrections I, 11.
Gases, compressibility measurements IV, 9 — cooling effect of sudden expansion V, 4 — equations of state for I, 9–10; IV, 3, 4 — isotherms of I, 3 — Joule-Kelvin effect V, 3; XIII, 4–5 — liquefaction of V, 2–6 — model of III, 2 — pressure variation in vertical column of III, 7 — ratio of viscosity and thermal conductivity XI, 9 — state defined by pressure and volume I, 2 — thermal conductivity XI, 5–7 — virial expansion I, 10; IV, 1, example 3; XVIII, 16, example — viscosity XI, 8 — use of, in thermometers I, 5–8 — see *Inversion temperature* — see *Perfect* — see *Virial expansion*.
Gay Lussac's law III, 1.
Gayler, see *Jenkins*.
Geddes, see *Maas*.
Geiger, see *Behn* — see *Rutherford*.
Gerlach, measurement of Stefan-Boltzmann constant XX, 13.
Giauque, principle of magnetic cooling V, 16 — size of degree I, 4.
Giauque and MacDougall, magnetic and thermodynamic temperatures V, 17 — thermodynamic scale below 1° K. V, 16.
Giauque and Wiebe, specific-heat anomalies XXII, 12.
Giauque, Buffington and Schultze, use of thermocouples below ice point V, 8, 9.
Giauque, MacDougall, Stout, and Clark, magnetic and thermodynamic temperatures V, 17.
Giauque, Stout and Barieau, rate of flow of liquid helium XVII, 2.
Gibbs free energy, characteristic function XVI, 12 — defined XVI, 4 — expressed

in terms of partial potential XVI, 15 — for electrons in superconductor XVII, 9 — for superconducting transition in magnetic field XVII, 8.

Gibbs function, magnetic V, examples 4, 6; XVI, 11; XVII, 8.

Gibbs, introduction of partial potential XVI, 12 — phase rule XVI, 14.

Gibbs paradox XV, 4.

Gibbs-Duhem formula XVI, 15.

Giebe, see *Grüneisen*.

Ginnings, Douglas, and Ball, ice calorimeter IX, 3.

Ginnings, see *Osborne, N. S.*

Goens, see *Grüneisen*.

Goetz and Hergenrother, expansion of crystals by X-ray method X, 6 — fusion XXIII, 14.

Gold, freezing-point I, 22.

Goldschmidt, thermal conductivity of liquids XI, 12.

Gorrie, expansion engine V, 4.

Gorter, model of second-order transition XVII, 4 — nuclear demagnetization V, 19 — thermal switch V, 18 — thermodynamical functions of a superconductor XVII, 9 — see *Casimir* — see *De Klerk*.

Gorter and Casimir, transition of a superconductor in a magnetic field XVII, 7.

Gray, see *Melville*.

Gregory and Archer, thermal conductivity of gases XI, 6.

Griffiths, E. H., electrical equivalent II, 13 — measurement of latent heat of vaporization VIII, 15 — see *Callendar*.

Griffiths, E. H., and Griffiths, Ezer, specific heats of solids VII, 4.

Griffiths, Ezer, constant-temperature baths I, 20 — ice calorimeter IX, 3 — mercury-in-glass thermometers I, 33 — thermal conductivity XI, 2; XXII, 4 — total-radiation pyrometer XX, 19 — see *Awbery* — see *Griffiths, E. H.* — see *Sherratt*.

Griffiths, Ezer, and Awbery, measurement of flame temperature XX, 21.

Grilly, see *Mills*.

Grilly, Hammel and Sydoriak, vapour pressure of helium 3 IV, 7; VIII, 25.

Grimm, rates of vaporization VIII, 25.

Gröber, convection XI, 27.

Grüneisen, latent heat of vaporization at absolute zero XXIII, 12 — proportionality of expansion coefficient and

specific heat at constant pressure VII, 5; X, 5; XXIII, 9, 10 — theory of solid state XXIII, 3.

Grüneisen and Giebe, the faraday XVIII, 22.

Grüneisen and Goens, thermal conductivity of metals XI, 13, 19 — thermal expansion of anisotropic bodies XXIII, 11.

Guard ring, use in measuring thermal conductivity XI, 5.

Guggenheim, partition functions XXIII, 15 — principle of corresponding states IV, 7 — virial coefficients IV, 7.

Guggenheim and McGlashan, virial coefficients and principle of corresponding states IV, 7.

Gunther, specific heat of mercuric oxide XIX, 2.

Gurney, see *Mott*.

Gutowsky and Pake, nuclear magnetic resonance and reorientation of molecules in solids XXII, 12.

Haber, reaction constant of ammonia equilibrium XVIII, 17 — heat of reaction XVIII, 26 — specific heat of ammonia VI, 10.

Hall, J. A., fixed points I, 15 — thermodynamic temperature scale I, 36 — see *Barber*.

Hall, J. A., and Barber, joule as unit of heat II, 5.

Hall, H. T., see *Bundy*.

Halpern and Buckingham, second virial coefficient IV, 6.

Hamilton, see *Buckingham*.

Hammel, see *Grilly*.

Hardy, Telfair, and Pielemeier, velocity of sound VI, 17.

Harker, latent heat of vaporization VIII, 18 — see *Chappuis*.

Harkins, see *Mulliken*.

Harlow, expansion of mercury X, 9.

Harmonic oscillator, approximation for atoms in crystal XXII, 1 — energy at absolute zero XXII, 10 — vibrations of a continuum XXI, 1, 4.

Harper, see *Dickinson*.

Harteck, vapour pressure of silver and copper VIII, 6 — see *Bonhoeffer* — see *Clusius*.

Hartree, numerical integration of heat conduction equation XI, 28 — see *Eyres* — see *James*.

Hatton, see *Darby*.

Hausen, increase of entropy in natural processes XV, 5.

Heat conduction, equation of XI, 28.

Heat, conversion into work XII, 1, 3–4 — nature of II, 1–6, 18 — propagation in conducting medium XI, 28 — quantity of, defined II, 18 — unit of II, 5 — international joule II, 12.

Heat content, see *Enthalpy*.

Heat engine, efficiency of XII, 3, 5; XIV, 1 — see *Engine*.

Heat losses, in calorimetry II, 8; VIII, 18 — in steam and internal-combustion engines XIV, 20.

Heat of reaction, at constant pressure and volume XVIII, 27 — defined XVIII, 3 — effect of temperature on XVIII, 3, 12 — for reaction involving condensed phases XVIII, 11 — measurement of XVIII, 26 — sign convention XVIII, 3.

Hebb, velocity of sound in free air VI, 17.

Hein, critical phenomena IV, 12.

Helfgott, radiation XX, 21.

Helium 3, calculation of molar volumes and vapour pressure IV, 7 — vapour pressure measured IV, 7; VIII, 25.

Helium 4, cannot be solidified under equilibrium vapour pressure IV, 7; V, 5, 13 — condensation of to supply energy V, 17 — desorption of V, 12 — effect of pressure on lambda point V, 13; XVII, 2 — energy spectrum of XVII, 2 — equilibrium diagram V, 13, 15 — inversion temperature of V, 5 — isotherm V, 1, 11 — lambda point V, 13; XVII, 1 — liquefaction V, 5 — liquid, excitations in and theory of XVII, 2 — melting-pressure curve V, 13; XVII, 2; XIX, 6 — phase transition in liquid V, 14; XVII, 1, 2; XIX, ٤; XXII, 12 — rapid change in gradient of melting-pressure curve as evidence for third law XIX, 6 — second sound XVII, 2 — specific heat of liquid XVII, 1; XXII, 12 — thermal conductivity of XI, 5 — transport properties of liquid XVII, 2 — vapour pressure and formulæ for V, 11; VIII, 25.

Helium liquefiers V, 6.

Helmholtz free energy, characteristic function XVI, 12 — defined XVI, 3 — equal to work done in isothermal change XVI, 3.

Henglein, see *v. Wartenberg*.

Henning, gas constant I, 38 — heat of reaction XVIII, 26 — linear expansion, comparator method X, 2 — measurement of latent heat of vaporization VIII, 15 — vapour pressure of nitrogen and hydrogen V, 9 — see *Holborn*.

Henning and Heuse, measurement of vapour pressure VIII, 2 — use of vapour-pressure thermometers V, 8.

Henning and Otto, vapour pressure of nitrogen and hydrogen V, 9.

Henning and Stock, vapour-pressure thermometry V, 8.

Henning and Tingwaldt, measurement of flame temperature XX, 21.

Henry, P. S. H., velocity of sound by tube method VI, 18 — vibrational specific heat VI, 29 –– see *Blackett*.

Henshaw, energy spectrum of liquid helium XVII, 2.

Herbst, melting- and boiling-points of carbon VIII, 6.

Hercus, effect of dissolved air on specific heat of water II, 11 — mechanical equivalent II, 11 — radiation during adiabatic expansion XX, 14 — see *Laby*.

Hercus and Laby, guard-ring method to measure thermal conductivity of gases XI, 5 — hot-wire method to measure thermal conductivity of gases XI, 6.

Hercus and Sutherland, guard-ring method to determine thermal conductivity of gases XI, 5.

Hergenrother, see *Goetz*.

Herzfeld, molecular forces and second virial coefficient IV, 9.

Herzfeld and Rice, theory of vibrational specific heat VI, 30.

Hettner, vibrational specific heat VI, 29.

Hettner and Simon, specific-heat anomalies and transparency of crystals XXII, 12.

Heuse, see *Henning* — see *Scheel*.

Heuse and Otto, comparison of international and gas scales below ice point V, 7 — measurement of vapour pressure VIII, 2 — pressure and volume coefficients I, 35.

Hevesy, see *Brønsted*.

Heycock and Neville, measurement of melting-point of gold with platinum thermometer I, 24.

Higgins, see *Kaye, G. W. C.*

Hildebrandt, melting-point and latent heat of fusion VIII, 21.

Hiller, see *Clusius* — see *Eucken.*

Hirschfelder, see *Dahler.*

Hirschfelder, Stevenson and Eyring, theory of melting XXIII, 15.

Hoare, measurement of Stefan-Boltzmann constant XX, 13.

Hoffman, see *Eucken.*

Hoge and Brickwedde, comparison of platinum thermometers I, 23 — sulphur point determination I, 18.

Holborn and Baumann, saturation pressure of steam IV, 12 — vapour pressure of water VIII, 2.

Holborn and Henning, linear expansion of solids X, 2 — specific heats of gases VI, 9 — sulphur point I, 18.

Holborn and Otto, Boyle temperature IV, 6 — compressibility measurements IV, 5, 9 — departure from Boyle's law I, 14 — gas thermometer corrections I, 14 — gas thermometry I, 8, 12.

Holborn and Schultze, compressibility of gases IV, 9.

Holland, Huggill, Jones, G. O., and Simon, solidification of helium V, 15.

Holm, thermal conductivity of metals at high temperatures XI, 17.

Holst, see *Onnes.*

Hoover, see *Fairchild.*

Hori, moment of inertia of hydrogen molecule VI, 28.

Hoxton, Joule-Kelvin effect XIII, 4 — specific heats of gases VI, 3.

Hubbard, see *Stewart.*

Hudson, see *Ambler* — see *de Klerk.*

Huggill, see *Holland.*

Hulett, see *Taylor, G. B.*

Hull, magnetic cooling V, 16, 17 — see *Bleaney.*

Hume-Rothery, use of Grüneisen's law X, 5.

Hund, statistical weight of rotational states VI, 28.

Hutchison, Stewart, Urey and Cohen, separation of isotopes XVIII, 8.

Hyde, Cady and Forsythe, apparent and true temperatures of tungsten filaments XX, 22.

Hydrogen, calculation of chemical constant VIII, 24 — cooling by desorption of V, 12 — electrode XVIII, 24 — entropy difference between equilibrium

and metastable mixtures of ortho- and para-molecules XIX, 3 — latent heat of vaporization at low temperatures VIII, 16 — liquefaction of V, 2, 3 — moment of inertia of molecule VI, 28 — ortho-and para-mixtures VI, 28; XIX, 3 — phase diagram V, 15 — specific heat at low temperatures VI, 10, 27; VIII, 24; XIX, 3.

Hypsometer I, 17.

Ice, different kinds of XVI, 14 — latent heat of fusion IX, 4.

Ice point, defined I, 15, 16, 22, 35 — determination of, on thermodynamic scale I, 34; XIII, 8, 9.

Iceland spar, contraction normal to axis as temperature rises X, 5.

Indicator diagram I, 3; XIV, 11 — see *Enthalpy-entropy diagram* — see *Entropy-temperature diagram.*

Induction heater, to warm salt in demagnetization experiment V, 17.

Infinitesimal changes, adiabatic conditions XVI, 2 — isothermal conditions XVI, 4.

Ingham, see *Eyres.*

Ingold, vapour pressure of metals VIII, 4.

Integrals used in kinetic theory III, 25.

Intermolecular forces, Lennard-Jones expression IV, 7; XXIII, 3 — determination from thermal diffusion coefficient III, 24 — relation to validity of principle of corresponding states IV, 7.

Internal-combustion engine, efficiency for Carnot cycle XIV, 17 — efficiency for Diesel cycle XIV, 19 — efficiency for Otto cycle XIV, 18.

Internal energy, additive property II, 18 — as function of pressure V, 3 — arising from molecular interactions IV, example 3 — change in equal to work done adiabatically II, 18 — characteristic function for particular choice of independent variables XVI, 12 — defined as function of state II, 18 — for mixture of perfect gases XV, 3; XVIII, 1 — of gas varies linearly with pressure V, 3 — of ideal gas depends only on temperature III, 1; V, 3.

International temperature scale, at high temperatures XX, 17 — departure from thermodynamic scale I, 22; V, 7 — from ice to oxygen points V, 7 — specified I, 22 — use of radiation formulæ XX, 15.

Interpolation instruments, use of, to realize international temperature scale I, 22.

Invar, expansion of X, 5.

Inversion temperature, and liquefaction of gases V, 3, example 2 — defined V, 3; XIII, 6 — relation to critical temperature V, examples 1, 2.

Ionization, heat of XXIII, 13.

Iridium, freezing-point I, 22.

Isentropic change, equivalent to reversible adiabatic change XIII, 2.

Isochore of reaction, for gaseous reactions XVIII, 4, 6 — for reactions involving condensed phases XVIII, 11 — integration of XIX, 3 — numerical calculations XVIII, 13.

Isotherm, adsorption VIII, 27 — corresponding I, 3 — critical IV, 2, 3 — defined I, 3 — of carbon dioxide IV, 2 — of fluid IV, 8.

Isotopes, separation of, by rate of evaporation VIII, 25 — by thermal diffusion III, 24 — exchange reactions XVIII, 8.

Isotopic abundance, natural variation VIII, 25; XVIII, 8.

Jackson, see *Eyres*.

Jacob, see *Knoblauch*.

Jacobus, see *Beattie*.

Jaeger, F. M., and Rosenbohm, specific heats of solids VII, 8.

Jaeger, W., and Diesselhorst, ratio of thermal and electrical conductivities XI, 18 — thermal conductivity of metals XI, 15.

Jaeger, W., and Steinwehr, electrical equivalent II, 14, 16; VII, 1 — specific heat of water II, 17.

James, Waller and Hartree, zero-point energy of crystals XXII, 10.

Jaquerod, see *Travers*.

Jay, see *Bradley*.

Jeans, distribution law and mean free path III, 14 — dynamical theory of gases III, 4; XXI, 1 — equipartition of energy VI, 25 — theory of thermal conductivity and viscosity of gases XI, 7–9.

Jenkins and Gayler, high-temperature melting-points XX, 22.

Jesse, see *Richards, T. W.*

Jessel, effect of dissolved air on specific heat of water II, 15 — refuted II, 11.

Jets, theory of XIV, 16.

Johannson and Linde, superlattice lines XVII, 5.

Jones, G. O., thermal switch V, 18 — see *Holland*.

Jones, G. O., Larsen and Simon, hydrogen liquefier V, 3.

Jones, H., properties of liquid helium V, 14 — see *Allen, J. F.* — see *Mott*.

Jones, H., and Miller, A. R., internal energy arising from molecular interactions IV, example 3 — reacting gases at high temperatures and pressures XVIII, 16, example.

Jones, H. A., and Langmuir, temperature of tungsten filaments XX, 22 — see *Langmuir*.

Jones, J. H., electron velocity from hot filament III, 13.

Joule, as unit of heat II, 5, 12, 18.

Joule effect, defined V, 3 — use of, in expansion liquefier V, 6.

Joule, experiments decisive against caloric theory II, 6 — experimental establishment of first law II, 6, 18, 19 — experiments on mechanical equivalent II, 4 — significance of experiments for second law XII, 12 — test of accuracy of electrical standards II, 12.

Joule-Kelvin effect, and liquefaction of gases V, 3, 6 — experiments on XIII, 4 — for Van der Waals gas V, 3 — relation to enthalpy XIII, 6 — theory XIII, 5 — to determine thermodynamic temperatures XIII, 8 — to maintain temperatures between liquid hydrogen and liquid nitrogen V, 12 — used to assign value to triple point of water XIII, 9.

Joule-Thomson expansion valve V, 6.

Joule's law, departure from causes cooling of gas V, 3; XIII, 6 — intermolecular attractions cause departure from V, 3 — obeyed by perfect gas VI, 2; XII, 7 — statement III, 1.

Justi, cooling by desorption of hydrogen V, 12 — triple points of oxygen and nitrogen V, 9.

Kaischew and Simon, entropy difference between solid and liquid helium XIX, 6 — entropy of helium V, 11.

Kammerlingh Onnes, see *Onnes*.

Kannuluik, ratio of coefficients of thermal conductivity and viscosity XI, 9 —

thermal conductivity of deuterium XI, 6 — thermal conductivity of metals XI, 15.

Kannuluik and Carman, thermal conductivity of rare gases using thick wire XI, 6, 9.

Kannuluik and Laby, thermal conductivity of metals XI, 13 — thermal conductivity of single crystals and aggregates XXII, 4.

Kannuluik and Law, thermal conductivity of gases XI, 6.

Kannuluik and Martin, thermal conductivity of gases, hot-wire method XI, 6 — thermal conductivity of powders XI, 21.

Kanolt, optical pyrometer to measure melting-points XX, 22.

Kapitza, helium liquefier V, 6 — radiomicrometer XX, 4.

Kármán, v., see Born.

Karwat, see Eucken.

Katz, see Clark.

Kaufman, see Onsager.

Kaye, G. W. C., and Higgins, thermal conductivity of liquids XI, 12 — thermal conductivity of solids XI, 21.

Kaye, G. W. C., and Laby, critical data IV, 3 — molecular diameter and mean free path from thermal conductivity and viscosity of gases XI, 10 — tables for use in platinum thermometry I, 23.

Kaye, G. W. C., and Roberts, thermal conductivity of non-metals XI, 21 — thermal conductivity of single crystals and aggregates XXII, 4.

Kaye. J., see Blaisdell — see Beattie.

Keene, measurement of Stefan-Boltzmann constant XX, 13.

Keesom, W. H., compressibility measurements and gas thermometry I, 10 — magnetic and thermodynamic temperatures V, 17 — properties of helium V, 14 — transition of a superconductor in a magnetic field XVII, 7 — vapour pressure of helium V, 11 — see Onnes — see Schmidt.

Keesom, W. H., and Clusius, phase transition in liquid helium V, 14.

Keesom, W. H., and Dammers, comparison of international and gas scales below the ice point V, 7.

Keesom, W. H., and Keesom, A. P., solidification of helium V, 13 — specific heat of helium V, 11.

Keesom, W. H., and Lignac, vapour pressure of helium V, 11.

Keesom, W. H., and Tuyn, ice point I, 35.

Keesom, W. H., and van den Ende, resistance thermometers at liquid helium temperature V, 11 — specific heats of solids VII, 7.

Keesom, W. H., Weber, Nøgaard and Schmidt, vapour pressure of helium V, 11.

Keller, temperature scale below 5° K. V, 11.

Kellerman, lattice theory of specific heats XXII, 11.

Kelvin, absolute temperature XII, 6 — second law XII, 4 — specification of degree I, 4 — see Joule-Kelvin effect — see Joule-Thomson valve.

Kemble and van Vleck, vibrational specific heat VI, 29.

Kendall, latent heat of vaporization and boiling-point VIII, 21.

Kennard, kinetic theory III, 8.

Kerr, see Yarnell.

Keyes, reduction of sulphur-point measurements I, 18 — see Slater.

Keyes and Collins, S. C., Joule-Kelvin effect XIII, 5.

Khalatnikov, see Landau.

Kingdon, see Langmuir.

Kippert, see Simon.

Kirchhoff, correction to sound velocity in tube VI, 18 — radiation law XX, 8 — vapour pressure formula VIII, 9.

Kirkwood, second virial coefficient IV, 9 — see Slater.

Kirschman, see Bates.

Kistemaker, vapour pressure of helium V, 11.

Kistiakowsky and Rice, measurement of ratio of specific heats VI, 15.

Kittel, relaxation time for conduction electrons and lattice V, 19 — ultrasonic vibrations VI, 29.

Klein and Rosseland, detailed balancing XX, 10.

Klinkhardt, specific heats of metals VII, 8.

Kneser, ultrasonic dispersion VI, 29.

Knietsch, measurement of equilibrium constants XVIII, 16.

Knipping, see Frank.

Knoblauch and Jacob, Mollier, Winkhaus and Raisch, specific heat of steam VI 10.

Knudsen, absolute manometer III, 22 —
accommodation coefficient XI, 11 —
conductivity of gases at very low
pressures XI, 11 — cosine law III,
17 — measurement of condensation coefficient VIII, 7 — molecular effusion
III, 21 — streaming of gas through
narrow tube III, 19, 20 — thermomolecular pressure III, 23 — use of
apparatus small compared with mean
free path III, 18 — vapour pressure
of metals VIII, 5, 9.

Kobe and Lynn, critical data IV, 3, 11.

Koenigsberger, thermal conductivity of
metals XI, 19.

Kohlrausch, thermal conductivity of
metals XI, 14, 17.

Konnertz, see Clusius.

Konno, thermal conductivity of metals
at high temperatures XI, 17.

Kopp and Neumann, specific heat of
chemical compounds VII, 6.

Korsching and Wirtz, separation of isotopes III, 24.

Kothari, see Chowdri.

Kramers, see De Haas.

Kruger, see Frank.

Kruis, see Clusius.

Kuhn, see Eucken.

Kundt, velocity of sound VI, 20.

Kundt and Warburg, effect of pressure on
cooling thermometers XI, 6 — velocity
of sound in mercury vapour VI, 20.

Kürti, anomalous specific heat of gadolinium sulphate XXII, 12 — distribution of ions over quantum states in
adiabatic demagnetization V, 16 —
see Rollin.

Kürti and Gardiner, measurements on
chromium methyl ammonium sulphate
V, 17.

Kürti and Simon, effect of shape of
specimen on susceptibility V, 16 —
heating paramagnetic salt by γ-rays
V, 16, 17 — magnetic and thermodynamic temperatures V, 17 — nuclear
demagnetization V, 19.

Kürti, Laîné and Simon, magnetic and
thermodynamic temperatures V, 17.

Kürti, Robinson, Simon, and Spohr,
nuclear demagnetization V, 19.

Laby, calorimetry, heat losses in II, 8 —
tables for use in platinum thermometry I, 23 — thermal conductivity of

gases XI, 6 — vapour pressure of
mercury VIII, 4 — see Aberdeen — see
Hercus — see Kannuluik — see Kaye,
G. W. C.

Laby and Hercus, dissolved air has negligible effect on specific heat of water
II, 11, 16 — mechanical equivalent II,
11, 16 — ratio of thermal conductivity
and viscosity of gases XI, 9.

Laîné, see Kürti.

Lambert, see Alexander.

Landau, quantum hydrodynamics and
theory of liquid helium XVII, 2.

Landau and Khalatnikov, explanation of
properties of liquid helium XVII, 2.

Landé, temperature concept I, 3.

Lang, see Martin.

Lange, see Simon.

Lange and Simon, measurement of
chemical constant VIII, 23 — specific
heat of solids VII, 7.

Langley, bolometer XX, 3.

Langmuir, degree of dissociation XXIII,
13 — measurement of equilibrium constants XVIII, 17 — monomolecular
film VIII, 27 — thermal conductivity
of metals at high temperatures XI, 17
— vapour pressure of metals VIII, 6.

Langmuir and Kingdon, adsorption VIII,
27.

Langmuir, Mackay and Jones, H. A.,
vapour pressure of metals VIII, 6, 25.

Langmuir, MacLane and Blodgett, temperature of tungsten filaments XX,
22.

Larmor, distribution of radiation XX, 14.

Larsen, see Jones, G. O.

Larsen, Simon and Swenson, rate of
evaporation of hydrogen due to ortho-
and para-conversion VI, 28.

Larson and Dodge, equilibrium constant
of ammonia XVIII, 17.

Lasarew and Esselson, low temperature
reached by pumping off helium V, 5.

Latent heat, at transition of superconductor in magnetic field XVII, 8 —
Clausius-Clapeyron equation VIII, 8;
XVI, 8 — early observations II, 3 —
of fusion of ice IX, 4.

Latent heat of fusion, defined IX, 1 —
measurement of IX, 2–6 — of metals
IX, 5.

Latent heat of sublimation VIII, 1.

Latent heat of vaporization, and boiling-
point VIII, 21 — at absolute zero

VIII, 12; XXIII, 12 — defined VIII, 1 — measurement of, for liquids VIII, 13–20 — measurement of, for metals VIII, 4–6 — measurement of, for non-metals VIII, 2–3.

Laue, independent vibrations of continuous medium XXI, 2.

Law, see *Kannuluik*.

Laws of thermodynamics, zeroth I, 2, 3 — first II, 22 — second XII, 4, 12 — third XIX, 1.

Lawson, specific-heat anomalies in ammonium salts XXII, 12.

Lead, freezing-point I, 22 — resistance thermometer V, 9; VII, 2 — wire of used as thermal switch V, 18.

Le Chatelier's principle XVIII, 6.

Lee, see *Egerton*.

Lees, thermal conductivity of liquids XI, 12 — of metals XI, 13 — of solid non-metals XI, 21.

Lenihan, velocity of sound V, 17.

Lennard-Jones, interatomic forces IV, 7; XXIII, 3 — second virial coefficient and law of force between molecules IV, 7.

Lennard-Jones and Dent, law of force between atoms XXIII, 9.

Lennard-Jones and Devonshire, theory of melting and liquids XXIII, 15.

Lennard-Jones and Taylor, P. A., crystal energies XXIII, 13.

Lewis, G. N., activity XVIII, 14, 16 — second law XII, 4.

Lewis, G. N., and Randall, activity XVIII, 16 — equilibrium constants XVIII, 24—molecular heats XIX, 2.

Lewis, G. N., and Rupert, chlorine electrode XVIII, 25.

Lewis, G. N., Gibson and Latimer, entropy of chlorine from different reactions XIX, 2.

Lewis, W. C. M., " Physical Chemistry " IV, 8.

Liebmann, black-body radiation XX, 9 — optical pyrometer to measure melting-points XX, 22.

Lignac, see *Keesom*.

Linde, see *Johannson*.

Linde method V, 3.

Lindemann, theory of fusion XXIII, 14 — see *Nernst*.

Linear expansion, anisotropic crystals X, 6 — measurement of X, 2–4.

Liquefaction of gases V, 2–6.

Liquids, cell theory of XXIII, 15 — compressibility of IV, 10; XXIII 15.

Littwin, see *Brüche*.

Logan, J. K., low temperatures V, 11.

London, F., liquid helium XVII, 2 — molecular forces XXIII, 3 — superconductivity XVII, 9.

Lorentz, theory of metals XI, 18.

Lorenz, ratio of thermal and electrical conductivities XI, 18.

Lossing, see *Thode*.

Lüde, see *Eucken*.

Ludin, specific heat of water II, 20.

Lummer, radiation XX, 21 — see *Wien*.

Lummer and Pringsheim, measurement of ratio of specific heats VI, 15.

Lynn, see *Kobe*.

Lyppe, second-order transitions XVII, 1.

Maas, see *Mason* — see *Naldrett*.

Maas and Geddes, critical phenomena IV, 12.

MacDougall, see *Giauque*.

MacGillavry, entropy differences for hydrogen XIX, 3.

MacGillivray and Swallow, constant-temperature baths V, 12.

Mackay, see *Langmuir*.

MacLane, see *Langmuir*.

MacLeod gauge, does not measure pressure of mercury vapour III, 22.

MacNair, see *Nix*.

Macnamara, see *Thode*.

Magnetic balance, to measure properties of paramagnetic salts V, 16.

Magnetic cooling, see *Adiabatic demagnetization*.

Magnetic interactions V, 16.

Magnetic temperature, defined V, 16 — relation to thermodynamic temperature V, 17.

Magnus and Holzman, specific heats at high temperatures VII, 8.

Manometer, absolute III, 22; IV, 9 — hot-wire XI, 11 — low-pressure VIII, 2 — open mercury IV, 9 — piston (pressure balance) IV, 9.

Martin, see *Kannuluik*, see *Caro*.

Martin and Lang, conductivity of liquids XI, 12.

Mason, Naldrett and Maas, critical phenomena IV, 12.

Mass action, law of, derived XVIII, 2.

Massey, see *Buckingham*.

Mathias, see *Cailletet*.

Roman figures refer to chapters, and Arabic figures to sections within these chapters

Mathias and Onnes, measurement of vapour density VIII, 22.

Maulard, velocity of sound at low pressures VI, 17.

Maxwell, distribution of velocities III, 8 — equipartition of energy VI, 25 — thermodynamic relations derived from differentials of thermodynamical functions XVI, example 12 — thermodynamic relations XIII, 2 — verification of velocity-distribution law III, 13, 19, 20.

Mayer, H., vapour pressure of metals VIII, 5.

Mayer, J. E., and Wintner, energy of crystalline salts XXIII, 13 — vapour pressure of metals VIII, 5.

Mayer, J. R. v., calculation of mechanical equivalent VI, 2.

McCrea, vibrational specific heat VI, 29.

Mean free path, see Free path.

Mechanical equivalent, as determination of specific heat II, 9, 18 — experimental determination II, 4, 6, 10–15.

Megaw, zero-point energy of helium XVII, 3.

Megaw and Simon, zero-point energy of helium XVII, 3.

Meissner effect in a superconductor XVII, 7.

Meissner, thermal conductivity of copper at low temperatures XI, 16, 19.

Meissner and Ochsenfeld, magnetic induction in a superconductor XVII, 7.

Melting, of pure substances IX, 1 — theory of XXIII, 15.

Melting-points, measurement at high temperatures I, 21 — used as fixed points I, 20, 22; IX, 1 — use of optical pyrometer to measure XX, 22 — see under particular substances.

Melting pressure curves, of hydrogen V, 15 — of helium V, 15; XVII, 3 XIX, 6.

Melville, see Bolland.

Melville and Gray, vapour pressure of metals VIII, 6.

Mendelssohn, cooling by desorption of helium V, 12 — see Daunt — see Simon.

Mendenhall, measurement of Stefan-Boltzmann constant XX, 13 — optical pyrometer to measure melting-points XX, 22.

Mendenhall and Forsythe, pyrometers XX, 20.

Meniscus, disappearance of indicates complete miscibility of liquid and vapour IV, 12.

Mercury, condensing-point I, 22 — vapour pressure VIII, 9.

Mercury-in-glass thermometry I, 33.

Merritt, linear expansion of solids X, 3.

Metals, theory of conductivities and comparison with experiment XI, 18–20.

Method of mixtures, see Mixtures.

Meyer, see Cooke.

Michels, A., see De Boer.

Michels, A. and C., dependence on density of virial coefficient of carbon dioxide IV, 5.

Microscopic reversibility, principle of III. 23.

Mie, atomic forces XXIII, 3.

Milford, see Egerton.

Milford, Bracey, Cunnold and Egerton, disappearing filament pyrometer XX, 18.

Miller, A. R., adsorption VIII, 27; XI, 11; XVII, 6 — co-operative assemblies XVII, 6 — existence of liquid state down to absolute zero and third law XVII, 2; XIX, 6 — temperature concept I, 3 — see Daunt — see Jones, H.

Miller, J. T., see Ferguson.

Millikan, electronic charge III, 7.

Mills and Grilly, melting-pressure curves V, 15.

Mitscherlich, effect of anisotropy on expansion of crystals X, 6.

Mixtures, method of, and latent heat of ice IX, 2 — and latent heat of metals IX, 5 — at high temperatures, to measure specific heats of solids VII, 1, 8 — early work on II, 4 — specific heats of gases VI, 7, 8.

Moelwyn-Hughes, critical data IV, 3 — entropy of solid body XXIII, 10 — latent heat of fusion IX, 7 — mean free path III, 14 — negligible difference between values of entropy on Einstein and Debye theories XXIII. 10.

Molecular diameter, from thermal conductivity and viscosity of gases XI, 10.

Molecular effusion III, 21.

Molecular heat VI, 2.

Molecular theory III, 2.

Moles, Toral and Escribano, gas constant I, 38.

Mollier, see Knoblauch.

Mollier diagram, for paramagnetic salt V, example 7 — for steam XIV, 10 — used to study processes in refrigerator XIV, 24–25.

Moorby, see *Reynolds*.

Moser, depression of freezing-point of water XVI, 8 — platinum thermometer specification I, 24.

Motion, third law of IV, 3.

Mott, theory of metals XI, 20 — transitions between two solid states XXII, 12 — theory of liquids XXIII, 15.

Mott and Gurney, entropy change on melting XXIII, 15.

Mott and Jones, H., theory of metals XI, 20.

Müller, A., second virial coefficient IV, 6.

Müller, E., chlorine electrode XVIII, 25.

Müller bridge I, 29.

Mulliken and Harkins, separation of isotopes VIII, 25.

Multiple-expansion engines XIV, 12.

Murphy and Rice, law of corresponding states applied to frozen rare gases IV, 7.

Murril, see *Roebuck*.

Naldrett, see *Mason*.

Naldrett and Maas, critical phenomena IV, 12.

Naphthalene, boiling-point I, 19 — vapour, condensing-point I, 22.

Nernst, calorimeter VII, 2 — dissociation of ammonium hydrosulphide XVIII, 10 — evaluation of Debye function XXII, 4, 8 — integration of adiabatic relations VI, 14 — lead resistance thermometer V, 9 — measurement of equilibrium constants XVIII, 17 — relation between equilibrium constants at different pressures and temperatures XVIII, 18 — specific heat of ammonia VI, 9 — specific heat of solids VII, 1.

Nernst and Lindemann, difference between specific heats for solids VII, 5 — two-line spectrum for solids XXII, 1.

Nernst and v. Wartenburg, measurement of equilibrium constants XVIII, 17.

Nernst and Wohl, values of specific heats of gases VI, 26.

Nernst heat theorem, and liquid helium transition XVII, 2 — and unattainability of absolute zero XIX, 1, 9 — experimental verification from chemical reactions XIX, 2–4 — experimental verification by low-temperature phenomena XIX, 5–9 — historical and statement XIX, 1.

Nettleton, thermal conductivity of liquids XI, 12.

Neumann, see *Kopp*.

Neutrons, inelastic scattering of and energy spectrum of helium XVII, 2.

Neville, see *Heycock*.

Newton, fixed points I, 1 — law of cooling II, 8 — linseed-oil thermometer I, 2 — third law of motion IV, 3.

Nickel, freezing-point I, 22 — use of optical pyrometer to measure freezing point XX, 22.

Nicolson, J., see *Callendar*.

Nicolson, P., see *Crank*.

Nier, see *Aldrich*.

Nix and MacNair, linear expansion of solids X, 3.

Nix and Shockley, order-disorder transitions XVII, 5.

Nøgaard, see *Keesom*.

Nozzle, expansion through XIV, 15–16.

Nuclear demagnetization, possible use of superconductor as thermal switch for XVII, 7 — suggested V, 19.

Nuclear magnetic resonance and reorientation of molecules in solids XXII, 12.

Nuclei, polarization of and errors in temperature scale V, 11.

Ochsenfeld, see *Meissner*.

Onnes, compressibility measurements and gas thermometry I, 10; IV, 9 — departure from Boyle's law I, 14 — lead resistance thermometer V, 9 — liquefaction of helium V, 5 — superconductivity XVII, 7 — virial expansion I, 10; IV, 5 — see *Mathias* — see *Woltjer*.

Onnes and Boks, density of liquid helium XVII, 1.

Onnes and Crommelin, use of thermocouples at low temperatures V, 9.

Onnes and Holst, thermal conductivity of mercury XI, 19.

Onnes and Keesom, compressibility measurements and gas thermometry I, 10.

Onnes and von Gulik, solidification of helium V, 13.

Onnes and Weber, vapour pressure of helium V, 11.

Onnes, Dorsman and Holst, measurement
of critical data IV, 11.
Onsager, co-operative assemblies XVII,
6 — microscopic reversibility III, 23 —
theory of paramagnetism V, 17 — see
Watson.
Onsager and Kaufman, order-disorder
transitions XVII, 5.
Optical lever, to measure thermal ex-
pansion X, 4.
Optical pyrometer, use as interpolation
instrument I, 22; XX, 18 — to
measure freezing-points XX, 22.
Order-disorder phenomena XVII, 5;
XXIII, 15.
Ornstein and van Wyk, spectrum of gas
discharge III, 13.
Ortho-hydrogen VI, 28; XIX, 3.
Osborne, D. V., second sound in liquid
helium XVII, 2.
Osborne, D. W., see *Abraham.*
Osborne, D. W., Weinstock and Abraham,
flow properties of liquid helium XVII, 2.
Osborne, N. S., latent heat of fusion of
ice IX, 4 — see *Dickinson* — see *Yost.*
Osborne, N. S., Stimson and Ginnings,
electrical equivalent II, 15, 16 —
specific heat of water II, 17.
Osborne, N. S., Stimson, Sligh and
Cragoe, specific heat of ammonia VI, 10.
Otto, cycle for gas or petrol engine XIV,
18 — see *Henning* — see *Heuse* — see
Holborn.
Otvos, see *Stevenson.*
Owen and Richards, expansion of crystals
by X-ray method X, 6.
Oxygen, boiling-point I, 22 — isotherms
of I, 38; IV, 5 — triple point V, 9.

Palladium, freezing-point I, 22 — use of
optical pyrometer to measure freezing
point XX, 22.
Pake, see *Gutowsky.*
Para-hydrogen, fraction of at different
temperatures VI, 28.
Paramagnetic relaxation and hysteresis
V, 17.
Paramagnetic salts used in demagnetiza-
tion experiments V, 16–19.
Parfianowitsch, see *Arzybyschew.*
Parr, heats of reaction XVIII, 26.
Partial potential, condition of equilibrium
between phases XVI, 13 — defined
XVI, 12 — in superconducting phase
XVII, 9.

Partial pressures, heterogeneous equilibrium XVIII, 7 — law of III, 1.
Partington, measurement of ratio of
specific heats VI, 15.
Partington and Schilling, correction of
velocity of sound in tube VI, 18 —
measurement of equilibrium constants
XVIII, 17 — specific heats of gases
IV, 4; VI, 3, 17, 21 — values of
specific heats and their ratio VI, 26 —
velocity of sound VI, 17, 18, 20.
Partition function VI, 28; XXIII, 15.
Pauli, exclusion principle XI, 20 — thermal conductivity of crystal lattice XI,
23.
Pauling, specific-heat anomalies in am-
monium salts XXII, 12.
Peierls, thermal conductivity of crystal
lattice XI, 23.
Pelham, see *de Klerk.*
Penney, see *Van Vleck.*
Perfect gas, change of entropy XV, 2–4
— defined III, 1 — difference between
specific heats VI, 2 — equation for adi-
abatic change in VI, 13 — internal
energy independent of volume III, 1.
Perlick, see *Clusius.*
Perrin, determination of Avogadro's
number III, 7.
Peshkov, second sound in liquid helium
XVII, 2.
Peters, see *Fairchild.*
Pfaffian differential equations, condition
for integration XII, 12.
Phase, defined XVI, 10 — description of
XVI, 11 — equilibrium between XVI,
13.
Phase rule XVI, 14.
Phonons XVII, 2.
Pickard and Simon, quantitative study
of performance of expansion liquefier V,
6 — specific heat of helium V, 11.
Pictet process V, 2.
Pielemeier, vibrational specific heat VI,
29 — see *Hardy.*
Pier, bomb calorimeter VI, 6.
Pierce, ultrasonic dispersion VI, 29.
Pippard, see *Daunt.*
Pirani, specific heats of metals VII, 8.
Pirani and v. Wangenheim, thermal con-
ductivity of solid non-metals XI, 21.
Pitzer, principle of corresponding states
IV, 7.
Planck, absorption and emission of radia-
tion XX, 8 — energy distribution for-

mula XX, 15 — quantization of energy XXI, 4 — radiation formula XXI, 4 — second law XII, 4.

Platinum, freezing-point I, 22 — use of optical pyrometer to measure freezing point XX, 22.

Platinum resistance thermometer, calibration of I, 23 — described I, 23 — used as interpolation instrument I, 22; V, 7.

Platinum-rhodium platinum thermocouple I, 22.

Platinum thermometry, at high temperatures I, 24 — below ice point V, 7 — characteristics of wire I, 23; V, 7 — compensation of leads I, 26 — difference formulæ I, 23; V, 7 — measuring current, heating effect of I, 27 — platinum temperature I, 23 — thermoelectric effects in I, 28.

Platzmann, γ-ray heating V, 17.

Porter, effect of pressure on expansion coefficient of liquids X, 9 — see Callendar.

Prandtl, convection XI, 27.

Pressure, and expansion coefficient of liquids X, 9 — of perfect gas III, 3 — vapour VIII, 1.

Pressure coefficient I, 35.

Preuner and Schupp, measurement of equilibrium constants XVIII, 17.

Prévost, theory of exchanges XX, 6.

Pringsheim, see Lummer.

Pyrometer, comparison of XX, 20 — optical XX, 18 — optical, to determine melting-points XX, 22 — total radiation XX, 19 — used to measure temperature of sun XX, 23.

Quantal system, entropy as function of temperature for XIX, 1 — hydrodynamics of and theory of liquid helium XVII, 2 — principle of corresponding states for IV, 7.

Quantity of heat II, 5, 18.

Quantum theory, and equation of state for solids XXIII, 10 — and metallic conduction XI, 20 — of radiation XXI, 4 — of specific heats of gases VI, 28–29 — of specific heats of solids XXII, 1–3, 6, 11.

Quasi-static process, defined XII, 2.

Radiant energy, density of given wavelength depends only on temperature XX, 8 — emission and absorption of XX, 7 — measurement XX, 2–5 — nature of XX, 1 — other than black bodies XX, 21 — total density and temperature XX, 11 — to warm paramagnetic salt V, 17 — wave-length distribution XX, 14 — see Black body.

Radiation constants, experimental determination XX, 16 — use in international temperature scale I, 22; XX, 15.

Radiation, number of independent vibrations of continuous medium XXI, 2 — Planck's formula XX, 15; XXI, 4 — Rayleigh's formula XXI, 3 — transfer of heat by XI, 1.

Radiator, full, defined XX, 9 — emissive power of XX, 12 — partition of energy XXI, 4 — wedge as XX, 22.

Radiometer XX, 5.

Radio-micrometer XX, 4.

Rai, see Eumorfopoulos.

Raisch, see Knoblauch.

Ramsay, velocity of sound in argon and helium VI, 20.

Randall, see Lewis, G. N.

Rankine cycle, efficiency XIV, 7, 9 — specified XIV, 4 — with superheated steam XIV, 6.

Rankine, molecular diameters XI, 10.

Rayleigh, free vibrations of system of particles XXII, 6 — low-temperature manometer VIII, 2 — method of dimensions in studying convection XI, 24 — radiation formula XXI, 3.

Reaction constant, see Equilibrium constant.

Reaction, heat of, at constant pressure and volume XVIII, 27 — calculations of XVIII, 13 — defined XVIII, 3 — measurement XVIII, 26 — related to equilibrium constant XVIII, 4, 5, 7, 11 — variation with temperature XVIII, 13.

Reaction isochore XVIII, 4, 7, 11 — integration of XIX, 3 — numerical calculations XVIII, 12.

Rectilinear diameters, law of IV, 11; XXIII, 15.

Reduced equation of state IV, 3, 4.

Refrigerator, actual cycle XIV, 23 — choice of working substance XIV, 22 — efficiency for Carnot cycle XIV, 21 — Electrolux XIV, 26.

Regnault, absolute expansion of liquids X, 9 — specific heats of gases at constant pressure VI, 8.

Reheat factor XIV, 15.
Relaxation phenomena VI, 30.
Relaxation time, for different vibrational modes of a molecule VI, 29 — for conduction electrons and lattice V, 19.
Resistivity, thermal XI, 3.
Reversible process, defined XII, 2 — for transition of superconductor XVII, 7 — for galvanic cell XVIII, 20 — see *Quasi-static process.*
Reynolds, discharge through nozzles XIV, 16 — thermomolecular pressure III, 23.
Reynolds and Moorby, mechanical equivalent II, 10.
Rhodium, freezing-point I, 22.
Riccoboni, see *Clusius.*
Rice, second virial coefficient IV, 6 — see *Herzfeld* — see *Kistiakowsky* — see *Murphy.*
Richards, T. L., see *Owen.*
Richards, T. W., and Jesse, heats of reaction XVIII, 26.
Richards, W. T., ultrasonic vibration VI, 29.
Richardson, distribution of radiation XX, 14.
Richardson and Brown, electron velocity from hot filament III, 13.
Rideal, see *Blackett.*
Ritter, see *Crenshaw.*
Roberts, J. K., accommodation coefficient XI, 11 — adsorption VIII, 27; XVII, 6 — co-operative phenomena XVII, 6 — distribution of ions over quantum states during adiabatic demagnetization V, 16 — expansion of solids determined by optical lever X, 4 — thermal conductivity of single crystals and aggregates XXII, 4 — thermal expansion of bismuth X, 4; XXII, 4 — see *Kaye, G. W. C.*
Roberts, L. D., see *Erickson.*
Roberts, T. R., see *Sydoriak.*
Robinson, see *Kürti.*
Rodebush and Walters, measurement of chemical constants VIII, 23.
Rodebush, Dixon and Fiock, vapour pressure of liquids VIII, 3.
Roebuck, Joule-Kelvin effect XIII, 4.
Roebuck and Murrill, ice point I, 35.
Roeser, thermocouples I, 30 — see *Wensel.*
Roeser, Caldwell and Wensel, disappearing filament pyrometer XX, 18 — optical pyrometer to measure melting-points XX, 22.

Roger, constant-temperature bath at ice point I, 4.
Rollin, see *Darby.*
Rollin, Kürti and Simon, helium film XVII, 2.
Rosenbohm, see *Jaeger, F. M.*
Rosseland, see *Klein.*
Rossini and Fransden, internal energy of a gas as a function of the pressure V, 3.
Roth, heats of reaction XVIII, 26 — temperature variation of specific heat of water II, example.
Rotons XVII, 2.
Rowland, mechanical equivalent II, 10.
Rubin, see *Yost.*
Rüchardt, adiabatic changes in gases VI, 15.
Ruhemann, constant-temperature bath at low temperatures V, 12 — see *Simon.*
Rumford, test of caloric theory II, 2.
Rundle, variation of ratio of specific heats with pressure and relation to equation of state VI, 15; XIII, example 7.
Rupert, see *Lewis, G. N.*
Russell, see *Yost.*
Rutgers, transition of superconductor in magnetic field XVII, 7.
Rutherford and Geiger, determination of Avogadro's number III, 7.

Salsburg, see *Cohen, E. G. D.*
Sand, measurement of equilibrium constants XVIII, 17.
Sarjant, see *Eyres.*
Scheel and Heuse, measurement of vapour pressure VIII, 2 — specific heat of hydrogen at low temperatures VI, 27 — specific heats of gases VI, 10.
Schiller, convection XI, 27.
Schiller and Burbach, convection XI, 27.
Schleiermacher, thermal conductivity of gases XI, 6.
Schmekel, convection XI, 27.
Schmidt, see *Keesom.*
Schmidt and Keesom, vapour pressure of helium V, 11.
Schmidt and Schnell, specific heats of gases VI, 26.
Schnell, see *Schmidt.*
Schofield, optical pyrometer to measure melting-points XX, 22 — thermal conductivity of non-metals XI, 21.
Scholes, bomb calorimeter XVIII, 26.
Schottky, electron velocity from hot

filament III, 13 — specific-heat anomalies XXII, 12 — statistical weights VIII, 23.

Schrödinger, specific heats of solids VII, 5; XXII, 4, 5, 7.

Schultze, see *Holborn*.

Schupp, see *Preuner*.

Schuster and Gannon, electrical equivalent II, 13.

Schwartz, see *Fajans*.

Schwers, see *Eucken*.

Scott and Brickwedde, constant-temperature baths V, 12.

Scott and Cooke, expansion liquefier V, 6.

Searle, theory of flow methods VI, 8.

Second-order transitions, for superconductor XVII, 7, 9; XIX, 7 — in liquid helium XVII, 1; XIX, 3 — in various systems XVII, 5 — model of XVII, 3 — thermodynamical functions for XVII, 1.

Semi-permeable membrane, condition of equilibrium across XVI, 13 — use in measurement of reaction constant XVIII, 17.

Senter, see *Travers*.

Seymour, see *Darby*.

Shakespear, measurement of Stefan-Boltzmann constant XX, 13.

Sherratt and Griffiths, Ezer, vibrational specific heats VI, 29.

Shilling, velocity of sound VI, 21 — see *Partington*.

Shockley, see *Nix*.

Shoenberg, see *Daunt*.

Siegel, measurement of equilibrium constants XVIII, 17.

Siemens, platinum thermometry I, 23.

Sih Ling Ting, electron velocity from hot filament III, 13.

Silsbee, see *Darby*.

Silver, freezing-point I, 22.

Simon, calculation of chemical constant of hydrogen VIII, 24 — calculations on nuclear demagnetization V, 19 — cooling by desorption of helium V, 12 — determination of absolute from magnetic temperature V, 17 — expansion liquefier V, 6 — internal energy of helium V, 13 — measurement of chemical constants VIII, 23 — nuclear demagnetization V, 19 — specific-heat anomalies XXII, 12 — third law XIX, 1, 3, 4, 6 — two-stage demagnetization V, 18 — zero-point energy of helium

XVII, 3 — see *Berman* — see *Bleaney* — see *Hettner* — see *Holland* — see *Jones, G. O.* — see *Kaischew* — see *Kürti* — see *Lange* — see *Larsen* — see *Megaw* — see *Pickard* — see *Rollin*.

Simon and Ahlberg, expansion liquefier V, 6.

Simon and Bergmann, linear expansion of solids X, 2 — specific-heat anomalies XXII, 12.

Simon and Kippert, solids under pressure XXIII, 8.

Simon and Lange, adiabatic vacuum calorimeter VII, 3; VIII, 16 — latent heat of fusion at low temperatures IX, 6 — latent heat of vaporization at low temperatures VIII, 16 — thermal measurements on gases VII, 2.

Simon and Ruhemann, specific heat of solids VII, 1.

Simon and Swain, specific-heat anomalies XXII, 12.

Simon and Swenson, change in gradient of melting-pressure curve as evidence for third law XIX, 6 — solidification of helium V, 13; XVII, 3; XIX, 6.

Simon, Mendelssohn and Ruhemann, anomaly in specific heat of hydrogen XIX, 3.

Simon, Ruhemann and Edwards, solidification of helium V, 15.

Simon, von Simson, and Ruhemann, specific heat anomalies XXII, 12.

Sinden, linear expansion of solids X, 4.

Slater, Kirkwood and Keyes, interatomic forces IV, 6.

Sligh, see *Osborne, N. S.*

Smith, F. E., bridge for thermometric work I, 29.

Smoluchowski, absolute manometer III, 22 — conduction of gases at very low pressures XI, 11 — streaming of gas through narrow tube III, 19 — thermal conductivity of non-metallic crystals XI, 23.

Smyth, separation of isotopes III, 24; XVIII, 8 — see *Coster*.

Soddy and Berry, conductivity of gases at low pressures XI, 11.

Sodium sulphate decahydrate, transition point I, 22.

Solar constant XX, 23.

Sommerfeld, theory of metals XI, 20.

Sosman, measurements at high temperatures XX, 22 — see *Day*.

Sound, dispersion of, in gas VI, 30.

Sound, velocity of, in gas, formula VI, 16 — free-air measurement VI, 17 — measurement in tube VI, 18.

Specific heat, at constant pressure and constant volume VI, 1, 2, 3; VII, 5; XIII, 3 — defined II, 5; VI, 1 — Dulong and Petit's law VII, 6 — of liquids and difference from solid at melting-point VII, 9 — of metals VII, 8 — of saturated vapours XVI, 9 — of water II, 17.

Specific heats of gases, difference between at constant volume and constant pressure for perfect gas VI, 2 — experimental values VI, 26 — difference between for actual gas VI, 3; XIII, 3 — internal vibrations VI, 29 — measurement of VI, 4–11 — measurement of ratio VI, 15, 17, 26 — relation of ratio to molecular degrees of freedom VI, 25 — theory of ratio VI, 12–14 — used in determining equilibrium constants XVIII, 18.

Specific heat of liquids VII, 9.

Specific heat of solids, anomalies XXII, 12 — at high temperatures XXII, 6, 9 — cubic law at low temperatures VII, 7; XIX, 1, 3; XXII, 5, 7 — departure from Dulong and Petit's law near melting-points XXII, 9 — lattice theory of XIX, 3; XXII, 11 — quantum theory introduced by Einstein XXII, 1 — spurious T^3 regions XIX, 1, 3; XXII, 5, 11 — theory of Born and v. Kármán XXII, 6 — theory of Debye XXII, 3.

Spohr, see *Kürti*.

Stäckel, see *Trautz*.

Stanton, convection XI, 27.

Stationary vibrations, to measure velocity of sound VI, 19.

Steam, saturation pressure IV, 12 — thermodynamic tables for XIV, 9; Appendix 3 — properties of Appendix 2.

Steam engine, measurement of performance XIV, 11 — multiple expansion XIV, 12 — reciprocating XIV, 3.

Steam point I, 17, 22 — effect of pressure on I, 17.

Steam tables, use of XIV, 8.

Steam turbine, efficiency XIV, 15 — impulse XIV, 13 — reaction XIV, 14.

Steenland, see *De Klerk*.

Stefan-Boltzmann law, derived XX, 11, 12 — experimental study XX, 13.

Steinwehr, see *Jaeger, W.*

Stern, chemical constant VIII, 23; XIX, 3 — entropy differences for hydrogen XIX, 3 — see *Estermann*.

Stevenson, see *Hirschfelder*.

Stevenson, Wagner, Beeck and Otvos, separation of isotopes XVIII, 8.

Stewart, relaxation of rotational degrees of freedom VI, 29 — see *Hutchison*.

Stewart and Cohen, separation of isotopes XVIII, 8.

Stewart, Stewart and Hubbard, relaxation of rotational degrees of freedom VI, 29.

Stille, values of physical and chemical constants I, 38; III, 7; XIII, 9; XVIII, 22.

Stimson, international and thermodynamic temperature scales I, 36 — joule as unit of heat II, 5 — size of degree I, 4 — ice point I, 36 — see *Osborne, N. S.*

Stoner, theory of metals XI, 20.

Stoodley, see *Carpenter*.

Stout, see *Giauque*.

Stracciati, see *Bartoli*.

Streaming of gases, through nozzles III, 19.

Strong, see *Bundy*.

Sulphur point I, 18, 22; V, 7 — effect of pressure on I, 18.

Sun, black-body temperature of XX, 23.

Superconductivity, properties of a superconductor XVII, 7; XXII, 12 — transition in magnetic field, thermodynamical relations XVII, 8 — transition in magnetic field, relation to third law XIX, 7 — thermodynamical functions of a superconductor XVII, 9.

Superconductor as thermal switch V, 18.

Sutherland, see *Hercus*.

Swain, see *Simon*.

Swallow, see *MacGillivray*.

Swann, specific heats of gases VI, 10.

Swenson, see *Larsen* — see *Simon*.

Sydoriak, see *Grilly*.

Sydoriak and Roberts, T. R., vapour pressure of helium isotope 3 IV, 7.

Sydoriak, Grilly, and Hammel, vapour pressure of helium isotope 3 IV, 7; VIII, 25.

Tabor, see *Bowden*.

Tammann, different kinds of ice XVI, 14. — superlattice lines XVII, 5.

Tate, see *Fairbairn.*

Taylor, G. B., and Hulett, dissociation pressure of mercuric oxide XIX, 2.

Taylor, G. I., convection XI, 27.

Taylor, P. A., see *Lennard-Jones.*

Taylor, W. J., theory of liquids XXIII, 15.

Teichner, critical phenomena IV, 12.

Telfair, see *Hardy.*

Temperature, absolute thermodynamical scale I, 34–6; XII, 6 — and kinetic energy of molecules III, 6 — celsius I, 4 — concept of I, 1, 3 — empirical scale I, 3 — fahrenheit I, 4 — international scale I, 22 — scale agreed on for use in helium range V, 11 — standard interval I, 4 — see *Absolute temperature* — see *Fixed points* — see *Magnetic temperature.*

Temperature radiation, defined XX, 8 — Kirchhoff's law XX, 8.

ter Haar, intermolecular energy IV, 7 — virial coefficients IV, 6.

Teske, see *Clusius.*

Tetrode, chemical constant VIII, 23.

Thacher, see *Dahler.*

Thatte, expansion coefficients of liquids X, 9.

Thermal capacity II, 5.

Thermal conductivity, defined XI, 2 — measurement of, for gases XI, 5, 6 — of gases at very low pressures XI, 11 — of liquids XI, 12 — of metals XI, 13–18 — of metals at high temperatures XI, 17 — of metals at very low temperatures XI, 16 — of metals, theory XI, 18 — of non-metals XI, 21 — ratio of thermal to electrical conductivity XI, 19 — theory of parallel-plate method XI, 7 — used in analysis of fractions of ortho- and para-hydrogen VI, 28.

Thermal diffusion III, 24.

Thermal equilibrium, defined I, 2 — existence of, basis of temperature concept I, 3 — law of I, 2.

Thermal expansion, see *Expansion coefficient.*

Thermal switch V, 18.

Thermal transpiration, see *Thermomolecular pressure.*

Thermodynamical functions, electronic contribution to in a superconductor XVII, 9 — in phase transition XVI, 8; XVII, 1 — relations between XVI, 12;

Appendix, 1 — see particular thermodynamical functions.

Thermodynamical potential, see *Gibbs free energy.*

Thermodynamics, zeroth law I, 2, 3 — first law, II, 19 — second law XII, 4, 11; XVI, 8; XVIII, 18 — third law XIX, 1.

Thermo-electric thermometry, at high temperatures I, 32 — below ice point V, 8 — copper constantan thermocouple I, 30 — platinum platinum-rhodium thermocouple I, 30 — sources of error I, 31.

Thermometer, constant-pressure I, 6 — constant-volume I, 7 — gas I, 5–8 — independent of particular gas I, 8, 10, 12 — mercury-in-glass I, 33 — numerical values of corrections I, 14 — platinum resistance I, 12, 22, 23–29 — reduced pressure, extrapolation to I, 8 — theory of gas thermometer corrections I, 11 — thermo-electric I, 30–32 — to measure temperature I, 2, 3 — see particular kinds of thermometer.

Thermomolecular pressure, and measurement of temperature III, 23; V, 11 — defined III, 23.

Thermopile XX, 4.

Third law, adiabatic demagnetization and unattainability of absolute zero XIX, 8 — equilibrium between liquid and solid helium XIX, 6 — experimental verification from chemical reactions XIX, 2, 3 — statement of XIX, 1 — superconducting transition in magnetic field XIX, 7 — verification from low-temperature phenomena XIX, 5–9.

Thirring, specific heats at high temperatures XXII, 6.

Thode, exchange reactions VIII, 25 — separation of isotopes XVIII, 8.

Thode and Urey, separation of isotopes XVIII, 8.

Thode, Macnamara, Lossing and Collins, natural variations in isotopic abundance XVIII, 8.

Thomsen, see *Bearden.*

Thomson, W., see *Kelvin.*

Thomson, heats of reaction XVIII, 26.

Tin, freezing-point I, 22.

Tin resistance thermometers V, 10.

Tingwaldt, see *Henning.*

Tisza, two-fluid theory of helium XVII, 2.

Todd, measurement of Stefan-Boltzmann constant XX, 13.

Tolman, statistical mechanics XXIII, 10.
Toral, see *Moles*.
Total heat, see *Enthalpy*.
Traube, critical phenomena IV, 12.
Trautz and Stäckel, measurement of equilibrium constants XVIII, 17.
Trautz and Zündel, thermal conductivity of gases XI, 5.
Travers, Senter and Jaquerod, gas thermometer corrections I, 14.
Triple point, and phase rule XVI, 14 — of helium V, 14 — of hydrogen V, 15 — of oxygen and nitrogen V, 9 — of water I, 4, 22, 34; XII, 6; XIII, 9.
Trkal, see *Ehrenfest*.
Trouton's rule VIII, 21.
Tungsten, melting-point I, 22; XX, 22.
Tutton, linear expansion of solids X, 3.
Twigg, conductivity and gas analysis VI, 28.
Two-fluid model, of liquid helium XVII, 2 — of superconductor XVII, 9.
Two-stage demagnetization V, 18.

Ubbelhode, see *Egerton*.
Ubbink and De Haas, thermal conductivity of gases at low temperatures XI, 5.
Ultrasonic waves VI, 29.
Umino, latent heat of fusion IX, 5.
Uranium, separation of isotopes of III, 24.
Urey, exchange reactions VIII, 25; XVIII, 8 — see *Hutchison* — see *Thode*.
Urey and Grieff, difference between thermodynamical functions of isotopes XVIII, 8.
Utterback, radiation XX, 21.

Van Cittert, see *Burger*.
Van der Waals equation, agreement with experiment IV, 3 — Boyle temperature for IV, 6, example 2 — critical parameters IV, 3, example 1 — derivation IV, 3 — Joule-Kelvin effect V, 3; XIII, example 5 — properties IV, 3.
Van Dijk, triple point of water I, 35.
Van Dijk and Durieux, temperature scale below 5° K. V, 11.
Van Itterbeek and Vermaelen, relaxation of rotational degrees of freedom VI, 29.
Van't Hoff, reaction isochore XVIII, 4, 7, 11; XIX, 3.
Van Vleck, theory of paramagnetism V, 17 — see *Kemble*.

Van Vleck and Penney, paramagnetism V, 17.
Van Wyk, see *Ornstein*.
Vapour density, measurement of VIII, 22.
Vapour pressure, Clausius-Clapeyron equation VIII, 8 — defined VIII, 1 — general equation VIII, 10 — Kirchhoff formula VIII, 9 — measurement of VII, 2–6 — of helium, see *Helium*.
Varet, heat of reaction XIX, 2.
Variables, macroscopic I, 2.
Vaughan, see *Clusius*.
Velocities, distribution of III, 8 — experimental test III, 13, 20–21 — expressions for III, 11 — graphical representation III, 12.
Velocity of gas molecules, mean III, 9 — most probable III, 10 — root mean square III, 8.
Velocity of sound VI, 16–22 — in free space independent of pressure VI, 17.
Vermaelen, see *Van Itterbeek*.
Vertical column of gas, distribution of pressure in III, 7.
Vibrations, internal of molecules, related to degrees of freedom VI, 25 — internal theory of VI, 29 — of continuous medium XXI, 2.
Villars and Schultze, specific heat of methane VI, 28.
Virial coefficients I, 10, example; IV, 1, 5; VI, 3 — of helium IV, 6 — second and equation of state IV, 6.
Virial expansion I, 10; IV, 5.
Virial law, of Clausius XXIII, 1, 2.
Viscosity of gases, kinetic theory XI, 8 — ratio of coefficient of to thermal conductivity XI, 9.
Volatile compounds, thermal diffusion used to study properties of III, 24.
Volker, see *Wenman*.
Volmer and Estermann, measurement of condensation coefficient VIII, 7.
Von Elbe, see *Wohl*.
v. Kármán, see *Born*.
Von Simson, see *Simon*.
v. Wangenheim, see *Pirani*.
v. Wartenberg, latent heat of vaporization and boiling-point VIII, 21 — measurement of equilibrium constants XVIII, 17 — vapour pressure of metals VIII, 6 — see *Nernst*.
v. Wartenberg and Henglein, measurement of equilibrium constants XVIII, 17; XXIII, 13.

Roman figures refer to chapters, and Arabic figures to sections within these chapters

Wagner, latent heat of vaporization and boiling-point VIII, 21 — see *Stevenson.*

Wagstaff, see *Eyres.*

Waidner and Burgess, measurement of Stefan-Boltzmann constant XX, 13.

Waller, specific heats at high temperatures XXII, 9 — see *James.*

Walters, see *Rodebush.*

Wannier, co-operative assemblies XVII, 6 — order-disorder transitions XVII, 5.

Warburg, see *Kundt.*

Washburn, internal energy as a function of pressure V, 3.

Water, anomalous expansion X, 10 — dissociation of vapour XVIII, 25 — triple point I, 35; XII, 6; XIII, 9; XVI, 8 — vaporization and freezing of as test of second law XVI, 8 — variation of specific heat II, 17 example.

Watson, Onsager and Zucker, separation of isotopes III, 24.

Watt, indicator diagram XIV, 11.

Wave function, for liquid helium examined by Feynman XVII, 2.

Weber, thermal conductivity of gases XI, 6 — thermomolecular pressure III, 23 — see *Keesom.*

Webster, fusion XXIII, 14.

Weight thermometer X, 8.

Weinstock, see *Abraham* — see *Osborne, D. W.*

Wenman and Volker, vapour pressure of mercury VIII, 9.

Wensel, radiation constants XX, 15 — see *Roeser.*

Wensel and Roeser, optical pyrometer to measure melting-points XX, 22.

Wentorf, see *Bundy.*

Westphal, distribution of radiation XX, 14 — measurement of Stefan-Boltzmann constant XX, 13.

Weyl, number of independent vibrations of continuous medium XXI, 2.

Whaples, temperature concept I, 3.

Whiffen, see *Fenning.*

Wiebe, see *Giauque.*

Wiedemann-Franz law XI, 18.

Wien, distribution of radiation XX, 14 — formula (approximate) XX, 17.

Wien and Lummer, black body XX, 9.

Wiersma, see *De Haas.*

Williams, see *Bragg.*

Wilner and Borelius, thermal conductivity of gases XI, 6.

Wilson, A. H., theory of metals XI, 18, 20.

Wilson, A. J. C., specific-heat anomalies XXII, 12.

Wilson, E. B., see *Bichowsky.*

Wilson, H. A., experimental verification of Wien's law XX, 16 — quantum theory of radiation XXI, 4.

Winkhaus, see *Knoblauch.*

Wintner, see *Mayer, J. E.*

Wirtz, see *Korsching.*

Witt, radio-micrometer XX, 4.

Wohl, measurement of equilibrium constants XVIII, 17 — measurement of heats of dissociation XXIII, 13 — see *Nernst.*

Wohl and von Elbe, specific heats of gases VI, 6.

Wolf, see *Cooke.*

Wolfe, see *Balamuth.*

Woltjer and Onnes, susceptibility of gadolinium sulphate V, 16.

Womersley, specific heats of gases VI, 6.

Wood, Alex., vibrations in sound wave adiabatic VI, 16.

Workman, specific heats of gases VI, 3.

Worthing, optical pyrometer to measure melting-points XX, 22 — specific heats of metals VII, 8 — thermal conductivity of metals at high temperatures XI, 17.

Yarnell, Arnold, Bendt and Kerr, energy spectrum of liquid helium XVII, 2.

Yost, Garner, Osborne, N. S., Rubin and Russell, comparison of international and gas scales below ice point V, 7.

Zartman, distribution of velocities III, 13.

Zemansky, temperature concept I, 1.

Zero-point energy, deviation of light elements from classical principle of corresponding states IV, 7 — effect on properties of liquid helium XVII, 3 — energy levels of simple harmonic vibration XXI, 4; XXII, 10 — experimental evidence for XXII, 10.

Zinc, freezing-point I, 22.

Zündel, see *Trautz.*

Zwikker, specific heats of metals VII, 8.